Frontiers in Neuroendocrinology, 1969

Frontiers in
Neuroendocrinology, 1969

EDITED BY
WILLIAM F. GANONG

Department of Physiology
University of California School of Medicine
San Francisco Medical Center

AND
LUCIANO MARTINI

Istituto di Farmacologia e di Terapia
Università degli Studi, Milan

New York
OXFORD UNIVERSITY PRESS
London   Toronto   1969

Contributors

Carlos Beyer, Institute for Biological and Medical Studies, University of Mexico, Mexico, D. F.

Julian M. Davidson, Department of Physiology, School of Medicine, Stanford University, Stanford, California

David de Wied, Rudolf Magnus Institute for Pharmacology, Medical Faculty, University of Utrecht, Vondellaan 6, Utrecht, The Netherlands

Franco Fraschini, Università degli Studi, Istituto di Farmacologia e di Terapia, Via Vanvitelli, 32, Milan, Italy

Kjell Fuxe, Department of Histology, Karolinska Institutet, Stockholm, Sweden

Irving I. Geschwind, Department of Animal Husbandry, University of California, Davis, California

John R. Gill, Jr., Endocrinology Branch, National Heart Institute, Bethesda, Maryland

Seymour M. Glick, Metabolism and Endocrinology Laboratory, Coney Island Hospital, Ocean and Shore Parkways, Brooklyn, New York

Béla Halász, Department of Anatomy, University Medical School, Pécs, Hungary

Tomas Hökfelt, Department of Histology, Karolinska Institutet, Stockholm, Sweden

Hideshi Kobayashi, Zoological Institute, Faculty of Science, University of Tokyo, Tokyo, Japan

Luciano Martini, Università degli Studi, Istituto di Farmacologia e di Terapia, Via Vanvitelli, 32, Milan, Italy

Tokuzo Matsui, Zoological Institute, Faculty of Science, University of Tokyo, Tokyo, Japan

Marcella Motta, Università degli Studi, Istituto di Farmacologia e di Terapia, Via Vanvitelli, 32, Milan, Italy

Charles H. Sawyer, Department of Anatomy, Center for Health Science, University of California, Los Angeles, California

Leonard Share, Department of Physiology, School of Medicine, Western Reserve University, Cleveland, Ohio

Preface

This book is the first of a projected series of biennial volumes surveying
the frontiers of the new and rapidly expanding science of neuroendocrinology. This science is concerned not only with neural control of endocrine secretion, but also with the effects of hormone on behavior and
with the broader problem of the interactions between the brain and the
internal environment. In a two-volume survey (*Neuroendocrinology*,
L. Martini and W. F. Ganong, eds., Academic Press, New York, Volume
I, 1966, Volume II, 1967) the subject was reviewed in detail. We plan
to update this survey every two years by publishing in this new series a
collection of chapters reviewing the areas in which there have been
advances, innovations, or controversies. The first volume, *Frontiers in
Neuroendrocrinology, 1969,* surveys a number of such areas. Rapid
publication has made it possible to combine the features of review mono-
graphs and current journals. The contributors are experts in their fields,
and they have been encouraged to include not only published data, but,
where pertinent, the results of their own current research as well. This
will make the book of particular value to investigators engaged in research
in neuroendocrinology. However, the book should also interest psychol-
ogists, psychiatrists, neurophysiologists, biochemists, and all those concerned with any of the multiple facets of the interaction between the brain
and the endocrine glands.

March 1969   WILLIAM F. GANONG

                                                          LUCIANO MARTINI

Contents

Frontiers in Neuroendocrinology, 1969

1

Fine Structure of
the Median Eminence
and Its Functional Significance

HIDESHI KOBAYASHI and TOKUZO MATSUI

Introduction

Neurosecretory neurons in the ventral hypothalamus transform afferent neural signals into neurohormonal information in the form of neurohypophyseal hormones and releasing factors for adenohypophyseal hormones. The neural lobe is a depot of neurohypophyseal hormones and the median eminence is a storage site of releasing factors. Further, the median eminence is the place where releasing factors are discharged into the hypophyseal portal vessels, through which they are transported to the adenohypophysis.

The neurohypophyseal hormones exist in granules (Barer *et al.*, 1963; Ishii, Su. *et al.*, 1962a; Weinstein *et al.*, 1961; Poisner and Douglas, 1968), and it seems likely that releasing factors stored in the median eminence are also carried in granules. If this is true, electron microscopy of the median eminence should reveal granules carrying those factors. In this review we will present recent anatomical studies of the median eminence and describe some experiments based on electron microscopic observations.

Comparative Anatomy of the Median Eminence

Gross Anatomy

In most fish the neurohypophysis has not been differentiated into the pars nervosa and the median eminence. Exceptions are selachians (Meurling,

3

1960; Mellinger, 1960a,b, 1963) and lungfish (Green, 1951; Wingstrand, 1966), which possess a structure similar to the tetrapod median eminence. In tetrapods the neurohypophysis has evolved into the pars nervosa and the median eminence, and these animals have a true hypophyseal portal system (Green, 1951). In the tetrapod median eminence, the following layers can generally be recognized with the light microscope (Fig. 1-1): (1) Ependymal layer, consisting of one layer of ependymal cells. (2) Hypendymal layer, consisting of one or two layers of hypendymal cells. This layer is seen in the turtle, birds, mouse, and rat, but in the salamander, toad, and frog it has not developed. (3) Fiber layer, consisting mostly of fine nerve fibers including the supraoptico-hyophyseal tract. (4) Reticular layer, a network of Gomori-positive and -negative nerve fibers. This layer is not seen in the salamander. (5) Palisade layer, consisting of Gomori-positive and -negative nerve fibers in addition to processes of glial and ependymal cells. This layer is most conspicuous in the turtle, birds, mouse, and rat. The glial cells are scattered in the latter three layers, except in the salamander, in which glial cells are rare. A few neurons of the arcuate nucleus are observable in the lateral peripheral margins of the median eminence in birds, the mouse, and the rat; in the middle portion of the

Figure 1-1   Diagram of the layers of the median eminence and the pars tuberalis, based on light-microscope observations in the bird. Black dots are Gomori-positive neurosecretory material. Large dots are Herring bodies.   E, ependymal layer; H, hypendymal layer; F, fiber layer; R, reticular layer; P, palisade layer; PT, pars tuberalis.

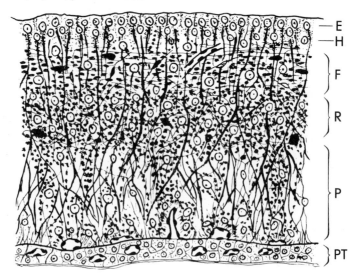

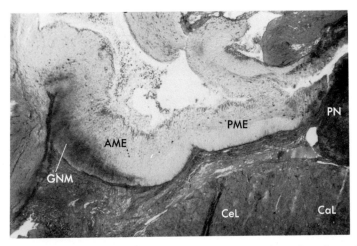

Figure 1-2   Sagittal section of the hypothalamo-hypophyseal region of the pigeon.   AME, anterior division of median eminence; CaL, caudal lobe of adenohypophysis; CeL, cephalic lobe of adenohypophysis; GNM, Gomori-positive neurosecretory material; PME, posterior division of median eminence; PN, pars nervosa.   × 77.

median eminence neuronal cell bodies are very rare. On the surface of the palisade layer lies the primary capillary network of the hypophyseal portal vessels. In the turtle, birds, mouse, and rat the pars tuberalis covers most of the basal surface of the median eminence and the primary capillary network. The structure of the median eminence has also been described by Wingstrand (1951, 1966), Diepen (1962), and Sloper (1966).

Anatomical Relations between the Median Eminence and the Pars Distalis of the Adenohypophysis

In birds, the median eminence is divided into distinct divisions, anterior and posterior (Fig. 1-2). Although the fibers from tuberal nuclei terminate in both anterior and posterior divisions, the fibers of Gomori-positive neurosecretory nuclei terminate mostly in the anterior division (Oksche, 1962, 1967). Wilson (1967) has presented evidence that the posterior division of the median eminence is important in regulation of gonadotropin release.

In the turtle, the median eminence is not anatomically divisible, but the anterior portion stores Gomori-positive neurosecretory material and the posterior portion does not (Hirano, 1966a). Since the primary capillary network lies on the basal surface of both portions, as it does in birds, it is likely that the posterior portion of the turtle median eminence is equivalent to the posterior division of the avian median eminence. In the frog *Rana catesbeiana*, the region immediately posterior to the portion containing much Gomori-positive material is drained by the primary capillary network on its surface. Therefore, this infundibular stem region seems to be morphologically equivalent to the avian posterior median eminence (Matsui, 1966a; Farner *et al.*, 1967). Electron microscopy may reveal the significance of this region, which could be the posterior median eminence of the turtle and the frog. It seems possible that among all tetrapod vertebrates there are at least two functionally differentiated divisions in the neural stalk (see below and Fig. 1-11).

The avian adenohypophysis is divided into cephalic and caudal lobes (Fig. 1-2; Wingstrand, 1951; see Farner *et al.*, 1967). In the duck and white-crowned sparrow, the capillaries covering the anterior division of the median eminence drain mostly into the cephalic lobe, and those covering the posterior division drain mostly into the caudal lobe (Benoit and Assenmacher, 1953; Assenmacher and Tixier-Vidal, 1964; Vitums *et al.*, 1965). In several species of birds, the cells manufacturing prolactin, adrenocorticotropin (ACTH), follicle stimulating hormone (FSH), and thyrotropin (TSH) are in the cephalic lobe (Tixier-Vidal, 1963). These cells are probably controlled by neurohormones released from the axonal endings in the anterior division of the median eminence. The cells manufacturing

Figure 1-3   Hypothalamo-hypophyseal region of the fish *Oryzias latipes*. ANH, anterior neurohypophysis; PI, pars intermedia; PNH, posterior neurohypophysis; PPD, proximal pars distalis; RPD, rostral pars distalis.   × 315.

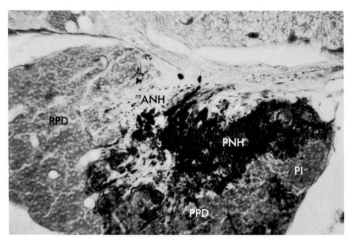

luteinizing hormone (LH) and growth hormone (STH, GH) are in the caudal lobe (Tixier-Vidal, 1963), so these cells are probably controlled by neurohormones liberated from the endings in the posterior division of the median eminence. There are also a few TSH-manufacturing cells in the caudal lobe. Although Mikami (1958) reported different conclusions from those of Tixier-Vidal about the distribution of different cell types in the domestic fowl, both investigators agree that there are conspicuous differences in cell types between the lobes.

The same anatomical relationship between the median eminence and the pars distalis may be present in the turtle, since in the turtle the median eminence probably has two divisions, and the pars distalis has two lobes (see Wingstrand, 1951, 1966; Saint-Girons, 1963; Grignon, 1963).

In certain fish the neurohypophysis is clearly divisible into two portions: one portion with much Gomori-positive material, the other without this material (Fig. 1-3; see Wingstrand, 1966; Sloper, 1966). The former portion is mostly associated with the pars intermedia; the latter interdigitates with the pars distalis, which is divisible into two or more zones (see Kobayashi *et al.*, 1959; Bern and Knowles, 1966; Follenius, 1965a,b, 1967; Knowles and Vollrath, 1966; Wingstrand, 1966; Kawamoto, 1967). These anatomical observations suggest that the Gomori-negative neurohypophyseal portion, which seems to be equivalent to the tetrapod median eminence, may have further regional differentiation in function. In the newt *Triturus*, there is some division of the pars distalis, and the distribution of cell types is different among the divisions (Dent, 1961). In mammals, it has been shown that specific groups of long or short portal-blood vessels, which arise in the median eminence and the lower infundibular stem, respectively, supply fairly specific regions of the pars distalis (see Daniel, 1966).

Thus, fish, amphibians, reptiles and mammals may resemble the birds in having functional relationships between the divisions of the pars distalis and various divisions of the median eminence–stem region. Examination of the capillary distribution in the tetrapod median eminence–stem region and in the fish neurohypophysis should be carried out with special attention to the divisions of the pars distalis.

Electron Microscopy of Gomori-positive Neurosecretory Neurons

The fine structure of the Gomori-positive neurosecretory system has been studied extensively by many investigators in different animals, and much knowledge has been accumulated (see Bargmann, 1966; Bern and

Knowles, 1966; Oota *et al.*, 1966; Scharrer, 1966). In this section, some recent findings that may provide some insight into the control of pituitary function are described.

Neurosecretory Cells and Monoaminergic Fibers

Synapses have recently been found between Gomori-positive neurosecretory cell perikarya and the endings of axons containing small granules measuring about 1000 Å in diameter and small vesicles measuring 500 Å in the rat and mouse (Murakami, 1962; Kawabata, 1964; Peterson, 1965; Polenov and Senchik, 1966). Because of their profiles and size, the granules and vesicles are considered to contain monoamines and acetylcholine, respectively (see below). In the frog, there are synaptic junctions between axon terminals containing small monoamine granules and neurosecretory fibers containing large granules (Oota and Kobayashi, 1963). Carlsson *et al.* (1962), Falck (1964), and Fuxe and Hökfelt (1967) have described many monoaminergic fibers around the neurosecretory cells of the supraoptic nucleus in mammals. More recently, Urano (1968) has demonstrated that, in birds and the mouse, monoamine oxidase activity is strong around the neurosecretory cell perikarya. These findings suggest that the neurosecretory cells are regulated by monoaminergic neurons.

Figure 1-4 Synapse (S) between a neurosecretory axon containing intermediate granules (IG) and an ordinary axon in the hypothalamus near the median eminence of the turtle *Clemmys japonica*. Note that the neurosecretory axon containing intermediate granules is presynaptic. SG, small granule. × 18,900.

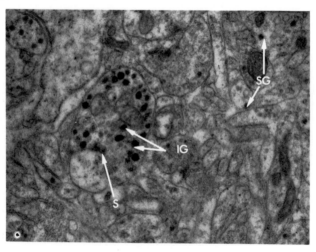

Other observations suggest a cholinergic innervation of the supraoptic neurons. Feldberg and Vogt (1948) found high acetylcholine synthesizing activity in the supraoptic region. Injection of acetylcholine, physostigmine, or diisopropyl fluorophosphate directly into the supraoptic region causes release of antidiuretic hormone from the dog neural lobe (Pickford, 1947; Duke et al., 1950). Gomori-positive neurosecretory cell perikarya show strong acetylcholinesterase activity (Abrahams et al., 1957; Arvy, 1963; Kobayishi and Farner, 1964; Uemura, 1964, 1965). However, synapses between cholinergic fibers containing exclusively synaptic vesicles and the neurosecretory cell perikarya have not been reported. Acetylcholine injected into the supraoptic region may have caused the monoaminergic fibers to release monoamines, resulting in stimulation of neurosecretory peikarya. There are many experiments reporting contradictory effects of norepinephrine, acetylcholine, antiadrenergic substances and anticholinergic substances on the neurosecretory system (see Sawyer and Mills, 1966; Konstantinova, 1967). Since the injections in these experiments were all systemic or ventricular, it is not known whether the effects were in fact due to direct action of the reagents on the neurosecretory cells.

Neurosecretory Axons

In the turtle and frog, neurosecretory axons containing large granules end on fibers of ordinary neurons (Fig. 1-4; Oota, 1963c; Oota and Kobayashi, 1963). Knowles (1965), Knowles and Vollrath (1966), and Follenius (1967) have shown that the neurosecretory axons containing large granules form synaptoid contacts with cells of the adenohypophysis in certain fishes, with ependymal elements in the neurointermediate lobe in the fresh water eel, and with ependymal cells of the neural lobe in the slender loris (Knowles, 1967). Nishioka et al. (1964) have described synaptic-like contacts between neurosecretory fibers containing large granules and the ependymal cells of the pars nervosa in the white-crowned sparrow. These findings suggest that neurosecretory neurons are capable of conducting information to ordinary neurons, glandular cells, and ependymal cells. Conduction of impulses in neurosecretory cells has been demonstrated by several investigators (Ishibashi, 1962; Kandel, 1964; Bern and Yagi, 1965; Yagi et al., 1966).

Electron Microscopy of the Median Eminence

General observations on the fine structure of the avian median eminence and the mammalian median eminence have been reported by several investigators (Kobayashi et al., 1961; Barry and Cotte, 1961; Oota and Koba-

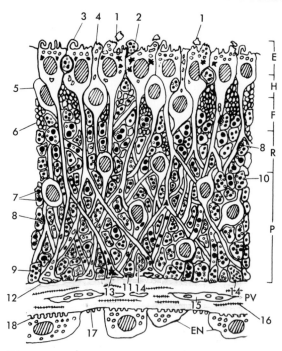

Figure 1-5   Diagram of the fine structure of the rat median eminence. E, ependymal layer; EN, endothelial cell; F, fiber layer; H, hypendymal layer; P, palisade layer; PV, perivascular space; R, reticular layer. 1, cytoplasmic masses released from ependymal cells into the third ventricle; 2, monoaminergic axons protruding into the third ventricle; 3, marginal fold; 4, process of hypendymal cell; 5, hypendymal cell; 6, mass of fine fibers; 7, large granules (these may be grouped into two types); 8, synaptoid contacts; 9, small granule; 10, small vesicle; 11, active point; 12, ependymal endfoot containing vesicles; 13, ependymal or glial endfoot containing dense bodies; 14, unidentified fiber ending containing peculiarly shaped granules; 15, fibroblast; 16, collagen fiber; 17, fenestration; 18, pinocytosis.

yashi, 1962; T. Kobayashi *et al.,* 1963; Oota, 1963b; Nishioka *et al.,* 1964; Bern and Nishioka, 1965; Duffy and Menefee, 1965; Mazzuca, 1965; Röhlich *et al.,* 1965; Seitz, 1965; Tsuji, 1965; Bern *et al.,* 1966; Kobayashi *et al.,* 1966; Matsui, 1966a,b; Rinne, 1966; T. Kobayashi *et al.,* 1967; Monroe, 1967; Oksche, 1967; Streefkerk, 1967). In lower vertebrates the observations are mostly confined to the palisade layer (Nishioka and Bern, 1966; Oota, 1963a, Oota and Kobayashi, 1963; Mellinger, 1963; Smoller, 1966). A general scheme of the fine structure of the median eminence is presented in Fig. 1-5.

Ependymal Secretion

With a light microscope, Leveque and Hofkin (1962) have observed PAS-positive substance in the ependymal cells of the rat infundibular recess. They further showed (1) that gonadectomy, adrenalectomy, hypophysectomy, and cortisone injection had no effect on the amount of this substance; (2) that cold stress increased the amount; and (3) that propylthiouracil decreased the amount. From these findings, they suggested the involvement of ependymal secretion in the regulation of adenohypophyseal function. Vigh *et al.* (1963) have also discussed ependymal secretion in relation to the anterior pituitary.

Several investigators have reported that the ependymal cells of the median eminence have microvilli or protrusions instead of cilia. Leveque *et al.* (1965, 1966) and Matsui and Kobayashi (1968) emphasized the glandular character of the ependymal cells of the infundibular recess in the rat. The ependymal cells of the median eminence seem to have some important role in the regulation of adenohypophyseal function, since their apical surfaces face the third ventricle and their thick processes terminate at the wall of capillaries of the primary plexus. In the median eminence of the pigeon, white-crowned sparrow, and rat the ependymal cells generally protrude finger-like microvilli including marginal folds. In addition to the microvilli, bleb-like or bulbous protrusions containing vacuoles or vesicles are frequently seen at the apical surface of the ependymal cells. Along the base of the protrusion small vesicles in a linear arrangement are often observed. These findings suggest that the ependymal cells secrete substances into or absorb substances from the cerebrospinal fluid of the third ventricle. Supporting the concept of ependymal absorption and secretion, vesicles or vacuoles near the microvilli and the protrusions are sometimes continuous with the vesicular tubes of the Golgi apparatus (Matsui and Kobayashi, 1969).

On the other hand, the processes of the ependymal cells contain many vesicles or vacuoles in their terminals which abut on the capillary wall of the primary plexus of the hypophyseal portal vessels. The vacuoles seem to be secreted from the feet into the perivascular space of the capillaries (Fig. 1-6). Since endocytosis is not visible at the terminal membrane of the feet, absorption by the ependymal feet from the capillaries seems unlikely.

Ependymal cells situated near the arcuate nucleus have similar characteristics to the ependymal cells of the median eminence. Their processes penetrate the arcuate nucleus and proceed to the capillaries of the primary plexus. It is not known whether there is functional contact between the processes and the neurons of the arcuate nucleus.

At the moment, the significance of the apparent absorption and bi-directional secretion of the ependymal cells is not known. Since it has been demonstrated with the electron microscope that Gomori-positive neuro-secretory substance is released into the third ventricle (Smoller, 1965; Öztan, 1967), there is the possibility that releasing factors may be secreted into the ventricular fluid. These neurohormones could be absorbed by the ependymal cells of the median eminence and transferred to the adenohy-pophysis. Recently, Kumar and Knowles (1967) described the specialized ependymal cells located anterolaterally in the tuber cinereum of the rhesus monkey. These ependymal cells have long processes which extend to the region of the pars tuberalis or to the wall of the hypothalamo-hypophyseal blood vascular system. Kumar and Knowles found that when labeled estro-gen was injected in ovariectomized monkeys a high concentration of the estrogen was found in the specialized ependyma.

Figure 1-6 Endfeet of ependymal or glial process (GP) containing many granules, vesicles, and other organelles of various shapes in the median eminence of the normal rat. Such inclusions are closely associated with the perivascular space (PV). EN, endothelial cell; Gly, glycogen granules; SG, small granule; UP, process containing inclusions of peculiar forms. × 16,310.

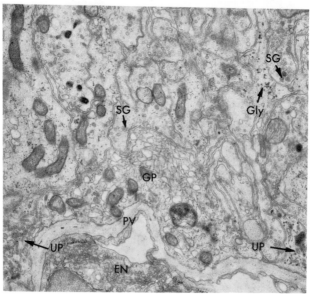

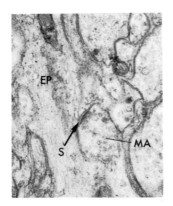

Figure 1-7. Synaptoid contact (S) between a monoaminergic axon (MA) and an ependymal process (EP) found in the fiber layer of the pigeon posterior median eminence.   × 17,500.

Synaptoid Contacts between the Ependymal Cells and the Neurosecretory Fibers Containing Small or Large Granules

The axons containing small, presumably monoaminergic, granules form synaptoid contacts with the ependymal, hypendymal, and glial cell bodies and also with their processes in the median eminence of the rat, mouse, and pigeon (Fig. 1-7; Matsui, 1966a,b; Kobayashi and Matsui, 1967). In some instances the membrane of the axons disappears at the point of the contacts and small vesicles are observed in the ependymal cytoplasm near the contact region. Similar contacts between neurosecretory fibers and pituicytes have been reported in eels (*Anguilla* and *Conger*) by Knowles and Vollrath (1966). Some of the hypendymal cells have protrusions into the third ventricle. (Because there is much similarity between ependymal and hypendymal cells, for the sake of convenience both are designated as ependymal cells in this section.) The synaptoid contacts mentioned above suggest that the ependymal secretion or absorption may be controlled by the monoaminergic fibers. Since monoaminergic neurons are present in the arcuate nucleus (Löblich and Knezevic, 1960; Fuxe, 1964; Lichtensteiger and Langemann, 1966; T. Kobayashi *et al.*, 1967; Mazzuca, 1967), fibers forming the synaptoid contacts may originate at the arcuate nucleus. However, it is possible that the monoaminergic fibers arise in the other hypothalamic nuclei, because neurons with their cell bodies in several hypothalamic nuclei innervate the median eminence (see Christ, 1966). Knowles (1967) has also reported synaptoid contacts between the monoaminergic fibers and ependymal elements in the paraventricular region in the slender loris.

There are synaptoid contacts between the neurosecretory fibers containing large granules and pituicytes in fish (Knowles, 1965; Knowles and Vollrath, 1966; Follenius, 1967) and between neurosecretory fibers and ependymal cells in the neural lobe of the white-crowned sparrow (Nishioka *et al.*, 1964).

Neurohemal Region of the Fish Neurohypophysis and Tetrapod Median Eminence

In the neurohypophysis of fish, four types of axons have been observed: (1) fibers containing large granules measuring 1500 to 1800 Å in diameter

Figure 1-8.   Pars nervosa of the frog *Rana catesbeiana.* There are two types of neurosecretory axons, containing large and intermediate granules (LG and IG, respectively). The monoaminergic axon containing small granules (SG) may be a vasomotor nerve.   × 23,625.

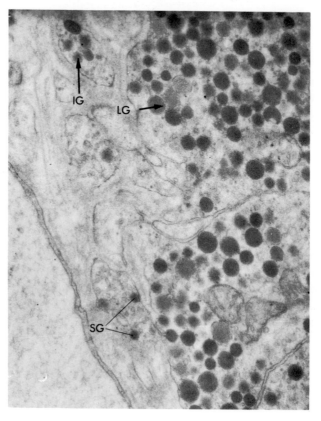

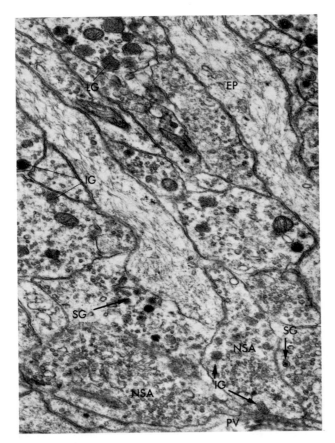

Figure 1-9 Neurohemal region of turtle (*Clemmys japonica*) median eminence. There are two types of neurosecretory axons containing large and intermediate granules (LG and IG, respectively), and monoaminergic axons containing small granules (SG). Neurosecretory axons (NSA) are attached directly
to the perivascular space (PV).   EP, ependymal process.   ×28,000.

and small vesicles measuring about 500 Å; (2) fibers containing intermediate granules measuring 1000 to 1200 Å in diameter and small vesicles
measuring 500 Å; (3) fibers containing small granules measuring less than
1000 Å and small vesicles measuring 500 Å; and (4) fibers containing
exclusively small vesicles measuring 500 Å. The small granules generally
contain electron-dense cores measuring approximately 600 to 800 Å in
diameter and the cores do not fill the boundary membrane. The first and
second types of fibers were originally lumped together and called Type A
fibers (Knowles, 1965). The third type was called Type B. On the basis of

studies in the eel *Anguilla anguilla*, Knowles and Vollrath (1966) subsequently divided Type A fiber into Type A_1 and Type A_2 fibers. These were observed to contain granules of 1600 to 1800 Å and granules of 1200 Å, respectively. Lederis (1964) observed two types of large granules (1400 and 1900 Å) in the rainbow trout neurohypophysis. Recent careful evaluation has shown two types of large granules (measuring 1200 and 1500 Å) in the neurohypophysis of the fish *Oryzias*. Thus, it seems likely that the large granules are generally divisible into two groups, large and intermediate, on the basis of their diameters. It may be possible that these granules are carriers of isotocin and arginine vasotocin, respectively. Most

Figure 1-10   Reticular layer of the pigeon anterior median eminence. Two types of neurosecretory axons containing large and intermediate granules (LG and IG, respectively), and monoaminergic axons containing small granules (SG) are intermingled.   × 14,000.

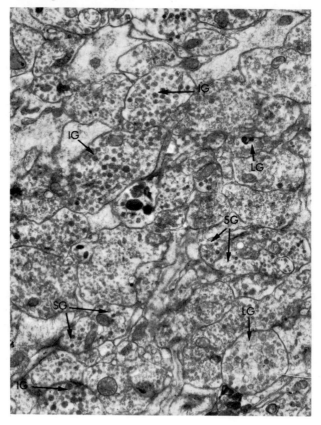

investigators are of opinion that both large and intermediate granules are produced in the preoptic nucleus and are carriers of neurohypophyseal hormones, while the small granules are produced in the lateral tuberal nuclei and are carriers of monoamines (Mellinger, 1963; Knowles and Vollrath, 1966).

In the *Conger* eel, synaptoid contacts between Type A fibers and cells of the pars intermedia have been demonstrated (Knowles and Vollrath, 1966). In the sea horse *Hippocampus guttulatus*, many synaptoid contacts between Type B fibers and cells of the pituitary have been observed (Vollrath, 1967). However, in most fish there is a wide connective tissue space, the so-called extravascular channel (Knowles and Vollrath, 1966), between these fibers and the secretory cells (Oota, 1963a; Bargmann and Knoop, 1957; Follenius, 1965a,b, 1967; Knowles and Vollrath, 1966). This wide connective tissue space is probably a continuation of the perivascular connective tissue space, and it is probable that substances released from the neurosecretory axon endings diffuse into this space and enter either the adenohypophyseal cells or the capillaries.

In amphibians there seem to be four kinds of fibers in the median eminence. In the frog *Rana catesbeiana*, most of the fibers contain two types of large granules, with diameters of about 1200 and 1500 Å, respectively. A few fibers contain small granules (1000 Å), which probably carry monoamines. The fibers containing only the small vesicles (500 Å) are rare (Oota and Kobayashi, 1963). The granules of 1200 Å and those of 1500 Å are both found in the pars nervosa (Fig. 1-8). In the tree frog *Hyla,* the median eminence contains numerous fibers containing small granules and a smaller number of fibers containing large granules (Smoller, 1966). The difference in granule distribution between *Rana* and *Hyla* may have to do with the difference in their habitats; *Rana* lives in the water more than *Hyla*. All those fibers containing either small or large granules include the small vesicles (500 Å). The descriptions mentioned above are based mainly on the median eminence containing Gomori-positive neurosecretory material. The fine structure of the infundibular–stem region should be examined; the importance of this region has been discussed above. Cohen (1967) reported that in the clawed frog *Xenopus*, fibers containing the small granules penetrate the pars intermedia, but fail to make direct synaptoid contacts with the intermedia cells. However, he observed many fibers enveloped by pars intermedia cells and is of the opinion that there are functional contacts between them. This observation is in good agreement with the observations of monoaminergic innervation at cells of the pars intermedia as observed with the fluorescence technique (Enemar and Falck, 1965; Enemar et al., 1967).

In the turtle it now appears that, instead of the two types of granules postulated to be present (Oota, 1963c), there are three types in the neurons. The sizes are about 1000, 1200, and 1500 Å, respectively (Fig. 1-9). The smallest granules are conceivably carriers of monoamines. The larger granules (1200 and 1500 Å) may be carriers of neurohypophyseal hormones, since both types of granules are observed in the pars nervosa. Fibers containing only the small vesicles (500 Å) are occassionally observed. All the fibers containing any type of granule include the small vesicles. Electron microscopy of the posterior portion of the median eminence has not yet been done. This study must be done in the light of the importance of the posterior division of the avian median eminence (Farner *et al.* 1967; Wilson, 1967).

In birds (Fig. 1-10), recent studies have revealed that there are four types of fibers in the median eminence: (1) fibers containing granules approximately 1500 Å in diameter and small vesicles measuring 500 Å; (2) fibers containing granules approximately 1200 Å in diameter and small vesicles measuring 500 Å; (3) fibers containing small granules approximately 1000 Å in diameter and small vesicles measuring 500 Å; and (4) fibers containing mainly small vesicles measuring 500 Å (Kobayashi *et al.*, 1961; Kobayashi, 1963; Bern *et al.*, 1966; Matsui, 1966a). All these fibers are intermingled with processes of glial and ependymal cells. In the posterior division of the median eminence, fibers of the third type are predominant in number and the fibers containing large granules are rare.

In mammals, the fine structure of the median eminence is almost the same as that of the posterior division of the avian median eminence (Matsui, 1966b). In the rat, the large granules are found mainly in the fiber layer. This is due to the fact that in mammals Gomori-positive material is not prominent in the external layer; instead, the capillaries penetrate into the parenchyma of the median eminence to reach the neurosecretory tract in the fiber layer. There are three types of electron-dense granules and small vesicles in the rat median eminence (Rinne, 1966). Synaptoid contacts have been described in the neurohemal region, as well as in the fiber layer, of the rat median eminence. In recent studies, we found terminals of either glial or neuronal processes which were filled with peculiar-shaped inclusions (Fig. 1-6). However, the biological significance of these inclusions is not clear.

In summary, it has become apparent that there are at least four types of axon endings in the fish neurohypophysis and in the tetrapod median eminence and pars nervosa (Fig. 1-11): (1) endings containing large granules measuring 1500 Å in diameter and small vesicles measuring 500 Å; (2) endings containing intermediate granules measuring 1200 Å in

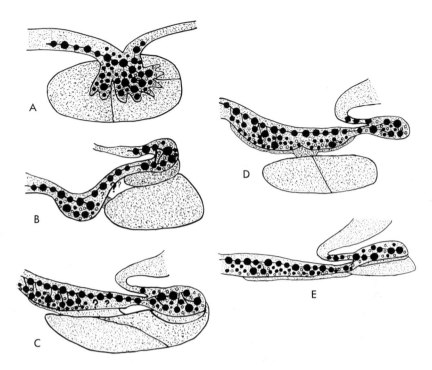

Figure 1-11   Diagram of distribution of granules and vesicles in the pars nervosa and median eminence. There are three types of granules (about 1500, 1200, and 1000 Å) and one type of small vesicle (500 Å). The large and the intermediate granules are believed to contain neurohypophyseal hormones; the small granules contain monoamines and the small vesicles contain acetylcholine. However, these granules or vesicles may also contain the releasing or inhibiting factors.

A. Possible distribution of granules and vesicles in the anterior and posterior portions of the neurohypophysis of the fish *Oryzias latipes*. This figure is based on histological observations that the anterior portion contains a small amount of Gomori-positive material and the posterior portion a large amount.

B. Hypothalamus and pituitary of the frog *Rana catesbeiana*. The fine structure of the outer layer of the stem region has not yet been studied.

C. Hypothalamus and pituitary of the turtle *Clemmys japonica*. The fine structure of the outer layer of the posterior division of the median eminence has not been examined.

D. Hypothalamus and pituitary of birds. Note the difference in granule distribution between the anterior and posterior divisions of median eminence.

E. Hypothalamus and pituitary of the rat. The fine structure is very much similar to the posterior division of the bird median eminence.

diameter and small vesicles measuring 500 Å; (3) endings containing small granules measuring 1000 Å in diameter and small vesicles measuring 500Å; and (4) endings containing exclusively small vesicles measuring 500Å. Both large and intermediate granules are conceivably carriers of at least neurohypophyseal hormones, the small granules are carriers of at least monoamines, and the small vesicles are carriers of at least acetyl-choline (see below).

Nature of Granules and Vesicles in the Fish Neurohypophysis and in the Tetrapod Median Eminence

Large and Intermediate Granules in the Median Eminence

The large granules (about 1500Å) and intermediate granules (about 1200Å) in the fish neurohypophysis and in the tetrapod median eminence must be granules carrying at least neurohypophyseal hormones. The reasons are as follows: (1) the distribution of the granules is the same as that of aldehyde-fuchsin stainable material in the median eminence (Matsui, 1966a,b); (2) the sizes of the granules in the median eminence are about the same as the sizes of the two types of granules in the neural lobe (Matsui, 1966a,b); (3) the median eminence contains neurohypophyseal hormones (Su. Ishii et al., 1962b; Hirano, 1964, 1966a; Kobayashi, et al., 1965); and (4) the large granules separated by centrifugation from the horse median eminence contain neurohypophyseal hormones. However, there is the possibility that these large granules may also contain releasing factors (Ishii, Su. et al., 1969).

Small Granules in the Median Eminence

The small granules (1000 Å) in the median eminence appear to be carrier granules of at least monoamines, judging from the following observations: (1) the size and the profile of the granules are similar to those of the granules carrying monoamines in the anterior hypothalamus (Pellegrino de Iraldi et al., 1963; Aghajanian and Bloom, 1966; Ishii, Se 1967); (2) the distribution of the small granules is the same as that of monoamines revealed in the median eminence with fluorescence microscopy (Fuxe, 1964); (3) a decrease in the number of the small granules is induced by reserpine injection (Rinne and Arstilla, 1966; Matsui, 1967b; Sano et al., 1967) and the fluorescence of monoamines in the median eminence is also decreased by the injection (Akmayev and Donáth, 1965; Sano *et al.*, 1967); and (4) the distribution of monoamine oxidase in the median eminence revealed by histochemistry is almost the same as that of the small granules (Matsui and Kobayashi, 1965; Follett *et al.*, 1966; Urano, 1968). The view that the small granules contain monoamines is shared by a number of investigators (Matsui, 1966a,b; Rinne, 1966; Knowles, 1967; Sano *et al.*, 1967). However, they may also contain releasing factors. Further studies are needed to clarify this possibility.

Small Vesicles in the Median Eminence

There is still some disagreement among investigators on the nature of the small vesicles (500Å). De Robertis and his associates (de Robertis *et al.*, 1963; de Robertis, 1964) argued that the small vesicles contained acetylcholine. This concept is supported by the following observations: (1) the rat median eminence contains about 10 μg of acetylcholine per gram of fresh tissue (Kobayashi *et al.*, 1966), and the fish urophysis, which contains numerous vesicles, has a high titer of acetylcholine (100 to 300 μg/gm) (Kobayashi *et al.*, 1963); (2) Uemura *et al.* (1963), studying the cow, and Lederis (1967), studying the rabbit, both found acetylcholine in the neural lobes; (3) the distribution of acetylcholinesterase is almost the same as that of the vesicles in the median eminence (Kobayashi and Farner, 1964; Uemura, 1964, 1965); and (4) the vesicles in the axon endings containing either large or small granules form clusters (active points) against the perivascular connective tissue space (Palay, 1955; Oota, 1963d). However, another interpretation of these vesicles (Holmes and Knowles, 1960; Knowles, 1963; Holmes, 1964; Lederis, 1965; Bern *et al.*, 1966) is that they are the result of fragmentation of larger neurosecretory granules. Electrical stimulation of neurosecretory axons of the mantis-shrimp *Squilla* induced fragmentation of neurosecretory granules and the formation of the smaller vesicles (Knowles, 1963). Palay (1957) showed that antidiuretic hormone release led to the disappearance of neurosecretory granules and a concomitant increase in the number of the small vesicles. Conversely, Oota and Kobayashi (1966) showed that deprivation of drinking water from the mouse led to the fragmentation and then the disappearance of the larger granules, but did not cause any increase of the small vesicles. They found an increase in the number of active points, which are formed by an aggregation of small vesicles against the perivascular space. Recently, Lederis (1967) separated the small vesicles from the rabbit neural lobe by means of centrifugation and presented evidence that the isolated vesicles contained acetylcholine. From these observations, it may be concluded that, in all probability, the small vesicles in the median eminence contain acetylcholine. It has not been determined whether the small vesicles also contain releasing factors.

Granules Carrying Releasing Factors

If it is assumed that the releasing and inhibiting factors in the median eminence are carried like other peptide hormones, they must be contained in either the granules or the small vesicles described above. To study this problem, Ishii, Su. *et al.* (1969) have separated out the granules in the horse median eminence. A homogenate of the horse median eminence, which contains much Gomori-positive neurosecretory material (Muramatsu, 1961), was fractionated by a series of differential centrifugations. Corticotropin releasing factor (CRF) and vasopressor activities were found in highest concentration in a sediment obtained at 41,000 G.

Figure 1-12   Vasopressor activity of ten fractions obtained from the homogenate of horse median eminence by means of ultracentrifugation using a continuous gradient of sucrose solutions from 1.04 to 2.00 M. Fraction 4 is a layer of sucrose solutions between 1.44 and 1.55 M. Size distribution curve of the granules in this fraction showed a peak at 1350 Å.

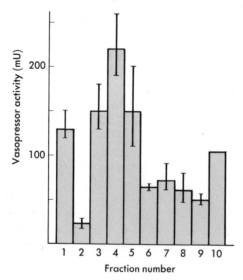

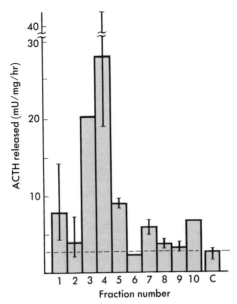

Figure 1-13   CRF activity of the same ten fractions as used for vasopressor activity. The broken line shows a blank level.

This sediment was resuspended in a 0.8 M sucrose solution, and then the solution was further fractionated by means of ultracentrifugation using a continuous gradient of sucrose solutions from 1.04 to 2.00 M. After the centrifugation, ten fractions were obtained. Both CRF and vasopressor activities were highest in fraction 4, which was a layer of sucrose between 1.44 and 1.55 (Figs. 1-12 and 1-13). The granules in this fraction had a peak at 1350 Å in their size distribution curve. It is therefore possible that, among the large granules, all of which were previously considered to be carrier granules of neurohypophyseal hormones, there are a certain number that contain CRF. However, it has not yet been proved that the CRF activity was not due to vasopressin. Recently, Ishii, Su. (personal communication) found that luteinizing hormone-releasing factor (LRF) is also associated with granules in the horse median eminence. These findings give us the idea that, among the small, intermediate, and large granules and the small vesicles, there must be those containing releasing factors other than CRF.

Biological Significance of Neurohormones and Neurohumors
in the Median Eminence

Releasing Factors

Much attention has been paid to the chemistry and the properties of
releasing factors, and these aspects of the subject need not be reviewed
here. However, an interesting point has been raised by Endröczi and
Hilliard (1965), who showed that, in the dog, LRF activity is distributed
not only in the median eminence, but also in other regions of the brain.
They therefore suggested that LRF and presumably other releasing factors
might have other roles in the brain in addition to releasing hormones from
the pars distalis.

Neurohypophyseal Hormones

The median eminence contains neurohypophyseal hormones, the only
difference between it and the pars nervosa being that the vasopressin/oxy-
tocin ratio is significantly higher in the median eminence in every species
examined (Hirano, 1964, 1966a). The biological significance of this
difference is uncertain.

Axon endings containing large granules of neurohypophyseal hormones
terminate at the capillaries of the primary plexus (Fig. 1–5). The number
of the terminals abutting on the capillaries depends upon the species
(Kobayashi, 1964). This finding suggests that neurohypophyseal hormones are secreted into the capillaries of the primary plexus and carried
to the pars distalis. It has been demonstrated that neurohypophyseal
hormones in the median eminence change in amount coincident with
changes in adenohypophyseal function (Hirano et al., 1962; Ishii, Su.
et al., 1962c; Kobayashi, 1963; Hirano, 1966b), although Follett and
Farner (1966) found evidence to the contrary in birds. The possibility
that the neurohypophyseal hormones act as releasers of the adenophypo-
physeal hormones is extensively discussed by Martini (1966). The hypothesis that such control exists is supported by the fact that in fish the
neurosecretory fibers innervate cells of the pars distalis (Knowles and
Vollrath, 1967). Several other possible effects of neurohypophyseal hormones on adenohypophyseal function deserve mention: (1) they may
change the permeability of the membrane of the adenohypophyseal cells;
(2) they may modify the general metabolism of pars distalis cells by their

effects on the mitochondria (Greenbaum and Dicker, 1962), or by glucose oxidation (Barondes, 1962); or (3) they may constrict or dilate the capillaries of the primary plexus (Worthington, 1955, 1960, 1963) or the sinuses in the pars distalis.

Another suggested role for vasopressin in the median eminence has been advanced by Hedge et al. (1966). These investigators demonstrated that injection of vasopressin into the rat median eminence induced ACTH secretion from the adenohypophysis. Secretion of ACTH was not induced by direct application of vasopressin to the adenohypophysis. They concluded that vasopressin caused the median eminence to release CRF. Endröczi and Hilliard (1965) observed that, in the rabbit, intratuberal vasopressin injection produced LH release, while intrapituitary injection did not. These two experiments suggest that vasopressin may influence the ending in the median eminence of the axons that contain releasing factors.

Acetylcholine

The vesicles carrying acetylcholine coexist with the small, intermediate, or large granules in the axon endings. Clusters of small vesicles (active points) were often encountered against the inner surface of the membranes of the axon bulbs abutting on the capillary wall (Palay, 1955; Oota, 1963d). It has been suggested that acetylcholine liberated from the clusters of the vesicles penetrates the axon membrane and changes its permeability, facilitating in some way the passage of neurohypophyseal hormones, releasing factors, or monoamines. This hypothesis was first presented by Koelle (1962).

Some of the axonal endings in the median eminence contain only small vesicles. These axons are probably purely cholinergic. Their function is not clear, but they may affect the capillaries of the primary plexus. It seems unlikely that acetylcholine reaches the adenohypophysis via the portal vessels, since acetylcholine is rapidly destroyed by acetylcholinesterase in the blood.

Monoamines and Other Biologically Active Substances

Synaptoid contacts are found mostly in the hypendymal and fiber layers of the median eminence in the pigeon, white-crowned sparrow, mouse, and rat (Fig. 1–7; Matsui, 1966a,b; Oota and Farner, unpublished data). The presynaptic axons are probably noradrenergic, judging from the results of Fuxe and Hökfelt (1967). The postsynaptic structures appear to be ependymal processes of hypendymal cell bodies. It is possible, therefore, that monoaminergic axons regulate ependymal secretion or absorption.

The roles of the monoamines, and especially of the dopamine found in the palisade layer of the median eminence (Fuxe, 1964; Fuxe and Hökfelt, 1967), are uncertain. Considering the fine structure of the median eminence, it seems likely that dopamine in the palisade layer is transferred to the adenohypophysis and affects the cells directly. This view is supported by the observation that, in lower vertebrates, monoaminergic fibers terminate directly on endocrine cells of the adenohypophysis (see above). An alternate view is that they may be concerned with secretion of releasing factors from the axon endings in the median eminence.

Substance P, serotonin, histamine, and γ-aminobutyric acid have been detected in the hypothalamus (see Ganong and Lorenzen, 1967). Serotonin implanted in the median eminence has no effect on LH release, but melatonin and 5-hydroxytryptophol implants reduce LH release (Fraschini et al., 1968). Additional studies of possible endocrine effects of these substances are needed.

Implantation of Monoamines and Dibenamine in the Median Eminence

To investigate the action of monoamines in the median eminence, we have implanted norepinephrine, dopamine, and dibenamine in the rat median eminence (Matsui, 1967a; Kobayashi, 1969; Uemura and Kobayashi, unpublished data). When the tips of the cannulae containing a mixture of norepinephrine (NA) and cholesterol (1 to 1 by weight) were placed in the median eminence, the rats showed irregular estrous cycles with prolonged estrous and diestrous phases (Fig. 1-14). The ovaries showed small corpora lutea, moderate interstitial tissue, and follicles of normal size. The ovarian weight was one-third that of control rats bearing cannulae which were empty or which contained only cholesterol. These control rats showed regular estrous cycles (Fig. 1-15). The rats with implanted cannulae containing a mixture of 3 parts NA to 1 part cholesterol showed prolonged diestrous phases with intermittent estrus when the tips of the cannulae were placed in the median eminence (Fig. 1-16). The ovaries had no functional corpora lutea and the interstitial tissue was abundant. The ovarian weight was one-third that of the control rats. These results suggest that the release of LH was inhibited to some extent by implanted NA and, further, that the inhibitory effect was stronger when the concentration of NA in the mixture was higher. Matsui (1967a) observed a disturbance in rat estrous cycles when cannulae containing

Figure 1-14   Estrous cycles of rats receiving implants of a mixture of norepinephrine and cholesterol (1 to 1) in the median eminence. Tallest black bar
shows estrus and shorter one proestrus. The rat number is shown at the left
side of the figures.   Op, date of operation.

Figure 1-15   Estrous cycles of rats receiving implants of cholesterol in the
median eminence.

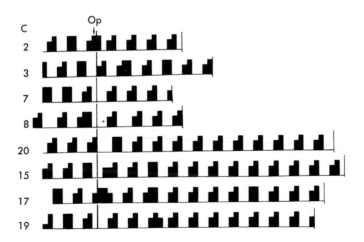

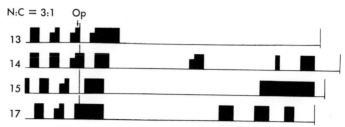

Figure 1-16   Estrous cycles of rats receiving implants of a mixture of norepinephrine and cholesterol (3 to 1) in the median eminence.

NA—in what was probably a lower concentration than ours—were implanted into the median eminence. NA implants in the arcuate nucleus induced weaker effects than in the median eminence. The rats bearing cannulae containing NA showed regular estrous cycles when the tips of the cannulae were placed in the adenohypophysis (Fig. 1-17) and in hypothalamic nuclei other than the arcuate nucleus. Implantation of dopamine mixed with cholesterol (2 to 1 or 5 to 1) provoked effects that were similar to those of NA on estrous cycles and ovarian weight (Fig. 1-18). Donovan and Harris (1956) found that slow injection of NA into the rabbit adenohypophysis had no effect on LH release. Therefore, the effects of NA implanted in the median eminence or arcuate nucleus are probably not exerted directly on the adenohypophysis.

Another possibility is that NA reduces the amount of LRF reaching the adenohypophysis by constricting the capillaries of the primary plexus. This seems unlikely because in rats that had had NA implants for two

Figure 1-17   Estrous cycles of rats receiving implants of a mixture of norepinephrine and cholesterol (1 to 1) into the pars distalis.

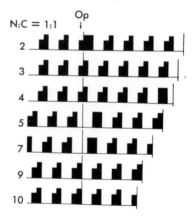

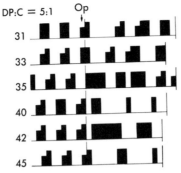

Figure 1-18   Estrous cycles of rats receiving implants of a mixture of dopamine and cholesterol (5 to 1) in the median eminence.

weeks the weights of the adrenals and thyroids were not affected. Presumably, therefore, NA acts on some neural mechanism involved in LRF release in the arcuate nucleus or the median eminence.

Implantation of the adrenergic blocking agent dibenamine mixed with cholesterol (1 to 10, 2 to 1, or 4 to 1 by weight) brought about prolonged diestrus only when the tips of the cannulae were in the arcuate nucleus–median eminence region (Fig. 1-19). The uterus showed deciduoma when it was traumatized. The ovary had large functional corpora lutea. Implants placed in regions nearby had no effect on the estrous cycle. These findings suggest that dibenamine induces the release of prolactin, and hence it is reasonable to speculate that NA stimulates the release of PIF. Our findings

Figure 1-19   Estrous cycles of rats receiving implants of a mixture of dibenamine and cholesterol (2 to 1 or 4 to 1) in the median eminence.

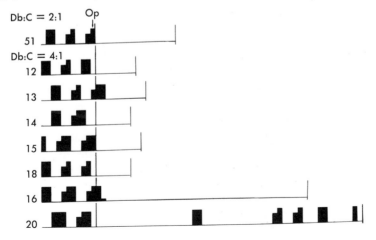

are in good agreement with the effects obtained by injection of monoamine depletors, which induce pseudopregnancy in the rat (Barraclough and Sawyer, 1959; Meites *et al.*, 1963; Yoshida, 1964; Coppola *et al.*, 1965).

It should be noted here that, in our implantation experiments, all the reagents were implanted for 2 to 4 weeks. Different results may be obtained with different routes and periods of administration. Actually, Sawyer *et al.* (1949, 1950) observed that systemic but not local injection of NA induced ovulation in the rabbit, indicating LH release. Endröczi and Hilliard (1965) injected NA into the rabbit tuberal region and observed no effect on LH release. Comparison of results should be cautious, however, when the routes and periods of administration vary.

Experimental Studies on the Fine Structure of the Median Eminence

Effect of Adrenalectomy, Thyroidectomy, and Other Experimental Treatments on Axonal Inclusions

There are scattered data on ultrastructural changes induced in the median eminence of animals by various experimental manipulations. Akmayev *et al.* (1967) observed that in the adrenalectomized rats the size of granules in the palisade layer ranged from 900 to 1500 Å, whereas the size in control rats was 600 to 1200 Å. Furthermore, in the experimental rats, almost half of the granules lost their central cores and appeared to be vesicular. From these results it seems likely that CRF is associated with some of the granules in the median eminence. In our separation experiments, CRF is associated with the large granules about 1350 Å in diameter (see above). Thyroidectomy did not cause any significant ultrastructural change in the rat median eminence (Akmayev *et al.*, 1967). Streefkerk (1967) could not detect any change in the ultrastructure of the rat median eminence following dehydration or injection of formalin.

Harris and Campbell (1966) compared the ultrastructure of the median eminence of normal estrous rabbits with that of female rabbits 5 to 30 minutes after coitus. They observed a decrease in the number of electron-lucent neurosecretory vesicles (about 1000Å) and increases in the numbers of small vesicles and of their clusters. In many cases, clusters of vesicles were impinging on the membrane of the nerve terminals. Bern *et al.* (1966) observed that the median eminence of photorefractory white-crowned sparrows contained many more small granules (800 to 1000Å) than that of the photosensitive birds kept under an 8-hour or 20-hour photoperiod. However, osmotic stress did not change the size and population of the granules in the median eminence of birds kept under an 8-hour photoperiod. These data suggest that the small granules (1000 Å), which have been considered to contain monoamines, may also be involved in release of LH or other gonadotropins from the adenohypophysis.

Castration and Axonal Inclusions

Akmayev *et al.* (1967) could find no noticeable change in the fine structure of the rat median eminence 2 weeks after castration. However, T. Koba-

Figure 1-20   Neurohemal area of the median eminence of the normal rat. Many monoaminergic axons containing small granules (SG) are observed. Neurosecretory axons containing intermediate granules (IG) are intermingled, but those containing large granules are not visible in this figure.   AP, clusters of small vesicles (active point); EN, endothelial cell; PV, perivascular space. × 18,900.

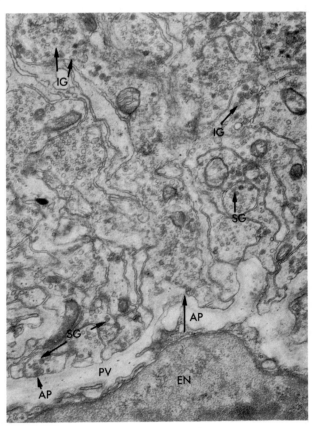

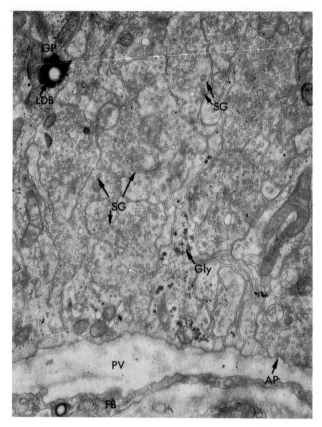

Figure 1-21   Neurohemal region of the rat median eminence three weeks after castration. Compare with that of normal rat (Figure 1-20). Most monoaminergic axons contain many small granules (SG). Synaptic vesicles are markedly increased.   AP, active point; FB, fibroblast; Gly, glycogen granules; LDB, large dense body with electron-lucent matrix; GP, glial process; PV, perivascular space.   × 18,900.

yashi *et al.* (1967) have reported that in rats the number of vesicles with diameters of 600 to 1000 Å is remarkably increased 2 weeks after castration. No significant change in the population and structure of the larger dense granules was observed. Our recent studies (Matsui and Kobayashi, unpublished data) have demonstrated that there were marked increases in the numbers both of the small vesicles (500 Å) and of small granules with or without cores (1000 Å) 3 weeks after castration in rats (Figs 1-20 and 1-21). Daily injections of 10 μg of estradiol-17β during the period suppressed the increase of the small granules; however, an increase of the small vesicles was not abolished by the treatment. These results also suggest that the granules with a diameter of about 1000 Å are related to gonadotropin release.

Castration, Estrogen, and Ependymal or Glial Secretion

Three weeks after castration, cytoplasmic organelles such as the Golgi apparatus, large vesicles of rough-surfaced endoplasmic reticula, poly-

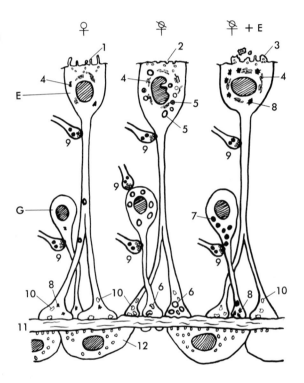

Figure 1-22   Diagram of the ependymal (E) and glial (G) cells in the median eminence of the normal female rat (♀), the rat three weeks after ovariectomy (♀), and the rat receiving daily injections of estrogen for three weeks beginning the day after castration (♀ + E).   1, microvilli; 2, pit forming pinocytotic vesicle; 3, bulbous protrusion; 4, Golgi apparatus; 5, developing and mature stages of large electron-dense bodies with electron-lucent matrix; 6, deforming stage of electron-dense body with electron-lucent matrix; 7, solid electron-dense body; 8, deforming stage of solid electron-dense body; 9, synaptoid contact of monoaminergic axon with ependymal and glial elements; 10, unknown cytoplasmic inclusion in the ependymal and glial processes; 11, perivascular connective tissue space; 12, endothelial cell.   See text for explanation.

somes, and glycogen granules became prominent in the ependymal and hypendymal cells of the rat median eminence. Furthermore, large round electron-dense bodies were noticeably increased around both the Golgi apparatus and the rough-surfaced endoplasmic reticula (Fig. 1-22). The bodies had a electron-dense margin and the matrix was electron-lucent. In these castrated rats the cytoplasmic protrusions, such as the microvilli seen in normal rats, were poorly developed. Instead, small pinocytotic vesicles or small pits were often observed at the apical surface of the epen-dymal cells. After castration the terminals of the ependymal and hypen-dymal processes showed increases in the numbers of glycogen granules, small granules, large electron-dense bodies with electron-lucent matrix, and vesicles with various shapes. Some of the dense bodies were deformed

Figure 1-23   Ependymal cells of the median eminence of the rat given daily injections of estrogen for three weeks beginning the day of castration. Cyto-plasm is filled with well-developed organelles. At the apical surface, many bulbous protrusions (BP) were induced by estrogen. In their neck portion, small vesicles tend to make a line from one side to the other (LV). The small vesicles near the apical surface are seemingly extensions of Golgi vesicles (ExGA). Dense bodies (DB) are usually irregular.   GA, Golgi apparatus; III, third ventricle.   × 16,100.

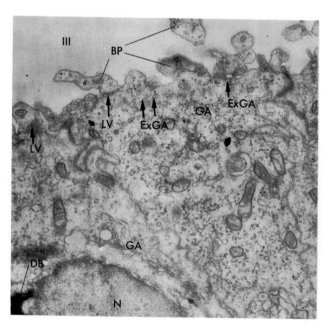

stellate masses of lipid that had no limiting membrane. Vacuoles or vesicles and dense bodies were closely associated with the membrane of the endfeet (Fig. 1-22). At the moment we cannot attach any physiological meaning to the changes caused by castration in the rat ependymal and hypendymal cells.

Daily injections of estrogen for 3 weeks did not alter the appearance of the cytoplasmic organelles in the ependymal cells of the castrated rats, except that estrogen brought about large irregular solid electron-dense bodies that were different in shape from those found in the castrated rats. The ependymal and hypendymal cells had more numerous bleb-like and bulbous protrusions than those seen in the control or castrated, uninjected rats (Figs. 1-22 and 1-23). Masses of cytoplasm detached from the cells were frequently observed in the ventricular cavity. They contained endoplasmic reticula and many vacuoles or vesicles. These findings suggest that estrogen stimulates ependymal secretion into the third ventricle. In the terminals of processes of these cells, an increase in the number of solid bodies and glycogen granules was obvious. Kumar and Knowles (1967) have reported that in the ovariectomized rhesus monkey the specialized ependymal cells located anterolaterally in the tuber cinereum show many irregular globular electron-dense masses after injection of labeled estrogen. They also demonstrated that a large amount of estrogen was found in those ependymal cells.

Some glial cells located in the fiber and palisade layers responded to castration in a similar manner to the ependymal cells; they had well-developed cytoplasmic organelles, and elaborated a number of round dense bodies with electron-lucent matrix. Around such bodies many glycogen granules were gathered. Injections of estrogen to these animals did not induce any appreciable change in cytoplasmic inclusions, except for induction of many irregular-shaped and solid dense bodies (Fig. 1-22) that were different from the dense bodies in the ependymal and glial cells of the uninjected, castrated rats. The endfeet of the glial cells responded to castration and estrogen in a similar way to those of the ependymal cells.

Although at the present time it is difficult to attach biological meanings to any of the phenomena mentioned above, the evidence suggests that the ependymal and glial cells of the median eminence are involved in the hypothalamo-hypophyseal-gonadal interrelationship.

Conclusions

Although it is well known that the median eminence contains high titers of releasing factors, we have very little information about the precise sites of production of these factors and the neural mechanisms governing their secretion. It may be helpful to consider the Gomori-positive neurosecretory system as a model for the releasing factor of the neurosecretory system. Monoaminergic fibers form synaptic contacts with the perikarya and axons of Gomori-positive neurosecretory cells (see above), and may control them. Monoamine oxidase activity is high around Gomori-positive neurosecretory perikarya. The small vesicles carrying acetylcholine are present in the terminals of both Gomori-positive neurosecretory axons and monoaminergic axons. The acetylcholine in the terminals may be involved in the mechanism releasing neurohypophyseal hormones or monoamines from the axon endings. Gomori-positive neurosecretory neurons show a strong reaction to acetylcholinesterase.

The findings of Barry *et al.* (1965, 1966) are pertinent to this problem. They found that the cells of the hypothalamic laterodorsal interstitial nucleus of the guinea pig, which are Gomori-negative, contain secretory granules and show a strong acetylcholinesterase activity. The cells of the nucleus showed increases in secretory activity and acetylcholinesterase after castration. Androgen injection suppressed the effects of castration. Furthermore, Barry *et al.* (1965) have shown that an extract of the hypothalamic laterodorsal interstitial nucleus provokes a decrease in the amount of ascorbic acid and cholesterol in the rat ovary. They are of the opinion that the nucleus may elaborate LRF.

Neurohormones and neurohumors such as neurohypophyseal hormones, acetylcholine, and monoamines are usually carried by granules or vesicles visualized under the electron microscope. Releasing factors are probably carried by some kind of granule, and stored in the median eminence. We have found that in the tetrapod median eminence there are three types of granules and one type of small vesicles. We feel that the large and intermediate granules contain neurohypophyseal hormones, and the small granules contain monoamines. The small vesicles contain acetylcholine. The populations of the granules and small vesicles in the rat median eminence are altered by adrenalectomy and castration. This suggests intragranular localization of CRF and gonadotropin releasing factor. Finally, it has been demonstrated that CRF and LRF are associated with granules isolated by ultracentrifugation from the horse median eminence.

The avian median eminence is divisible into anterior and posterior divisions; the anterior division has a functional relationship with the cephalic lobe and the posterior division with the caudal lobe of the pars distalis. These findings led us to consider regional differentiation in function in the median eminence of other animal classes, and several aspects of this subject have been discussed above. The studies emphasize the importance of the comparative approach in investigations of the hypo-thalamo-hypophyseal relationship.

The presence of monoamine granules in the median eminence stimulated us to explore the roles of monoamines. We have obtained evidence that NA and dopamine decrease the release of LH from the rat pars distalis, and that dibenamine induces the release of prolactin. Further experiments are needed to clarify definite roles and sites of action of monoamines in the median eminence.

Considering the data collected so far, it may be stated that a great deal of interest has been uncovered, but there is a great deal more to be done.

Acknowledgments

Investigations by the senior author and his co-workers were supported by a grant from the Ministry of Education of Japan and a grant (A-3678) from United States Public Health Service. The authors are indebted to Drs. H. Uemura, Su. Ishii, Y. Oota, and T. Hirano, and Mr. A. Urano, Mr. K. Yokoyama, and Mr. T. Asai for their collaboration in the investigations, and Miss Y. Osada for her kind help in preparing the manuscript.

References

Abrahams, V. C., G. B. Koelle, and P. Smart (1957). Histochemical demonstrations of cholinesterases in the hypothalamus of the dog. *J. Physiol. (London) 139*, 137-44.

Aghajanian, G. K., and F. E. Bloom (1966). Electron-microscopic autoradiography of rat hypothalamus after intraventricular H^3-norepinephrine. *Science 153*, 308-10.

Akmayev, I. G., and T. Donáth (1965). Die Katecholamine der Zona palisadica der Eminentia mediana des Hypothalamus bei Adrenalektomie, Hydrocortison-verabreichung und Stress. *Z. mikr.-anat. Forsch. 74*, 83-91.

Akmayev, I. G., R. Réthelyi, and K. Majorossy (1967). Changes induced by adrenalectomy in nerve endings of the hypothalamic median eminence (Zona palisadica) in the albino rat. *Acta Biol. Hung. 18*, 187-200.

Arvy, L. (1963). *Histo-enzymologie des Glandes Endocrines.* Gauthier-Villars, Paris.

Assenmacher, I., and A. Tixier-Vidal (1964). Hypothalamic-pituitary relations. *Proc. 2nd Int. Cong. Endocrinol., Excerpta Medica, Int. Cong. Ser. 83*, Part 1, 131-45.

Barer, R., H. Heller, and K. Lederis (1963). The isolation, identification and properties of the hormonal granules of the neurohypophysis., *Proc. Roy. Soc.* B *158*, 388-416.

Bargmann, W. (1966). Neurosecretion. *Int. Rev. Cytol. 19*, 183-201.

Bargmann, W., and A. Knoop (1957). Elektronmikroskopische Beobachtungen an der Neurohypophyse. *Z. Zellforsch. 46*, 242-51.

Barondes, S. H. (1962).　The influence of neuroamines on the oxidation of glucose by the anterior pituitary. *J. Biol. Chem. 237*, 204-7.

Barraclough, C. A., and C. H. Sawyer (1959).　Induction of pseudopregnancy in the rate by reserpine and chlorpromazine. *Endocrinology 65*, 563-71.

Barry, J., and G. Cotte (1961).　Étude préliminaire, au microscope électronique, de l'éminence médiane du cobaye. *Z. Zellforsch. 53*, 714-24.

Barry J., and J. Léonardelli (1966).　Variation de l'activité acétylcholinestérasique de l'hypothalamus chez le cobaye mâle, castré ou soumis à l'action d'androgenes. *C. R. Soc. Biol. (Lille) 160*, 1608-10.

Barry, J., C. Lefranc, J. Léonardelli, and J. C. Fourlinnie (1965).　Effets de l'injection d'extraits frais de noyau hypothalamique latérodorsal interstitiel de cobaye sur le taux de cholestérol ovarien de rattes préparée pour le test de Bell, Mukerji et Loraine. *C. R. Soc. Biol. 1159*, 1152.

Benoit, J., and I. Assenmacher (1953).　Rapports entre la stimulation préhypophysaire et la neurosécrétion chez l'oiseau.　*Arch. Anat. micr. Morph. exp. 42*, 334-86.

Bern, H. A., and F. G. W. Knowles (1966).　Neurosecretion.　In *Neuroendocrinology* (L. Martini and W. F. Ganong, eds.), *1*, pp. 139-86.　Academic Press, New York, London.

Bern, H. A., and R. S. Nishioka (1965).　Fine structure of the median eminence of some passerine birds. *Proc. Zool. Soc.* (Calcutta) *18*, 107-19.

Bern, H. A., and K. Yagi (1965).　Electrophysiology of neurosecretory systems. *Proc. 2nd Int. Cong. Endocrin., Excerpta Medica, Int. Cong. Ser. 83*, Part 1, 577-83.

Bern, H. A., R. S. Nishioka, L. R. Mewaldt, and D. S. Farner (1966).　Photoperiodic and osmotic influences on the ultrastructure of the hypothalamic neurosecretory system of the white-crowned sparrow, *Zonotrichia leucophrys gambelii*. *Z. Zellforsch. 69*, 198-227.

Carlsson, A., B. Falck, and N.-Å. Hillarp (1962).　Cellular localization of brain monoamines. *Acta Physiol. Scand.* Suppl. *56*, 196.

Christ, J. F. (1966).　Nerve supply, blood supply and cytology of the neurohypophysis.　In *The Pituitary Gland* (G. W. Harris and B. T. Donovan, eds.), *3*, pp. 62-130.　Butterworths, London.

Cohen, A. G. (1967).　Observations on the pars intermedia of *Xenopus laevis*. *Nature 215*, 55-56.

Coppola, J. A., R. G. Leonardi, W. Lippmann, J. W. Perrine, and I. Ringler (1965).　Induction of pseudopregnancy in rats by depletors of endogenous catecholamines. *Endocrinology 77*, 485-90.

Daniel, P. M. (1966).　The anatomy of the hypothalamus and pituitary gland.　In *Neuroendocrinology* (L. Martini and W. G. Ganong, eds)., *1*, pp. 15-80.　Academic Press, New York, London.

Dent, J. N. (1961).　Seasonal and sexual variation in the pituitary gland of *Triturus viridescens*. *Anat. Rec. 141*, 85-96.

de Robertis, E. (1964).　*Histophysiology of Synapses and Neurosecretion.*　Pergamon Press, Oxford, London, Edinburgh, New York, Paris, Frankfurt.

de Robertis, E., L. Salganicoff, L. M. Zieher, and G. Rodriguez de Lores Arnaiz (1963).　Acetylcholine and cholinesterase content of synaptic vesicles. *Science 140*, 300-301.

Diepen, R. (1962). Der Hypothalamus.　In *Handb. mikr. Anat. des Menschen* (W.

Möllendorff and W. Bargmann, eds.), Bd. *4*, T. 6.   Springer-Verlag, Berlin, Göttingen, Heidelberg.

Donovan, B. T., and G. W. Harris (1956).   Adrenergic agents and the release of gonadotrophic hormone in the rabbit.   *J. Physiol.* (London) *132*, 577-85.

Duffy, P. E., and M. Menefee (1965).   Electron microscopic observations of neurosecretory granules, nerve and glial fibers, and blood vessels in the median eminence of the rabbit.   *Am. J. Anat. 117*, 251-86.

Duke, H. N., M. Pickford, and J. A. Watt (1950).   The immediate and delayed effects of di-iso-propylfluorophosphate injection in the supraoptic nuclei of dogs.   *J. Physiol.* (London) *111*, 81-88.

Endröczi, E., and J. Hilliard (1965).   Luteinizing hormone releasing activity in different parts of rabbit and dog brain.   *Endocrinology 77*, 667-73.

Enemar, A., and B. Falck (1965).   On the presence of adrenergic nerves in the pars intermedia of the frog, *Rana temporaria*.   *Gen. Comp. Endocrinol. 5*, 577-83.

Enemar, A., B. Falck, and F. C. Iturriza (1967).   Adrenergic nerves in the pars intermedia of the pituitary in the toad, *Bufo arenarum*.   *Z. Zellforsch. 77*, 305-30.

Falck, B. (1964).   Cellular localization of monoamines.   *Prog. Brain Res. 8,* 28-44.

Farner, D. S., F. E. Wilson, and A. Oksche (1967).   Neuroendocrine mechanisms in birds.   In *Neuroendocrinology* (L. Martini and W. F. Ganong, eds.), *2*, pp. 529-82.   Academic Press, New York, London.

Feldberg, W., and M. Vogt (1948).   Acetylcholine synthesis in different regions of the central nervous system.   *J. Physiol. (London) 107*, 372-81.

Follenius, E. (1965a).   Bases structurales et ultrastructurales des correlations hypothalamo-hypophysaires chez quelques espèces de téléostéens.   *Thèse de Sciences*, in *Ann. Sci. Nat. Zool. 180*, Série 7, 1-150.

Follenius, E. (1965b).   Bases structurales et ultrastructurales des correlations diencéphalo-hypophysaires chez les sélaciens et les téléostéens.   *Arch. Anat. micr. Morph. exp. 54*, 195-216.

Follenius, E. (1967).   Cytologie des systèmes neurosécreteurs hypothalamo-hypophysaires des poissons téléostéens.   In *Neurosecretion* (F. Stutinsky, ed.), pp. 42-55.   Springer-Verlag, Berlin, Heidelberg, New York.

Follett, B. K., and D. S. Farner (1966).   The effects of the daily photoperiod on gonadal growth, neurohypophysial hormone content, and neurosecretion in the hypothalamo-hypophysial system of the Japanese quail, *Coturnix coturnix japonica*.   *Gen. Comp. Endocrinol. 7*, 111-24.

Follett, B. K., H. Kobayashi, and D. S. Farner (1966).   The distribution of monoamine oxidase and acetylcholinesterase in the hypothalamus and its relation to the hypothalamo-hypophysial neurosecretory system in the white-crowned sparrow, *Zonotrichia leucophrys gambelii*.   *Z. Zellforsch. 75*, 57-65.

Fraschini, F., B. Mess, F. Piva, and L. Martini (1968).   Brain receptors sensitive to indole compounds: function in control of luteinizing hormone secretion.   *Science 159*, 1104-5.

Fuxe, K. (1964).   Cellular localization of monoamines in the median eminence and the infundibular stem of some mammals.   *Z. Zellforsch. 61*, 710-24.

Fuxe, K., and T. Hökfelt (1967).   The influence of central catecholamine neurons on the hormone secretion from the anterior and posterior pituitary.   In *Neurosecretion* (F. Stutinsky, ed.), pp. 165-77.   Springer-Verlag, Berlin, Heidelberg, New York.

Ganong, W. F., and L. Lorenzen (1967). Brain neurohumors and endocrine function. In *Neuroendocrinology* (L. Martini and W. F. Ganong, eds.), *2*, pp. 583-640. Academic Press, New York, London.

Green, J. D. (1951). The comparative anatomy of the hypophysis, with special reference to its blood supply and innervation. *Am. J. Anat. 88*, 225-311.

Greenbaum, A. L., and S. E. Dicker (1962). The effects of mammalian posterior lobe hormones on the swelling of liver and kidney mitochondria, in the rat and the dog. *Biochim. Biophys. Acta 74*, 519-24.

Grignon, G. (1963). Cytophysiologie de l'adenohypophyse des Reptiles. In *Cytologie de l'Adenohypophyse* (J. Benoit and C. Da Lage, eds.), *Colloq. Int. C.N.R.S. (Paris) 128*, pp. 287-300.

Harris, G. W., and H. J. Campbell (1966). The regulation of the secretion of luteinizing hormone and ovulation. In *The Pituitary Gland* (G. W. Harris and B. T. Donovan, eds.), *2*, pp. 99-165. Butterworths, London.

Hedge, G. A., M. B. Yates, R. Marcus, and F. E. Yates (1966). Site of action of vasopressin in causing corticotropin release. *Endocrinology, 79*, 328-40.

Hirano, T. (1964). Further studies on the neurohypophysial hormones in the avian median eminence. *Endocrinol. Japon. 11*, 87-95.

Hirano, T. (1966a). Neurohypophysial hormones in the median eminence of the bullfrog, turtle and duck. *Endocrinol. Japon. 13*, 59-74.

Hirano, T. (1966b). Neurohypophysial hormones in the pigeon median eminence in relation to reproductive cycle and formalin stress. *J. Fac. Sci., Univ. Tokyo*, Sec. IV, *11*, 43-48.

Hirano, T., Su Ishii, and H. Kobayashi (1962). Effects of prolongation of daily photoperiod on gonadal development and neurohypophysial hormone activity in the median eminence and the pars nervosa of the passerine bird, *Zosterops palpebrosa japonica. Annot. Zool. Japon. 35*, 64-71.

Holmes, R. L. (1964). Comparative observations on inclusions in nerve fibers of the mammalian neurohypophysis. *Z. Zellforsch. 64*, 474-92.

Holmes, R. L., and F. G. W. Knowles (1960). "Synaptic vesicles" in the neurohypophysis. *Nature* (London) *185*, 710-11.

Ishii, Se. (1967). Morphological studies on the distribution and properties of the granulated vesicles in the brain. *Arch. histol. jap. 28*, 355-76.

Ishii, Su., T. Iwata, and H. Kobayashi (1969). Intragranular localization of corticotropin releasing factor and vasopressin in the horse median eminence. *Endocrinol. Jap. 15*, in press.

Ishii, Su., I. Yasumasu, H. Kobayashi, Y. Oota, T. Hirano, and A. Tanaka (1962a). Isolation of neurosecretory granules and nerve endings from bovine posterior lobe. *Annot. Zool. Japon. 35*, 121-27.

Ishii, Su., T. Hirano, and H. Kobayashi (1962b). Neurohypophyseal hormones in the avian median eminence and pars nervosa. *Gen. Comp. Endocrinol. 2*, 433-40.

Ishii, Su., T. Hirano, and Kobayashi (1962c). Preliminary report on the neurohypophysial hormone activity in the avian median eminence. *Zool. Mag. (Dobutsugaku Zasshi) 71*, 206-11 (in Japanese with English summary).

Ishibashi, T. (1962). Electrical activity of the caudal neurosecretory cells in the eel, *Anguilla japonica*, with special reference to synaptic transmission. *Gen. Comp. Endocrinol. 2*, 415-24.

Kandel, E. R. (1964). Electrical properties of hypothalamic neuroendocrine cells. *J. Gen. Physiol. 47*, 691-717.

Kawabata, I. (1964). Electron microscopy of the rat hypothalamic neurosecretory system. I. The supraoptic nuclei of normal and dehydrated rats. *Gunma Symp. Endocrinol. 1*, 51-58.

Kawamoto, M. (1967). Zur Morphologie der Hypophysis Cerebri von Teleostieren. *Arch. histol. jap. 28*, 123-50.

Knowles, F. G. W. (1963). Techniques in the study of neurosecretion. In *Techniques in Endocrine Research* (P. Eckstein and F. G. W. Knowles, eds.), pp. 57-65. Academic Press, London, New York.

Knowles, F. G. W. (1965). Evidence for a dual control, by neurosecretion, of hormone synthesis and hormone release in the pituitary of the dogfish, *Scylliorhinus stellaris. Phil. Trans.* B *249*, 435-56.

Knowles, F. G. W. (1967). Neuronal properties of neurosecretory cells. In *Neurosecretion* (F. Stutinsky, ed.), pp. 8-19. Springer-Verlag, Berlin, Heidelberg, New York.

Knowles, F. G. W., and L. Vollrath (1966). Neurosecretory innervation of the pituitary of the eels, *Anguilla* and *Conger.* I.The structure and ultrastructure of the neuro-intermediate lobe under normal and experimental conditions. II. The structure and innervation of the pars distalis at different stages of the life-cycle. *Phil. Trans.* B *250*, 311-42.

Kobayashi, H. (1963). Median eminence of birds. *Proc. XIIIth. Int. Ornithol. Cong.*, 1069-84.

Kobayashi, H. (1964). Histochemical, electron microscopic and pharmacologic studies of the median eminence. *Proc. 2nd Int. Cong. Endocrinol., Excerpta Medica, Int. Cong.* Ser. *83*, Part 1, 570-76.

Kobayashi, H. (1969). Fine structure and adrenergic mechanism of the median eminence in relation to gonadotropic activity of the adenohypophysis. In *La Photoregulation des Cycles Sexuels chez les Oiseaux et les Mammifères* (J. Benoit and I. Assenmacher, eds.). *Colloq. Int. C.N.R.S. (Paris),* in press.

Kobayashi, H., and D. S. Farner (1964). Cholinesterases in the hypothalamo-hypophysial neurosecretory system of the white-crowned sparrow, *Zonotrichia leucophrys gambelii. Z. Zellforsch. 63*, 965-73.

Kobayashi, H., and T. Matsui (1967). Synapses in the rat and pigeon median eminence. *Endocrinol. Japon. 14*, 279-83.

Kobayashi, H., Su. Ishii, and A. Gorbman (1959). The hypothalamic neurosecretory apparatus and the pituitary gland of a teleost, *Lepidogobius lepidus. Gunma J. Med. Sciences 8*, 301-21.

Kobayashi, H., H. A. Bern, R. S. Nishioka, and Y. Hyodo (1961). The hypothalamo-hypophysial neurosecretory system of the parakeet, *Melopsittacus undulatus. Gen. Comp. Endocrinol. 1*, 545-64.

Kobayashi, H., H. Uemura, Y. Oota, and Su. Ishii (1963). Cholinergic substance in caudal neurosecretory storage organ of fish. *Science 141*, 714-15.

Kobayashi, H., T. Hirano, and Y. Oota (1965). Electron microscopic and pharmacological studies on the median eminence and pars nervosa. *Arch. Anat. micr. Morph. exp. 54*, 277-94.

Kobayashi, H., Y. Oota, H. Uemura, and T. Hirano (1966). Electron microscopic and pharmacological studies on the rat median eminence. *Z. Zellforsch. 71*, 387-404.

Kobayashi, T., T. Kobayashi, K. Yamamoto, and M. Inatomi (1963). Electron microscopic observation on the hypothalamo-hypophyseal system in the rat. I. The ultrafine structure of the contact region between the external layer of the infundibulum and pars tuberalis of the anterior pituitary. *Endocrinol. Japon. 10*, 69-80.

Kobayashi, T., T. Kobayashi, K. Yamamoto, M. Kaibara, and Y. Kameya (1967). Electron microscopic observation on the hypothalamo-hypophyseal system in the rat. II. Ultrafine structure of the median eminence and of the nerve cells of the arcuate nucleus. *Endocrinol. Japon. 14*, 158-77.

Koelle, G. B. (1962). A new general concept of the neurohumoral functions of acetylcholine and acetylcholinesterase. *J. Pharm. (London) 14*, 65-90.

Konstantinova, M. (1967). The effect of adrenaline and acetylcholine on the hypothalamic-hypophysial neurosecretion in the rat. *Z. Zellforsch. 83*, 549-67.

Kumar, T. C. A., and F. G. W. Knowles (1967). A system linking the third ventricle with the pars tuberalis of the rhesus monkey. *Nature (London) 215*, 54-55.

Lederis, K. (1964). Fine structure and hormone content of the hypothalamo-neurohypophysial system of the rainbow trout (*Salmo irideus*) exposed to sea water. *Gen. Comp. Endocrinol. 4*, 638-61.

Lederis, K. (1965). An electron microscopical study of the human neurohypophysis. *Z. Zellforsch. 65*, 847-68.

Lederis, K. (1967). Beziehung zwischen der Ultrastruktur der Neurohypophyse und der subcellulären Verteilung von biologisch aktiven Substanzen. *Naunyn-Schmiedebergs Arch. Pharmak. Exp. Pathol. 257*, 83-93.

Leveque, T. F., and G. A. Hofkin (1962). A hypothalamic periventricular PAS substance and neuroendocrine mechanisms. *Anat. Rec. 142*, 252.

Leveque, T. F., F. Stutinsky, M. E. Stoeckel, and A. Porte (1965). Sur les caractères ultrastructuraux d'une formation glandulaire periventriculaire dans l'éminence médiane du rat. *C. R. Acad. Sci. (Paris) 260*, 4621-23.

Leveque, T. F., F. Stutinsky, A. Porte, and M. E. Stoeckel (1966). Morphologie fine d'une differenciation glandulaire du recessus infundibulaire chez le rat. *Z. Zellforsch. 69*, 381-94.

Lichtensteiger, W., and H. Langemann (1966). Uptake of exogenous catecholamines by monoamine-containing neurons of the central nervous system: uptake of catecholamines by arcuato-infundibular neurons. *J. Pharmacol. Exp. Therap. 151*, 400-408.

Löblich, H. J., and M. Knezevic (1960). Elektronenoptische Untersuchungen nach akuter Schädigung des Hypophysen-Zwischenhirnsystems (Befunde an der Hypophyse und am Zwischenhirn des Kaninchens nach Gefäss- und Dünndarmunterbindung). *Beiträge zur path. Anat. 122*, 1-30.

Martini, L. (1966). Neurohypophysis and anterior pituitary activity. In *The Pituitary Gland* (G. W. Harris and B. T. Donovan, eds.), *3*, pp. 535-77. Butterworths, London.

Matsui, T. (1966a). Fine structure of the posterior median eminence of the pigeon, *Columba livia domestica. J. Fac. Sci., Univ. Tokyo*, Sec. IV, *11*, 49-70.

Matsui, T. (1966b). Fine structure of the median eminence of the rat. *J. Fac. Sci., Univ. Tokyo*, Sec. IV, *11*, 71-96.

Matsui, T. (1967a). Effects on the rat estrous cycle of implants of norepinephrine placed in the median eminence. *Annot. Zool. Japon. 40*, 74-81.

Matsui, T. (1967b). Effect of reserpine on the distribution of granulated vesicles in the mouse median eminence. *Neuroendocrinology 2*, 99-106.

Matsui, T., and H. Kobayashi (1965). Histochemical demonstration of monoamine oxidase in the hypothalamo-hypophysial system of the tree sparrow and the rat. *Z. Zellforsch. 68*, 172-82.

Matsui, T., and H. Kobayashi (1969). Surface protrusions from the ependymal cells of the median eminence. *Arch. Anat. micro. Morph. exp.*, in press.

Mazzuca, M. (1965). Structure fine de l'éminence médiane du cobaye. *J. Micr. 4*, 225-38.

Mazzuca, M. (1967). Étude préliminaire au microscope électronique du noyau infundibulaire chez le cobaye. In *Neurosecretion* (F. Stutinsky, ed.), pp.36-41. Springer-Verlag, Berlin, Heidelberg, New York.

Meites, J., C. S. Nicoll, and P. K. Talwalker (1963). The central nervous system and the secretion and release of prolactin. In *Advances in Neuroendocrinology* (A. V. Nalbandov, ed.), pp. 238-77. University of Illinois Press, Urbana.

Mellinger, J. C. A. (1960a). Contribution à l'étude de la vascularisation et du développement de la région hypophysaire d'un Sélacien, *Scylliorhinus caniculus* (L.). *Bull. Soc. Zool. Fr. 85*, 123-39.

Mellinger, J. C. A. (1960b). Esquisse structurale de l'appareil hypophysaire d'un Sélacien, *Scylliorhinus caniculus* (L.), pour servir de base à une étude expérimentale des correlations neuro-endocriniennes. *C. R. Acad. Sci. (Paris) 251*, 2422-24.

Mellinger, J. C. A. (1963). Première thèse. Les relation neuro-vascule-glandulaires dans l'appareil hypophysaire de la rousette, *Scylliorhinus caniculus* (L.). Deuxième thèse. Étude histophysiologique du système hypothalamo-hypophysaire de *Scylliorhinus caniculus* (L.) en état de melanodis persion permanente. *Thèses, Faculté des Sciences de l'Université de Strasbourg* No. 238– Série E.

Meurling, P. (1960). Presence of a pituitary portal system in elasmobranchs. *Nature (London) 187*, 336-37.

Mikami, S. (1958). The cytological significance of regional patterns in the adenohypophysis of the fowl. *J. Fac. Agr., Iwate Univ. 3*, 473-545.

Monroe, B. G. (1967). A comparative study of the ultrastructure of the median eminence, infundibular stem and neural lobe of the hypophysis of the rat. *Z. Zellforsch. 76*, 405-32.

Murakami, M. (1962). Electronenmikroskopische Untersuchung der neurosekretorischen Zellen im Hypothalamus der Maus. *Z. Zellforsch. 56*, 27-229.

Muramatsu, T. (1961). Comparative morphological studies on the hypothalamic nuclei of domestic mammals. *Special bulletin of the College of Agriculture, Utsunomiya Univ. 13*, 1-38 (in Japanese with English summary).

Nishioka, R. S., and H. A. Bern (1966). Fine structure of the neurohemal areas associated with the hypophysis in the hagfish, *Polistotrema stoutii. Gen. Comp. Endocrinol. 7*, 457-62.

Nishioka, R. S., H. A. Bern, and L. R. Mewaldt (1964). Ultrastructural aspects of the neurohypophysis of the white-crowned sparrow, *Zonotrichia leucophrys gambelii*, with special reference to the relation of neurosecretory axons to ependyma in the pars nervosa. *Gen. Comp. Endocrinol. 4*, 304-13.

Oksche, A. (1962). The fine nervous, neurosecretory and glial structure of the median eminence in the white-crowned sparrow. In *Neurosecretion* (H. Heller and R. B. Clark, eds.), *Mem. Soc. Endocrinol. 12*, pp. 199-208, Academic Press, London, New York.

Oksche, A. (1967). Eine licht- und elektronenmikroskopische Analyse des neuro-endokrinen Zwischenhirn-Vorderlappen-Komplexes der Vögel. In *Neurosecretion* (F. Stutinsky, ed.), pp. 77-78. Springer-Verlag, Berlin, Heidelberg, New York.

Oota, Y. 1963a). Electron microscopic studies on the region of the hypothalamus contiguous to the hypophysis and the neurohypophysis of the fish, *Oryzias latipes. J. Fac. Sci., Univ. Tokyo*, Sec. IV, *10*, 143-53.

Oota, Y. (1963b). Fine structure of the median eminence and the pars nervosa of the mouse. *J. Fac. Sci., Univ. Tokyo*, Sec. IV, *10*, 155-68.

Oota, Y. (1963c). Fine structure of the median eminence and the pars nervosa of the turtle, *Clemmys japonica. J. Fac. Sci. Univ. Tokyo*, Sec. IV, *10*, 169-79.

Oota, Y. (1963d). On the synaptic vesicles in the neurosecretory organs of the carp, bullfrog, pigeon and mouse. *Annot. Zool. Japon. 36*, 167-72.

Oota, Y., and H. Kobayashi (1962). Fine structures of the median eminence and pars nervosa of the pigeon. *Annot. Zool. Japon. 35*, 128-38.

Oota, Y., and H. Kobayashi (1963). Fine structure of the median eminence and the pars nervosa of the bullfrog, *Rana catesbeiana. Z. Zellforsch. 60*, 667-87.

Oota, Y., and H. Kobayashi (1966). On the synaptic vesicle-like structures in the neurosecretory axon of the mouse neural lobe. *Annot. Zool. Japon. 39*, 193-201.

Oota, Y., I. Kawabata, and K. Kurosumi (1966). Electron microscope studies on the rat hypothalamo-hypophyseal neurosecretory system. *Japan. J. Exp. Morph. 20*, 65-83 (in Japanese).

Öztan, N. (1967). Neurosecretory processes projecting from the preoptic nucleus into the third ventricle of *Zoarces viviparus* (L.). *Z. Zellforsch. 80*, 458-60.

Palay, S. L. (1955). An electron microscope study of the neurohypophysis in normal, hydrated and dehydrated rats. *Anat. Rec. 121*, 348.

Palay, S. L. (1957). The fine structure of the neurohypophysis. In *Ultrastructure and Cellular Chemistry of Neural Tissue* (H. Waelsch, ed.), *Prog. Neurobiology 2*, pp. 31-49. Hoeber-Harper, New York.

Pellegrino de Iraldi, A., H. F. Duggan, and E. de Robertis (1963). Adrenergic synaptic vesicles in the anterior hypothalamus of the rat. *Anat. Rec. 145*, 521-31.

Peterson, R. P. (1965). Synapses in the rat supraoptic nucleus. *Anat. Rec. 151*, 399.

Pickford, M. (1947). The action of acetylcholine on the supraoptic nucleus of the chloralosed dog. *J. Physiol. (London) 106*, 264-70.

Poisner, A. M., and W. W. Douglas (1968). Adenosine triphosphate and adenosine triphosphatase in hormone-containing granules of posterior pituitary gland. *Science 160*, 203-4.

Polenov, A. L., and J. I. Senchik (1966). Synapses on neurosecretory cells of the supraoptic nucleus in white mice. *Nature (London) 211*, 1423-24.

Rinne, U. K. (1966). Ultrastructure of the median eminence of the rat. *Z. Zellforsch. 74*, 98-122.

Rinne, U. K., and A. U. Arstila (1966). Electron microscopic evidence of the significance of the glandular and vesicular inclusions of the neurosecretory nerve endings in the median eminence of the rat. I. Ultrastructural alterations after reserpine injection. *Med. Pharmacol. Exp. 15*, 357-69.

Röhlich, P., B. Vigh, I. Teichmann, and B. Aros (1965). Electron microscopy of the median eminence of the rat. *Acta Biol. Hung. 15*, 431-57.

Saint-Girons, H. (1963). Histologie comparée de l'adenohypophyse chez les Reptiles. In *Cytologie de l'Adenohypophyse* (J. Benoit and C. Da Lage, eds.), *Colloq. Int. C.N.R.S. (Paris) 128*, pp. 275-86.

Sano, Y., G. Odake, and S. Takemoto (1967). Fluorescence microscopic and electron microscopic observations on the tuberohypophysial tract. *Neuroendocrinology 2*, 30-42.

Sawyer, C. H., J. E. Markee, and B. F. Townsend (1949). Cholinergic and adrenergic components in the neurohumoral control of the release of LH in the rabbit. *Endocrinology 44*, 18-37.

Sawyer, C. H., J. E. Markee, and J. W. Everett (1950). Further experiments on blocking pituitary activation in the rabbit and rat. *J. Exp. Zool. 113*, 659-82.

Sawyer, W. H., and E. Mills (1966). Control of vasopressin secretion. In *Neuroendocrinology* (L. Martini and W. F. Ganong, eds.), *1*, pp. 187-216. Academic Press, New York, London.

Scharrer, E. (1966). Principles of neuroendocrine integration. In *Endocrines and the Central Nervous System* (Association for Research in Nervous and Mental Disease) *43*, pp. 1-35. Williams and Wilkins, Baltimore.

Seitz, H. M. (1965). Zur elektronenmikroskopischen Morphologie des Neurosekrets in Hypophysenstiel des Schweins. *Z. Zellforsch. 67*, 351-66.

Sloper, J. C. (1966). The experimental and cytopathological investigation of neurosecretion in the hypothalamus and pituitary. In *The Pituitary Gland* (G. W. Harris and B. T. Donovan, eds.), *3*, pp. 131-239. Butterworths, London.

Smoller, C. G. (1965). Neurosecretory processes extending into third ventricle: secretory or sensory? *Science 147*, 882.

Smoller, C. G. (1966). Ultrastructural studies on the developing neurohypophysis of the Pacific treefrog, *Hyla regilla*. *Gen. Comp. Endocrinol. 7*, 44-73.

Streefkerk, J. G. (1967). Functional changes in the morphological appearance of the hypothalamo-hypophyseal neurosecretory and catecholaminergic neural system, and in the adenohypophysis of the rat. A light, fluorescence and electron microscopic study. *ter verkrijging van de graad van doctor in de geneeskunde aan de Vrije Universiteit te Amsterdam.*

Tixier-Vidal, A. (1963). Histophysiologie de l'adenohypophyse des oiseaux. In *Cytologie de l'Adenohypophyse* (J. Benoit and C. Da Lage, eds.), *Colloq. Int. C.N.R.S. (Paris) 128*, pp. 255-73.

Tsuji, S. (1965). Histologisch-Elektronenmikroskopische Untersuchungen am Infundibulum bei Hund und Katze. *J. Kyoto Pref. Med. Univ. 74*, 446-56 (in Japanese with German summary).

Uemura, H. (1964). Cholinesterases in the hypothalamo-hypophysial neurosecretory system of the bird, *Zosterops palpebrosa japonica*. *Zool. Mag. (Dobutsugaku Zasshi) 73*, 118-26 (in Japanese with English summary).

Uemura, H. (1965). Histochemical studies on the distribution of cholinesterase and alkaline phosphatase in the vertebrate neurosecretory system. *Annot. Zool. Jap. 38*, 79-96.

Uemura, H., H. Kobayashi, and Su. Ishii (1963). Cholinergic substance in the neurosecretory storage-release organs. *Zool. Mag. (Dobutsugaku Zasshi) 72*, 204-12 (in Japanese with English summary).

Urano, A. (1968). Monoamine oxidase in the hypothalamic neurosecretory system and the adenohypophysis of the Japanese quail and the mouse. *J. Fac. Sci., Univ. Tokyo*, Sec. IV, *11*, 437-51.

Vigh, B., B. Aros, T. Wenger, S. Koritsansky, and G. Cegledi (1963). Ependymo-secretion (Ependymal secretion). IV. The Gomori-positive secretion of the hypothalamic ependyma of various vertebrates and its relation to the anterior pituitary. *Acta Biol. Hung. 13*, 407-19.

Vitums, A., S. Mikami, A. Oksche, and D. S. Farner (1965). Vascularization of the hypothalamo-hypophysial complex in the White-crowned Sparrow, *Zonotrichia leucophrys gambelii*. *Z. Zellforsch. 64*, 541-69.

Vollrath, L. (1967). Über die neurosekretorische Innervation der Adenohypophyse von Teleostiern, insbesondere von *Hippocampus cuda* und *Tinca tinca*. *Z. Zellforsch. 78*, 234-60.

Weinstein, H., S. Malamed, and H. Sachs (1961). Isolation of vasopressin-containing granules from the neurohypophysis of the dog. *Biochim. Biophys. Acta 50*, 386-89.

Wilson, F. E. (1967). The tubero-infundibular neuron system: A component of the photoperiodic control mechanism of the white-crowned sparrow, *Zonotrichia leucophrys gambelii*. *Z. Zellforsch. 82*, 1-24.

Wingstrand, K. G. (1951). *The Structure and Development of the Avian Pituitary*. C. W. K. Gleerup, Lund.

Wingstrand, K. G. (1966). Comparative anatomy and evolution of the hypophysis. In *The Pituitary Gland* (G. W. Harris and B. T. Donovan, eds.), *1*, pp.58-126. Butterworths, London.

Worthington, W. C., Jr. (1955). Some observations on the hypophyseal portal system in the living mouse. *Bull. Johns Hopkins Medical Hosp. 97*, 347-57.

Worthington, W. C., Jr. (1960). Vascular responses in the pituitary stalk. *Endocrinology 66*, 19-31.

Worthington, W. C., Jr. (1963). Functional vascular fields in the pituitary stalk of the mouse. *Nature (London) 199*, 461-65.

Yagi, K., T. Azuma, and K. Matsuda (1966). Neurosecretory cell: Capable of conducting impulse in rats. *Science 154*, 778-79.

Yoshida, K. (1964). The effects of reserpine on reproductive function in female rats. *Endocrinol. Japon. 11*, 216-36.

2
Catecholamines in the Hypothalamus and the Pituitary Gland

KJELL FUXE and TOMAS HÖKFELT

Introduction

For more than ten years norepinephrine (noradrenaline, NA) has been known to exist in high concentrations in the mammalian hypothalamus (Vogt, 1954), and adrenergic mechanisms have been postulated to regulate endocrine function in view of results obtained with α-adrenergic blocking agents and drugs depleting monoamine stores in the brain (Markee et al., 1948; Sawyer et al., 1949; Sawyer, 1963; Everett, 1964; Meites et al., 1963). However, until about five years ago it was difficult to evaluate the role played by the catecholamines (CA), dopamine (DA), and NA in the hypothalamus and in the brain as a whole, since the cellular localization of the CA was unknown. In 1962, Carlsson, Falck, and Hillarp, by the use of the histochemical fluorescence technique (Falck et al., 1962; see reviews by Hillarp et al., 1966; Corrodi and Jonsson, 1967), obtained some evidence for the view that the NA in the hypothalamus, mainly in the nucleus supraopticus and the nucleus paraventricularis, is localized in nerve terminals. These workers also observed a diffuse green specific fluorescence in the external layer of the median eminence. In subsequent studies more concrete evidence of the fact that NA in the mammalian hypothalamus is localized to nerve terminals was obtained when it was shown that the hypothalamic NA terminals disappeared after lesions were made in the tegmentum of the mesencephalon, the lateral hypothalamic area, and the subthalamus (Dahlström et al., 1964; Andén et al., 1965a; Andén et al., 1966a,b). Furthermore, the morphological characteristics and the distribution pattern of NA nerve terminals in the hypothalamus were demonstrated (Fuxe, 1965a,b,c). These studies showed that the NA nerve terminals in the hypothalamus to a large extent arise from fibers ascending mainly in the medial forebrain bundle, most of them originating from NA cell bodies in the pons and the medulla oblongata. Moreover, it was shown that the green CA fluorescence in the external layer of the median eminence was localized to nerve terminals belonging to tuberoinfundibular DA neurons (Fuxe, 1963, 1964; Fuxe and Hökfelt, 1966; Lichtensteiger and Langemann, 1966), the cell bodies of which are localized mainly in the arcuate nucleus and have a faint, green fluorescence. In pharmacological studies evidence was obtained that these neurons contain DA and not NA (Fuxe, 1964; Carlsson et al., 1965a).

These morphological results give evidence for the view that CA and especially NA in the hypothalamus, have a transmitter function. The localization of the DA nerve terminals around the primary capillary plexus of the hypophyseal portal system in the external layer of the median eminence suggests that they play an important role in the neuroendocrine regulation of the anterior pituitary. Electron microscopic studies (Hökfelt, 1967a) indicated that the DA neurons form axo-axonic contacts, so it is likely that the DA participates in local transmission mechanisms within the median eminence. The present review deals mainly with findings from our own laboratory and with those obtained in cooperation with Dr. A. Carlsson's department in Göteborg (especially with Dr. Andén), and with Dr. O. Nilsson in Uppsala (Department of Anatomy).

Morphological Studies

NA Afferents to the Hypothalamus

The NA nerve terminals of the hypothalamus have essentially the same morphological features as those present in the other parts of the brain (Fuxe, 1965a,b,c). Thus, the main store of NA is found in enlargements of the axons, the so-called "varicosities" (Figs. 2-1, 2-2, 2-3), whereas the intervaricose parts have a very weak green fluorescence which makes them barely visible. The varicosities, mainly around 1 to 1.5 μ in diameter as measured in the fluorescence microscope, seem to make both axosomatic (e.g. in the nucleus supraopticus and the nucleus paraventricularis) and axodendritic contacts (e.g. in the nucleus periventricularis and in the retrochiasmatic area). Hökfelt (1967b, 1968) has recently been able to identify NA boutons (Fig. 2-4) in the hypothalamus at the ultrastructural level using the permanganate technique (see Richardson, 1966). Thanks to these studies strong evidence now exists that a large store of NA in the vari-

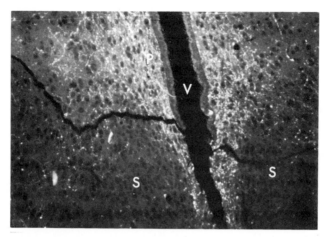

Figure 2-1 Cross section of the nucleus periventricularis hypothalami (P) and the nucleus suprachiasmaticus (S) of normal rats. There is a high density of strongly fluorescent NA nerve terminals in the periventricular nucleus, whereas the suprachiasmatic nucleus is empty of NA nerve terminals. The density is low in the anterior hypothalamic nucleus, lying lateral to the periventricular part. V, third ventricle. × 120.

Figure 2-2 Cross section of the area dorsal to the fornix (F) at the level of the middle part of the median eminence in the normal rat. There is a medium density of fine to fairly thick NA nerve terminals, forming a plexus which lies mainly in between the nonfluorescent cell bodies. × 120.

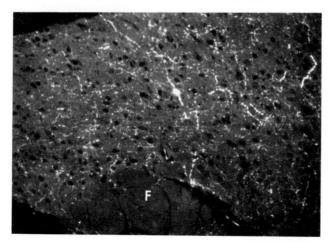

cosity is localized to small granular vesicles (about 500 Å in diameter), which, using ordinary fixation techniques (e.g. glutaraldehyde) appear empty and then are called "synaptic vesicles." A second type of vesicle, the so-called large granular vesicle (diameter of about 1000 Å), may also contain NA. The smaller granular vesicles can be seen aggregated at the presynaptic surface of synaptic axodendritic junctions (Hökfelt, 1968), which further supports the view that NA acts as a transmitter substance in the central nervous system.

The distribution of the NA nerve terminals in the hypothalamus is uneven. High to very high densities are found in these areas of the hypothalamus (Fuxe, 1965c): nucleus supraopticus, nucleus paraventricularis (Fig. 2-5), nucleus dorsomedialis hypothalami (Fig. 2-6), nucleus periventricularis hypothalami, and retrochiasmatic area. A very low to medium density is found in the mammillary body, the anteiror hypothalamic nucleus, and the lateral hypothalamic area. Few NA nerve terminals are found, for example, in the nucleus ventromedialis hypothalami (see Figs. 2-7 to 2-11; Table 2-1).

The NA nerve terminals in the hypothalamus arise from fibers in the medial forebrain bundle. It is not known if these NA fibers exclusively innervate the hypothalamus, or whether they only give collaterals to this area and innervate other areas such as the limbic system. The exact pathway of the NA fibers from their site of origin to their innervation areas in the hypothalamus is also not known. Although the NA nerve terminals proba-

Figure 2-3   Higher magnification of the same area shown in Figure 2-2. The NA nerve terminals have varicosities of varying diameters and a strong fluorescence intensity. Arrows point to large (↗) and small (↙) varicosities. These probably belong to two separate nerve terminals.   × 300.

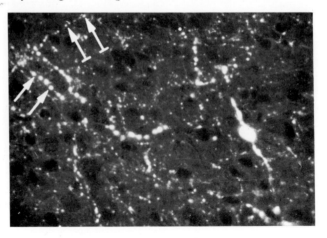

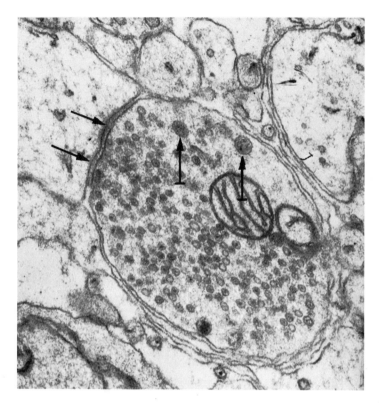

Figure 2-4 Periventricular hypothalamic nucleus (From Hökfelt, *Z. Zellforsch.* 91, 1-74, 1968). A bouton containing large numbers of small granular vesicles (500 Å in diameter) can be seen, probably making an axodendritic junction (↗). Some large granular vesicles (1000 Å in diameter) are also present (↙). There is good evidence (Hökfelt, 1968) that this type of bouton stores NA, and that the main store is localized to the small granular vesicles. × 56,000.

bly mainly have a rhombencephalic origin, some may also arise in the mesencephalon (Andén *et al.*, 1965a; 1966b).

It is interesting to note that the ascending NA fiber systems mainly traverse the lateral hypothalamic area in the medial forebrain bundle, not in the periventricular fiber system. Furthermore, the NA afferents show no pattern indicating a special innervation of the interneurons in the lateral hypothalamic area that have reciprocal connections with the medial hypothalamus. Thus, in contrast to other afferents in the medial forebrain bundle, the NA afferents directly connect with several nuclei of the medial hypothalamus.

The nonterminal CA axons are difficult to visualize in normal animals, since, in contrast to the terminals, they contain very low amine concentrations and thus exhibit only a weak green fluorescence. There are several

Figure 2-5   Cross section of the paraventricular nucleus of normal rat. There is a high density of strongly fluorescent NA nerve terminals in this nucleus, particularly in the parvicellular part.   V, third ventricle.   × 120.

Figure 2-6   Cross section of the nucleus dorsomedialis hypothalami of normal rat. In contrast to the previous illustrations, this illustration is from a thin plastic section (1 to 2 μ), which accounts for the relatively low density observed in the picture. The nucleus ventromedialis hypothalami, which contains practically no fluorescent nerve terminals, is in the bottom portion of the picture. V, third ventricle.   × 80.

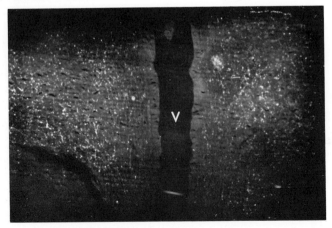

ways, however, in which the amine levels in the fibers can be increased so that they are easily visualized in the microscope and their pathway easily mapped out. One way is to increase the amine levels pharmacologically by injecting a monoamine oxidase (MAO) inhibitor (e.g. nialamide) com-

---

Figures 2-7 to 2-11   Schematic illustrations of the distribution of CA nerve terminals in the hypothalamus. The CA nerve terminals are indicated by dots. Their topography and relative density are shown (From Fuxe, 1965b).

ABBREVIATIONS

ACO, nucleus amygdaloideus corticalis
AM, nucleus amygdaloideus medialis
ARC, nucleus arcuatus
BL, nucleus amygdaloideus basolateralis
CA, commissura anterior
CAI, capsula interna
CAIR, capsula interna, pars lenticularis
CF, columna fornicis
CO, chiasma opticus
CSDV, commissura supraopticus dorsalis, pars ventralis
EM, eminentia mediana
FMP, fasciculus medialis prosencephalici
FMT, fasciculus mammillo-thalamicus
FMTG, fasciculus mammillo-tegmentalis
FR, fasciculus solitarius
G, nucleus gelatinosus
GPA, globus pallidus
H₁, Forel's field H₁
H₂, Forel's field H₂
HA, nucleus anterior hypothalami
HD, nucleus dorsomedialis hypothalami
HL, nucleus lateralis hypothalami
HP, nucleus hypothalamicus posterior
HPV, nucleus periventricularis hypothalami
HVM, nucleus ventromedialis hypothalami

LM, lemniscus medialis
MML, nucleus mammillaris medialis, pars lateralis
MMM, nucleus mammillaris medialis, pars medialis
MPL, nucleus mammillaris prelateralis
POL, nucleus preopticus lateralis
POM, nucleus preopticus medialis
POP, nucleus preopticus periventricularis
POSC, nucleus preopticus suprachiasmaticus
PV, nucleus premammillaris ventralis
PVM, nucleus paraventricularis, pars magnocellularis
PVP, nucleus paraventricularis, pars parvicellularis
PVS, nucleus paraventricularis, pars stellatocellularis
RC, retrochiasmatic area
RE, nucleus reuniens
SC, nucleus suprachiasmaticus
SGP, substantia grisea periventricularis
SO, nucleus supraopticus
STR, nucleus triangularis septi
SUM, area supramammillaris
SUT, nucleus subthalamicus
TO, tractus opticus
TRD, tractus diagonalis
ZI, zona incerta

From K. Fuxe.   Evidence for the existence of monoamine neurons in the central nervous system. IV. Distribution of monoamine nerve terminals in the central nervous system. *Acta Physiol. Scand. 64, Suppl.* 247, 1965.

_{H₁}

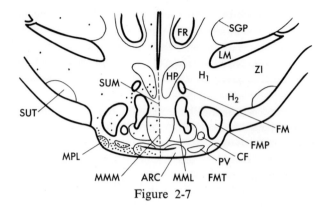

Figure 2-7

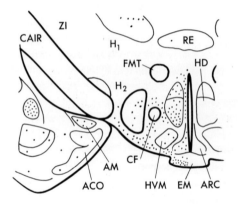

Figure 2-8

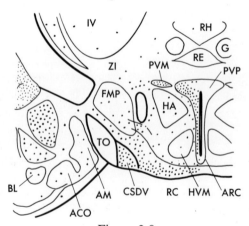

Figure 2-9

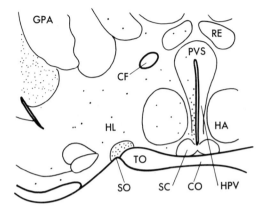

Figure 2-10

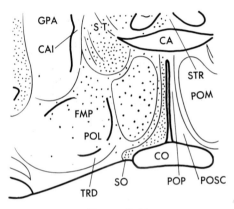

Figure 2-11

bined with the CA precursor 3,4-dihydroxyphenylalanine (1-dopa). In such animals high amounts of CA are formed intraneuronally in the *entire* neuron (Fuxe, 1965c), due to the action of the intraneuronal dopadecarboxylase (Andén *et al.,* 1965b, 1966b; Heller *et al.,* 1965). In the NA neurons, part of the DA formed is further β-hydroxylated to NA by the DA-β-oxidase, which probably also is located intraneuronally and close to the storage sites, at least in the adrenal medulla (Carlsson *et al.,* 1963; Kirshner, 1962; Carlsson and Waldeck, 1963). The first rate-limiting enzyme in CA biosynthesis, tyrosine hydroxylase, is also probably located intraneuronally (Goldstein *et al.,* 1966). Due to the intraneuronal accumu-

Table 2-1   The distribution of CA and 5-HT nerve terminals in the hypo-thalamus: 5 + = very high density; 4 + = high density; 3 + = medium density; 2 + = low density; 1 + = very low density; — = no detectable terminals.

Hypothalamus	Density of CA-terminals	Density of 5-HT terminals
A. Mammillary complex		
1. Nucleus premammillaris ventralis	3+, fine (NA)	1+, very fine
2. Nucleus mammillaris prelateralis	3+, fine (NA)	1+, very fine
3. Nucleus mammillaris lateralis	2+, very fine to fine (NA)	1+, very fine
4. The rest of the mammillary complex	1+ to 2+, very fine to fine (NA)	1+ to 3+, very fine
B. Vegetative hypothalamus		
1. Nucleus posterior hypothalamus (ventral part)	3+, fine (NA)	2+, very fine
2. Nucleus ventromedialis hypothalami, all parts	scattered to 2+, fine (NA)	scattered to 1+, very fine
3. Nucleus dorsomedialis hypothalami, pars ventralis	5+, fine to fairly thick (NA)	2+, very fine
4. Nucleus dorsomedialis hypothalami, pars dorsalis	4+, fine to fairly thick (mainly NA)	2+, very fine
5. Nucleus arcuatus	3+, fine (NA)	scattered, very fine
6. Nucleus periventricularis hypothalami	4+ to 5+, fine to fairly thick	scattered to 1+, very fine
7. The part just dorsal to the fornix	3+ to 4+, fine (NA)	scattered
8. The part ventral to the fornix between the nucleus ventromedialis and the nucleus lateralis hypothalami	5+, fine to fairly thick (mainly NA)	1+, very fine
9. Nucleus lateralis hypothalami	1+ to 3+, fine to thick (NA)	scattered to 1+, very fine
10. The retrochiasmatic area	4+ to 5+ fine to thick (mainly NA)	1+ to 2+, very fine
11. The external layer of the median eminence (see Fuxe, 1964)	dotted fluorescence of strong intensity (mainly DA, probably some NA)	—
12. Nucleus anterior hypothalami	+1 to 2+, fine (NA)	scattered to 2+, very fine
13. Nucleus paraventricularis	4+ to 5+, fine to fairly thick (mainly NA)	—
14. Nucleus supraopticus (Fig. 22 in Fuxe, 1965c)	4+ to 5+, fine mainly NA)	—
15. Nucleus suprachiasmaticus	—	4+, very fine
16. Nucleus preopticus medialis	3+ to 4+, fine (NA)	scattered, very fine
17. Nucleus preopticus lateralis	2+ to 4+, fine (NA)	—
18. Nucleus preopticus suprachiasmaticus	4+, fine (NA)	scattered, very fine
19. Nucleus preopticus periventricularis (Fig. 8 in Fuxe, 1965c)	4+, fine (NA)	—
20. Nucleus commissurae anterioris	3+, fine (NA)	—

From K. Fuxe, Evidence for the existence of monoamine neurons in the central nervous system. IV. Distribution of monoamine nerve terminals in the central nervous system, *Acta Physiol. Scand. 64*, Suppl. 247, 1965.

lation of CA after nialamide-dopa treatment, the nonterminal axons become strongly green-fluorescent and can be easily visualized.

Another way to make fibers easily visible is to damage them either by transection or by making a thermal lesion. After the damage there is a rapid accumulation of fluorescence on the cell body side of the lesion, probably due to damming up of amine storage granules which are produced in the cell bodies and transported down to the terminals via the axons (Dahlström and Fuxe, 1964a; Dahlström, 1966). The CA axons are probably unmyelinated and very thin. If they are cut in the lateral hypothalamic area, there is a marked accumulation of green fluorescence in the CA axons caudal to the lesion. Accumulation of fluorescence can only be observed a few millimeters away from the lesion, however. The tissue close to the lesion is sometimes distorted, making it difficult to determine the exact localization of the axons.

As stated above, the NA axons have mainly a rhombencephalic origin, and some of the NA cell bodies in this region lie in various parts of the reticular formation. Thus, the reticular formation may exert at least some of its influence on the hypothalamus by way of these NA afferents. It must be remembered, however, that many ascending NA fiber systems may bypass the hypothalamus to innervate the limbic lobe and the neocortex. The NA afferents to the hippocampal formation and the amygdaloid cortex may influence the activity of the hypothalamus via the prominent pathways from them to the hypothalamus (deGroot, 1966). In a similar way, the

Figure 2-12   Cross section of the median eminence of normal rat. Araldite-embedded tissue, section thickness 2 to 3 μ. There is a strong green fluorescence in the external layer of the median eminence due to the accumulation of DA nerve terminals (↗). V, third ventricle.   × 80.

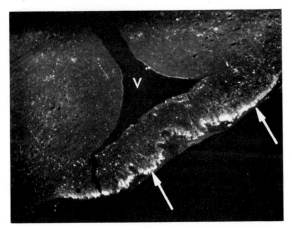

NA nerve terminals in the reticular formation of the lower brain stem and the limbic midbrain area may modify the input to the hypothalamus.

DA Afferents to the Median Eminence

In the rat median eminence the DA nerve terminals are mainly concentrated in the lateral parts of the external layer of the median eminence. The terminals are also quite evident in the midline, and as a rule the DA nerve terminals approach the capillary plexus on the borderline between the median eminence and the pars lateralis (Figs. 2-12, 2-13, 2-14). Not so many follow the capillary loops into the internal layer of the median eminence. In the rat, large NA varicosities (1 to 2 μ) are mainly found in the internal layer. However, these are only present in a low to medium density.

Using the potassium permanganate fixation in combination with the incubation technique it has been possible to localize the DA-containing boutons in the median eminence at the ultrastructural level (Hökfelt, 1967a). Thus, the main store of DA in the varicosities is probably localized to small granular vesicles (500 Å) which represent the main type of vesicle found. Large granular vesicles (1000 Å) are also observed in these DA boutons. It has been shown that the DA boutons are closely related not only to the pericapillary space of the capillary plexus but more particularly to other boutons that do not contain monoamines (Fig. 2-15). These neurons probably represent the neurons that manufacture and release

Figure 2-13   Cross section of the dorsal lip of the median eminence of normal rat. Araldite-embedded tissue, section thickness 2 to 3 μ. In this illustration the fluorescent NA varicosities of the internal layer are well illustrated (↗). × 100.

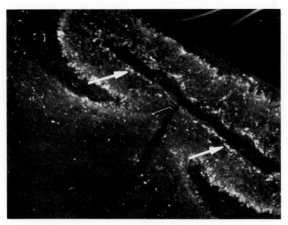

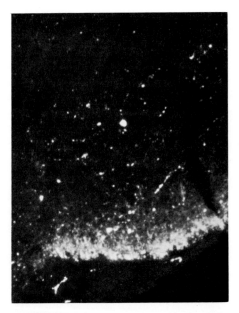

Figure 2-14   Higher magnification of the lateral part of the median eminence in the normal rat in cross section. The closely packed fluorescent varicosities of the DA nerve terminals can be seen.   × 300.

various types of hypothalamic releasing and inhibiting factors that affect anterior pituitary secretion.

The DA afferents mainly derive from axons which originate from faintly fluorescent, rounded cell bodies in the arcuate nucleus and the anterior periventricular nucleus, ventral part. The existence of faintly green-fluorescent cell bodies in this region of the brain was first discovered by Carlsson *et al.*, (1962a). However, to obtain a good localization of this cell group it is necessary to increase the amine levels in the cell bodies. This can be accomplished by nialamide-dopa treatment, by intravenous CA injections (since the blood-brain barrier is lacking in this region), or by intraventricular injections of CA (see Fuxe and Hillarp, 1964; Fuxe and Hökfelt, 1966; Fuxe *et al.*, 1966; Fuxe and Ungerstedt, 1968a). Experiments with the intraventricular CA technique have shown that CA cell bodies probably exist not only in the ventral but also in the dorsal part of the anterior periventricular nucleus. It is not known if these cell bodies send axons to the median eminence. The axons of the tuberoinfundibular DA neurons can be visualized with similar methods—for example, by nialamide-dopa treatment, by injections of CA (Fuxe and Hökfelt, 1966; Lichtensteiger and Langemann, 1966), or by lesions of the infundibular stalk (Fuxe and Hökfelt, 1966). Exogenous CA increase the amine levels in the CA neurons because there is a potent amine-concentrating mechanism at the nerve cell membrane along the entire monoamine neuron (Carlsson *et al.*, 1966a; Hamberger, 1967; Fuxe and Ungerstedt, 1966). Exogenous amines are also taken up and accumulated in the major dendrites of the DA cell bodies, indicating that the mechanism exists also in this part of the neuron.

Most of the DA cell bodies in the arcuate nucleus are found in the ante-

Figure 2-15 The external layer of the rat median eminence. The boutons (b) containing the small granular vesicles (500 Å in diameter) are in all probability identical with the DA varicosities. Some of these are lying in close contact with other axons (↗), indicating possible axo-axonic contacts.   × 28,000.

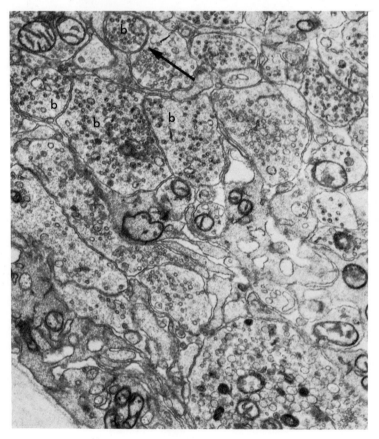

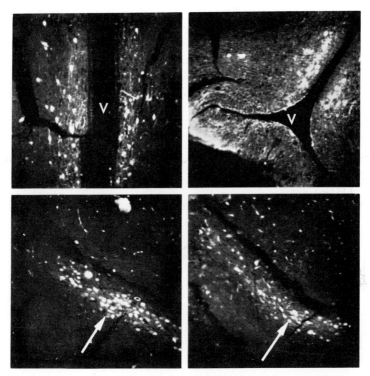

Figure 2-16 (Top Left) Periventricular hypothalamic nucleus of a reserpine pre-treated rat after an intraventricular injection of α-methyl-NA 30 minutes before sacrifice (From Fuxe and Ungerstedt, unpublished data). There is a strong accumulation of fluorescence in CA cell bodies of the dorsal and ventral part of the periventricular hypothalamic nucleus. V, third ventricle. × 40.

Figure 2-17 (Top Right) The ventromedial hypothalamus of rat under the same conditions as described in Figure 2-16 (from Fuxe and Ungerstedt, unpublished data). There is a marked accumulation of fluorescence (α-methyl-NA) in the DA cell bodies of the arcuate nucleus and in the DA nerve terminals of the external layer. V, third ventricle. × 40.

Figure 2-18 (Bottom Left) Cross section of dorsal hypothalamus of rat treated with nialamide-dopa. After the dopa injection there is an accumulation of strong fluorescence in the CA cell bodies (↗) lying dorsal to the nucleus dorsomedialis hypothalami (A13). × 80.

Figure 2-19 (Bottom Right) Dorsal hypothalamus after treatment with nialamide-dopa. There is an accumulation of strong fluorescence in CA cell bodies (↗) lying ventral to the tractus mammillothalamicus. × 80.

rior part of the nucleus. Practically no DA cell bodies are found rostral to the arcuate nucleus. Since the DA cell bodies in the arcuate nucleus represent only a small percentage of the total amount of cell bodies found in this nucleus, many other types of tuberoinfundibular systems must also exist. So far no evidence has been obtained that the NA afferents innervate the DA cell bodies in the arcuate nucleus. However, it cannot be excluded that the NA nerve terminals in this nucleus make contact with the fine dendritic branches of the DA cell bodies.

In the pigeon, no evidence of the existence of the tuberoinfundibular DA neuron system could be found (Fuxe and Ljunggren, 1965). However, it has recently been possible to visualize this system in the avian hypothalamus (Björklund et al., 1968; Enemar and Ljunggren, 1968). In the pigeon, neuroendocrine regulating mechanisms are different, since the hypothalamus appears to secrete a prolactin-releasing factor (see Meites and Nicoll, 1966).

CA Cell Groups in the Hypothalamus

There are CA cell groups in addition to those already described in the arcuate and periventricular nuclei (Figs. 2-16, 2-17). There is a cell group in the medial part of the zona incerta just dorsal to the nucleus dorsomedialis hypothalami (Fuxe, 1965c). These cells lie closely packed, have a faint green fluorescence, are small (10 to 15 μ in diameter), and are rounded in shape. After nialamide-dopa treatment, these cell bodies develop a strong green fluorescence (Fig. 2-18). Close to this group and partly in continuity with it lies a small group of cells with similar morphological features. They mainly lie just ventral to the tractus mamillothalamicus (Fig. 2-19). Scattered large CA cell bodies are found in the posterior hypothalamic nuclei (Fuxe, 1965c). It is not known which areas of the brain all these CA cell bodies innervate. No CA cell groups are found in the lateral hypothalamic area, including the laterodorsal interstitial nucleus.

An interesting finding has been made in the area within and dorsolateral to the nucleus premammillaris ventralis of the rat, using intraventricular amine injections (Fuxe and Ungerstedt, 1968a). Normally the cell bodies in this area do not seem to contain any amine stores. However, some of these cell bodies are able to take up and accumulate exogenous CA in a way similar to that observed in cells known to store CA. This may mean that they store another type of amine (e.g. histamine) and therefore possess an amine-concentrating mechanism at the cell membrane. They may also represent true CA cell bodies with normally very low amounts of CA in the perikarya.

Biochemically very small amounts of epinephrine have been found in the mammalian hypothalamus (Gunne, 1963; Häggendal, 1963). The cel-

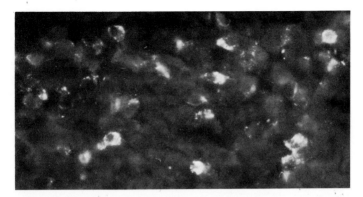

Figure 2-20. The anterior lobe of the rat adenohypophysis. The tissue has been incubated with a high concentration of α-methyl-NA (100 μg/ml). This results in an accumulation of strong fluorescence in certain cells. × 500.

lular localization of this epinephrine is unknown. However, in the frog hypothalamus epinephrine nerve terminals are abundant (Falck *et al.*, 1963).

CA Stores in the Pituitary Gland

The Anterior Lobe of the Adenohypophysis.   Large numbers of PAS-positive cells in the anterior lobe of some mammals, especially the cat and the dog, exhibit a strong green to yellow-green fluorescence after exposure to formaldehyde treatment. The fluorescence has an emission and activation spectrum similar to that of the CA. Furthermore, many of the histochemical criteria are fulfilled for the specificity of the fluorescence reaction (Dahlström and Fuxe, 1966; Ritzén, 1966, unpublished data). Thus there is support for the idea that these cells may store CA. The concentrations are probably low, in spite of the relatively high fluorescence intensity, since only low CA concentrations have been found biochemically in the anterior lobe of the cat (Häggendal, unpublished data) and the pig pituitary gland (Björklund *et al.*, 1967). The fluorescence is not depleted by reserpine or dopa-analogues, as is the fluorescence in the adrenergic neurons. One explanation for this may be that the CA are stored in the glycoprotein granules of the PAS-positive cells by a mechanism that is insensitive to reserpine; for instance, the cationic amines might be bound to the acid mucopolysaccharides present in these granules (Dahlström and Fuxe, 1966). Practically no CA nerve terminals are present in this part of the adenohypophysis.

In the anterior lobe of the rat there are no gland cells exhibiting a specific fluorescence. However, most of the PAS positive cells can take up

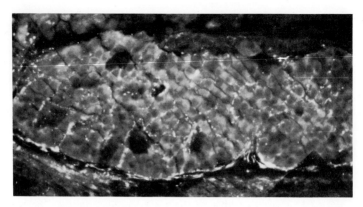

Figure 2-21   The intermediate lobe of the adenohypophysis. The fluorescent gland cells are observed to be innervated by a plexus of green fluorescent CA nerve terminals with a single CA nerve terminal in each strand.   × 300.

L-dopa and decarboxylate it to DA, which is stored in the cells for many hours (Dahlström and Fuxe, 1966) giving rise to a strong green fluorescence in the cells. Some of the cells are also able to take up 5-hydroxytryptophan (5-HTP) and decarboxylate it to 5-hydroxytryptamine (5-HT), causing the appearance of a yellow fluorescence in these cells. DA or α-methyl-NA given systemically is not taken up and accumulated within these cells. However, when pituitaries are incubated in high concentrations of α-methyl-NA (100 µg/ml), most of the PAS-positive cells take up the amine (Fig. 2-20) and become strongly fluorescent (Fuxe, Hamberger and Hökfelt, unpublished data). Thus there exists a possibility for the presence of monoaminergic mechanisms in most of the PAS-positive cells of the anterior pituitary. More investigations are needed to elucidate this possibility.

The Intermediate Lobe of the Adenohypophysis.   In the rat and mouse, the intermediate lobe consists mainly of PAS-positive gland cells exhibiting a green to yellow-green fluorescence, which satisfies the histochemical criteria for the specificity of the fluorescence reaction (Dahlström and Fuxe, 1966). It is therefore possible that these cells may contain CA. However, the activation and emission spectra of the fluorescence from these cells have as yet not been determined. In the rat and mouse pituitary (Fuxe, 1964; Dahlström and Fuxe, 1966), these fluorescent cells have been found to be innervated by a plexus of CA nerve terminals (Fig. 2-21) that probably have a central origin (Hillarp and Jacobsohn, 1943). Such a plexus also exists in the intermedia of the frog pituitary (Enemar and Falck,

1965; Iturriza, 1966). A plexus of CA nerve terminals of somewhat lesser density is found in the pars intermedia of the pig pituitary (Falck and Owman, 1968). Since considerable amounts of DA have been found in the pars intermedia in this species, it has been suggested that these CA nerve terminals store DA and not NA (Björklund *et al.*, 1967). From results obtained with α-methyl-metatyrosine treatment (Dahlström and Fuxe, 1966, see below), it has been suggested that in the rat at least part of the CA terminal plexus may contain DA. A dopaminergic innervation of the intermediate lobe has also been postulated by Smelik (1966). However,

Figure 2-22   The posterior lobe of rat after incubation with a high concentration of DA (100 μg/ml). There is a marked accumulation of amine within dots that become green fluorescent. Some of these dots may belong to nerve terminals.   × 180.

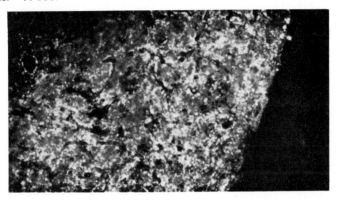

Figure 2-23   The posterior lobe of normal rat (dorsomedial part) after incubation with DA (10 μg/ml). CA nerve terminals are observed both surrounding the vessels (↗) and probably also in the parenchyma itself (↙).   × 180.

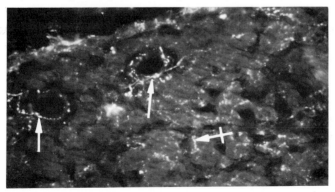

unpublished observations from this laboratory on the effect of desipramine on α-methyl-NA uptake (Fuxe, Hamberger, and Hökfelt, unpub.) indicate that part of the terminals may also contain NA. Since considerably more terminals are found after methylene blue staining (Hillarp and Jacobsohn, 1943) than after formaldehyde treatment, terminals containing other transmitter substances may also exist in this area of the pituitary gland.

The Posterior Lobe of the Adenohypophysis. Adrenergic vasomotor nerve terminals in the posterior lobe have been described previously (Dahlström and Fuxe, 1966). In this study, no certain parenchymal innervation could be established. However, after incubating the posterior lobe *in vitro* with CA, a parenchymal plexus of fluorescent varicose dots can be observed (Fig. 2-22). Some of them presumably belong to nerve terminals (Fig. 2-23). They are mainly in the dorsal central part of the lobe (Fuxe, Hamberger, and Hökfelt, unpublished data). On re-investigating the posterior lobe of normal rats, strands of very fine to fine green-fluorescent nerve terminals could in fact be observed in this area of the posterior lobe, which are probably identical with some of the fine fluorescent dots observed after *in vitro* incubation with CA (Fuxe and Hökfelt, 1968, unpublished data). However, the large fluorescent droplets observed after incubation with CA probably belong mainly to the terminals of the magnocellular neurosecretory neurons. Various types of CA nerve terminals have also been observed in normal rat posterior lobes (Björklund *et al.*, 1967). These authors observed that, besides the adrenergic vasomotor terminals and the very fine CA nerve terminals, there also exist large CA nerve terminals with droplet-like varicosities. From biochemical studies (Björklund *et al.*, 1967) and microspectrofluorimetric studies (Björklund, 1968, personal communication), it is probable that these large fluorescent droplets belong to central DA neurons.

In several species, the infundibular stem has been found to contain both DA and NA, the major CA being DA (Laverty and Sharman, 1965). DA nerve terminals have also been found lying close to the capillary plexus on the surface of the infundibular stem and also close to the capillary loops, especially in the cat (Fuxe, 1964). The blood of this system is drained by the short portal vessels into the sinuoids of the adenohypophysis (see Daniel, 1966).

Pharmacological Studies

It is well known that *reserpine* depletes the CA and 5-HT stores in the brain (see Carlsson, 1966). However, the hypothalamic NA nerve terminals are less sensitive to reserpine than are other terminals in the brain (Fuxe, 1965b; Andén, 1967). They are depleted considerably more slowly than, for instance, the neocortical NA nerve terminals. Furthermore, with a moderate dose of reserpine (1 mg/kg), little depletion is obtained in the hypothalamic NA nerve terminals compared to that obtained in the nerve terminals of the cortical areas. The large NA varicosities in the internal layer of the median eminence and in the lateral hypothalamic area and the subthalamus are particularly resistant to reserpine. This may partly be due to the fact that these varicosities contain large numbers of NA storage granules with an exceptionally high content of NA. Thus, NA may compete successfully with reserpine at the uptake sites of the granular membrane, the probable location at which the drug acts. This would retard the onset of, and/or partly prevent the blockage of, the uptake-storage mechanism after reserpine (Dahlström et al., 1965a; Carlsson, 1966). Since reserpine blocks the re-uptake into the granules, amine depletion is probably caused by the constant normal rapid leakage of amines out of the granules into the cytoplasm, where they are deaminated by MAO. Even within one and the same brain nucleus, the NA terminals are depleted at various speeds. This is true, for instance, in the nucleus paraventricularis and the nucleus dorsomedialis hypothalami (Fuxe, 1965c). On the other hand, the NA nerve terminals in the nucleus supraopticus are practically all depleted at the same rapid speed and, in contrast to the other hypothalamic NA terminals, exhibit about the same marked sensitivity to reserpine as the cortical NA nerve terminals (Fuxe, 1965c). It may be pointed out that the nervous impulse flow is of little importance for the amine depletion obtained by reserpine (Andén et al., 1967a).

The DA nerve terminals in the median eminence are very sensitive to reserpine. Doses as low as 0.1 mg/kg cause them to be partly depleted of DA, and they show a rapid rate of depletion; the fluorescence disappears after 1 to 2 hours, at which time little depletion has occurred in the NA nerve terminals (Carlsson et al., 1962a; Fuxe, 1964, 1965c). The recovery of amines, however, is rapid and occurs after only 36 to 48 hours. At this time no fluorescent NA nerve terminals are observed in the hypothalamus (Fuxe, 1965c). This suggests that the functional recovery after reserpine is earlier in the tuberoinfundibular DA neurons than in the NA afferents to the hypothalamus.

An important discovery made in connection with the reserpine experiments is that the cell bodies recover almost normal fluorescence intensity 24 to 36 hours after reserpine injection, whereas the terminals regain fluorescence only after many days. This is particularly true of the NA cell bodies in the rhombencephalon (Dahlström and Fuxe, 1964b; Dahlström et al., 1965a) which give rise to most of the NA afferents to the hypothalamus. These cells are in the area of the nucleus reticularis lateralis in the medulla oblongata. The explanation for the early recovery is probably that newly formed intact amine storage granules are produced in the cell bodies shortly after reserpine injection, whereas in the terminals, only blocked granules are present, and they cannot store amines. It is possible that the newly synthesized granules at least partly replete the amine stores in the terminals.

Tetrabenazine, in contrast to reserpine, only causes a brief blockade of the uptake-storage mechanism of the granules (see review by Carlsson, 1966). Following its administration, there is an initial depletion, followed by a rapid and simultaneous recovery of fluorescence in the various hypothalamic NA afferents and the NA cell bodies in the rhombencephalon (Dahlström and Fuxe, 1964b; Dahlström *et al.*, 1965a).

Depletion of the fluorescence in the NA and DA nerve terminals can also be brought about by treatment with *dopa analogues* such as *metatyrosine* and *α-methyl-meta-tyrosine* (α-MMT), although the depletion is not as complete as that produced by reserpine. These analogues are taken up in the CA-neurons, decarboxylated, and in the NA neurons β-hydroxylated into the corresponding m-tyramine derivatives, which displace the endogenous amines and do not develop any green fluorescence on exposure to formaldehyde gas (Carlsson and Lindqvist, 1962). The displacement is not influenced significantly by nervous activity (Andén, Fuxe, and Henning, to be published). After treatment with m-tyrosine there is a brief disappearance of the specific fluorescence in both DA and NA nerve terminals. Recovery starts 4 hours after the last dose of m-tyrosine (Fuxe, 1965c). After α-methyl-meta-tyrosine treatment, there is a long-lasting disappearance of fluorescence from the NA, but not from the DA terminals. This is due to the fact that the α-methyl-β-hydroxy-meta-tyramine (metaraminol) formed in NA neurons does not disappear as rapidly as the α-methyl-meta-tyramine formed in the DA neurons. There are few effects on gross behavior after treatment with these drugs, possibly due to the fact that the small amine pool immediately important for function is not affected (see below). Therefore, CA transmission is relatively undisturbed. A possible false transmitter function of the amine analogues cannot be excluded, however.

Histochemically, it is not yet possible to differentiate between DA and NA in the central nervous system, since DA and NA both give rise to the same strong green fluorescence with identical activation and emission spectra (see Corrodi and Jonsson, 1967). Treatment with α-MMT constitutes one of the pharmacological methods by which DA and NA nerve terminals can be separated from one another; there are differences in the rate at which the terminals recover (Fuxe, 1965b). Another pharmacological method to differentiate DA from NA nerve terminals is to treat the animals with α-methyl-dopa and inject reserpine 24 hours later. This method is based on differences in recovery rate between DA and NA neurons and on the fact that the α-methylated analogues are not broken down by MAO. Since the α-methyl-DA and α-methyl-NA formed from α-methyl-dopa in the DA and NA neurons (Carlsson and Lindqvist, 1962) give the fluorescence reaction, there is no depletion of fluorescence in animals treated only with α-methyl-dopa. If reserpine is given 24 hours after the last injection of α-methyl-dopa there is depletion in the DA neurons, because α-methyl-DA disappears rapidly from the DA neurons and is replaced by newly synthesized DA, which is sensitive to MAO. Alpha-methyl-NA, on the other hand, remains in the NA neurons and, since this compound is not broken down by the MAO, there is no depletion of fluorescence after reserpine treatment in the NA neurons (Carlsson et al., 1965a). A third way is to inject a DA-β-oxidase inhibitor, diethyldithiocarbamate, which to a large extent depletes selectively the fluorescence in the NA neurons. DA does not accumulate in the NA neurons in such a degree as to compensate for the decrease in the NA content even if the MAO is inhibited (Carlsson et al., 1966b; 1967). A fourth way is to use desipramine. If brain slices from reserpine-pretreated rats are incubated with α-methyl-NA together with desipramine there will be a selective blockade of uptake and accumulation of the amine in the NA nerve terminals. The DA nerve terminals, on the other hand, become strongly green-fluorescent (Hamberger, 1967).

There is, of course, an important difference between treatment with reserpine and with dopa analogues, in that 5-HT neurons are only slightly affected by treatment with m-tyrosine or α-MMT. Another difference is the degree of blockade of transmission. After treatment with reserpine, there is a transmission blockade in the DA and NA neurons in the brain for at least 24 hours. After treatment with dopa analogues, however, it is uncertain if the transmission in the CA neurons is decreased to such a degree that a functional blockade is present (Carlsson, 1964). There probably exists in the monoamine boutons a small pool of transmitter which is of immediate importance for function, and this pool is probably not impaired even if the bulk of the transmitter is replaced by other amines such as metaraminol or α-methyl-NA. Furthermore, functional recovery after reserpine returns at a time when the amine levels are low (Häggendal and Lindqvist, 1964; Andén and Henning, 1966; Dahlström et al., 1967). This small pool has been disclosed in chronic reserpine experiments (Häggendal and Lindqvist, 1964). It is probably the result of the fact that the amine granules start to take up amines 24 to 48 hours after reserpine treatment is stopped (Andén and Henning, 1966; Dahlström et al., 1967).

Uptake into the granules is probably necessary for function to recover, since the amines have to be localized in the granules to be released by the nerve impulse (Malmfors, 1965). These facts have to be taken into consideration when evaluating the effects of reserpine and dopa analogues on endocrine function.

In the hypothalamus, as elsewhere in the central nervous system, *chlorpromazine* and *haloperidol* probably interfere with CA neurotransmission by causing a postsynaptic blockade of the DA and NA receptors (Carlsson and Lindqvist, 1963; Andén et al., 1964a, 1966c). This probably results in a compensatory activation of the presynaptic CA neurons due to a nervous feedback on the cell bodies and dendrites of these neurons (Carlsson and Lindquist, 1963; Corrodi et al., 1967a; Andén et al., 1967a). Some of the NA cell bodies even show increased amounts of amines, presumably due to an increased production of amine storage granules (Andén et al., 1966c). In contrast to the case with reserpine, the transmission in the 5-HT neurons does not appear to be blocked after chlorpromazine and haloperidol (Andén et al., 1967a). Therefore the neuroendocrine effects of these drugs are probably due to an effect on CA neurotransmission.

When using drugs to study adrenergic mechanisms in endocrine function it may be helpful to use the α-adrenergic blocking agent *phenoxybenzamine*, since recent evidence indicates that phenoxybenzamine selectively blocks NA receptors in the brain and the spinal cord (Andén et al., 1967a). The β-adrenergic blocking agent *propranolol* does not seem to block NA receptors in the brain or the spinal cord (Andén and Fuxe, unpublished data).

The drugs described above tend to decrease monoamine neurotransmission in the brain. There are also drugs which act mainly by facilitating central monoamine neurotransmission.

Amphetamine is a potent releaser of amines both from hypothalamic DA and NA nerve terminals and other CA nerve terminals. Amphetamine is especially effective (in doses down as low as 0.25 to 0.5 mg/kg) in releasing reserpine resistant stores of NA (Figs. 2-24 and 2-25; Carlsson et al., 1965b, 1966a,c; Fuxe and Ungerstedt, 1968b). The NA cortical nerve terminals are more sensitive to amphetamine than the hypothalamic NA nerve terminals are (Carlsson et al., 1966b). Since the central stimulant action of amphetamine on conditioned avoidance behavior is blocked by treatment with reserpine plus inhibitors of tyrosine hydroxylase (Hanson, 1967) but not by reserpine alone, it must have a presynaptic action; furthermore, the pool released by amphetamine is probably dependent on newly synthesized amines, at least in this experimental situation.

Desipramine and *protriptyline*, on the other hand, facilitate central NA neurotransmission selectively, by blocking the uptake of amine at the nerve cell membrane of the NA neurons (Carlsson *et al.*, 1965c, 1966a,b; Hamberger, 1967; Fuxe and Ungerstedt, 1968b; Glowinski and Baldessarini, 1966). It should be pointed out that the reserpine-resistant amine-concentrating mechanism at the nerve cell membrane is an important inactivating mechanism for released amines, which after re-uptake are either broken down by the intraneuronal MAO (Fuxe and Hillarp, 1964; Hamberger and Masuoka, 1965) or are taken up again in the amine granules. The DA neurons are not affected, and the uptake at the cell membrane of the 5-HT neurons is only slightly blocked. However, the amine-concentrating mechanism at the cell membrane of the 5-HT neurons is markely blocked by imipramine and amitriptyline (Carlsson *et al.*, 1968; Corrodi and Fuxe, 1968; Fuxe and Ungerstedt, 1968b). Therefore, treatment with desipramine does not prevent the uptake and accumulation of amines in the DA afferents to the median eminence, and a specific uptake is observed histochemically after pretreatment with desipramine (Fuxe *et al.*, 1966, 1967a). The amine-concentrating mechanism of these DA nerve terminals is blocked by cocaine. Compounds of this type should be useful in establishing whether dopaminergic or noradrenergic mechanisms are involved in the control of various endocrine functions.

Figure 2-24   The rat median eminence after treatment with reserpine-α-methyl-NA (0.5 mg/kg, 1 hour before sacrifice). There is an accumulation of α-methyl-NA in the DA nerve terminals which results in the appearance of fluorescence in the external layer (↗).   × 180.

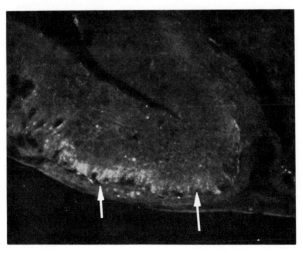

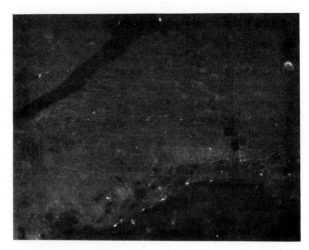

Figure 2-25   The rat median eminence after treatment with reserpine-α-methyl-NA (0.5 mg/kg, 1 hour before sacrifice) and amphetamine (1 mg/kg, given 15 minutes after the amine injection). There is a rapid release of amine after amphetamine, which results in an almost complete disappearance of the fluorescence.   × 180.

It is obvious that by giving the precursor dopa together with a MAO inhibitor, which prevents the oxidative deamination of the amines formed from dopa, facilitation of CA transmission can be produced. There are increased amine levels in the entire CA neuron, and the fluorescence intensity is markedly increased in the CA fibers and CA cell bodies in areas such as the hypothalamus.

Another way to increase CA neurotransmission in the brain is to inject drugs which stimulate the receptor sites themselves. There is good evidence that apomorphine selectively stimulates DA receptors in the brain (Ernst, 1967; Andén et al., 1967b). This drug is known to induce compulsive gnawing behavior in rats and its action is independent of presynaptic stores of DA. Since it seems likely that DA acts as a transmitter substance in the median eminence, it would be particularly valuable to analyze the endocrine actions of apomorphine. Such a study could contribute to elucidating the neuroendocrine role played by the dopaminergic neurons in the brain. Recent evidence indicates that the anti-hypertensive agent, catapresan, stimulates central NA receptors (Andén, Corrodi, Fuxe, Hökfelt, and Hökfelt, unpublished data). The neuroendocrine effects of this drug are now being studied.

A detailed pharmacological analysis has been performed on the tuberoinfundibular-DA neurons (Fuxe and Hillarp, 1964; Fuxe et al.,

1966, 1967a; Lichtensteiger and Langemann, 1966). These neurons, like the central NA neurons (Hamberger and Masuoka, 1965; Hamberger, 1967) possess a reserpine-resistant amine-concentrating mechanism, which is energy-dependent, at the cell membrane. This mechanism is blocked by cocaine, but not by guanethidine, desipramine, or chlorpromazine. The latter three drugs are able to block this mechanism in peripheral adrenergic neurons (Malmfors, 1965). High doses of estrogen, progesterone, or testosterone have not been found to block the amine-concentrating mechanism (Fuxe and Hökfelt, unpublished data). In the DA neurons and NA neurons this mechanism is not stereospecific. It may be relatively specific for CA, however, since high doses of 5-HT or α-methyl-5-HT (Fuxe and Hökfelt, unpublished data) have to be given before any accumulation is observed. The reserpine-resistant accumulation of 5-HT in the tuberoinfundibular neurons is released by amphetamine in the same manner as the reserpine-resistant accumulation of DA.

Functional Studies

Studies that aim at elucidating the function of neuron systems in the central nervous system present great difficulties. However, some principal methods may be mentioned. One is selective interruption of pathways, with observation of the functional deficit thus produced. A second is intracerebral injection of substances that specifically interfere with a certain type of transmission known to exist in that area. Problems of specificity are great in such experiments, but successful experiments have been performed in the nucleus caudatus putamen of the rat (Ungerstedt et al., 1969). A third method, which has been successfully used in a large number of various types of experiments, is based on the idea that the function of a neuron system might be disclosed by recording changes in its activity caused by various experimental and physiological conditions.

Methods of Studying Turnover of CA

One way to study the over-all activity in the monoamine terminals is to use inhibitors of amine synthesis and study the disappearance rate of the amines. In our studies, the *methylester* of *α-methyl-p-tyrosine* (H 44/68), an inhibitor of tyrosine hydroxylase, has been used (Andén et al., 1966d; Corrodi and Hanson, 1966). The amine depletion obtained after treatment with this inhibitor is highly dependent on the nervous impulse flow. This was demonstrated in rats in which the spinal cord had been transected. In such animals, the NA terminals in the spinal cord that are caudal to the transection lack nervous impulse flow because all the NA nerve terminals in the spinal cord belong to descending bulbospinal systems. It was observed that the NA nerve terminals cranial but not caudal to the transection were depleted by the synthesis inhibitor. Similar results have been obtained after treatment with dopa-decarboxylase inhibitors and DA-β-oxidase inhibitors (diethyldithiocarbamate) (Andén *et al.*, 1967c). Furthermore, electrical stimulation of the medulla oblongata in rats treated with the synthesis inhibitor results in enhanced amine depletion only from the NA nerve terminals cranial to the spinal transection (Dahlström *et al.*, 1965b).

A large number of papers have been published about the use of synthesis inhibitors to study turnover of monoamines (e.g. Corrodi *et al.*, 1966a,b; 1967 a,b; Andén *et al.*, 1967a,b,c). Theoretically, this technique has the drawback of using a drug that interferes with the equilibrium state of the monoamine nerve terminal and which therefore may cause effects that are not related to the actual state of activity in the neuron. However, the studies are generally performed before the pharmacological effects are apparent. Other models to measure turnover should also be used. Another way to measure turnover is to study the decline in specific activity of intraventricularly injected, isotopically labeled CA. In one study this method was compared with the others and found to give similar results (Iversen and Glowinski, 1966). However, one drawback involved in studies using intraventricular injections is that only the zone close to the ventricles and the ventral part of the subarachnoid space is reached by the amine (Fuxe and Ungerstedt, 1966, 1967, 1968a). Thus, the activity in the majority of the monoamine neuron systems in the brain cannot be studied with this technique. This may not be too important when the effects of drugs are analyzed, since the drugs usually affect the terminal systems similarly in all parts of the brain. A comparable problem is involved when the acid DA and 5-HT metabolites are measured in the cerebrospinal fluid, since these acids are probably mainly derived from terminals lying close to the ventricles.

Intraventricular amine injections can be avoided if systemic injections of radioactive tyrosine or l-dopa are given and the decline in specific activity of the radioactive NA or DA formed in the brain is studied (Nybäck *et al.*, 1967). However, such studies also involve problems. There are insufficient data on when the synthesis of labeled precursors ceases; only small amounts of radioactive NA are formed from tyrosine in the brain; and the use of labeled precursors in turnover experiments requires further study.

It is also possible to measure the amounts in the brain of the 3-0-methylated CA metabolites, 3-methoxytyramine (formed from DA), and normetanephrine (formed from NA), and the acid DA and 5-HT metabolites, 3,4-dihydroxyphenylacetic acid (DOPAC), 5-hydroxyindolacetic acid, and homovanillic acid (HVA). These metabolites have been found in areas rich in CA nerve terminals and are therefore probably related to central CA neurotransmission (Roos, 1962; Andén et al., 1963a,b; Carlsson and Lindqvist, 1963). The acid DA and 5-HT metabolites are transported out of the brain with the help of an energy-dependent mechanism, which is blocked by probenicid (Neff et al., 1964; Sharman, 1967; Werdinius 1967). The rate of accumulation of acid DA metabolites after inhibition of the transport system probably reflects the turnover of DA. No acid metabolites of NA are found in the brain; NA is oxidatively deaminated to 3,4-dihydroxy-phenylglycol and its 3-0-methylated derivative. The derivatives are lipid soluble and probably diffuse out of the brain with ease (Rutledge and Jonason, 1967). These studies were performed *in vitro* on rabbit brain slices. The oxidative deamination in the CA neurons occurs intraneuronally and precedes the 3-0-methylation, which occurs extraneuronally, since after reserpine treatment followed by dopa injection there is first a peak of DOPAC and then a peak of HVA (Carlsson and Hillarp, 1962). Furthermore, after a blockade of the amine-concentrating mechanism in the NA neurons by desipramine, there is a decrease in the formation of the 3,4-dihydroxyphenylglycols from added NA in the incubation bath, indicating that the oxidative deamination mainly occurs inside the neuron (Jonason and Rutledge, 1969). Normetanephrine is the principal product formed when exogenous CA are added to the incubation bath (Rutledge and Jonason, 1967).

Direct evidence has recently been obtained that normetanephrine is related to activity in the NA neurons; when the nerve impulse flow to the spinal cord is reduced by a spinal transection in rats, the levels of normetanephrine decrease (Andén, Börjeson, and Magnusson, to be published). However, the methods used in this study are not very sensitive, and large numbers of rat brains have to be pooled to measure the level of normetanephrine in the hypothalamus. In previous studies on metabolism of labeled DA and NA, brain regions devoid of monoamine nerve terminals were not studied. Therefore, it has as yet not been possible to distinguish adequately between the intraneuronal and extraneuronal component of metabolism of administered labeled precursors of DA and NA or the labeled amines themselves.

In view of the above discussion it seems that, at the present time, the use of synthesis inhibitors is a convenient way to study at least semi-quantitatively the over-all activity in the central monoamine neurons. If possible, labeled CA precursors or labeled CA should also be used, so that the results obtained by the two techniques can be compared. In the case of the DA afferents to the median eminence, labeled DA can be used instead of labeled precursors, since the blood-brain barrier is lacking in this region. So far, the results obtained from studies on these afferents with synthesis inhibitors and labeled DA agree (Fuxe, Hökfelt, and Jonsson, unpublished data, see below).

In several studies, there are indications that increased amounts of amines in CA cell bodies reflect an increased nervous activity in that neuron system. Thus, whenever an increased fluorescence intensity has been observed in the CA cell bodies, e.g. after haloperidol in the NA cell bodies of the reticular formation in the medulla oblongata or during pregnancy in the arcuate DA cell bodies (Andén *et al.*, 1966c; Fuxe *et al.*, 1967b), an increased rate of depletion of CA after treatment with amine synthesis inhibitors has always been observed (Corrodi *et al.*, 1967a; Fuxe and Hökfelt, 1967; Fuxe *et al.*, 1967b).

NA Afferents to the Hypothalamus

Various Types of Stress. The NA nerve terminals in the hypothalamus and the rest of the NA nerve terminals in the brain show an increased rate of amine depletion after H 44/68 under the influence of immobilization stress (Corrodi *et al.*, 1968). Thus the NA nerve terminals in the hypothalamus, as elsewhere in the brain, probably are in a state of high activity during this type of stress. Previous reports (Maynert and Levi, 1964) on decreases of NA levels during such types of stress seem to be in agreement with this view. Persistent increases of NA turnover in various regions of the brain in response to electroconvulsive shock treatment, using intraventricular injections of labeled NA, have also been reported (Kety *et al.*, 1967).

Acute exposure to a cold environment at $+3°C$, on the other hand, does not seem to influence the activity of the hypothalamic NA nerve terminals (Corrodi *et al.*, 1967b), whereas exposure to a hot environment ($+40°C$) has about the same effect on the hypothalamic and other central NA terminals as immobilization stress (Corrodi *et al.*, 1968). It is uncertain if this response to heat is a nonspecific stress response, or if, instead, it indicates a role of the hypothalamic NA nerve terminals in thermoregulation. The fact that cold stress was ineffective may support the latter alternative. Furthermore, Iversen and Simmonds (1968) have recently reported selective changes in turnover of hypothalamic NA nerve terminals in rats kept at an environmental temperature of 24°C during intraventricular injections of labeled NA. In this connection it may be pointed out that the peripheral adrenergic neurons show signs of increased activity on exposure of the rats to cold (Corrodi and Malmfors, 1966) whereas the central CA neurons do not show any change.

It is not known if the increased activity in the hypothalamic NA nerve terminals in response to stress is of importance for the increased output of adrenocorticotropic hormone (ACTH; see Mangili *et al.*, 1966) and growth hormone (GH; see Müller *et al.*, 1967a) observed in response to stresses such as immobilization. However, studies with drugs interfering with the CA metabolism support this possibility (see Gold and Ganong, 1966; Müller *et al.*, 1967b).

Osmotic Stimulation. In view of the high density of NA nerve terminals surrounding the nucleus supraopticus and the importance of this nucleus in the regulation of antidiuretic hormone (ADH) secretion, it was of interest to study the activity of the supraoptic NA nerve terminals and the rest of the hypothalamic NA nerve terminals under the influence of osmotic stimuli. When both hypotonic and hypertonic sodium chloride solutions were infused intravenously for 2 hours to awake animals, there was diffuse activation of a large number of NA nerve terminal systems, including those of the hypothalamus (Figs. 2-26, 2-27; Andén, Fuxe, and Hökfelt, 1968, unpublished). Isotonic sodium chloride infusions did not produce such effects. Thus it seems that osmotic stimuli, whether hypotonic or hypertonic, triggered the same diffuse activation response of the NA neurons as did the immobilization stimulus. Consequently, the NA neurons do not seem to be involved in the osmotic control of ADH secretion, but

Figure 2-26 Nucleus supraopticus of normal male rat after treatment with H 44/68 (250 mg/kg, i.p., 4 hours before sacrifice). A medium density of faintly to strongly fluorescent NA nerve terminals still remains. O, optic chiasm. × 180.

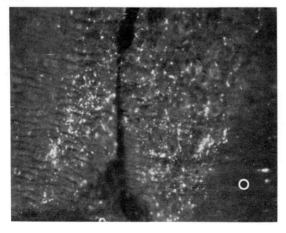

they may be involved in its neural control. Some workers (Mills and Wang, 1966) have reported that the effects of electrical stimulation of ascending pathways from the rhombencephalon that mediate ADH release can be blocked by adrenergic blocking agents such as phenoxybenzamine. These findings support the view that NA afferents to the hypothalamus participate in the neural control of ADH secretion. The results of experiments with infusions of isotonic sodium chloride solution indicate that stimulation of volume receptors is not of great importance for activation of the central NA neurons. In this connection it should be pointed out that ethanol, which inhibits ADH secretion, increases the rate of depletion of NA from hypothalamic NA nerve terminals after H 44/68 treatment (Corrodi et al., 1966b) Thus, it is possible that increased release of NA from NA terminals in the supraoptic nucleus partly mediates the inhibitory effect of ethanol on ADH secretion.

Removal of Olfactory Stimuli.   Removal of olfactory bulbs, as studied with synthesis inhibitors, has not been found to influence the activity in the hypothalamic NA afferents markedly (Andén, Fuxe, Larsson, and Ungerstedt, unpublished data).

Electrically Induced Defense Reaction (Sham Rage).   During the sham rage response produced by stimulation of the amygdala, NA appears to

Figure 2-27   Nucleus supraopticus of rat after intravenous infusion of hyperosmotic sodium chloride solution and H 44/68 treatment as described in caption to Figure 2-26. Now only a low density of weakly fluorescent NA nerve terminals can be seen, probably due to an increased turnover of NA and increased activity in these supraoptic NA nerve terminals.   O, optic chiasm. × 180.

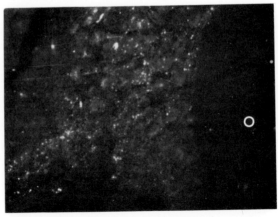

be released from practically all the NA nerve terminal systems of the brain, including the hypothalamic NA nerve terminals (Gunne and Reis, 1963; Fuxe and Gunne, 1964; Gunne and Lewander, 1966). NA is depleted from the terminals and normetanephrine is increased. The released NA is probably of importance in eliciting rage behavior, since the behavior is rapidly blocked by a low dose of haloperidol (Reis and Fuxe, 1967, unpublished data). Other evidence for electrically induced release of CA and 5-HT from central CA and 5-HT nerve terminals have been obtained mainly from electrical stimulation of the mouse spinal cord (Andén et al., 1964b), the medulla oblongata (Dahlström et al., 1965b), and brain slices (Baldessarini and Kopin, 1967; Chase et al., 1968). The same effects are obtained by adding K^+ to the medium, which causes depolarization of the membranes. Removal of Ca^{++} from the incubation bath inhibits NA release, whether induced by K^+ or electrical stimulation.

Lactation. Preliminary analyses with synthesis inhibitors indicate that no clear changes occur in the activity of the hypothalamic NA nerve terminals during the first 15 days of lactation, and during pregnancy (Andén, Fuxe and Hökfelt, unpublished data). Furthermore, ethanol, which blocks oxytocin secretion (Fuchs, 1966), may increase the activity in the NA afferents to the hypothalamus and thus also in the paraventricular NA nerve terminals, since the rate of depletion of NA is increased after H 44/68 (Corrodi et al., 1966b). It is tempting to suggest that the NA released at least partly mediates the inhibitory effect on oxytocin secretion.

Castration and Effect of Gonadal Hormones. Increases in NA levels in the anterior hypothalamus of male and female rats have been reported after castration (Stefano et al., 1965; Donoso et al., 1967). The increased NA levels in the female can be restored to normal by treatment with high doses of estrogen and progesterone (Donoso and Stefano, 1967). Furthermore, Anton-Tay and Wurtman (1968) have given intraventricular injections of labeled NA to castrated rats and have reported that, compared with controls, these rats show an increased rate of disappearance from whole brain of the labeled amine. These workers therefore suggest that after castration there is an increased activity in the NA neurons. Our group, on the other hand, found no clear-cut change in the rate of disappearance of NA after treatment with H 44/68 in castrated male rats and in castrated female rats as compared with sham operated controls (Corrodi et al., 1969). Furthermore, in our studies the levels of NA in the whole hypothalamus was not increased after castration. Preliminary results from studies using synthesis inhibitors indicate that the activity in the NA terminals of the hypothalamus of the castrated female rat cannot be changed by treatment with high doses of estrogen. Testosterone in moderate doses does not cause a significant change in the activity of the NA neurons after castration (unpub. data). In view of the data presented above, it is important that experiments with radioactive tyrosine be performed and that the decline of radioactive brain NA after intraventricular injection be studied at various time intervals from the time of injection until 24 hours after injection. In the meantime, it is unclear whether the hypothalamic NA nerve terminals participate in some way in the regulation of gonadotropin secretion.

Hypophysectomy.   The effect of hypophysectomy on hypothalamic NA has been studied in female and male rats. Histochemical results demonstrate a clear-cut retardation of amine depletion in the hypothalamic NA terminals after H 44/68. This indicates that the activity of the hypothalamic NA terminals is decreased after removal of the pituitary gland (Fuxe and Hökfelt, 1968, to be published).

Estrous Cycle.   Stefano and Donoso (1967) have reported increased NA levels in the anterior hypothalamus during metestrus and diestrus. Diurnal changes in NA concentrations in the hypothalamus have also been reported (Reis and Wurtman, 1968). As yet the cycle has not been analyzed with the help of amine synthesis inhibitors.

Pregnancy.   No increases in NA levels have been observed during pregnancy, and results with synthesis inhibitors indicate that no marked changes in activity occur in the NA neurons of the hypothalamus (Andén, Fuxe, and Hökfelt, 1968, unpublished).

DA afferents to the median eminence

Stress.   The effects on the DA afferents of a large number of different stresses have been studied. These include heat, cold, immobilization, and hypoglycemia plus bone injury. So far these conditions have not been found to change the rate of amine depletion after H 44/68, although they do increase ACTH and GH secretion. Therefore no support exists for the view that these neurons participate in the regulation of ACTH or GH secretion (Fuxe and Hökfelt, 1967).

Adrenalectomy and Treatment with Glucocorticoids. No change in the activity of the DA neurons could be demonstrated after adrenalectomy or cortisol treatment (Fuxe and Hökfelt, 1967). This is further evidence that these DA neurons are not involved in the regulation of ACTH

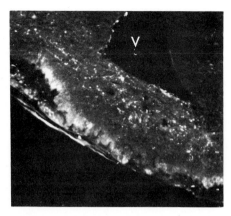

Figure 2-28   The median eminence of a castrated female rat after treatment with H 44/68 as described in caption to Figure 2-26. A weak to medium fluorescence intensity still remains in the external layer. V, third ventricle. × 120.

secretion. High doses of dexamethasone (1 mg/rat, twice a day for 2 days) have produced an increase in the activity of the DA neurons in castrated male animals (Fuxe and Hökfelt, unpublished data). However, such high doses probably can exert a negative feedback action on gonadotropin

Figure 2-29   The median eminence of a lactating rat (day 10) after treatment with H 44/68. Practically no fluorescence remains in the external layer, probably because of the increased DA turnover and activity in the tuberoinfundibular DA neurons during lactation. Note that the NA nerve terminals in the internal layer are still comparatively strongly fluorescent. V, third ventricle. × 180.

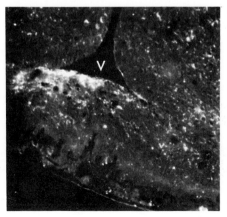

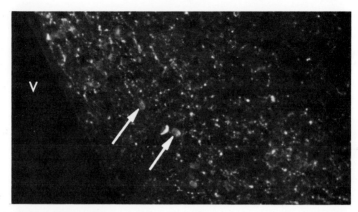

Figure 2-30   The arcuate nucleus of a female rat at estrous of the ovarian cycle. A very low fluorescence intensity can be seen in the DA cell bodies (↗). V, third ventricle.   × 180.

secretion (Hagino, 1968). Studies with osmotic stimuli have so far given negative results.

Effect of Thyroxine and Thiouracil.   Treatment with high doses of thyroxine and thiouracil has not been found to change to any extent the rate of amine depletion from the tuberoinfundibular DA neurons after H 44/68. These treatments have also failed to produce any changes in the amine content of the DA cell bodies of the arcuate nucleus (Fuxe and Hökfelt, unpublished data).

Lactation.   There is a marked increase in the rate of DA depletion after H 44/68 during the first 20 days of lactation (Fig. 2-28, 2-29), and on

Figure 2-31   The arcuate nucleus of a lactating rat (day 10). An increased fluorescence intensity is observed in the DA cell bodies (↗) of the arcuate nucleus compared to normally cycling rats.   V, third ventricle.   × 180.

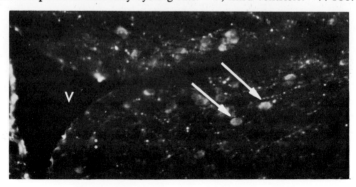

days 10 through 15 there are increases in the number and intensity of DA cell bodies (Fig. 2-30, 2-31; Fuxe *et al.*, 1967b). Furthermore, there is an increase in the decline of radioactive DA from the median eminence after an initial normal accumulation (Fuxe, Hökfelt, and Jonsson, 1969, to be published). However, the first days after delivery, during which the postpartum ovulation occurs, have not been analyzed in detail.

The activation of the DA neurons during lactation is at least partly dependent on stimuli from the breast, since, compared with normally lactating rats, the rate of depletion of amines decreases in the absence of such stimuli. Ovariectomy on day 2 of lactation, on the other hand, has not been found to decrease the activation; 8 days after the operation the rate of depletion of DA is the same as that in lactating rats with intact ovaries (Fuxe *et al.*, 1969a). Treatment with estrone, progesterone, or gonadotropins on days 2 through 4 also does not seem to influence the activity; at least it does not during the 5-day period following the last injection. It is known that prolactin and ACTH secretion are increased during lactation, whereas FSH and LH secretion are low and ovulation is blocked. The release of FSH and LH is decreased by the milking stimulus (see Meites, 1966). Furthermore, the concentration of prolactin inhibiting factor (PIF) is decreased by suckling and estradiol treatment (see Meites, 1966).

Castration and Treatment with Gonadal Hormones. In the male rat, castration 3 to 10 weeks before sacrifice does not produce any observable effects on the activity of the DA neurons.

In the female rat, the changes in activity observed during the estrous cycle (described below) disappear, and the system remains in a state of low activity like that observed during certain periods of proestrus and estrus (Fuxe *et al.*, 1969b). After castration there is a marked rise in the plasma and pituitary levels of FSH and LH (see McCann *et al.*, 1968). These effects are probably mediated via increased release of follicle-stimulating hormone releasing factor (FSHRF) and luteinizing hormone releasing factor (LRF) from the median eminence. Since the activity in the NA neurons and in the DA afferents to the median eminence is not markedly changed after castration, the NA afferents and the DA afferents probably do not participate in mediating this response. After treatment with estradiol (down to a total of 0.15 µg/rat), testosterone (down to 0.3 mg/rat), or progesterone (15 mg/rat), the activity in the DA neurons of the castrated rat is probably increased; at any rate, there is an increased depletion rate after inhibition of amine synthesis (Fuxe *et al.*, 1967b). Furthermore, the disappearance rate of i.v. injected ^{3}H-DA from the median eminence is considerably increased (Fuxe, Hökfelt, and Jonsson, to be published). It may be, there-fore, that the negative feedbacks of the gonadal hormones on FSH and LH release are mediated, at least in part, by an activation of these tubero-infundibular DA neurons. It is probable that the sex hormones mainly act centrally by decreasing release of FSHRF and LRF (McCann *et al.*, 1968). It is a fascinating possibility that contraceptive steroids may at least partly act by activating the DA afferents to the median eminence, since one of the actions of these steroids is to inhibit the release of the LRF from the median eminence (Schally *et al.*, 1968). Cortisol (30 mg/rat) has no observable effect on the DA tuberoinfundibular neurons of the castrated rat, and dexamethasone is effective only in high doses (Fuxe and Hökfelt, unpublished), suggesting that a certain specificity exists in the response to the sex hormones. The low doses of estradiol and testosterone which activate the tuberoinfundibular DA neurons have been found to be ineffective in influencing the activity in the hypo-thalamic NA afferents of castrated rats (Corrodi *et al.*, 1969). Negative feedback of the sex hormones is therefore probably not mediated via the NA afferents. Injected gonadotropins, human chorionic gonado-tropin (HCG), and/or pregnant mares' serum (PMS) have so far proved to be ineffective in influencing the activity of the DA neurons in the castrated male or female rat. However, these negative results may be due to the existence of a species specificity in the response to HCG and PMS. It is possible that the gonadal hormones may act directly on the DA neurons, since ^{3}H-estrogen is accumulated in many arcuate cell bodies. Studies have been performed to see if at least some of these are identical with the DA cell bodies. The distribution of tritiated estrogen or tritiated testosterone in the central nervous system has previously been reported by investigators such as Stumpf (1968) and Pfaff (1968a; 1968b). The amine-concentrating mechanisms in the DA nerve terminals, whether at the granular or the cell membrane level, do not seem to be effected by estrogen or testosterone (Fuxe and Hökfelt, unpublished data). Thus the hormones probably do not act on the DA terminals but on the DA cell bodies and/or on a nervous circuit in which the DA neurons participate.

The reactivity of the DA neurons to the gonadal hormones is increased after castration. Thus, considerably higher doses of estrogen and testo-sterone have to be given to activate the tuberoinfundibular DA neurons of normal male rats. The DA neurons of androgen-sterilized rats (see Barraclough, 1967) which exhibit no cyclic changes and an activity similar to that observed in diestrus do not react to treatment with estrogen, progesterone or testosterone (Fuxe *et al.*, 1969c). After castration of androgen-sterilized rats, however, the DA neurons react to estrogen, but the activation is less than that obtained by giving a similar dose to a castrated normal rat (Fuxe *et al.*, 1969c).

Hypophysectomy.   Seven to ten days after removal of the pituitary gland there is a considerable decrease in the rate of amine depletion after treatment with H 44/68, suggesting a decrease in the activity of tuberoinfundibular DA neurons. This is also suggested by the fact that only a few, faintly green-fluorescent DA cell bodies are observed in the arcuate nucleus (Fuxe, Hökfelt and Nilsson, unpublished). Treatment of the hypophysectomized rats with high doses of HCG and PMS has not been found to restore the activity in the DA neurons. The results obtained with hypophysectomy suggest that FSH and LH act on the hypothalamus to activate the DA* tuberoinfundibular neurons not only via release of gonadal hormones but also directly via a short feedback loop. This possibility has to be checked by continued experiments involving gonadotropin treatments of various types.

Estrous cycle.   In studies in which the stages of ovarian cycle were determined solely from light microscopy on sections of the vagina, no marked changes were observed in the number and intensity of DA cell bodies. However, the CA cell bodies appear to be slightly increased in number and intensity in diestrus (Fuxe *et al.*, 1967b). Other workers have described the opposite (Lichtensteiger, 1968). Our own findings, however, agree well with results obtained with amine synthesis inhibitors (Fuxe *et al.*, 1969b). Thus the rate of amine depletion at diestrus is higher than that at certain periods of proestrus and estrus. This decrease

Figure 2-32   The arcuate nucleus of a pregnant rat (day 8). An increased fluorescence intensity is observed in the DA cell bodies (↗) compared to normally cycling rats.   V, third ventricle.   × 180.

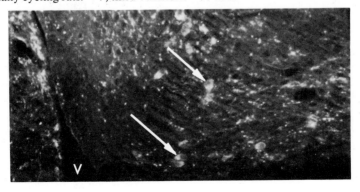

in activity at proestrus may be related to the ovulatory release of LH occurring at this time. It is tempting to speculate that withdrawal of an inhibitory action of DA at the median eminence level is of at least some importance for the release of LRF that triggers the ovulation-producing burst of LH secretion (Fuxe *et al.*, 1969b).

Pregnancy.   From the day 3 until the end of pregnancy there is a marked increase in the activity of the tuberoinfundibular DA neurons, as revealed by acceleration of amine depletion after synthesis inhibition (Fuxe *et al.*, 1967b) and increased disappearance rate of radioactive DA from the median eminence (Fuxe, Hökfelt, and Jonsson, to be published). Furthermore, there are marked increases (Fig. 2-32) in the number and intensity of DA cell bodies in the arcuate nucleus (Fuxe *et al.*, 1967b). If the rats are hysterectomized on day 12 of pregnancy the activation of the DA neurons decreases (Fuxe *et al.*, 1969a). However, this is only observed after a period of 6 to 8 days. The mechanism behind this effect is being analyzed by performing embryotomy, by removal of the placenta-embryo, and by distension of the uterus with plastic devices.

The importance of stimulation of the vagina and cervix for the activation is illustrated by the fact that the DA neurons are also activated during pseudopregnancy produced either by sterile mating or mechanical stimulation of the cervix (Fuxe *et al.*, 1969a). The mechanical stimulation has to be performed at estrus to result in an activation of the DA neurons, which may indicate that the neurons are sensitized by estrogen. The period of activation of the DA neurons largely coincides with the period of pseudopregnancy. If the period of pseudopregnancy is prolonged by hysterectomy or by causing deciduomata the activation of the DA neurons also lasts longer. In experiments on early pregnancy, hormone treatments and ovariectomy have so far not been found to influence the activity in the DA neurons (Fuxe *et al.*, 1967b).

The fact that drugs such as reserpine (which blocks DA and NA transmission) and dibenamine (which blocks NA transmission) inhibit ovulation and produce pseudopregnancy and lactation (see Gold and Ganong, 1966) seems difficult to reconcile with our findings of an increased activity in the tuberoinfundibular DA neurons during pseudopregnancy and lactation. However, the effects obtained with drugs are difficult to interpret, since other types of monoamine neurons such as NA and/or 5-HT neurons and the large ascending DA neurons of the brain are usually also affected. This criticism also holds true for the implantation of pellets of reserpine in the ventromedial hypothalamus (Smelik and Van Mannen, 1968), although now the effects are restricted to the hypothalamic mono-amine nerve terminals. The problems involved with drug injections are well illustrated by the fact that amphetamine, which markedly increases DA and NA transmission, produces lactation in the same way as reserpine (see Gold and Ganong, 1966).

The DA afferent input to the basal ganglia and the basal telencephalon is not changed during pregnancy and lactation or after castration and treatment with sex hormones. Thus the changes occurring in the median eminence are specific. The changes in turnover in the median eminence are specific also, in view of the fact that no definite changes in activity are observed under situations which markedly change the rate of ACTH, GH, and TSH secretion. Marked changes are only observed in endocrine situations involving changes in the secretion of FSH, LH, and prolactin from the anterior pituitary. The DA nerve terminals in the median eminence seem to establish axo-axonic contacts with other terminals (Hökfelt, unpublished data). Therefore the best present explanation of the increased DA release when ovulation is blocked is that the DA released by the nervous impulse flow in the tuberoinfundibular DA neurons inhibits the release of FSHRF and LRF into the primary capillary plexus from nerve terminals in the median eminence. However, an inhibitory effect by DA on nerve terminals storing PIF in the external layer of the median eminence cannot be excluded. The inhibitory action of DA may be viewed as a special form of presynaptic inhibition. When DA is discharged it may partly depolarize the nerve membrane of the "peptidergic" neurons, and thus less releasing factor may be discharged into the primary capillary plexus by the nervous impulse flow in the "peptidergic" neurons.

Conclusions

The DA tuberoinfundibular neuron system appears to be specifically involved in the regulation of gonadotropin secretion from the anterior pituitary, since the activity of the system is increased in pregnancy, pseudopregnancy, lactation, after androgen sterilization, and after treatment with sex hormones. Furthermore, the activity undergoes cyclic changes during the ovarian cycle (activity is increased at diestrus), and these changes are lost after castration. Also, the activity is decreased after hypophysectomy. The hypothesis has been advanced that the DA boutons in the median eminence establish axo-axonic contacts, and that the DA released inhibits the release of FSHRF and/or LRF into the primary capillary plexus by way of a depolarizing action on the cell membrane of nerve terminals containing FSHRF and LRF, respectively. The action potentials reaching these terminals are postulated to be decreased, and less releasing factor is delivered per impulse. These synaptic events could best be described as a special form of presynaptic inhibition. An effect by DA on PIF-storing terminals cannot be excluded.

The NA afferent input to the hypothalamus also seems to participate in neuroendocrine regulation. The activity of these NA neurons in hypophysectomized rats is probably decreased, whereas, in lactating and pregnant rats, it is not clearly affected. Furthermore the NA afferents are fairly insensitive to testosterone and particularly estradiol treatment, especially when compared with the DA afferents to the median eminence. These NA neurons may also participate in the neural control of the ACTH, GH, oxytocin, and ADH secretion, in view of the increased activity these neurons exhibit to different types of stress and osmotic stimulation and to ethanol. It has been postulated that the hypothalamic NA nerve terminals, especially in the perifornical area, are involved in the control of food intake, since increased food intake and decreased water intake is obtained after an intracerebral NA injection into this area (see Miller, 1965). Furthermore, a theory that the NA afferents to the hypothalamus have a role in thermoregulation has been advanced by Feldberg and Myers (1963) and is supported by results obtained in a study on the effect of environmental temperature on NA turnover using synthesis inhibitors (Corrodi et al., 1967b). Thus, the NA neurons may participate in many of the complex functions of the hypothalamus. Their exact role, however, remains to be determined.

References

Andén, N.-E. (1967). Effects of reserpine and a tyrosine hydroxylase inhibitor on the monoamine levels in different regions of the rat central nervous system. Europ. J. Pharmacol. 1, 1-5.

Andén, N.-E., and M. Henning (1966). Adrenergic nerve function, noradrenaline level and noradrenaline uptake in cat nictitating membrane after reserpine treatment. Acta. Physiol. Scand. 67, 498-504.

Andén, N.-E., B.-E. Roos, and B. Werdinius (1963a). 3-4-Dihydroxylphenylacetic acid in rabbit corpus striatum normally and after reserpine treatment. Life Sci. 2, 319-25.

Andén, N.-E., B.-E. Roos, and B. Werdinius (1963b). On the occurrence of homovanillic acid in brain and cerebrospinal fluid and its determination by a fluorometric method. Life Sci. 2, 448-58.

Andén, N.-E., B.-E. Roos, and B. Werdinius (1964a). Effects of chlorpromazine, haloperidol and reserpine on the levels of phenolic acids in rabbit corpus striatum. Life Sci. 3, 149-58.

Andén, N.-E., A. Carlsson, N.-Å. Hillarp, and T. Magnusson (1946b). Noradrenaline release by nerve stimulation of the spinal cord. Life Sci. 4, 129-32.

Andén, N.-E., A. Dahlström, K. Fuxe, and K. Larsson (1965a). Mapping out of catecholamine and 5-hydroxytryptamine neurons innervating the telencephalon and diencephalon. Life Sci. 4, 1275-79.

Andén, N.-E., T. Magnusson, and E. Rosengren (1965b). Occurrence of dihydroxyphenylalanine decarboxylase in nerves of the spinal cord and sympathetically innervated organs. Acta. Physiol. Scand. 64, 127-35.

Andén, N.-E., A. Dahlström, K. Fuxe, L. Olson, and U. Ungerstedt (1966a). Ascending noradrenaline neurons from the pons and the medulla oblongata. *Experientia 22*, 44.

Andén, N.-E., A. Dahlström, K. Fuxe, K. Larson, L. Olson, and U. Ungerstedt (1966b). Ascending monoamine neurons to the telencephalon and diencephalon. *Acta. Physiol. Scand. 67*, 313-26.

Andén, N.-E., A. Dahlström, K. Fuxe, and T. Hökfelt (1966c). The effect of haloperidol and chlorpromazine on the amine levels of central monoamine neurons. *Acta. Physiol. Scand. 68*, 419-20.

Andén, N.-E., H. Corrodi, A. Dahlström, K. Fuxe, and T. Hökfelt (1966d). Effects of tyrosine hydroxylase inhibition on the amine levels of central monoamine neurons. *Life Sci. 5*, 561-68.

Andén, N.-E., H. Corrodi, K. Fuxe, and T. Hökfelt (1967a). Increased impulse flow in bulbospinal NA neurons by catecholamine receptor blocking agents. *Europ. J. Pharmacol. 2*, 59-64.

Andén, N.-E., K. Fuxe, T. Hökfelt, and A. Rubensson (1967b). Evidence for dopamine receptor stimulation by apomorphine. *J. Pharm. Pharmacol. 19*, 335-37.

Andén, N.-E., K. Fuxe, and T. Hökfelt (1967c). Effect of some drugs on monoamine nerve terminals lacking nerve impulse flow. *Europ. J. Pharmacol. 1*, 226-32.

Anton-Tay, F., and R. J. Wurtman (1968). Norepinephrine: Turnover in rat brains after gonadectomy. *Science 159*, 1245.

Baldessarini, R. J., and I. J. Kopin (1967). The effect of drugs on the release of norepinephrine-H^3 from central nervous system tissues by electrical stimulation in vitro. *J. Pharmacol. Exp. Ther. 150*, 31-38.

Barraclough, C. A. (1967). Modification in reproductive function after exposure to hormones during the prenatal and early postnatal period. In *Neuroendocrinology*, (L. Martini and W. F. Ganong, eds.), pp. 62-100. Academic Press, New York.

Björklund, A., B. Falck, and E. Rosengren (1967). Monoamines in the pituitary gland of a pig. *Life Sci. 6*, 2103-10.

Björklund, A., B. Falck, and L. Ljunggren (1968). Monoamines in the bird median eminence, failure of cocaine to block the accumulation of exogenous amines. *Z. Zellforsch. 89*, 193-201.

Carlsson, A. (1964). Functional significance of drug-induced changes in brain monoamine levels. *Prog. Brain Res. 8*, 9-27.

Carlsson, A. (1966). Drugs which block the storage of 5-hydroxytryptamine and related amines. In *Handbook of experimental Pharmacology* (O. Eichler and A. Farah, eds.), *19*, 529-92. Springer Verlag, Berlin, Heidelberg, Göttingen.

Carlsson, A., and N.-Å. Hillarp (1962). Formation of phenolic acids in the brain after administration of 3,4-dihydroxyphenylalanine. *Acta Physiol. Scand. 55*, 95-100.

Carlsson, A., and M. Lindqvist (1962). In vivo decarboxylation of α-methyl-DOPA and α-methyl-meta-tyrosine. *Acta Physiol. Scand. 54*, 87-94.

Carlsson, A., and M. Lindqvist (1963). Effect of chlorpromazine or haloperidol on formation of 3-methoxy-tyramine and normetanephrine in mouse brain. *Acta. Pharmacol. Toxicol. 20*, 140-44.

Carlsson, A., and B. Waldeck (1963). β-hydroxylation of tyramine in vivo. *Acta Pharmacol. Toxicol. 20*, 371-74.

Carlsson, A., B. Falck, and N.-Å. Hillarp (1962a). Cellular localization of brain monoamines. *Acta Physiol. Scand.* 56, Suppl. 196, 1-28.

Carlsson, A., B. Falck, N.-Å. Hillarp, and A. Torp (1962b.) Histochemical localization at the cellular level of hypothalamic noradrenaline. *Acta Physiol. Scand.* 54, 385-86.

Carlsson, A., N.-Å. Hillarp, and B. Waldeck (1963). Analysis of the Mg^{++}-ATP dependent storage mechanism in the amine granules of the adrenal medulla. *Acta Physiol. Scand.* 59, Suppl. 215, 1-38.

Carlsson, A., A. Dahlström, K. Fuxe, and N.-Å. Hillarp (1965a). Failure of reserpine to deplete noradrenaline neurons of α-methyl-noradrenaline formed from α-methyl-DOPA. *Acta Pharmacol.* 22, 270-76.

Carlsson, A., M. Lindqvist, A. Dahlström, K. Fuxe, and D. Masuoka (1965b). Effects of the amphetamine group on intraneuronal brain amines *in vivo* and *in vitro*. *J. Pharm. Pharmacol.* 17, 521-24.

Carlsson, A., A. Dahlström, K. Fuxe, and M. Lindqvist (1965c). Histochemical and biochemical detection of monoamine release from brain neurons. *Life Sci.* 4, 809-16.

Carlsson, A., K. Fuxe, B. Hamberger, and M. Lindqvist (1966a). Biochemical and histochemical studies on the effects of imipramine-like drugs and (+)-amphetamine on central and peripheral catecholamine neurons. *Acta Physiol. Scand.* 67, 481-97.

Carlsson, A., A. Dahlström, K. Fuxe, and M. Lindqvist (1966b). Histochemical and biochemical effects of diethyldithiocarbamate on tissue catecholamines. *J. Pharmacol.* 18, 60-62.

Carlsson, A., K. Fuxe, B. Hamberger, and M. Lindqvist (1966c). The effect of (+)-amphetamine on various central and peripheral catecholamine-containing neurons. *J. Pharm. Pharmacol.* 18, 128-30.

Carlsson, A., K. Fuxe, and T. Hökfelt (1967). Effect of desmethylimipramine, protriptyline and (+)-amphetamine on fluorescence of central adrenergic neurons of rats pretreated with α-methyl-dopa and tetrabenazine or reserpine. *Europ. J. Pharmacol.* 2, 196-201.

Carlsson, A., K. Fuxe, and U. Ungerstedt (1968). The effect of imipramine on central 5-hydroxytryptamine neurons. *J. Pharm. Pharmacol.* 20, 150-51.

Chase, T. N., G. R. Breese, D. O. Carpenter, S. M. Schanburg, and I. J. Kopin (1968). Stimulation-induced release of serotonin. *Adv. in Pharmacol.* 6A, 351-64.

Corrodi, H., and K. Fuxe (1968). The effect of imipramine on central monoamine neurons. *J. Pharm. Pharmacol.* 20, 230-31.

Corrodi, H., and L. Hanson (1966). Central effects of an inhibitor of tyrosine hydroxylation. *Psychopharmacol. (Berlin)* 10, 116-25.

Corrodi, H., and G. Jonsson (1967). The formaldehyde fluorescence method for histochemical demonstration of biogenic monoamines. *J. Histochem. Cytochem.* 15, 65-78.

Corrodi, H., and T. Malmfors (1966). The effect of nerve activity on the depletion of the adrenergic transmitter by inhibitors of noradrenaline synthesis. *Acta Physiol. Scand.* 67, 352-57.

Corrodi, H., K. Fuxe, and T. Hökfelt (1966a). The effects of barbiturates on the activity of the catecholamine neurons in the rat brain. *J. Pharm. Pharmacol.* 18, 556-58.

Corrodi, H., K. Fuxe, and T. Hökfelt (1966b). The effect of ethanol on the activity of the central catecholamine neurons in rat brain. *J. Pharm. Pharmacol. 18,* 821-23.

Corrodi, H., K. Fuxe, and T. Hökfelt (1967a). The effect of neuroleptics on the activity of central catecholamine neurons. *Life Sci. 6,* 767-74.

Corrodi, H., K. Fuxe, and T. Hökfelt (1967b). A possible role played by central monoamine neurons in thermo-regulation. *Acta Physiol. Scand. 71,* 224-32.

Corrodi, H., K. Fuxe, and T. Hökfelt (1968). The effect of immobilization stress on the activity of central monoamine neurons. *Life Sci. 7,* 107-12.

Corrodi, H., K. Fuxe, and T. Hökfelt (1969). Castration, sex hormones and NA afferents to the hypothalamus, to be published.

Dahlström, A. (1966). *Studies on the intraneuronal distribution of noradrenaline and the transport and life-span of amine storage granules in the peripheral adrenergic neuron. A histochemical and biochemical study.* M.D. Thesis, Stockholm.

Dahlström, A., and K. Fuxe (1964a). A method for the demonstration of adrenergic nerve fibers in peripheral nerves. *Z. Zellforsch. 62,* 602-7.

Dahlström, A., and K. Fuxe (1964b). Evidence for the existence of monoamine containing neurons in the central nervous system. I. Demonstration of monoamines in the cell bodies of brain stem neurons. *Acta Physiol. Scand. 62,* Suppl. 232, 1.

Dahlström, A., and K. Fuxe (1966). Monoamines and the pituitary gland. *Acta Endocrinol. (Kbh.) 51,* 301-14.

Dahlström, A., K. Fuxe, L. Olson, and U. Ungerstedt (1964). Ascending catecholamine system from lower brain stem. *Acta Physiol. Scand. 62,* 485-86.

Dahlström, A., K. Fuxe, and N.-Å. Hillarp (1965a). Site of action of reserpine. *Acta Pharmacol. 22,* 277-92.

Dahlström, A., K. Fuxe., D. Kernell, and G. Sedvall (1965b). Reduction of the monoamine stores in the terminals of bulbospinal neurons following stimulation in the medulla oblongata. *Life Sci. 4,* 1207-12.

Dahlström, A., K. Fuxe, B. Hamberger, and T. Hökfelt (1967). Uptake and storage of catecholamines in rabbit brain after chronic reserpine treatment. *J. Pharm. Pharmacol. 19,* 345-49.

Daniel, P. M. (1966). The anatomy of the hypothalamus and pituitary gland. In *Neuroendocrinology* (L. Martini and W. F. Ganong, eds.), *1,* pp. 15-80. Academic Press, New York.

Donoso, A. O., and F. J. E. Stefano (1967). Sex hormones and concentration of noradrenaline and dopamine in the anterior hypothalamus of castrated rats. *Experientia 23,* 665-66.

Donoso, A. O., F. J. E. Stefano, A. M. Biscardi, and J. Cukier (1967). Effects of castration of hypothalamic catecholamines. *Amer. J. Physiol. 212,* 737-39.

Enemar, A., and B. Falck. (1965). On the presence of adrenergic nerves in the pars intermedia of the frog, *Rana temporaria. Gen. Comp. Endocrinol. 5,* 577-83.

Enemar, A., and L. Ljunggren (1968). Monoamines in the adult and developing neurohypophysis of *Gallus gallus. Z. Zellforsch. 91,* 496-506.

Ernst, A. M. (1967). Mode of action of apomorphine and dexamphetamine on gnawing compulsion in rats. *Psychopharmacol. 10,* 316-23.

Everett, J. W. (1964). Central neural control of reproductive functions of the adenohypophysis. *Physiol. Rev. 44,* 373-431.

Falck, B., and Ch. Owman (1968). 5-Hydroxytryptamine and related amines in endocrine cell systems. *Adv. in Pharmacol. 6A*, 211-31.

Falck, B., N.-Å. Hillarp, G. Thieme, and A. Thorp (1962). Fluorescence of catecholamines and related compounds condensed with formaldehyde. *J. Histochem. Cytochem. 10*, 348-54.

Falck, B., J. Häggendal, and Ch. Owman (1963). The localization of adrenaline in adrenergic nerves in the frog. *Quart. J. Exp. Physiol. 18*, 253-57.

Feldberg, W., and R. D. Myers (1963). A new concept of temperature regulation by amines in the hypothalamus. *Nature (London) 200*, 1325.

Fuchs, A.-R. (1966). The inhibitory effect of ethanol on the release of oxytocin during parturition in the rabbit. *J. Endocrinol. 35*, 125-34.

Fuxe, K. (1963). Cellular localization of monoamines in the median eminence and infundibular stem of some mammals. *Acta Physiol. Scand. 58*, 383-84.

Fuxe, K. (1964). Cellular localization of monoamines in the median eminence and infundibular stem of some mammals. *Z. Zellforsch. 61*, 710-24.

Fuxe, K. (1965a). *Evidence for the existence of central monoamine neurons.* M.D. Thesis, Stockholm.

Fuxe, K. (1965b). Evidence for the existence of monoamine neurons in the central nervous system. III. The monoamine nerve terminals. *Z. Zellforsch. 65*, 573-96.

Fuxe, K. (1965c). Evidence for the existence of monoamine neurons in the central nervous system. IV. The distribution of monoamine nerve terminals in the central nervous system. *Acta Physiol. Scand. 64*, Suppl. 247, 39-85.

Fuxe, K., and L.-M. Gunne (1964). Depletion of the amine stores in brain catecholamine terminals on amygdaloid stimulation. *Acta. Physiol. Scand. 62*, 493-94.

Fuxe, K., and N.-Å. Hillarp (1964). Uptake of L-dopa and noradrenaline by central catecholamine neurons. *Life Sci. 3*, 1403-6.

Fuxe, K., and T. Hökfelt (1966). Further evidence for the existence of tubero-infundibular dopamine neurons. *Acta. Physiol. Scand. 66*, 245-46.

Fuxe, K., and T. Hökfelt (1967). The influence of central catecholamine neurons on the hormone secretion from the anterior and posterior pituitary. In *Neurosecretion* (F. Stutinsky, ed.), pp. 165-77. Springer Verlag, New York.

Fuxe, K., and L. Ljunggren (1965). Cellular localization of monoamines in the upper brain stem of the pigeon. *J. Comp. Neurol. 125*, 355-82.

Fuxe, K., and U. Ungerstedt (1966). Localization of catecholamine uptake in rat brain after intraventricular injection. *Life Sci. 5*, 1817-24.

Fuxe, K., and U. Ungerstedt (1967). Localization of 5-HT uptake in rat brain after intraventricular injection. *J. Pharm. Pharmacol. 19*, 335-37.

Fuxe, K., and U. Ungerstedt (1968a). Histochemical studies on the distribution of catecholamines and 5-hydroxytryptamine after intraventricular injections. *Histochemie 13*, 16-28.

Fuxe, K., and U. Ungerstedt (1968b). Histochemical studies on the effect of (+)-amphetamine, drugs of the imipramine group and tryptamine on central catecholamine and 5-hydroxytryptamine neurons after intraventricular injection of catecholamine and 5-hydroxytryptamine. *Europ. J. Pharmacol. 4*, 135-44.

Fuxe, K., B. Hamberger, and T. Malmfors (1966). Inhibition of amine uptake in tubero-infundibular dopamine neurons and in catecholamine cell bodies of the area postrema. *J. Pharm. Pharmacol. 18*, 543-44.

Fuxe, K., B. Hamberger, and T. Malmfors (1967a). The effect of drugs on accumulation of monoamines in tubero-infundibular dopamine neurons. *Europ. J. Pharmacol. 1*, 334-41.

Fuxe, K., T. Hökfelt, and O. Nilsson (1967b). Activity changes in the tuberoinfundibular DA neurons of the rat during various states of the reproductive cycle. *Life Sci. 6*, 2057-61.

Fuxe, K., T. Hökfelt, and O. Nilsson (1969a). Factors involved in the control of the activity of the tubero-infundibular DA neurons, especially during pregnancy and lactation. *Neuroendocrinology*, in press.

Fuxe, K., T. Hökfelt, and O. Nilsson (1969b). Tubero-infundibular dopamine neurons and the estrous cycle. *Neuroendocrinology*, in press.

Fuxe, K., T. Hökfelt, and O. Nilsson (1968c). The effect of constant light and androgen sterilization on the tubero-infundibular DA neurons. *Neuroendocrinology*, in press.

Glowinski, J., and R. J. Baldessarini (1966). Metabolism of norepinephrine in the central nervous system. *Pharm. Rev. 18*, 1201-38.

Gold, E. M., and W. F. Ganong (1967). Effects of drugs on neuroendocrine processes. In *Neuroendrocrinology* (L. Martini and W. F. Ganong, eds.), *2*, 377-438. Academic Press, New York.

Goldstein, M. B., B. Anagnoste, W. S. Owen, and A. F. Battista (1966). The effects of ventromedial tegmental lesions on the biosynthesis of catecholamines in the striatum. *Life Sci. 5*, 2171-76.

deGroot, J. (1966). Limbic and other neural pathways that regulate endocrine function. In *Neuroendocrinology* (L. Martini and W. F. Ganong, eds.), *1*, pp. 81-106. Academic Press, New York.

Gunne, L. M. (1963). Catecholamines and 5-hydroxytryptamine in morphine tolerance and withdrawal. *Acta Physiol. Scand. 25*, Suppl. 204.

Gunne, L. M., and T. Lewander (1966). Monoamines in brain and adrenal glands of cats after electrically induced defense reaction. *Acta Physiol. Scand. 67*, 405-10.

Gunne, L. M., and D. J. Reis (1963). Changes in brain catecholamines associated with electrical stimulation of amygdaloid nucleus. *Life Sci. 11*, 804-9.

Häggendal, J. (1963). An improved method for fluorimetric determination of small amounts of adrenaline and noradrenaline in plasma and tissues. *Acta. Physiol. Scand. 59*, 242-54.

Häggendahl, J., and M. Lindqvist (1964). Disclosure of labile monoamine fractions in brain and their correlation to behaviour. *Acta Physiol. Scand. 60*, 351-57.

Hagino, N. (1968). Inhibition of gonadotrophin-induced ovulation by ACTH in immature female rats. *Excerpta Medica Int. Cong.* Ser. *157*, p. 61.

Hamberger, B. (1967). Reserpine-resistant uptake of catecholamines in isolated tissues of the rat. *Acta Physiol. Scand. 295*, 1-56.

Hamberger, B., and D. Masuoka (1965). Localization of catecholamine uptake in rat brain slices. *Acta Pharmacol. 22*, 363-68.

Hanson, L. C. F. (1967). Biochemical and behavioural effects of tyrosine hydroxylase inhibition. *Psychopharmacol. (Berlin) 11*, 8-17.

Heller, A., L. S. Seiden, W. Porcher, and R. Y. Moore (1965). 5-Hydroxytryptophan decarboxylase in rat brain: effect of hypothalamic lesions. *Science 147*, 887-88.

Hillarp, N.-Å., and D. Jacobsohn (1943). Über die Innervation der Adenohypophyse und ihre Beziehungen zur Gonadotropin Hypophysenfunktion. *Kgl. Fysiogr. Sällsk. Hal.* Bd *54*, 1-25.

Hillarp, N.-Å., K. Fuxe, and A. Dahlström (1966). Central monoamine neurons. In *Mechanisms of release of biogenic amines* (U. S. v. Euler, S. Rosell, and B. Uvnäs, eds.), pp. 31-37. Pergamon Press, New York.

Hökfelt, T. (1967a). The possible ultrastructural identification of tubero-infundibular dopamine containing nerve endings in the median eminence of the rat. *Brain Res. 5*, 121-23.

Hökfelt, T. (1967b). On the ultrastructural localization of noradrenaline in the central nervous system of the rat. *Z. Zellforsch. 79*, 110-17.

Hökfelt, T. (1968). *In vitro* studies on central and peripheral monoamine neurons at the ultrastructural level. *Z. Zellforsch., 91*, 1-74.

Iturriza, F. C. (1964). Electron-microscopic study of the pars intermedia of the pituitary of the toad *Bufo arenarum*. *Gen. Comp. Endocrinol. 4*, 492-502.

Iversen, L., and J. Glowinski (1966). Regional studies of catecholamines in the rat brain. II. Rate of turnover of catecholamines in various brain regions. *J. Neurochem. 13*, 671-82.

Iversen, L., and M. A. Simmonds (1968). Turnover studies using ³H-noradrenline. Paper presented at the Brain Metabolism Symposium. Edinburgh, July 1968.

Jonason, J., and C. O. Rutledge (1969). The effect of protriptyline on the metabolism of dopamine and noradrenaline in rabbit brain in vitro. *Brit. J. Pharmacol.*, in press.

Kety, S. S., F. Javoy, A. M. Thiery, J. Julon, and J. Glowinski (1967). A sustained effect of electroconvulsive shock on the turnover of norepinephrine in the central nervous system of the rat. *Proc. U.S. Nat. Acad. Sci. 58*, 1249-54.

Kirshner, N. (1962). Uptake of catecholamines by a particulate fraction of the adrenal medulla. *J. Biol. Chem. 237*, 2311-17.

Laverty, R., and D. F. Sharman (1965). The estimation of small quantities of 3,4-hydroxyphenylethylamine in tissues. *Brit. J. Pharmacol. 24*, 538-48.

Lichtensteiger, W. (1968). Mikrofluorimetrische Studien an katecholaminhaltigen hypothalamischen Nervenzellen der Ratte in den verschiedenen Phasen des viertägigen Oestruszyklus. *Helv. Physiol. Acta 25*, 423-25.

Lichtensteiger, W., and H. Langemann (1966). Uptake of exogenous catecholamines by monoamine containing neurons of the central nervous system: Uptake of catecholamines by arcuate infundibular neurons. *J. Pharmacol. Exp. Ther. 151*, 469-92.

Malmfors, T. (1965). Studies on adrenergic nerves. The use of rat and mouse iris for direct observations on their physiology and pharmacology at cellular and subcellular levels. *Acta Physiol. Scand. 64*, Suppl. 248, 1-93.

Mangili, G., M. Motta, and L. Martini (1966). Control of adenocorticotropic hormone secretion. In *Neuroendocrinology* (L. Martini and W. F. Ganong, eds.), *1*, pp. 297-370. Academic Press, New York.

Markee, J. E., C. H. Sawyer, and W. H. Hollinshead (1948). Adrenergic control of the release of luteinizing hormone from the hypophysis of the rabbit. *Recent Prog. Hormone Res. 2*, 117-31.

Maynert, E. W., and R. Levi (1964). Stress-induced release of brain norepinephrine and its inhibition by drugs. *J. Pharmacol. 143*, 90-95.

McCann, S. M., A. P. S. Dhariwal, and J. C. Porter (1968). Regulation of the adenohypophysis. *Ann. Rev. Physiol. 30*, 589-640.

Meites, J. (1966). Control of mammary growth and lactation. In *Neuroendocrinology* (L. Martini and W. F. Ganong, eds.), *1*, pp. 669-708. Academic Press, New York.

Meites, J., and C. S. Nicoll (1966). Adenohypophysis: prolactin. *Ann. Rev. Physiol. 28*, 57-88.

Meites, J., C. S. Nicoll, and P. K. Talwalker (1963). The central nervous system and the secretion and release of prolactin. In *Advances in Neuroendocrinology* (A. V. Nalbandov, ed.), pp. 238-277. University of Illinois Press, Urbana.

Miller, N. E. (1965). Chemical coding of behavior in the brain. *Science 148*, 328-38.

Mills, E., and S. C. Wang (1966). Liberation of antidiuretic hormone: pharmacologic blockade of ascending pathways. *Am. J. Physiol. 207*, 1405-10.

Müller, E. E., A. Ariumura, S. Sawano, T. Saito, and A. V. Schally (1967a). Growth hormone-releasing activity in the hypothalamus and plasma of rats subjected to stress. *Proc. Soc. Exp. Biol. Med. 125*, 874-78.

Müller. E. E., S. Sawano, A. Arimura, and A. V. Schally (1967b). Blockade of release of growth hormone by brain norepinephrine depletors. *Endocrinology 80*, 471-76.

Neff, N. H., T. N. Tozer, and B. B. Brodie (1964). Indole metabolism Part II. A specialized transport system to transfer 5-HIAA directly from brain to blood. *Pharmacologist 6*, 194.

Nybäck. H., G. Sedvall, and I. J. Kopin (1967). Accelerated synthesis of dopamine-C^{14} from tyrosine-C^{14} in rat brain after chlorpromazine. *Life Sci. 6*, 2307-12.

Pfaff, D. W. (1968a). Autoradiographic localization of radioactivity in rat brain after injection of tritiated sex steroids. *Science 161*, 1355-56.

Pfaff, D. W. (1968b). Uptake of ^{3}H-estradiol by the female rat brain. An autoradiographic study. *Endocrinology 82*, 1149-52.

Reis, D. J., and R. J. Wurtman (1968). Diurnal changes in brain noradrenaline. *Life Sci. 7*, 91-98.

Richardson, K. C. (1966). Electron microscopic identification of autonomic nerve endings. *Nature (London) 210*, 756.

Rinne, U. K. (1966). Ultrastructure of the median eminence of the rat. *Z. Zellforsch. 74*, 98-122.

Roos, B.-E. (1962). On the occurrence and distribution of 5-hydroxyindoleacetic acid in brain. *Life Sci. 1*, 25-27.

Rutledge, C. O., and J. Jonason (1967). Metabolic pathways of dopamine and norepinephrine in rabbit brain in vitro. *J. Pharmacol. Exp. Ther. 157*, 493-502.

Sawyer, C. H. (1963). Discussion of paper by P. L. Munson: Pharmacology of neuroendocrine blocking agents. In *Advances in Neuroendocrinology* (A. V. Nalbandov, ed.), pp. 444-59. University of Illinois Press, Urbana.

Sawyer, C. H., J. E. Markee, and B. F. Townsend (1949). Cholinergic and adrenergic components in the neurohumoral control of the release of LH in the rabbit. *Endocrinology 44*, 18-37.

Schally, A. V., W. H. Carter, and M. Saito (1968). On the site of action of oral contraceptive steroids. *Excerpta Medica Int. Cong.* Ser. *157*, p. 51.

Sharman, D. F. (1967). A discussion of the modes of action of drugs which increase the concentration of 4-hydroxy-3, methoxyphenylacetic acid in the striatum of the mouse. *Brit. J. Pharmacol. Chemother. 30*, 620-26.

Smelik, P. G. (1966). A dopaminergic innervation of the intermediate lobe of the pituitary? *Acta Physiol. Pharmacol. Neerl. 14*, 1, 1966.

Smelik, P. G., and J. H. Van Mannen (1968). Role of the tubero-infundibular dopaminergic neurons in the control of prolactin secretion. *Excerpta Medica Int. Cong. Ser. 157*, p. 135.

Stefano, F. J. E., and A. O. Donoso (1967). Norepinephrine levels in rat hypothalamus during the estrous cycle. *Endocrinology 81*, 1405-6.

Stefano, F. J. E., A. O. Donoso, and J. Cukier (1965). Hypothalamic noradrenaline changes in ovariectomized rats. *Acta Physiol. Latinoamer. 15*, 425-27.

Stumpf, W. E. (1968). Cellular and subcellular localization of ^{3}H-estradiol in target and non-target tissues by autoradiography. *Excerpta Medica Int. Cong. Ser. 157*, p. 10.

Ungerstedt, U., L. L. Butcher, S. G. Butcher, N.-E. Andén, and K. Fuxe (1969). Direct chemical stimulation of dopaminergic mechanisms in the neostriatum of the rat. *Brain Res.*, in press.

Vogt, M. (1954). The concentration of sympathin in different parts of the central nervous system under normal conditions and after the administration of drugs. *J. Physiol. (London) 123*, 451-81.

Werdinius, B. (1967). Effect of probenicid on the levels of monoamine metabolites in the rat brain. *Acta Pharmacol. et Toxicol. 25*, 18-23.

3
Effects of Peptide Hormones on Behavior

DAVID DE WIED

Introduction

Although the effect of noxious stimuli, including those of emotional origin, on pituitary function has been studied extensively, the concept that this gland and its polypeptide hormones may in turn influence behavior has received relatively little attention. My interest in the behavioral effect of peptide hormones originated in studies of the responsiveness of the anterior lobe of the pituitary gland to emotional stimuli in rats in which the posterior lobe had been extirpated. The release of adrenocorticotropic hormone (ACTH) from the pituitary gland of such rats was markedly reduced. This impaired reaction of the anterior pituitary was thought to result from the absence of posterior lobe principles involved in ACTH-release or to reflect a behavioral incompetence of the posterior lobecto-mized animal. Accordingly, studies were performed on the conditioned emotional behavior of the posterior lobectomized rat using techniques developed during a period of study with Dr. R. E. Miller in the laboratories of Dr. I. Arthur Mirsky in Pittsburgh. The initial studies demonstrated that rats deprived of their posterior lobe did indeed behave abnormally. Since the behavior of posterior lobectomized rats was restored to normal by treating them with anterior, intermediate, and posterior lobe principles, we were stimulated to explore the effect of specific pituitary peptides on conditioned emotional behavior.

Information about the effects of peptide hormones on behavior is sparse and limited primarily to what has been derived from studies on materials of pituitary origin. I shall, therefore, confine myself to a description of behavioral effects of pituitary hormones. Less attention will be paid to those data which seem the result of effects of the tropic hormones on their respective target organs. Since the behavioral effects of the absence of pituitary hormones following hypophysectomy and the influence of substitution therapy are pertinent to the elucidation of the problem, such studies are also included here. Most of the research concerned with the subject has been performed with animals and relatively little with man. Therefore, although there is obvious relevance to human behavior, the studies in man are not included in the following discussion.

The Anterior Pituitary and Behavior

Only a limited number of studies has been performed during the last 30 years on the effect of hypophysectomy on behavior. To our knowledge, the first investigators who called attention to the behavior of hypophysectomized rats were Richter and his associates (Richter and Wislocki, 1930; Richter and Eckert, 1937). They showed that, after hypophysectomy, female rats exhibited a marked decrease in spontaneous activity and in food and water intake. Daily injections of emulsions of fresh anterior lobe substance starting on the day of hypophysectomy restored their activity toward normal and increased their food and water intake. Hypophyseal transplants to the anterior chamber of the eye were virtually ineffective in these respects. A few years later, Burnham and Leonard (1941) reported that hypophysectomy did not interfere with the reverse learning of a simple black and white discrimination test, although the hypophysectomized rats made a greater number of errors in the early stages of the reverse learning. Only a few animals were used and no evidence was provided for the effectiveness of the operation.

More than 10 years later Stone and his associates performed an extensive study on the influence of hypohysectomy on several behavioral measures in rats (Stone and King, 1954; Stone and Obias, 1955; Stone and Mason, 1955). These authors found that rats hypophysectomized at 15, 30, or 35 days of age were significantly inferior to controls of the same age during the second part of their trial series in a 13-choice swimming maze. No difference was found between rats operated at 15 days of age, when cells in the CNS are still dividing, and rats hypophysectomized at 30 days of age, when mitosis in the CNS has ceased. The latter group of hypophysectomized rats was used in a second experiment, learning a 5-unit food-reinforced light discrimination problem. This group was also identical with controls. It thus appears that hypophysectomized rats are slightly inferior in learning swimming mazes but not in mazes in which strength and physical effort are not necessary. Nestbuilding ability, however, was superior in hypophysectomized rats of the same age at temperatures from 48° to 64°F. This difference disappeared at high ambient temperature, when nestbuilding is low in intact as well as in hypophysectomized rats. The investigators concluded that this behavior is prompted by the need for supplemental heat because of impairment of the mechanism for heat production. This was supported by the fact that hypophysectomized rats which could choose between a warm and a cold box in a runway, used the warm box more often than controls.

Stone et al. wondered whether the hypophysectomized rat had a real deficit in ability to learn or whether the impairment in maze performance was caused by a motivational disturbance. They stated that the deficit was not caused by differences in exploratory activity, nor due to an impairment of the various endocrine activities.

A more decisive behavioral defect in hypophysectomized rats was found by Applezweig and Baudry (1955) and Applezweig and Moeller (1959). These investigators showed that 5 days after hypophysectomy, rats exhibited a severe deficit in the rate of acquisition of a shuttle-box avoidance response. However, Bélanger (1958), using a somewhat different situation, found that the performance of hypophysectomized rats was nearly as good as that of control rats, although the reaction of the hypophysectomized rats to the conditioned stimulus (CS) was significantly slower. This apparent difference between the findings of Bélanger (1958) and those of Applezweig et al. may be explained by the fact that in Bélanger's study the time between CS and unconditioned stimulus (US) of shock was 10 seconds, while Applezweig et al. used only 2 seconds. In other words, if the hypophysectomized rat were allowed enough time, the response might have been made.

In view of the fact that the experiments above were performed with rats in which the whole pituitary gland had been removed and that results concerning the effect of the pituitary on conditioned avoidance behavior were apparently controversial, it was deemed of interest to investigate the influence of the removal of the adenohypophysis alone on avoidance and escape behavior of male rats (De Wied, 1964). Adenohypophysectomy was performed under ether anesthesia via the parapharyngeal route. Animals were allowed to recover for 1 week, during which they were treated with streptomycin to avoid infection at the site of operation. Avoidance training in a shuttle-box was begun 1 week after operation. The CS was a buzzer presented for 5 seconds prior to the US of shock. Ten trials were presented each day for 14 days, with a mean intertrial onset interval of 60 seconds during the first 3 days. Thereafter intertrial onset intervals were reduced by 10 seconds every 3 days. It appeared that adenohypophysectomized rats were far inferior to sham-operated controls in acquiring the avoidance response, thus confirming the results of Applezweig et al. (Fig. 3-1). However, 6 of the 21 adeno-

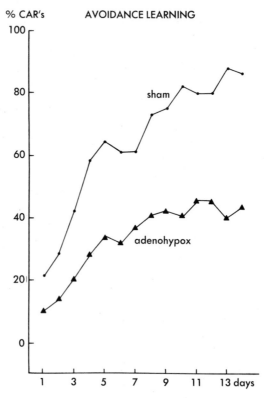

Figure 3-1   Effect of adenohypophysectomy on male rats' avoidance acquisition in a shuttle box. Avoidance acquisition was started 1 week following removal of the adenohypophysis.   CAR's, conditioned avoidance responses.

hypophysectomized rats performed identically to the control rats (Fig. 3-2). This could not be explained by the presence of adenohypophyseal remnants in these animals.

What factor or factors in the adenohypophysis cause the deficiency in conditioned avoidance behavior? Applezweig and Baudry (1955) found that the administration of ACTH 2 to 5½ hours before the sessions somewhat improved avoidance learning in hypophysectomized rats. However, the number of rats used was too small to draw a conclusion. The administration of a long-acting ACTH preparation (ACTH A_1) in a dose of 1.5 U per 2 days s.c. restored the rate of avoidance acquisition of the adenohypophysectomized rats toward normal levels (De Wied, 1964) (Fig. 3-3). This dose maintains the size of the adrenals of the adenohypophysectomized animal. These results suggested that products from the adrenal cortex rather than ACTH per se were the cause of the improved performance of the adenohypophysectomized rat. However, 3 I. U. of ACTH every two days, a dose which induced hypercorticism, had less effect than 1.5 I.U. If adenohypophysectomized rats were treated with a hormone replacement therapy consisting of cortisone, testosterone and thyroxin, avoidance learning was also significantly improved (Fig. 3-4). This treatment seemed to result in an improvement of the general physical state of the adenohypophysectomized rat. The observation that some nontreated adenohypophysectomized rats, which seemed to be in better physical condition than the others, learned better, and the observation that a maintenance dose of ACTH had a better effect than an overdose of this peptide, suggested that a general debilitation of the hypophysectomized organism was responsible for the inability of the adenohypophysectomized rat to acquire

Figure 3-2 Of the 21 adenohypophysectomized male rats subjected to avoidance training, 6 animals appeared to reach the conditioning criterion of 80 per cent or more avoidances during the last 3 days of avoidance training. As shown here, their curve was no different from that of sham-operated controls.

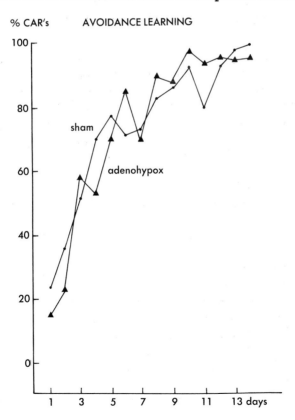

the avoidance response. Although Applezweig and Moeller (1959) had stated that this could not be the cause of the behavioral inability of the hypophysectomized rat, our hypothesis was supported by results obtained in a runway in which motor and/or sensory capacities were measured. The speed with which adenohypohysectomized rats escaped an unavoidable shock in a 2.4m long runway was far below that of sham-operated controls. Treatment with either the maintenance dose of ACTH or the replacement therapy improved the escape speed of adenohypophysectomized rats. This finding could be interpreted to indicate that motor and/or sensory capacities of the adenohypophysectomized rats were depressed and that the treatment had normalized these failing capacities considerably, although other factors might be involved as well. However, this hypothesis later appeared not to be tenable, as we shall see below.

As mentioned before, the adrenal gland per se bears no significant relationship to the acquisition of the avoidance response. This is in accord with findings of Moyer (1958) who showed that adrenalectomized rats were similar to sham-operated controls in learning an escape response. Others found the same (Applezweig and Moeller, 1957; Miller and Ogawa, 1962; De Wied, 1967), and Applezweig and Moeller (1959) suggested

Figure 3-3   Effect of ACTH (A_1 peptide), given subcutaneously as a long-acting Zn phosphate preparation every 2 days, on avoidance acquisition in a shuttle box experiment on adenohypophysectomized male rats. Note that the 3 U dose which caused adrenal hypertrophy was less effective than the 1.5 U dose.

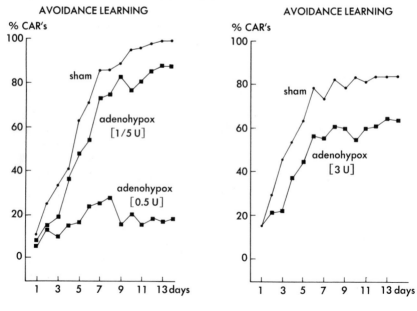

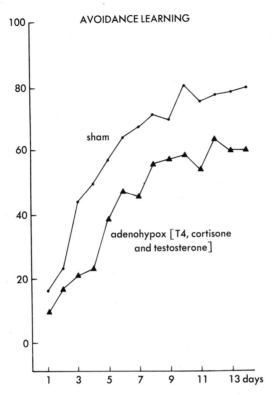

Figure 3-4   Effect of replacement therapy with cortisone 0.25 mg, testosterone propionate 0.2 mg, and L-thyroxin 10 μg, administered subcutaneously every other day, on avoidance acquisition in the shuttle box experiment on male adenohypophysectomized rats.

that ACTH may play a role in avoidance learning in some manner other than its tropic influence on the adrenal cortex.

When ACTH analogues devoid of corticotropic activity became available in recent years, it was possible to reinvestigate the behavioral effect of ACTH on avoidance learning, using animals deprived of endogenous ACTH, and to determine whether ACTH or a related peptide had a specific effect. The studies were done in animals in which the whole pituitary gland was removed, since it appeared that these animals were identical in avoidance learning to adenohypophysectomized rats. First it was determined whether synthetic ACTH β 1-24 had the same effect as the A_1 peptide used in previous experiments. The synthetic peptide, administered subcutaneously as a long-acting zinc phosphate preparation, in a dose of 20 μg per 2 days, had an effect similar to that of the A_1 peptide on the rate of avoidance learning in hypophysectomized rats. This amount

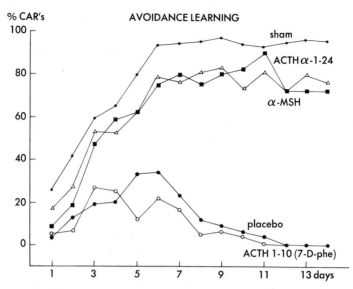

Figure 3-5   Effect of various peptides and placebo, administered subcutaneously as long-acting Zn phosphate preparation in a dose of 20 μg every other day, on the rate of acquisition of the avoidance response in the shuttle box experiment on male hypophysectomized rats. The rate of avoidance acquisition of sham-operated animals is also shown.

of ACTH maintained the size of the adrenal gland. A similar dose of long-acting α-MSH given in the same way exerted a similar action on avoidance learning without affecting adrenal weight. Accordingly, the effect of ACTH on avoidance acquisition is not mediated by the adrenal cortex and it must be regarded as an extra-adrenal effect. Smaller fragments of ACTH, like the sequence 1-10, also increased the rate of avoidance acquisition. In contrast, the sequence ACTH 1-10 in which the phenylalanine in the seventh position is replaced by the D-isomer failed to have an effect in this respect (Fig. 3-5). The smallest ACTH fragment so far studied that significantly facilitated avoidance learning in the hypophysectomized rat was ACTH 4-10. This peptide is capable of increasing the rate of avoidance acquisition in a way similar to a comparable dose of the synthetic ACTH β 1-24 (Fig. 3-6).

In hypophysectomized rats, escape speed in the runway was significantly increased when they were treated with the heptapeptide, although not to the level of that of sham-operated rats. The heptapeptide therefore might have improved motor and/or sensory capacities of the hypophysectomized rat, as in the foregoing experiments when ACTH or a replacement therapy was given. However, the improvement in performance in the runway with the heptapeptide was not as marked as the improvement with replacement therapy. In addition, the results may not indicate solely a deficiency in motor and/or sensory capacities. Motivational phenomena might be involved as well (Barry and Miller, 1965). It might well be, therefore, that the effect of the heptapeptide is on these phenomena rather than on motor and/or sensory functions. This is in accord with the observation that the treatment of hypophysectomized rats with ACTH 4-10 during avoidance learning not only improved avoidance acquisition but also increased the number of intertrial responses. That these peptides do not act by the mere increase in the level of general activity was shown in an experiment in which long-acting ACTH 1-10 was administered for 14 days to hypophysectomized rats. The animals were exposed to a circular open field for 3 minutes on 9 different days during the 14-day period of observation. The rate of ambulation of hypophysectomized rats was less than that of sham-operated controls only during the first minute of each session in the open field. When treatment with the decapeptide was compared with placebo treatment, it was found that the decapeptide did not affect the rate of ambulation.

Figure 3-6   Effect of 20 μg of ACTH 4-10 and of placebo, administered subcutaneously as a long-acting Zn phosphate preparation every other day, on the rate of acquisition of the avoidance response in the shuttle box experiment on male hypophysectomized rats.

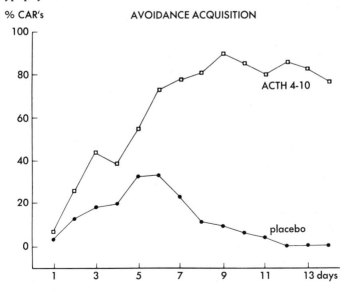

The heptapeptide ACTH 4-10, which exhibits a full behavioral effect, is completely devoid of corticotropic activity as determined by adrenal weight, plasma corticosterone, adrenal corticosteroid production *in vitro*, and thymus weight (De Wied, unpublished data). It does not seem to influence the gonads either, since atrophy of the testes in the hypophysectomized rat was not affected by treatment with the heptapeptide. Body weight loss resulting from hypophysectomy was also not affected by peptide treatment. Plasma insulin levels, which are significantly lower in hypophysectomized rats, were not restored to normal by treatment with ACTH 4-10. Accordingly, ACTH 4-10 does not affect endocrine functions so far studied. The behavioral effect of the heptapeptide may, therefore, not be due to an improvement of the physical condition of the hypophysectomized rat but may instead reflect a specific effect of a peptide derived from ACTH with neurotropic activities.

These results demonstrate that a deficiency caused by the removal of the pituitary gland can be restored to a great extent by treatment with a small peptide common to ACTH, α-MSH and β-MSH. Generally the effect of peptide hormones disappears if the size is reduced. For example ACTH β 1-24 loses its corticotropic effect if the chain length is reduced by 3-4 amino acids (Schwyzer, 1964). Smaller fragments only carry part of their original effect or lose the influence on their target organs completely. Here we are faced with the fact that a small entity of the ACTH molecule still carries full behavioral activity and a nearly adequate substitution is obtained if the sequence 4-10 is administered. Admittedly, on a molecular basis approximately 3 times more of the heptapeptide than of ACTH β 1-24 is used. However, since all peptides were injected as long-acting preparations and since small peptides are inferior in forming complexes with zinc phosphate, the comparison between ACTH 4-10 and its parent molecule on a weight basis may not be correct.

The above-mentioned results clearly establish that the pituitary is involved in conditioned behavior. A behavioral deficiency has been reported in some but not all studies with hypophysectomized rats. This presumably is related to the various experimental situations which have been used. Differences in kind and degree of difficulty of the task, kind and strength of punishment, kind of the reward, amount of physical exercise involved, time interval between CS and US, number of trials presented as massed or spaced trials, length of conditioning period, etc., etc., all may be of importance in this respect. Given the appropriate conditions, a behavioral deficiency might manifest itself. This deficiency certainly is linked to some extent to metabolic derangements in and physical weakness of the hypophysectomized organism. This hypothesis is supported by the favorable effect of a replacement therapy with cortisone, testosterone, and thyroxin on avoidance acquisition and escape behavior of hypophysectomized rats. However, pituitary peptides related to ACTH which neither visibly affect the metabolic disturbances nor the physical condition of the hypophysectomized rat restore the rate of avoidance acquisition to a nearly normal level. It may well be that similar peptides normally operate in the formation of conditioned and other adaptive responses. These peptides with neurogenic activities may be manufactured by the pituitary gland. Whether these peptides are represented by ACTH, α-MSH, and β-MSH, or by peptides closely resembling ACTH 4-10 cannot be determined at present. Such peptides which may be released from the pituitary upon adequate stimulation may affect central nervous structures involved in motivational, learning, or memory processes. The effect of ACTH, α-MSH, and β-MSH may then be regarded as an incidental finding because these hormones share the sequence 4-10. Proof for such an assumption can be obtained by isolation of such peptides from the adenohypophysis and by demonstrating a relationship between release of these pituitary neurogenic substances and acquisition of conditioned avoidance behavior.

The Posterior Pituitary and Behavior

In contrast to adenohypophysectomy, the removal of the posterior lobe—which includes the intermediate lobe—does not interfere with avoidance learning. However, a behavioral abnormality is found when extinction of the avoidance response is studied (De Wied, 1965). When normal rats are conditioned under a progressively diminished intertrial interval procedure, as used in the foregoing experiments in adenohypophysectomized rats, resistance to extinction occurs. Accordingly, in a 14-day period following learning in which only the CS is presented, no significant extinction of the avoidance response takes place (Murphy and Miller, 1956). Posterior lobectomized rats, however, conditioned under such circumstances, are not resistant to extinction and the avoidance response disappears within approximately 10 days. Escape behavior in the runway of posterior lobectomized rats does not differ from that of sham-operated controls, suggesting that motor and/or sensory factors are not involved.

Pitressin tannate in oil in a dose which restores the increased daily water intake of posterior lobectomized rats toward normal brings the rate of extinction of these rats back toward that found in sham-operated controls.

The rapid extinction of the avoidance response of posterior lobectomized rats might, therefore, be related to the disturbance in water metabolism as a result of the removal of the posterior lobe. Pitressin is a relatively crude extract prepared from posterior and intermediate lobes of the pituitary. The effect on extinction could therefore have been the result of substances derived from the intermediate lobe, such as MSH. In fact, treatment with long-acting α-MSH during extinction in different doses significantly inhibited the rate of extinction of the avoidance response in a dose dependent manner without affecting daily water consumption. However, purified lysine vasopressin given as a long-acting zinc tannate preparation had the same effect as the pitressin tannate in oil. ACTH was also capable of inhibiting the rapid rate of extinction of the avoidance response in posterior lobectomized rats.

How could these structurally different peptides have identical behavioral effects? It is known that the release of ACTH in response to neurogenic stimuli is reduced in posterior lobectomized rats (see for review De Wied, 1964). ACTH release as determined by plasma corticosterone content is also reduced in the posterior lobectomized rat during avoidance learning. It could be, therefore, that facilitation of extinction of the avoidance response in posterior lobectomized rats was due to a diminished release of ACTH and that the effect of vasopressin was the result of inherent corticotropin-releasing activities of this polypeptide (see for review Guillemin, 1966). To investigate this possibility an experiment was performed in completely hypophysectomized rats. These were treated with the replacement therapy, consisting of cortisone, testosterone, and thyroxin, in order to enable the animals to acquire the avoidance response. Extinction in these animals, like that in the posterior lobectomized rats, is fast. However, treatment with α-MSH or lysine vasopressin significantly inhibited extinction of the avoidance response in the hypophysectomized rats. These results ruled out the possibility that the effect of vasopressin was mediated by release of anterior pituitary ACTH. The posterior lobe thus exhibits an important effect on the maintenance of an avoidance response. This was confirmed in adenohypophysectomized rats. When these rats were treated with the replacement therapy, consisting of testosterone, cortisone, and thyroxin, to enable the animals to acquire the avoidance response, and were then subjected to extinction, the rate of extinction was equal to that of sham-operated control animals (Fig. 3-7).

In addition, it was found that treatment of posterior lobectomized rats with pitressin tannate in oil only during acquisition had the same effect on extinction of the avoidance response as treatment during the extinction period (Figs. 3-8 and 3-9). Treatment of posterior lobectomized rats with

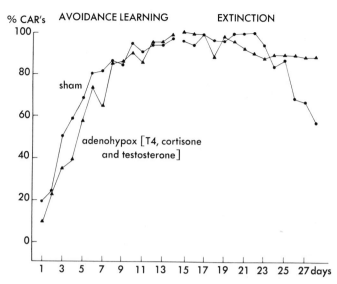

Figure 3-7   Effect of adenohypophysectomy on the rate of extinction of the avoidance response in the shuttle box as compared to sham-operated controls. Adenohypophysectomized rats received the replacement therapy throughout the whole experimental period. For details of treatment, see De Wied, 1964.

ACTH during acquisition only resulted in a significant inhibitory effect on the rate of extinction of the avoidance response also, but the effect was small. When injected during extinction it induced a much stronger inhibition (Figs. 3-10 and 3-11).

It was then considered of interest to further investigate whether the effect of vasopressin and of an ACTH-like peptide on extinction of the avoidance response might involve different mechanisms, as suggested by the foregoing experiments. For this study intact rats were used (De Wied and Bohus, 1966). These rats were conditioned in the shuttle box by a fixed intertrial onset interval procedure which makes the animals extinguish in approximately 10 days. As soon as the animals made 80 per cent or more avoidances for 3 consecutive days, extinction trials were run. Treatment with 20 μg long-acting α-MSH or 1 U Pitressin tannate in oil injected subcutaneously every other day during the extinction period inhibited extinction of the avoidance response. If these preparations were given during the learning period and the treatment was stopped when extinction trials were started, inhibition of extinction was found only in those

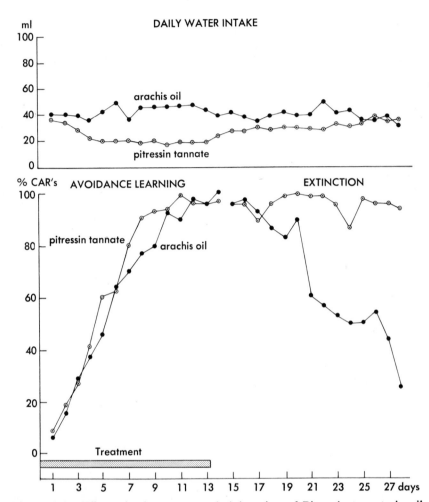

Figure 3-8   Effect of subcutaneous administration of Pitressin tannate in oil (1 U per 2 days) and of arachis oil (0.2 ml per 2 days), given during avoidance acquisition only, on daily water intake and on the rate of extinction of the avoidance response in the shuttle box experiment on posterior lobectomized rats. Note the effect of Pitressin on water intake, which disappears when treatment is stopped.

animals which had been treated with the Pitressin tannate. Moreover, if the rats were subjected to a second extinction period 21 days following the end of the first one, the rats which had been treated with the Pitressin preparation either during the acquisition or during the extinction period still exhibited retention of the avoidance response (Table 3-1). From this it

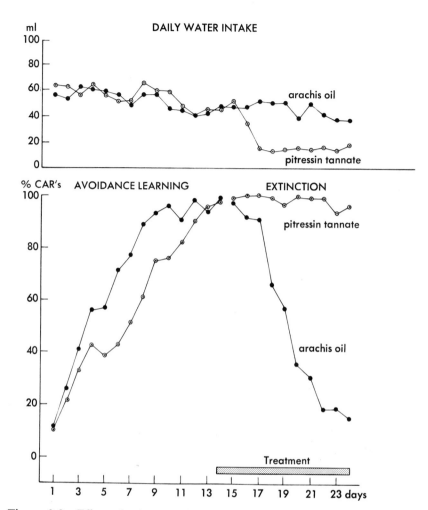

Figure 3-9   Effect of subcutaneous administration of Pitressin tannate in oil (1 U per 2 days) and of arachis oil (0.2 ml per 2 days), given during the extinction period, on daily water intake and on the rate of extinction of the avoidance response in posterior lobectomized rats (De Wied, 1965). Note the rapid normalization of the rate of water intake as soon as treatment is started.

was inferred that Pitressin preserves a conditioned avoidance response irrespective of the time of treatment, while α-MSH inhibits extinction only during the period of treatment. Accordingly, the mechanism by which Pitressin and ACTH-like peptides, or the posterior and anterior lobe of the pituitary, affect conditioned avoidance behavior is basically different.

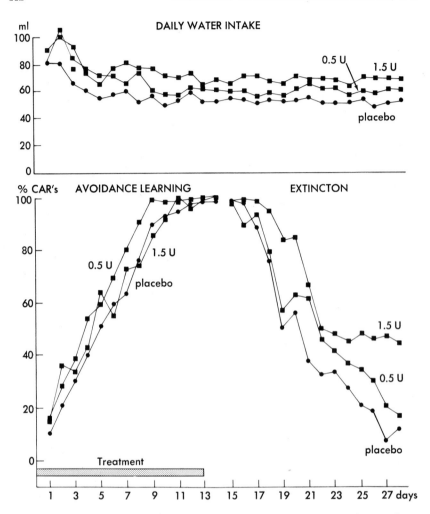

Figure 3-10   Effect of ACTH (A₁ peptide), given subcutaneously as a long-acting Zn phosphate preparation in 2-dose levels every other day during acquisition only, on daily water intake and the rate of extinction of the avoidance response in posterior lobectomized rats. No effect of ACTH was found on water intake. A slight but significant inhibition of the rate of extinction of the avoidance response was seen in animals treated with the highest dose of ACTH.

Whether vasopressin is responsible for the behavioral effect of Pitressin cannot be determined as yet. Although it has been shown that long-acting purified lysine vasopressin exhibits the same effect on extinction of the

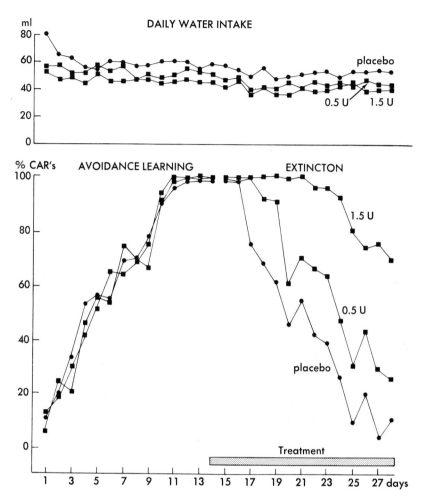

Figure 3-11   Effect of ACTH (A₁ peptide), given subcutaneously as a long-acting Zn phosphate preparation in 2-dose levels every other day during extinction only, on daily water intake and the rate of extinction of the avoidance response in posterior lobectomized rats. No effect of ACTH was found on water intake. A marked dose-related inhibitory effect of ACTH on the rate of extinction of the avoidance response was found.

avoidance response in posterior lobectomized rats as Pitressin tannate in oil does, experiments with a long-acting synthetic vasopressin preparation are needed to ascertain whether the behavioral effect of Pitressin is due to this octapeptide.

Table 3-1   Effect of Pitressin, α-MSH and placebo treatment on extinction and
retention of a shuttle box avoidance response
(For details, see De Wied and Bohus, 1966)

Treatment	Number of rats	First extinction CAR's*	Second extinction CAR's†
During acquisition			
Pitressin	9	126.5 ± 3.1‡	20.3 ± 1.9
α-MSH	10	59.5 ± 8.0	4.3 ± 1.7
Placebo	6	43.8 ± 0.9	2.8 ± 0.9
During extinction			
Pitressin	9	131.0 ± 2.0	22.1 ± 1.4
α-MSH	9	127.3 ± 2.2	4.1 ± 1.0
Placebo	8	57.0 ± 3.4	1.6 ± 0.6

* 140 trials.
† 30 trials.
‡ Mean ± Standard Error of the Mean.

Effects of ACTH and MSH and Their Structural Analogues

The first authors to demonstrate an effect of the pituitary-adrenal system
on fear-motivated behavior in monkeys were Mirsky *et al.* (1953). Monkeys were taught to press a bar which produced a tone of 1 second duration at the end of which a piece of grape was given as a reward. After they
had obtained sufficient practice, a group of animals received 15 mg of
ACTH in gelatin intramuscularly daily for 10 days. During this period the
animals received a shock at the end of the tone instead of the reward. The
treatment was stopped and the reward was given again in response to the
tone while the shock was omitted. It was found that, whereas the controls
had strong startle reactions in response to the tone, the monkeys previously
treated with ACTH performed the barpressing rapidly and efficiently.
Since ACTH did not impair the sensitivity to pain, it was inferred that it
prevented retention of a traumatic experience. In a subsequent experiment,
monkeys were trained to barpress to avoid shock. After they had reached
the conditioning criterion, i.e. 90 per cent positive avoidances during 3
consecutive days, extinction was studied by never presenting the shock. No
extinction was found in the control animals, but in those which had received 15 to 30 mg of ACTH in gelatin during the extinction period, rapid
extinction occurred. If the monkeys were made resistant to extinction by
reconditioning after they were extinguished, ACTH had no effect. In another experiment, rats were first trained to escape from a white to a black
compartment. After this fear-training procedure the animals could escape
to the black compartment by turning a wheel mounted above the door

which separated the two compartments. Treatment with 5 mg of ACTH in gelatin during the second period diminished the number of wheel-turning responses. This effect disappeared rather quickly when learning proceeded. From the studies in monkeys and rats the authors postulated that ACTH diminished the effectiveness of an anxiety-producing stimulus. Murphy and Miller (1955) subsequently found that the daily administration of 5 mg of ACTH in gelatin during the acquisition period of a shuttle box avoidance response did not affect acquistion, but that hormone-treated animals extinguished in a significantly longer period. Administration of ACTH during extinction had no significant effect on the rate of extinction of the avoidance response. No gross behavioral differences were found between ACTH-treated and placebo-treated rats. The results above suggest that ACTH exhibits an effect on fear-motivated behavior. However, whether this is caused by ACTH itself or by its effect on the adrenal cortex is not clear. In view of this Miller and Ogawa (1962) repeated the rat experiments in the shuttle box with adrenalectomized rats. It appeared that administration of ACTH during avoidance training had the same result in adrenalectomized rats—i.e. a delay of extinction of the avoidance response. The adrenals themselves apparently do not play a significant role in retention of a conditioned avoidance response, and, as suggested by the authors, ACTH might influence subcortical structures involved in emotional behavior. Meanwhile, Lissák et al. had made observations on the relation between the pituitary, the adrenal cortex, and behavior, using other behavioral situations. This group showed that a previously trained alimentary conditioned reflex in dogs was inhibited by the simultaneous application of the conditioned stimulus with a noxious stimulus that increases pituitary-adrenal activity. A relationship was found between the length of the inhibitory period of the alimentary conditioned reflex as induced by an electric shock on the hind leg of the dog and the ratio of cortisol to corticosterone in the adrenal venous effluent of these animals at the end of the experiment (Lissák and Endröczi, 1961). These experiments point to the adrenal cortex rather than to ACTH as the factor involved, but the authors did not discriminate between these factors. Bohus and Endröczi (1965) showed that ACTH in rats increased conditioned reflex activity while intertrial reactions disappeared. The avoidance response was established in a jumping box using a buzzer as the CS and an electric shock as the US. To avoid the US, rats were required to jump onto a 10-cm-high bench. Avoidance and intersignal (intertrial) reactions were recorded. Since intertrial reactions were regarded as spontaneous goal-directed motor activity, related to motivational phenomena, the reductions in these reactions might indicate that ACTH had a negative effect on motivation. Experiments in adrenalectomized rats maintained on deoxycorticosterone acetate revealed normal performance of the conditioned reflex, but an increase in the number of intersignal responses was found after stabilization of the conditioned reflex activity. This suggests that the negative effect of ACTH on inter-signal responses is mediated by the adrenal cortex. In experiments in cats, injection of ACTH on the third day of extinction of an alimentary conditioned reflex induced a temporary inhibition of both the conditioned and the intersignal activity. The authors suggested that the pituitary adrenal system would increase the intensity of internal inhibition since extinction according to the Pavlovian concept is considered the result of internal inhibitory processes.

Korányi et al. (1965, 1966) emphasized that, of the species studied, the rabbit shows the greatest sensitivity to the effect of ACTH on nervous function. This hormone in rabbits inhibits sexual drive and suppresses the conditional electroencephalographic (EEG) arousal reaction. It induces a rapid habituation to the CS, and the inhibitory effect manifests itself in inhibition of the conditioned avoidance response. ACTH administered in high doses to rabbits (Korányi and Endröczi, 1967) completely blocks not only conditioned reflex activity but also the unconditioned escape response. Furthermore, a marked reduction of the vasomotor reactions that accompany a conditioned emotional response was found in rabbits treated with ACTH. ACTH also inhibited a polysynaptic reflex arc. This finding led the authors to postulate that ACTH facili-tates the function of inhibitory neurons and/or synapses. The effect of ACTH could be counteracted by strychnine. This supported the postu-late that inhibitory processes in the nervous system are involved, because it is known that strychnine inhibits transmission at inhibitory synapses (Eccles et al., 1956). In this respect it is worth noting that Koltai and Minker (1966) have shown that ACTH inhibits synaptic transmission in the sympathetic ganglia of the cat; Krivoy et al. (1963) have shown that β-MSH stimulates evoked potentials from the dorsal root prepara-tion in the cat; Feldman et al. (1961) have shown that ACTH increases the amplitude of negative potentials in the multisynaptic system of neurons extending through the central part of the midbrain and dien-cephalon; and Wasserman et al. (1965) have shown that ACTH reduces the threshold for clonic electroshock seizures in young rats.

In a study in mice, Korányi et al. (1967) have shown that, in a novel situation in which mice had no previous experience, ACTH in-creased orienting activity and "freezing," resulting in longer latencies. In the second trial, the mice having experienced the situation before, ACTH treatment resulted in a more rapid reaction to the presentation of the CS. Accordingly, the effect of ACTH results in facilitation or inhibition of a behavioral reaction motivated by fear. Facilitation or inhibition, according to the authors, depends on the dose of ACTH and the complexity of the task and situation. Levine and Jones (1965) studied the effect of ACTH on passive avoidance learning in rats on a stabilized barpress response for water. If barpressing was followed by shock, subsequent barpressing was inhibited. Continuously administered ACTH (8 U per day in gelatin) markedly affected passive avoidance, in that this treatment resulted in a continuous inhibition. In a group of rats that received ACTH only during training, subsequent barpressing in response to the shock was improved in some but suppressed in others. Levine and Jones (1965) suggested that ACTH may have a specific effect on extinction in situations which have aversive components. Again, it may be said that the influence of the adrenal cortex in the experiments in dogs, cats, rabbits, rats, and mice was not taken into account sufficiently for us to determine the exact role of ACTH in conditioned emotional behavior.

Some effects of ACTH and related peptides on nonlearned behavior have been reported. Ferrari et al. (1961, 1963) discovered that intracisternal injection of ACTH and ACTH analogues in dogs produced a unique behavioral syndrome. Half an hour after injection of approximately 0.1 U per kg of ACTH the animals became apathic and exhibited diffuse tremors. The dogs were drowsy and yawned frequently. An hour after injection they began to stretch. This "stretching syndrome" persisted for 1 to 3 days depending on the dose of ACTH administered. Not only ACTH but also α-MSH induced the syndrome, but growth hormone, TSH, posterior pituitary extract, gonadotropic hormones, and insulin were inactive in this respect. Stressful stimuli similarly failed to elicit the syndrome. It was concluded that the stretching syndrome was an extra-adrenal effect of ACTH. The authors further showed that ACTH and α-MSH did not lose their behavioral effect when heated to 100°C for 30 minutes in 0.1 N NaOH. This destroys the corticotropic but not the melanotropic effect of ACTH. Heating in 0.1 N HCL, which destroys the other biological activities, abolishes the effect on behavior. The same behavioral activity of the ACTH molecule was found with the sequence ACTH 4-10, a heptapeptide common to ACTH, α-MSH, and β-MSH. Drugs capable of antagonizing the stretching syndrome included phenobarbital, atropine, scopolamine, chlorpromazine, diethazine and morphine. Since, according to the authors, these drugs block the reticular formation, the locus of action of the ACTH effect was sought in this structure. Recent experiments (Gessa and Ferrari, 1967) in which ACTH β 1-24 was injected in different areas of the brain of cats through chronically implanted cannulae indicated that the hypothalamic areas lining the third ventricle were most sensitive to the stretching effect of ACTH. According to the authors, stretching and yawning are physiological acts which may be considered as efforts to delay onset of sleep. Ferrari *et al.* (1963) suggested that the ACTH-like polypeptides may have an effect on the maintenance of wakefulness. In this respect it is worth noting that Dyster-Aas and Krakau (1965) found that the subcutaneous injection of α-MSH into rabbits also caused drowsiness, and that Sakamoto (1966) showed that the subcutaneous injection of β-MSH in very high doses in rats induced drowsiness. Sakamoto also reported that in mice, subcutaneous injection of large amounts of α-MSH or β-MSH caused hypersensitivity in response to noise, movement of the experimenter, etc.

An interesting study was performed by Krivoy *et al.* (1963) on the effect of MSH on the behavior of the Electric Knife Fish (*G. Eigenmannia*). This fish produces a sine wave of constant frequency. The amplitude of the wave depends on the behavioral situation. The amplitude is high when the fish is at rest and low when it is stimulated. When β-MSH was added to the aquarium, the amplitude decreased, indicating that the fish was stimulated. This effect on the nerve function of the fish was rather specific since α-MSH was without effect. Krivoy and Guillemin (1961) also reported that β-MSH caused an enhancement of the dorsal root potentials evoked by submaximal stimulation of the dorsal root preparation of the cat. ACTH, α-MSH, oxytocin, and vasopressin were without effect. However, substance P and bradykinin affected the intensity of dorsal root potentials under certain conditions. Chlorpromazine counteracts the effect of β-MSH on dorsal root potentials (Krivoy *et al.*, 1963), and since chlorpromazine inhibits monosynaptic activity in the spinal cord (Krivoy, 1957), these investigators suggested that the effect of β-MSH is on the monosynaptic reflex arc. Krivoy *et al.* (1963) also suggested that β-MSH augments excitability in the nervous system.

Whatever the experiments by Ferrari *et al.* (1965) and Sakamoto (1966) mean in terms of behavior, they indicate that ACTH and peptides derived from ACTH have an effect on behavior that is independent of the effect of this polypeptide on the adrenal cortex. This is in agreement with our results on the effect of ACTH and related peptides on extinction of conditioned avoidance behavior.

The effect of ACTH and MSH on extinction of the avoidance response in posterior lobectomized rats (De Wied, 1965) prompted us to investigate the effect of these peptides on extinction of the avoidance response in intact rats in which avoidance learning was established in such a way that extinction would take place in approximately 10 days (De Wied, 1966). ACTH administered during avoidance training did not affect the rate of avoidance acquisition but it significantly delayed extinction of the avoidance response. These results are in agreement with those of Murphy and Miller (1955). However, administration of ACTH during extinction had a much stronger inhibitory effect (Fig. 3-12). This effect was dose-dependent, but if ACTH were given in amounts high enough to elicit hypercorticism, facilitation rather than inhibition of extinction of the avoidance response occurred. In fact, injection of corticosterone in various dose levels during extinction facilitates extinction of the avoidance response in a dose-dependent manner (De Wied, 1967). Accordingly, glucocortico-steroids oppose the effect of ACTH on conditioned avoidance behavior. Further proof of the fact that the inhibitory effect on extinction of ACTH is not mediated by the adrenal gland was obtained in a study in which the effect of both α-MSH and β-MSH were studied. Both peptides inhibited the rate of extinction of the avoidance response. The administration of protamine zinc insulin was without effect (De Wied, 1966). In an attempt to determine the active part of the ACTH molecule responsible

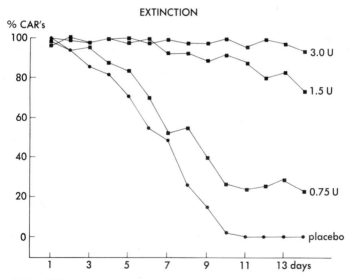

Figure 3-12   Effect of various dose levels of ACTH (A_1 peptide), given sub-cutaneously as a long-acting Zn phosphate preparation every other day, on the rate of extinction of the avoidance response in intact rats.

for the behavioral effect a pole-jumping avoidance procedure was used. Rats were trained in this situation to jump onto a pole within 5 seconds after presentation of the CS (a light emitted by a 60 watt bulb placed on top of the conditioning box). Rats which did not jump but remained on the floor received an electric shock which served as the US. Ten trials were given each day for 3 days with a variable intertrial onset interval averaging 60 seconds. Extinction was studied for the next 3 days using the same procedure as in the acquisition period except that the US was not presented. Structural analogues of ACTH were administered at the end of the third day of avoidance training as long-acting zinc phosphate preparations in a single dose of 10μg given subcutaneously. The sequence ACTH 1-10 significantly inhibited extinction of the avoidance response. It exhibited approximately equipotent effects as ACTH β 1-24. In contrast, ACTH 11-24 was without effect. ACTH 5-10 was less active than ACTH 1-10. Accordingly, the active part of ACTH was located in the N terminal part of the molecule, presumably in the first 10 amino acids. When further fragments of ACTH became available (Greven and De Wied, 1967) these studies were extended. The heptapeptide ACTH 4-10 appeared to be the shortest amino acid sequence possessing an inhibitory effect on extinction of the avoidance response comparable to that of ACTH β 1-24 or of ACTH 1-10 (Table 3-2).

During these studies it was found that the sequence ACTH 1-10, in which the amino acid phenylalanine in the seventh position is replaced by the D-isomer, had an opposite effect on extinction of the avoidance response in the shuttle box (Bohus and De Wied, 1966). Administration of this peptide as a long-acting preparation during the extinction period induced facilitation of extinction as long as it was injected

Table 3-2   Amino acid sequence of a number of ACTH analogues.

	1	2	3	4	5	6	7	8	9	10	11	12	13
α-MSH CH₃CO -	Ser -	Tyr -	Ser -	Met -	Glu -	His -	Phe -	Arg -	Trp -	Gly -	Lys -	Pro -	Val
ACTH 1-10	Ser -	Tyr -	Ser -	Met -	Glu -	His -	Phe -	Arg -	Trp -	Gly			
ACTH 2-10		Tyr -	Ser -	Met -	Glu -	His -	Phe -	Arg -	Trp -	Gly			
ACTH 3-10			Ser -	Met -	Glu -	His -	Phe -	Arg -	Trp -	Gly			
ACTH 4-10				Met -	Glu -	His -	Phe -	Arg -	Trp -	Gly			
ACTH 5-10					Glu -	His -	Phe -	Arg -	Trp -	Gly			
ACTH 6-10						His -	Phe -	Arg -	Trp -	Gly			
ACTH 7-10							Phe -	Arg -	Trp -	Gly			

Effect of these fragments was studied on the rate of extinction of a pole-jumping avoidance response. ACTH 4-10 and larger peptides were equipotent to ACTH 1-10 in inhibiting extinction of the avoidance response. Smaller peptides were less active.

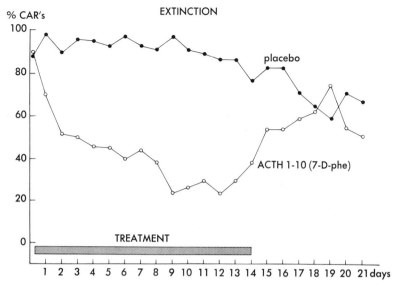

Figure 3-13   Effect of ACTH 1-10 (7-D-phe), and of placebo, both given subcutaneously as a long-acting Zn phosphate preparation in a dose of 20 μg per 2 days, on the rate of extinction of a shuttle box avoidance response in intact rats. Note that when treatment is stopped after 14 days, the rate of extinction of peptide-treated rats returns to the level of that of placebo-treated animals.

(Fig. 3-13). Extinction occurred rapidly and was demonstrable as early as 1 day after injection of the peptide. Since this effect might be caused by a direct antagonistic action of the 7-D-form peptide against naturally occurring hormones like ACTH or the MSH's, the 7-D-form peptide should be inactive in animals deprived of these hormones. Rats trained to criterion in the shuttle box were hypophysectomized or sham-operated. The hypophysectomized rats were treated with the replacement therapy consisting of cortisone, testosterone, and thyroxin. Two weeks after surgery the animals were retrained to criterion and thereafter subjected to extinction trials for 6 days.

The 7-D-form peptide administered during extinction appeared to act even more strongly in the hypophysectomized rats than in sham-operated controls. Accordingly, the effect of the 7-D-form decapeptide could not be explained by a direct antagonistic action between this peptide and structurally related L-form peptides of natural origin. A 14-day study showed that escape speed in the runway of rats under treatment with the 7-D- and L-form decapeptide was not different from that of placebo treated rats. Accordingly, the effect of the 7-D-form peptide on extinction of the avoidance response is not attributable to alteration in motor and/or sensory capacities. Gross behavior as studied in an open field 18 hours after a single injection of the two decapeptides, revealed no differences with respect to the rate of ambulation, rearing, grooming, or the number of fecal boluses during the 3 minute period of observation. Since these studies were performed a number of structural analogues of the 7-D-form decapeptide have become available (Table 3-3). Comparison between the effect of ACTH 1-10 (7-D-phe), ACTH 4-10 (7-D-phe), and ACTH 7-10 (7-D-phe) revealed that, as in the studies with the L-form, the sequence 4-10 possessed full behavioral activity (Fig. 3-14). Thus, in the present experiments the smallest peptide used that facilitates extinction of the avoidance response is the sequence 4-10. It is of interest to note that the decapeptide in which the amino acid tyrosine in the second position had been replaced by the D-isomer also exhibited facilitatory effects on extinction of the avoidance response. The effect was not as strong as with ACTH 1-10 (7-D-phe). The phenylalanine in the seventh position therefore seems to be more important than the tyrosine in the second position for the effect observed.

In an attempt to localize the site of action of ACTH-like peptides on extinction of the avoidance response, studies were performed in animals bearing lesions in the CNS. Since a number of observations suggested that thalamic reticular structures are involved in acquisition and retention of conditioned avoidance behavior (Thompson, 1963; Vanderwolf, 1964; Rich and Thompson, 1965; Cardo and Valade, 1965; Delacour and Santacana de Martinez, 1967; Cardo, 1967), and other studies suggested a role of these structures in motivational phenomena (Grossman et al., 1965;

Table 3-3   Amino acid sequence of a number of ACTH analogues with an amino acid in the D-form.

	1	2	3	4	5	6	7	8	9	10
ACTH 1-10	H - Ser -	Tyr -	Ser -	Met -	Glu -	His -	D Phe -	Arg -	Trp -	Gly - OH
ACTH 1-10	H - Ser -	D Tyr -	Ser -	Met -	Glu -	His -	Phe -	Arg -	Trp -	Gly - OH
ACTH 4-10				Met -	Glu -	His -	D Phe -	Arg -	Trp -	Gly - OH
ACTH 6-10						His -	D Phe -	Arg -	Trp -	Gly - OH
Amino acid sequence common to α-MSH, β-MSH, and ACTH				- Met -	Glu -	His -	Phe -	Arg -	Trp -	Gly -

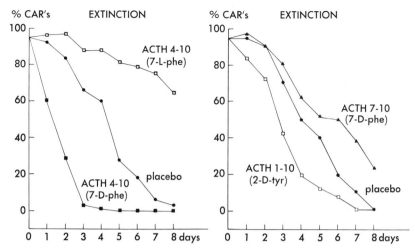

Figure 3-14   Effect of various ACTH analogues with D-form amino acids on the rate of extinction of the shuttle box avoidance response. All substances were administered subcutaneously as long-acting Zn phosphate preparations in a dose of 20 μg per 2 days.

Endröczi, 1965), lesions were placed in the thalamic area (Bohus and De Wied, 1967a). Lesions were made with the aid of a stereotaxic apparatus with high frequency cauterization (Bouman et al., 1957). Large lesions in the midline thalamic reticular area produced severe deficits in avoidance acquisition and escape behavior (Bohus and De Wied, 1967b). Small bilateral lesions in the same area also interfered with avoidance acquisition, but not with escape behavior. Bilateral destruction of the nuclei parafascicularis did not affect avoidance learning, but extinction was markedly facilitated. Administration of a α-MSH during the extinction period failed to delay the rate of extinction of the avoidance response in rats with lesions in the nuclei parafascicularis (Fig. 3-15). These results suggest that the CNS is involved in the behavioral effect of ACTH-like peptides, but the parafascicular nuclei need not necessarily be the site of action of these compounds. Interestingly, Cardo and Valade (1965) reported that the impairment in avoidance behavior of rats with lesions in the parafascicular nuclei could be partially restored by the administration of dexamphetamine. The failure of α-MSH to affect the rate of extinction in these rats suggests that the effect of ACTH-like peptides is of a more specific character than mere excitation of central nervous activity.

It is known that ACTH-analogues are capable of stimulating thyroid gland activity (Bowers et al., 1964; Cehović, 1962; 1967; Courrier and Cehović, 1960; Schally et al., 1967), and the thyroid has been implicated

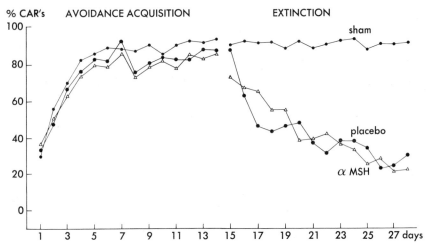

Figure 3-15   Acquisition and extinction of the shuttle box avoidance response of rats bearing lesions in the nuclei parafascicularis as compared to that of sham-operated controls. Extinction is rapid in the lesioned rats. Treatment with α-MSH (given subcutaneously as a long-acting Zn phosphate preparation in a dose of 20 μg per 2 days) failed to affect the rate of extinction.

in acquisition and retention of avoidance as well as spontaneous behavior (Bovet *et al.*, 1962; Eayrs, 1961; Eayrs and Lishman, 1955; Eayrs and Levine, 1963; Elrick *et al.*, 1960; Feuer and Broadhurst, 1962; Korn, 1967; Morrison and Cunningham, 1941; Richards and Stockburger, 1958; Sakata *et al.*, 1966; Thompson and Kenshalo, 1954). Therefore, it is possible that ACTH analogues exert their effect on extinction of the avoidance response by way of the thyroid gland. ACTH 1-10, however, delayed extinction of the pole-jumping avoidance response in thyroidectomized rats with or without replacement therapy with L-thyroxin; the behavior of these rats was similar to that of sham-operated animals (De Wied and Pirie, 1968). Accordingly, the inhibitory action of ACTH 1-10 and other analogues on the rate of extinction of the avoidance response is not mediated by an alteration in thyroid function.

Our data on ACTH and ACTH analogues indicate that ACTH affects conditioned behavior and that it does so by a mechanism which is not mediated by the adrenal cortex or by the thyroid gland. However, reports at variance with this conclusion have been published by other authors. Differences in reported behavioral effects may depend first of all upon the fact that ACTH, due to its intrinsic corticotropic effect, stimulates the secretion of adrenocortical steroids which themselves have an effect opposite to that of ACTH. Treatment of rats with dexamethasone or corticosterone daily during the extinction period of an avoidance response facilitates extinction of a shuttle box avoidance response. Aldosterone possesses only minor effects in this respect, indicating that glucocorticosteroids rather than mineralocorticoids are responsible for the facilitatory effect. Since daily treatment with glucocorticosteroids leads to a depression of ACTH release, these results might be interpreted as indicating that facilitation of extinction occurs as the result of a diminished ACTH release. However, the glucocorticosteroids also facilitate extinction of the avoidance response in hypophysectomized rats. Thus the effect of these steroids seems at least partly independent of pituitary ACTH (De Wied, 1967). A similar effect on avoidance behavior of rats under the influence of ACTH therefore might occur if supraphysiological amounts of this hormone are administered, consequently augmenting the secretion of adrenocortical steroids above the normal level. For example, the administration of ACTH in moderate, adrenal-maintaining doses improves the rate of avoidance learning in hypophysectomized rats better than large doses, which induce hypercorticism (De Wied, 1964). In addition, species differences in adrenal responsiveness to ACTH and differential sensitivity to hormones of the pituitary-adrenal system may markedly interfere with the observed behavioral effect of ACTH. The behavioral situation itself may also be of importance for the effect of ACTH. The use of passive or active avoidance behavior techniques, the use of reward or punishment, etc., all may contribute to differences in the resultant behavioral effect of ACTH. Since ACTH analogues have become available in recent years, studies with the aid of these analogues are necessary to elucidate the specific mechanism of ACTH action.

The biological meaning of the effects of ACTH and ACTH analogues on behavior is not clear. It is remarkable that the activity is demonstrable mainly in conditioned avoidance behavior. Avoidance conditioning, according to Mowrer's theory, is motivated by fear and reinforced by fear reduction (Mowrer, 1950). Emotional stimuli are among the most effective activators of the pituitary adrenal system. This system plays an essential role in adaptation when homeostasis of the organism is threatened during systemic or emotional stress. Learning, recognition, and experience are involved in the mechanism of adaptation. Modification of the rate of extinction of an avoidance response as induced by ACTH and ACTH analogues may therefore reflect a modification of an adaptive process.

Possible Mechanisms of Action

The mode of action of ACTH and ACTH-like peptides in their effect on conditioned behavior is unknown. Influence of β-MSH on evoked potentials in the spinal cord of cats (Krivoy and Guillemin, 1961), of ACTH on inhibitory neurons in the spinal cord of rabbits (Korányi and Endröczi, 1967), of ACTH on transmission in sympathetic ganglia of the cat (Koltai and Minker, 1966), and of ACTH on the threshold for clonic electroshock seizures of young rats (Wasserman *et al.*, 1965) indicate that these peptides affect neural processes through a direct action on transmission in nervous elements or by influencing the biochemical or the vascular environment of these elements. These studies, however, do not reveal the site or sites of action of ACTH. Feldman *et al.* (1961) found that ACTH, hydrocortisone, and adrenocortical extract increases the amplitude of negative potentials in the multisynaptic system of neurons extending through the central part of the midbrain and diencephalon. These authors suggested that the site of action of ACTH and adrenocortical steroids is in the mesencephalic reticular formation. Our results showing that the inhibitory effect of α-MSH is blocked in rats bearing lesions in the nuclei parafascicularis suggest that the thalamus also participates in the effect of ACTH and ACTH analogues on conditioned behavior.

In which way the peptides affect neural processes is unknown. It is possible that the peptides act via autonomic nervous transmission. Sakamoto and Prasad (1968) reported on the identical effects of β-MSH and norepinephrine. Rats treated with β-MSH or norepinephrine developed piloerection, tachypnea, and hypertension, and the effect of β-MSH could be reversed by adrenergic blocking agents. However, we have never been able to detect gross behavioral effects of ACTH-like peptides in the doses used (Bohus and De Wied, 1966).

Recent studies on behavioral processes that involve learning and memory indicate participation of RNA synthesis in the brain. Learning has been shown to increase RNA content of neurons in Deiters' nucleus in the rat, while base composition of nuclear RNA is changed (Hydén and Egyházi, 1962). Similar alterations were later also found in cortical neurons (Hydén and Egyházi, 1964). It has also been demonstrated that protein synthesis increases in the hippocampal pyramidal cells of rats subjected to a behavioral test (Hydén and Lange, 1968). Acquisition of new swimming skills in goldfish is accompanied by a change in base ratio of nuclear RNA of whole brain (Shashova, 1968). Zemp *et al.* (1966; 1967) have demonstrated increased RNA synthesis mainly located in the diencephalon of mice subjected to avoidance learning.

Further, it has been demonstrated that facilitation of avoidance acquisition by magnesium pemoline at the same time increased the amount of RNA in the brain (Glasky and Simon, 1966; Simon and Glasky, 1968; Plotnikoff, 1966a,b,c; Plotnikoff and Meekma, 1967). However, several studies on magnesium pemoline and RNA are conflicting, and further investigations are needed (Cain, 1967; Morris *et al.*, 1967; Stein and Jellin, 1967; Frey and Polidora, 1967; Beach and Kimble, 1967; Talland and McGuire, 1967; Segal *et al.*, 1967; Stein *et al.*, 1968; Smith, 1967; Burns *et al.*, 1967; Gelfand et al., 1968).

Blockade of RNA and protein synthesis in the brain also may interfere with learning or memory. Intracranial injection of 8-azoguanine impairs learning in rats (Dingman and Sporn, 1961; Warburton and Russell, 1968). Several authors demonstrated interference with consolidation of a learned response by intracranial injections of puromycin (Flexner *et al.*, 1963, 1967; Flexner and Flexner, 1968; Agranoff and Klinger, 1964; Davis *et al.*, 1965; Davis and Agranoff, 1966; Potts and Bitterman, 1967; Barondes and Cohen, 1966). The effect of puromycin, however, could not solely be explained by inhibition of protein synthesis (Flexner *et al.*, 1967). Other factors might be involved as well (Flexner and Flexner, 1968; Cohen and Barondes, 1967). Flexner and his associates (Flexner *et al.*, 1967; Flexner and Flexner, 1967) proposed an attractive hypothesis to explain the effect of puromycin. This group suggested that relatively small abnormal peptides might be found in the neurons in the presence of the antibiotic. These peptides might alter in a reversible way the characteristics of neuronal synapses. Such a synaptic alteration might be an important link in the process of consolidation of learned responses (Barondes, 1965). This is reminiscent of our observations with the D-form ACTH analogues, which have an effect opposite to that of naturally occurring ACTH-like peptides on extinction of the avoidance response (Bohus and De Wied, 1966). Although Flexner and associates failed to find an effect of the antibiotic acetoxycycloheximide on behavior, other investigations have shown that it not only interferes with protein synthesis but also with fixation of longer term memory processes (Barondes and Cohen, 1968; Cohen and Barondes, 1968).

It has been claimed that injection of RNA facilitates learning and delays extinction of an avoidance response (Cook *et al.*, 1963; Brown, 1966; Solyom *et al.*, 1966; Wagner *et al.*, 1966; Siegel, 1967, 1968). In addition, transfer of conditioned responses by injection of RNA extracts obtained from the brain of trained rats also suggests possible participation of RNA in learned behavior (Fjerdingstad *et al.*, 1965; Nissen *et al.*, 1965; Røigaard-Petersen *et al.*, 1965, 1968; Babich *et al.*, 1965; Babich, 1965; Jacobsen *et al.*, 1965). However, Rosenblatt *et al.* (1966a,b,c) and Rosenblatt and Miller (1966a,b) have demonstrated that the information-bearing molecule is not RNA but peptide material with a molecular weight between 1000 and 5000. These findings are in agreement with those of Ungar *et al.* (1965, 1966, 1967, 1968). These authors claimed purification of the peptide material responsible for the transfer of information.

This transfer molecule probably is a basic peptide containing 6 to 10 amino acid residues. The molecular weight of this peptide is well within the range of the ACTH and ACTH analogues we studied. It may be, therefore, that peptides like the ACTH analogues interfere with behavior as a result of their influence on the synthesis of macromolecules involved in neuronal activity within areas in the central nervous system that participate in the formation of conditioned responses.

Growth Hormone

Effects of a number of pituitary hormones on behavior have been described. In most of the studies, effects of these hormones on their respective target organs may have affected the results. A number of studies have been done with crude pituitary preparations, which makes it impossible to determine whether observed behavioral effects were due to peptide hormones or to other constituents of the extracts. Growth hormone is the only other pituitary factor which has been studied in relatively pure form and whose effect is not mediated by a specific target organ. The few studies on this hormone that are reported in the literature are cited below.

Zamenhof (1942) suggested that learning ability may be increased by an increase in the number of neural cells. Administration of a crude growth hormone preparation augmented the number of neurons and the amount of glia in the developing tadpole, as well as in the offspring of rats treated with this growth hormone preparation. However, no improvement in maze learning ability was found (Warden et al., 1942). In contrast, Clendinnen and Eayrs (1961) demonstrated that offspring of growth hormone treated rats are superior in learning a series of progressively more difficult problems. According to Block and Essman (1965) the lack of effect in Zamenhof's experiment may have been due to the complexity of the learning problem presented to the animals. Accordingly, Block and Essman (1965) reinvestigated the influence of growth hormone, using physiological amounts of this peptide and a simple response in offspring of growth hormone treated rats. A single trial avoidance conditioning technique was used. It was found that offspring of growth hormone treated rats extinguished more rapidly than their controls. This was not the result of an increase in the level of activity. Since extinction meant return to a dark, unrestrictive area, which rats prefer, the authors interpreted the findings as a more rapid return of the animals to the previously more adaptive behavior.

We have performed a number of studies in hypophysectomized rats with growth hormone. Treatment of these animals with growth hormone resulted in an improvement in avoidance learning. Administration of 0.2 and

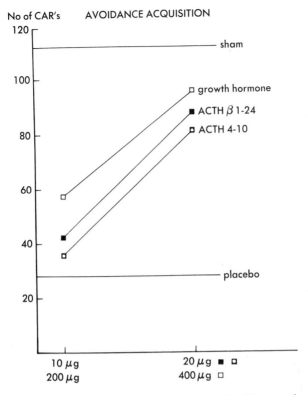

Figure 3-16   Effect of bovine growth hormone and of long-acting ACTH β 1-24 and ACTH 4-10 treatment for 14 days on avoidance acquisition of hypophysectomized rats as compared to that of placebo-treated hypophysectomized male rats and non-treated sham-operated animals. Growth hormone was injected subcutaneously every day; see text for details. Total number of positive avoidances in 140 trials (10 trials a day) indicates the rate of avoidance learning.

0.4 mg per rat per day to hypophysectomized rats caused a statistically significant increase in the rate of acquisition of a shuttle box avoidance response (Fig. 3-16). The preparation used was a bovine somatotropin containing 1.9 U/mg. The amounts administered were sufficient to cause either inhibition of weight loss or an increase in body weight in the hypophysectomized rats (Fig. 3-17). The influence of growth hormone therefore might be correlated with body weight growth and reflect a better physical condition of the hypophysectomized rat. The effect of growth hormone on avoidance acquisition in hypophysectomized rats resembles

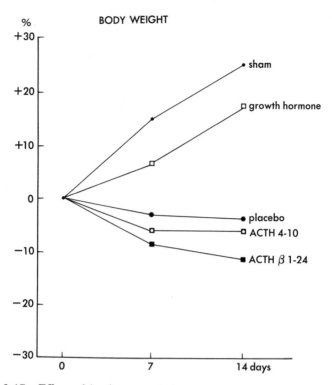

Figure 3-17   Effect of bovine growth hormone and of long-acting ACTH β 1-24 and ACTH 4-10 on body weight of hypophysectomized male rats as compared to that of placebo in hypophysectomized male rats and non-treated sham-operated animals. See text for details. Values expressed as per cent increase or decrease from initial body weight.

that of ACTH and ACTH analogues. It is of interest to note that growth hormone stimulates the rate of nuclear RNA and protein synthesis in the liver of hypophysectomized rats (see for review Tata, 1967). The seemingly identical behavioral effect of ACTH and growth hormone may indicate that neural elements involved in conditioned behavior do not discriminate between growth hormone and ACTH. It may also indicate that fragments of peptides that resemble each other in structure, size, or other characteristics cause the behavioral effects observed. It is known from other studies that structurally different peptides may have rather specific effects in common. For instance, it has been shown that insulin (Winegrad and Renold, 1958), prolactin, growth hormone, ACTH (Winegrad et al., 1959), glucagon (Hagen, 1961), oxytocin and lysine vasopressin (Mirsky and Perisutti, 1962) all are capable of stimulating glucose utilization in adipose tissue *in vitro*. Similarly, ACTH, α-MSH, vasopressin, and angiotensin II have been found to exhibit a positive inotropic action on isolated chicken heart muscle cells *in vitro* (Wollenberger and Halle, 1963). The mechanism of action of these compounds may be different, but the ultimate effect is identical. As we have seen, α-MSH and vasopressin, which have a seemingly identical effect on the rate of extinction of the avoidance response, affect the underlying processes in a different way; vasopressin has a much longer effect on the maintenance of an avoidance response than α-MSH (De Wied and Bohus, 1966). Such differences may also appear as more is learned about the effects of growth hormone on behavior. However, the present paucity of data does not permit further speculation in this respect in particular and on the behavioral effects of growth hormone in general.

Conclusions

In this paper I have reviewed studies concerned with the effect of the pituitary gland and of pituitary peptides on behavior. The anterior pituitary may interfere with learned behavior, inasmuch as the removal of the adenohypophysis alone or the whole pituitary inhibits or reduces the ability to acquire a conditioned avoidance response. If hypophysectomized rats are treated with ACTH and ACTH fragments devoid of corticotropic activities, their ability improves markedly. The similar response of ACTH analogues, however, indicates that the improvement in avoidance acquisition by ACTH is not mediated by the adrenal cortex. The general health and condition of the hypophysectomized rat is also involved in the ability to acquire a conditioned reflex. Substitution therapy with cortisone, testosterone, and thyroxin, which improves the physical condition of the hypophysectomized rat, also increases the rate of avoidance acquisition.

The heptapeptide ACTH 4-10, which is virtually devoid of endocrine and metabolic actions, enables the hypophysectomized rat to acquire the avoidance response. The facilitatory effect of this heptapeptide on avoidance learning in hypophysectomized rats seems to be a specific effect, and it might be that the pituitary manufactures peptides with neurogenic activities. These are either ACTH, α-MSH or β-MSH, or unknown peptides closely resembling the sequence ACTH 4-10. These neurogenic peptides may be released upon adequate stimulation to affect central nervous structures involved in motivational, learning, and memory processes.

The removal of the posterior pituitary does not interfere with avoidance acquisition, but the maintenance of an avoidance response is markedly disturbed. This abnormal behavior can be restored toward normal by treatment with anterior, intermediate, and posterior lobe principles. The mechanism of action of these structurally different groups of peptides is basically different, however. This difference lies in the duration of their effect on the maintenance of the avoidance response: Pitressin has a long lasting influence which is demonstrable several weeks after discontinuing the treatment, whereas the influence of ACTH or α-MSH manifests itself only during the treatment period.

Studies of pituitary hormones on learned behavior in intact animals have also revealed marked influences of these peptides. Some studies indicate that ACTH diminishes the effectiveness of an anxiety-producing stimulus, others suggest that it may have a specific effect in situations which have an aversive component, and others again implicate an effect on motivation. Unfortunately, most studies do not discriminate between the effect of ACTH per se and the effect of glucocorticosteroids that are produced by treatment with ACTH. These steroids in turn can oppose the behavioral activity of ACTH.

The effect of growth hormone in some respects resembles the effect of ACTH and its structural analogues on conditioned avoidance behavior. It has been shown to facilitate learning in intact as well as hypopophysectomized rats.

A number of studies indicate that ACTH and structural analogues may induce a stretching syndrome in dogs, drowsiness in rabbits and rats, and hypersensitivity in mice.

In regard to conditioned avoidance behavior, ACTH analogues have an inhibitory effect on the rate of extinction of an avoidance response. The amino acid sequence ACTH 4-10 again is the smallest peptide that possesses full behavioral activity in this respect. Curiously, replacement in this heptapeptide of the amino acid phenylalanine by its D-isomer reverses its effect and leads to facilitation of extinction.

The locus of action of the ACTH analogues in the CNS is unknown. The reticular formation and the thalamus have been implicated in this respect.

The mechanism of the behavioral effect of ACTH analogues on conditioned avoidance behavior also is not clear. It is possible that these peptides interfere with autonomic nervous transmission. However, ACTH facilitates the function of inhibitory neurons and/or synapses in the rabbit and β-MSH stimulates evoked potentials from the dorsal root preparation of the cat, suggesting that these peptides affect transmission in the nervous system by a direct action on the nerve cell or by influences on the biochemical and/or vascular environment of these cells. Finally it is intriguing to speculate that the peptides interfere with RNA and protein synthesis. These compounds might influence the synthesis of macromolecules involved in neuronal activity within certain CNS areas which participate in the formation of conditioned responses.

As yet, the relevance of these data to the over-all problem of behavior remains obscure. However, the increasing availability of synthetic polypeptides offers the opportunity for further insight into this exciting aspect of behavioral pharmacology. Such insights may help to unravel basic problems in animal and human psychology.

Acknowledgments

I wish to express my thanks to Drs. J. A. W. M. Weijnen and W. H. Gispen, Utrecht, for their help and critical remarks during the preparation of the manuscript, and to Dr. Alvin P. Shapiro, Pittsburgh, for his stimulating comments.

References

Agranoff, B. W., and P. D. Klinger (1964). Puromycin effect on memory fixation in the goldfish. *Science 146*, 952-53.

Applezweig, M. H., and F. D. Baudry (1955). The pituitary-adrenocortical system in avoidance learning. *Psychol. Rep. 1*, 417-20.

Applezweig, M. H., and G. Moeller (1957). Anxiety, the pituitary-adrenocortical system and avoidance learning. Fifteenth Int. Cong. Psych., Brussels, Belgium, August 1957.

Applezweig, M. H., and G. Moeller (1959). The pituitary-adrenocortical system and anxiety in avoidance learning. *Acta. Psychol. 15*, 602-3.

Babich, F. R. (1965). Cross-species transfer of learning: effect of ribonucleic acid from hamsters on rat behavior. *Proc. Nat. Acad. Sci. (Wash.) 54*, 1299-1302.

Babich, F. R., A. L. Jacobson, S. Bubash, and A. Jacobson (1965). Transfer of a response to naïve rats by injection of ribonucleic acid extracted from trained rats. *Science 149*, 656-57.

Barondes, S. H. (1965). Relationships of biological regulatory mechanisms to learning and memory. *Nature 205*, 18-21.

Barondes, S. H., and H. D. Cohen (1966). Puromycin effect on successive phases of memory storage. *Science 151*, 594-95.

Barondes, S. H. and H. D. Cohen (1968). Memory impairment after subcutaneous injection of acetoxycycloheximide. *Science 160*, 556-57.

Barry, H., III, and N. E. Miller (1965). Comparison of drug effects on approach, avoidance, and escape motivation. *J. Comp. Physiol. Psychol. 59*, 18-24.

Beach, G., and D. P. Kimble (1967). Activity and responsivity in rats after magnesium pemoline injections. *Science 155*, 698-701.

Bélanger, D. (1958). Effets de l'hypophysectomie sur l'apprentissage d'une réaction échappement-évitement. *Canadian J. Psychol. 12*, 171-78.

Block, J. B., and W. B. Essman (1965). Growth hormone administration during pregnancy: a behavioural difference in offspring rats. *Nature 205*, 1136-37.

Bohus, B., and E. Endröczi (1965). The influence of pituitary-adrenocortical function on the avoiding conditioned reflex activity in rats. *Acta Physiol. Acad. Sci. Hung. 26*, 184-89.

Bohus, B., and D. de Wied (1966). Inhibitory and facilitatory effect of two related peptides on extinction of avoidance behavior. *Science 153*, 318-20.

Bohus, B., and D. de Wied (1967a). Failure of α-MSH to delay extinction of conditioned avoidance behavior in rats with lesions in the parafascicular nuclei of the thalamus. *Physiology and Behavior 2*, 221-23.

Bohus, B., and D. de Wied (1967b). Avoidance and escape behavior following medial thalamic lesions in rats. *J. Comp. Physiol. Psychol. 64*, 26-29.

Bouman, P. R., J. H. Gaarenstroom, P. G. Smelik, and D. de Wied (1957). Hypothalamic lesions and ACTH secretion in rats. *Acta Physiol. Pharmacol. Neerl. 6*, 308-78.

Bovet, D., F. Bovet-Nitti, G. Bignami, and O. Orsingher (1962). Contributions à une pharmacologie de l'apprentisage fonctions thyroïdienne et conditionnement à une reaction de fuite et d'évitement chez le rat. In *Perspectives in Biology* (C. F. Cori, V. G. Foglia, L. F. Leloir, and S. Ochoa, eds.), pp. 210-21. Elsevier Publishing Co., Amsterdam.

Bowers, C. Y., T. W. Redding, and A. V. Schally (1964). Effects of α- and β-melanocyte stimulating hormones and other peptides on the thyroid in mice. *Endocrinology 74*, 559-66.

Brown, H. (1966). Effect of ribonucleic acid (RNA) on the rate of lever pressing in rats. *Psychol. Rec. 16*, 173-76.

Burnham, R. W., and S. L. Leonard (1941). Hypophysectomy and thyroidectomy as related to learning in the rat. I. Preliminary investigation. *J. Comp. Physiol. Psychol. 31*, 233-42.

Burns, J. T., R. F. House, F. C. Fensch, and J. G. Miller (1967). Effects of magnesium pemoline and dextroamphetamine on human learning. *Science 155*, 849-51.

Cain, D. F. (1967). Lack of effect of pemoline on the incorporation of $(H)^3$ uridine into RNA in brain slices. *Life Sci. 6*, 1919-26.

Cardo, B. (1967). Effets de la stimulation du noyau parafasciculaire thalamique sur l'acquisition d'un conditionnement d'évitement chez le rat. *Physiology and Behavior 2*, 245-48.

Cardo, B., and F. Valade (1965). Rôle du noyau thalamique parafasciculaire dans la conservation d'un conditionnement d'évitement chez le rat. *C.R. Acad. Sci. (Paris) 261*, 1399-1402.

Cehović, G. (1962). Action des hormones mélanophorétiques (MSH) sur la fonction thyroïdienne chez le Cobaye. *C.R. Acad. Sci. (Paris) 254*, 1872-74.

Cehović, G. (1967). Mechanism of action of MSH and certain other biologically active polypeptides on the thyroidal function. *International Symposium on the Pharmacology of Hormonal Polypeptides and Proteins,* Milan, September 14-16, p. 19.

Clendinnen, B. G., and J. T. Eayrs (1961). The anatomical and physiological effects of prenatally administered somatotrophin on cerebral development in rats. *J. Endocrinol. 22*, 183-93.

Cohen, H. D., and S. H. Barondes (1967). Puromycin effect on memory may be due to occult seizures. *Science 157*, 333-34.

Cohen, H. D., and S. H. Barondes (1968). Effect of acetoxycycloheximide in learning and memory of a light-dark discrimination. *Nature 218*, 271.

Cook, L., A. B. Davidson, D. J. Davis, H. Green, and R. J. Fellows (1963). Ribonucleic acid: effect on conditioned behavior in rats. *Science 141*, 268-69.

Courrier, R., and G. Cehović (1960). Action de l'hormone mélanophorotrope purifiée (α-MSH) sur la fonction thyroïdienne chez le lapin. *C.R. Acad. Sci. (Paris) 251*, 832-34.

Davis, R. E., and B. W. Agranoff (1966). Stages of memory formation in goldfish: evidence for an environmental trigger. *Proc. Nat. Acad. Sci. (Wash.) 55*, 555-59.

Davis, R. E., P. J. Bright, and B. W. Agranoff (1965). Effects of ECS and puromycin on memory in fish. *J. Comp. Physiol. Psychol. 60*, 162-66.

Delacour, J., and M. P. Santacana de Martinez (1967). Rôle du thalamus médian dans l'établissement et la retention de conditionnements defensifs, classiques et instrumentaux. *Neuropsychologia 5*, 237-52.

De Wied, D. (1964). Influence of anterior pituitary on avoidance learning and escape behavior. *Am. J. Physiol. 207*, 255-59.

De Wied, D. (1965). The influence of the posterior and intermediate lobe of the pituitary and pituitary peptides on the maintenance of a conditioned avoidance response in rats. *Int. J. Neuropharmacol. 4*, 157-67.

De Wied, D. (1966). Inhibitory effect of ACTH and related peptides on extinction of conditioned avoidance behavior in rats. *Proc. Soc. Exp. Biol (N. Y.) 122*, 28-32.

De Wied, D. (1967). Opposite effects of ACTH and glucocorticosteroids on extinction of conditioned avoidance behavior. Proc. 2nd Int. Cong. on Hormonal Steroids, Milan, May 1966. *Excerpta Medica Int. Cong. Ser. 132*, 945-51.

De Wied, D., and B. Bohus (1966). Long term and short term effects on retention of a conditioned avoidance response in rats by treatment with long acting pitressin and α-MSH. *Nature 212*, 1484-86.

De Wied, D., and G. Pirie (1968). The inhibitory effect of ACTH 1-10 on extinction of a conditioned avoidance response: its independence of thyroid function. *Physiology and Behavior 3*, 355-58.

De Wied, D., P. G. Smelik, J. Moll, and P. R. Bouman (1964). On the mechanism of ACTH release. In *Major Problems in Neuroendocrinology* (E. Bajusz and G. Jasmin, eds.) pp. 156-76. S. Karger, Basel.

Dingman, W., and M. B. Sporn (1961). The incorporation of 8-aza-guanine into rat brain, RNA and its effect on maze learning by the rat. An inquiry into the biochemical basis of memory. *J. Psychiat. Res. 1*, 1-11.

Dyster-Aas, H. K., and C. E. T. Krakau (1965). General effects of α-melanocyte stimulating hormone in the rabbit. *Acta Endocr. (Kbh) 48*, 609-18.

Eayrs, J. T. (1961). Age as a factor determining the severity and reversibility of the effects of thyroid deprivation in the rat. *J. Endocrinol. 22*, 409-19.

Eayrs, J. T., and S. Levine (1963). Influence of thyroidectomy and subsequent replacement therapy upon conditioned avoidance learning in the rat. *J. Endocrinol. 25*, 505-13.

Eayrs, J. T., and W. A. Lishman (1955). The maturation of behaviour in hypothyroidism and starvation. *Brit. J. Anim. Behav. 3*, 17-24.

Eccles, J. C., D. M. Eccles, and P. Fatt (1956). Pharmacological investigations on a central synapse operated by acetylcholine. *J. Physiol. (London) 131*, 154-69.

Elrick, H., D. Borda-Bossana, E. Diamant, L. Bernstein, and J. M. Whitehouse (1960). Effect of handling on the thyroidectomized rat. *Amer. J. Physiol. 198*, 13-14.

Endröczi, E. (1965). The role of the meso-diencephalic activating system in EEG and behavioral arousal, motivation and conditioned reflex processes. *Acta Physiol. Acad. Sci. Hung. 26*, 69-80.

Feldman, S., J. C. Todt, and R. W. Porter (1961). Effect of adrenocortical hormones on evoked potentials in the brain stem. *Neurology 11*, 109-15.

Ferarri, W., G. L. Gessa, and L. Vargiu (1961). Stretching activity in dogs intra-cisternally injected with a synthetic melanocyte-stimulating hexapeptide. *Experientia 17*, 90.

Ferrari, W., G. L. Gessa, and L. Vargiu (1963). Behavioral effects induced by intracisternally injected ACTH and MSH. *Ann. N.Y. Acad. Sci. 104*, 330-45.

Feuer, G., and P. L. Broadhurst (1962). Thyroid function in rats selectively bred for emotional elimination: III. Behavioral and physiological changes after treatment with drugs acting on the thyroid. *J. Endocrinol. 24*, 385-96.

Fjerdingstad, E. J., Th. Nissen, and H. H. Røigaard-Petersen (1965). Effect of ribonucleic acid (RNA) extracted from the brain of trained animals on learning in rats. *Scand. J. Psychol. 6*, 1-6.

Flexner, J. B., and L. B. Flexner (1967). Restoration of expression of memory lost after treatment with puromycin. *Proc. Nat. Acad. Sci. (Wash.) 57*, 1651-54.

Flexner, L. B., and J. B. Flexner (1968). Intracerebral saline: effect on memory of trained mice treated with puromycin. *Science 159*, 330-31.

Flexner, J. B., L. B. Flexner, and E. Stellar (1963). Memory in mice as affected by intracerebral puromycin. *Science 141*, 57-59.

Flexner, L. B., J. B. Flexner, and R. B. Roberts (1967). Memory in mice analyzed with antibiotics. *Science 155*, 1377-83.

Frey, P. W., and V. J. Polidora (1967). Magnesium pemoline: effect on avoidance conditioning in rats. *Science 155*, 1281-82.

Gelfand, S., L. D. Clark, E. W. Herbert, D. M. Gelfand, and E. D. Holmes (1968). Magnesium pemoline: stimulant effects on performance of fatigued subjects. *Clin. Pharmacol. Ther. 9*, 56-60.

Gessa, G. L., and W. Ferrari (1967). Effects of ACTH and MSH-peptides on nervous central system. *International Symposium on the Pharmacology of Hormonal Polypeptides and Proteins*, Milan, Italy, September 14-16, p. 42.

Glasky, A. J., and L. N. Simon (1966). Magnesium pemoline: enhancement of brain RNA polymerases. *Science 151*, 702-3.

Greven, H. M., and D. de Wied (1967). The active sequence in the ACTH molecule responsible for inhibition of the extinction of conditioned avoidance behaviour in rats. *Europ. J. Pharmacol. 2*, 14-16.

Grossman, S. P., R. H. Peters, P. E. Freedman, and N. E. Miller (1965). Behavioral effects of cholinergic stimulation of the thalamic reticular formation. *J. Comp. Physiol. Psychol. 59*, 57-65.

Guillemin, R. (1964). Hypothalamic factors releasing pituitary hormones. *Recent Prog. Hormone Res. 20*, 89-130.

Hagen, J. H. (1961). Effect of glucagon on the metabolism of adipose tissue. *J. Biol. Chem. 236*, 1023-27.

Hydén, H., and E. Egyházi (1962). Nuclear RNA changes of nerve cells during a learning experiment in rats. *Proc. Nat. Acad. Sci. (Wash.)* 48, 1366-73.

Hydén, H., and E. Egyházi (1964). Changes in RNA content and base composition in cortical neurons of rats in a learning experiment involving transfer of handedness. *Proc. Nat. Acad. Sci. (Wash.)* 52, 1030-35.

Hydén, H., and O. W. Lange (1968). Protein synthesis in the hippocampal pyramidal cells of rats during a behavioral test. *Science* 159, 1370-73.

Jacobson, A. L., F. R. Babich, S. Bubash, and A. Jacobson (1965). Differential-approach tendencies produced by injection of RNA from trained rats. *Science* 150, 636-37.

Koltai, M., and E. Minker (1966). The direct effect of some endocrine factors on synaptic transmission in the peripheral sympathetic ganglia. *Acta Physiol. Acad. Sci. Hung.* 29, 410.

Korányi, L., and E. Endröczi (1967). The effect of ACTH on neural processes. *Neuroendocrinology* 2, 65-75.

Korányi, L., E. Endröczi, and F. Tárnok (1966). Sexual behavior in the course of avoidance conditioning in male rabbits. *Neuroendocrinology* 1, 144-57.

Korányi, L., E. Endröczi, K. Lissák, and E. Szepes (1967). The effect of ACTH on behavioral processes motivated by fear in mice. *Physiology and Behavior* 2, 439-45.

Korn, J. H. (1967). Conditioned activity depression in hypothyroid and hyperthyroid rats. *J. Gen. Psychol.* 110, 169-80.

Krivoy, W. A. (1957). Actions of chlorpromazine and of reserpine on spinal reflex activity in the cat. *Proc. Soc. Exp. Biol. (N. Y.)* 96, 18-20.

Krivoy, W. A., and R. Guillemin (1961). On a possible role of β-melanocyte stimulating hormone (β-MSH) in the central nervous system of the mammalia: an effect of β-MSH in the spinal cord of the cat. *Endocrinology* 69, 170-75.

Krivoy, W. A., M. Lane, and D. C. Kroeger (1963). The actions of certain polypeptides on synaptic transmission. *Ann. N.Y. Acad. Sci.* 104, 312-29.

Levine, S., and L. E. Jones (1965). Adrenocorticotrophic hormone (ACTH) and passive avoidance learning. *J. Comp. Physiol. Psychol.* 59, 357-60.

Lissák, K., and E. Endröczi (1961). Neurohumoral factors in the control of animal behavior. In *Brain Mechanisms and Learning* (A. Fessard, R. W. Gerard, and J. Konorski, eds.), pp. 293-308. Blackwell, Oxford.

Miller, R. E., and N. Ogawa (1962). The effect of adrenocorticotrophic hormone (ACTH) on avoidance conditioning in the adrenalectomized rat. *J. Comp. Physiol. Psychol.* 55, 211-13.

Mirsky, J. A., and G. Perisutti (1962). Action of oxytocin and related peptides on epididymal adipose tissue of the rat. *Endocrinology* 71, 158-63.

Mirsky, A., R. Miller, and M. Stein (1953). Relation of adrenocortical activity and adaptive behavior. *Psychosom. Med.* 15, 574-88.

Morris, N. R., G. K. Aghajanian, and F. E. Bloom (1967). Magnesium pemoline: failure to affect in vivo synthesis of brain RNA. *Science* 155, 1125-26.

Morrison, G. W., and B. Cunningham (1941). Characteristics of the conditioned response in cretinous rats. *J. Comp. Psychol.* 31, 413-25.

Mowrer, O. H. (1950). *Learning Theory and Personality Dynamics*, Ronald, New York, p. 126.

Moyer, K. E. (1958). Effect of adrenalectomy on anxiety motivated behavior. *J. Genet. Psychol.* 92, 11-16.

Murphy, J. V., and R. E. Miller (1955). The effect of adrenocorticotrophic hormone (ACTH) on avoidance conditioning in the rat. *J. Comp. Physiol. Psychol. 48*, 47-49.

Murphy, J. V., and R. E. Miller (1956). Spaced and massed practice with a methodological consideration of avoidance conditioning. *J. Exp. Psychol. 52*, 77-81.

Nissen, Th., H. H. Røigaard-Petersen, and E. J. Fjerdingstad (1965). Effect of ribonucleic acid (RNA) extracted from the brain of trained animals on learning in rats. *Scand. J. Psychol. 6*, 265-72.

Plotnikoff, N. (1966a). Magnesium pemoline: enhancement of learning and memory of a conditioned avoidance response. *Science 151*, 703-4.

Plotnikoff, N. (1966b). Magnesium pemoline: antagonism of retrograde amnesia in rats. *Fed. Proc. 25*, 262.

Plotnikoff, N. (1966c). Magnesium pemoline: enhancement of memory after electroconvulsive shock in rats. *Life Sci. 5*, 1495-98.

Plotnikoff, N., and P. Meekma, Jr. (1967). Pemoline and magnesium hydroxide versus pemoline: enhancement of learning and memory of the conditioned avoidance response in rats. *J. Pharm. Sci. 56*, 290-91.

Potts, A., and M. E. Bitterman (1967). Puromycin and retention in the goldfish. *Science 158*, 1594-96.

Rich, I., and R. Thompson (1965). Role of the hippocamposeptal system, thalamus, and hypothalamus in avoidance conditioning. *J. Comp. Physiol. Psychol. 59*, 66-72.

Richards, W. J., and J. C. Stockburger (1958). Thyroid hormone and conditioning. *J. Comp. Physiol. Psychol. 51*, 445-47.

Richter, C. P., and J. F. Eckert (1937). The effect of hypophyseal injection and implants on the activity of hypophysectomized rats. *Endocrinology 21*, 481-88.

Richter, C. P., and G. B. Wislocki (1930). Anatomical and behavior changes produced in the rat by complete and partial extirpation of the pituitary gland. *Am. J. Physiol. 95*, 481-92.

Røigaard-Petersen, H. H., E. J. Fjerdingstad, and Th. Nissen (1965). Facilitation of learning in rats by intracisternal injection of "conditioned RNA." *Worm Runner's Digest 7*, 15-27.

Røigaard-Petersen, H. H., Th. Nissen, and E. J. Fjerdingstad (1968). Effect of ribonucleic acid (RNA) extracted from the brain of trained animals on learning in rats. III. Results obtained with an improved procedure. *Scand. J. Psychol. 9*, 1-16.

Rosenblatt, F., and R. G. Miller (1966a). Behavioral assay procedures for transfer of learned behavior by brain extracts I. *Proc. Nat. Acad. Sci. (Wash.) 56*, 1423-30.

Rosenblatt, F., and R. G. Miller (1966b). Behavioral assay procedures for transfer of learned behavior by brain extracts II. *Proc. Nat. Acad. Sci. (Wash.) 56*, 1683-88.

Rosenblatt, F., J. T. Farrow, and W. F. Herblin (1966a). Transfer of conditioned responses from trained rats to untrained rats by means of a brain extract. *Nature 209*, 46-48.

Rosenblatt, F., J. T. Farrow, and S. Rhine (1966b). The transfer of learned behavior from trained to untrained rats by means of brain extracts. I. *Proc. Nat. Acad. Sci. (Wash.) 55*, 548-55.

Rosenblatt, F., J. T. Farrow, and S. Rhine (1966c). The transfer of learned behavior from trained to untrained rats by means of brain extracts II. *Proc. Nat. Acad. Sci. (Wash.) 55*, 787-92.

Sakamoto, A. (1966). Hypersensitivity induced in albino mice by melanocyte-stimulating hormone. *Nature 211*, 1370-71.

Sakamoto, A., and K. N. Prasad (1968). The newly-observed catecholamine-like actions of β-melanocyte-stimulating hormone. In *Protein and Polypeptide Hormones*, Part 2 (M. Margoulies, ed.), Excerpta Medica Found. Int. Cong. Ser. No. 161, pp. 503-4.

Sakata, T., S. Agari, S. Kawasaki, H. Kuwahara, and N. Ogawa (1966). The effect of thyroidectomy on the acquisition of conditioned avoidance response in rats. *Fukuoka Acta Med. 57*, 752-56.

Schally, A. V., A. J. Kastin, T. W. Redding, C. Y. Bowers, H. Yajima, and K. Kubo (1967). Thyroid stimulating and pigmentary effects of synthetic peptides related to α-MSH and ACTH. *Metabolism 16*, 824-29.

Schwyzer, R. (1964). Chemistry and metabolic action of nonsteroid hormones. *Ann. Rev. Biochem. 33*, 259-86.

Segal, D. S., R. H. Cox, Jr., W. C. Stern, and R. P. Maickel (1967). Stimulatory effects of pemoline and cyclopropylpemoline on continuous avoidance behavior: similarity to effects of D-amphetamine. *Life Sci. 6*, 2567-72.

Shashova, V. E. (1968). RNA changes in goldfish brain during learning. *Nature 217*, 238-40.

Siegel, R. K. (1967). Yeast ribonucleic acid: effects on avoidance behavior of the neonate domestic chick. *Psychopharmacol. 12*, 68-77.

Siegel, R. K. (1968). Effects of ribonucleic acid (RNA) on interval scheduling in the domestic pigeon. *Psychol. Rec. 18*, 53-57.

Simon, L. N., and A. J. Glasky (1968). Magnesium pemoline: enhancement of brain RNA synthesis in vivo. *Life Sci. 7*, 197-202.

Smith, R. G. (1967). Magnesium pemoline: lack of facilitation in human learning, memory and performance tests. *Science 155*, 603-5.

Solyom, L., C. Beaulieu, and H. E. Enesco (1966). The effect of RNA on the operant conditioned behavior of white rats. *Psychonom. Sci. 6*, 341-42.

Stein, D. G., J. J. Brink, and A. Patterson (1968). Magnesium pemoline: facilitation of maze learning when administered in pure dimethylsulfonide. *Life Sci. 7*, 147-53.

Stein, H. H., and T. O. Jellin (1967). Pemoline and magnesium hydroxide: lack of effect on RNA and protein synthesis. *Science 157*, 96-97.

Stone, C. P., and F. A. King (1954). Effects of hypophysectomy on behavior in rats: I. Preliminary survey. *J. Comp. Physiol. Psychol. 47*, 213-19.

Stone, C. P., and W. A. Mason (1955). Effects of hypophysectomy on behavior in rats: III. Thermoregulatory behavior. *J. Comp. Physiol. Psychol. 48*, 456-62.

Stone, C. P., and M. D. Obias (1955). Effects of hypophysectomy on behavior in rats: II. Maze and discrimination learning. *J. Comp. Physiol. Psychol. 48*, 404-11.

Talland, G. A., and M. T. McGuire (1967). Tests of learning and memory with cylert. *Psychopharmacol. 10*, 445-51.

Tata, J. R. (1967). The formation and distribution of ribosomes during hormone-induced growth and development. *Biochem. J. 104*, 1-16.

Thompson, R. (1963). Thalamic structures critical for retention of an avoidance response in rats. *J. Comp. Physiol. Psychol. 56*, 261-67.

Thompson, R., and D. R. Kenshalo (1954). Discrimination learning and habit reversal as affected by thyroid hormone. *J. Comp. Physiol. Psychol. 47*, 36-40.

Ungar, G., and M. Cohen (1966). Induction of morphine tolerance by material extracted from brain of tolerant animals. *Int. J. Neuropharmacol. 5*, 183-92.

Ungar, G., and L. N. Irwin (1967). Transfer of acquired information by brain extracts. *Nature 214*, 453-55.

Ungar, G., and C. Oceguera-Navarro (1965). Transfer of habituation by material extracted from brain. *Nature 207*, 301-2.

Ungar, G., L. Galvan, and R. H. Clark (1968). Chemical transfer of learned fear. *Nature 217*, 1259-61.

Vanderwolf, C. H. (1964). Effect of combined medial thalamic and septal lesions on active avoidance behavior. *J. Comp. Physiol. Psychol. 58*, 31-37.

Wagner, A. R., J. B. Carder, and W. W. Beaty (1966). Yeast ribonucleic acid: effects on learned behavior in the rat. *Psychonom. Sci. 4*, 33-34.

Warburton, D. M., and R. W. Russell (1968). Effects of 8-aza-guanine on acquisition of a temporal discrimination. *Physiology and Behavior 8*, 61-63.

Warden, C. J., S. Ross, and S. Zamenhof (1942). The effect of artificial changes in the brain on maze-learning in the white rat. *Science 95*, 414-15.

Wasserman, M. J., N. R. Belton, and J. G. Millichap (1965). Effect of corticotropin (ACTH) on experimental seizures; adrenal independence and relation to intracellular brain sodium. *Neurology 15*, 1136-41.

Winegrad, A. I., and E. A. Renold (1958). Studies on rat adipose tissue in vitro. I. Effects of insulin on the metabolism of glucose by pyruvate and acetate. II. Effects of insulin on the metabolism of specifically labeled glucose. *J. Biol. Chem. 233*, 267-72.

Winegrad, A. I., W. N. Shaw, F. D. W. Lukens, W. C. Stadie, and A. E. Renold (1959). Effects of growth hormone in vitro on the mechanism of glucose in rat adipose tissue. *J. Biol. Chem. 234*, 1922-28.

Wollenberger, A., and W. Halle (1963). Wirkung von ACTH und verwandten Polypeptiden auf die spontane Rhythmik isoliertes Herzmuskelzellen in vitro. *Arch. exp. Path. Pharmak. 245*, 279-80.

Zamenhof, S. (1942). Stimulation of cortical-cell proliferation by the growth hormone. III. Experiments on albino rats. *Physiol. Zoöl. 15*, 281-92.

Zemp, J. W., J. E. Wilson, H. Schlesinger, W. O. Boggan, and E. Glassman (1966). Brain function and macromolecules, I. Incorporation of uridine into RNA of mouse brain during short-term training experience. *Proc. Nat. Acad. Sci. (Wash.) 55*, 1423-31.

Zemp, J. W., J. E. Wilson, and E. Glassman (1967). Brain function and macromolecules, II. Site of increased labeling of RNA in brains of mice during a short-term training experience. *Proc. Nat. Acad. Sci. (Wash.) 58*, 1120-25.

4

The Regulation of Growth Hormone Secretion

SEYMOUR M. GLICK

Introduction

The application of radioimmunoassay to the measurement of plasma growth hormone (GH) and the demonstration of the responsiveness of plasma growth hormone to acute stimuli have led to the rapid accumulation of data. Hundreds of papers concerning growth hormone secretion have appeared since the first review of our data (Glick *et al.*, 1965), written four years ago. The pre-immunoassay era has been thoroughly reviewed recently (Pecile and Müller, 1966a; Reichlin, 1966), but only the earliest papers utilizing immunoassay were included. The material covered by these authors is not discussed in any detail in the present review. Several other reviews, broader in scope than the present one, have touched upon the secretion of growth hormone with varying comprehensiveness (Knobil and Hotchkiss, 1964; Daughaday and Parker, 1965; Greenwood, 1967; Guillemin, 1967; McCann *et al.*, 1968). The present review concentrates on the more recent data, particularly those obtained with immunoassay techniques, and also comments upon areas of significant controversy and unsolved problems.

Most of the recently accumulated data resulted from the development of an immunoassay for human growth hormone and its application to clinical medicine. Immunoassays of non-primate GH were developed several years later, and there is currently considerable discordance between

This review and the author's work discussed in it were supported by Research Grant AMO-9219 from the National Institutes of Health.

141

the data in primates and the data in non-primates. There is also uncertainty about work in non-primates because of the discrepancies between the results obtained with bioassays and those obtained with immunoassays. Consequently, the more detailed and certain work on man and the monkey is reviewed first, and the work on non-primates is summarized at the end of the chapter.

Methodology

The factors affecting bioassay of GH are well known and need not be discussed here. Radioimmunoassay techniques have now been widely used for human growth hormone (HGH), with results which have, in general, been comparable in laboratories throughout the world, particularly with respect to relative changes in hormone levels in response to stimuli. Comparability of absolute values between laboratories presents several problems. Unfortunately, some authors do not specify the particular preparation of HGH used as their standard. In general, the Raben preparations are about 60 percent as potent as the newer Wilhelmi preparations, and appropriate corrections need to be made. Another source of differences between laboratories is the method used for separation of bound from free hormone. The test-tube methods, in contrast to the chromatoelectrophoretic method, do not provide quantitation of iodination damage and incubation damage to radioiodinated hormone, and may, therefore, result in falsely elevated levels of hormone. For these reasons comparisons of absolute levels of GH from one laboratory to another are often difficult, and may not be valid.

Although it is recognized that changes in plasma levels of hormone do not necessarily represent changes in secretory rate, the evidence suggests that in most cases they do. This assumption is accepted throughout this review, with awareness that, in selected instances, this interpretation may not be entirely appropriate.

Stimuli to GH Secretion

Stimuli Related to Energy Metabolism

Hypoglycemia.   Many investigators have substantiated the original observation (Roth *et al.*, 1963a) that acute, symptomatic, insulin-induced hypoglycemia is followed by an outpouring of GH into the circulation, and that this secretion is related to the hypoglycemia and not to the insulin. Because of the possibility that the secretion of GH under such circumstances may be merely a "nonspecific" response to stress rather than a primary glucoprival response, Luft and his co-workers (Luft *et al.*, 1966) examined the effects of very small doses of insulin. They reported that falls in blood glucose of 10 mg/100 ml, which were not symptomatic, were associated with significant elevations of plasma GH, suggesting a specific effect of glucopenia. Shortly thereafter, however, another group of investigators (Koh *et al.*, 1968) reported that changes of similar magnitude in plasma GH could be observed without insulin administration, and that there was no correlation between small decreases in blood glucose and significant elevations in plasma GH. Greenwood's data (Greenwood *et al.*, 1966), using graded doses of insulin, support Luft's findings in that the administration of .025 U/kg of insulin was associated with a definite rise of plasma GH, but was unaccompanied by elevation of plasma cortisol. However, more data are needed to settle this important point.

During chronic hypoglycemia, adaptation occurs and plasma GH is often normal (Marks *et al.*, 1967; Rosselin, *et al.*, 1967a). Acute falls in blood glucose beyond the chronic low levels (Marks *et al.*, 1967) and the infusion of arginine (Freychet *et al.*, 1967) do stimulate GH secretion in these patients.

Alcohol hypoglycemia has been reported to elicit only a weak GH response (Arky and Freinkel, 1964), but alcohol per se does not suppress the GH response to insulin hypoglycemia (Glick, 1968). It is likely that the failure of alcohol hypoglycemia to provoke a brisk GH response is related to the slowness of the fall in blood glucose.

Fructose given to fructose-sensitive individuals can provoke hypoglycemia with an associated GH elevation (Roth *et al.*, 1963a). In normal individuals fructose may suppress GH secretion and even prevent insulin-induced GH secretion (Baylis *et al.*, 1968), suggesting that fructose can substitute for glucose in the receptors.

Falling Blood Glucose.   Falling blood glucose even in the absence of hypoglycemia can stimulate GH secretion (Roth *et al.*, 1963b). In a detailed study of this stimulus it was observed that blood glucose had to be maintained at elevated levels for more than 3 minutes in most subjects in order for a subsequent fall of blood glucose to be an effective stimulus (Irie *et al.*, 1967a). Neither the magnitude of the fall nor the fall of blood glucose below the fasting value alone were sufficient to stimulate GH secretion if the initial high levels of blood glucose had been sustained for only a short time.

Interference with Glucose Utilization.   The administration of 2-deoxy-D-glucose stimulates GH secretion (Roth *et al.*, 1963b; Wegienka *et al.*,

1967) and may be useful for the testing of pituitary function in patients with insulin insensitivity (Wegienka et al., 1967). Diabetic acidosis, when severe, may also be accompanied by abnormally elevated levels of plasma GH (Unger, 1965), but a nonspecific response to severe stress, rather than specific interference with glucose utilization in an insulin-dependent hypothalamic center, may be the cause. The infusion of anti-insulin antibody into several monkeys, producing acute hyperglycemia by interference with glucose utilization, did not stimulate GH secretion (Glick, 1968). This experiment provides no support for the concept of a growth hormone regulatory center whose glucose utilization is dependent on insulin. On the other hand, neither does this experiment rule out the existence of such a center.

Exercise. Even moderate exercise without evident hypoglycemia stimulates GH secretion (Roth et al., 1963b; Hunter and Greenwood, 1964), to a degree roughly proportional to the severity of the exercise (Schalch, 1967). Concurrent administration of carbohydrate suppresses this GH secretion (Glick et al., 1965; Hunter et al., 1965), but the administration of fat does not (Hunter et al., 1965). The administration of protein may accentuate the stimulation of GH secretion even further (Hunter et al., 1965). The rise in GH occurs about 30 minutes after the onset of the exercise (Hunter et al., 1965; Hartog et al., 1967), and GH levels begin to fall 30 minutes later even with continuation of the exercise (Hunter et al., 1965; Hartog et al., 1967). Further increases of GH could be elicited at the end of exercise by administration of insulin (Hartog et al., 1967) suggesting that the fall in plasma GH observed was not the result of depletion of pituitary stores of GH. The rise in plasma free fatty acids and glycerol precedes that of GH (Hartog et al., 1967), and the suppression of fat mobilization by propanolol (Troyer et al., 1966) or by nicotinic acid (Hartog et al., 1967) does not have a significant effect on the initial rise of plasma GH. Nicotinic acid, which lowers free fatty acid levels, delays the fall in plasma GH that usually occurs 60 minutes after the onset of exercise (Hartog et al., 1967), leading to the speculation that free fatty acids may have an inhibitory effect on GH secretion.

Prolonged Fasting. Cahill's group (Cahill et al., 1966), in a careful metabolic and hormonal evaluation of prolonged starvation in six normal subjects, have cast doubt on the significance of the role of growth hormone in the metabolic response to fasting. Although they confirmed the previously well-documented rise in plasma growth hormone in response to starvation (Roth *et al.*, 1963b; Marks *et al.*, 1965; Landon *et al.*, 1966), they felt that the marked variability of the response suggested a minor role for growth hormone in the metabolic response to starvation. The crucial experiment, a detailed examination of the metabolic response to starvation in an individual with isolated growth hormone deficiency, remains to be done. Only if such an individual manifests a normal metabolic response to fasting can a role for GH during prolonged fasting be ruled out. Animal experiments (Russel, 1957) would seem to disagree with the conclusions of Cahill and his associates.

Stress-Related Stimuli

Surgery. Major surgery, performed under a variety of anesthetic agents, is associated with a rise in plasma GH (Glick *et al.*, 1965; Ketterer *et al.*, 1966; Schalch, 1967) in spite of concomitant hyperglycemia. There is a rough correlation between the severity of the surgical stress and the increase in plasma GH (Glick *et al.*, 1965; Ketterer *et al.*, 1966). Ketterer and his associates suggest teleologically that the increase in GH might (1) augment free fatty acid release; (2) reduce non-obligatory glucose utilization, thus contributing to greater cerebral glucose delivery; and (3) enhance tissue repair by its anabolic effects. However, it seems more likely that the release of GH is an incidental "nonspecific" response to stress.

Bacterial Endotoxins. GH secretion, like that of ACTH, is stimulated by the administration of bacterial endotoxin pyrogens (Greenwood and Landon, 1966a; Frohman *et al.*, 1967a; Kohler *et al.*, 1967). Nevertheless, dissociation between ACTH secretion and GH secretion exists. Individual subjects may respond to pyrogen with secretion of one or the other hormone (Kohler *et al.*, 1967; Kimball *et al.*, 1968). Neither the acute administration of glucose (Greenwood and Landon, 1966a; Kohler *et al.*, 1967) nor of dexamethasone (Baylis *et al.*, 1968) could suppress the GH response to pyrogen. Although the response to pyrogen is generally considered the prototype of a stress-related response, there is poor correlation between the degree of fever and the hormonal response (Kimball *et al.*, 1968). The production of fever by etiocholanolone, a more effective but more slowly acting pyrogen, is not associated with increases in plasma GH (Kimball *et al.*, 1968). The rise in GH is not produced by the fever itself, because the GH elevation usually precedes the rise in temperature (Baylis *et al.*, 1968; Kimball *et al.*, 1968) and is not prevented by salicylate-induced suppression of fever (Baylis *et al.*, 1968). In several experiments in pentobarbital-anesthetized monkeys the production of hyperthemia by exogenously applied heat was not associated with increases in plasma GH (Glick, 1968).

Vasopressin. Vasopressin, like bacterial endotoxins, has effects on both ACTH and GH secretion when given in rather large doses (Greenwood and Landon, 1966a; Meyer and Knobil, 1966). Although consistent responses have been reported (Gagliardino *et al.*, 1967) with Pitressin, more variable results were observed with synthetic lysine vasopressin (Brostoff *et al.*, 1968; Chakmajian and Bethune, 1968). The correlation of GH secretion with presence and severity of side effects (Brostoff *et al.*, 1968) suggests that the response to vasopressin is of the stress-induced type. Production of hyperosmolarity in monkeys to a degree sufficient to stimulate endogenous vasopressin secretion did not stimulate GH secretion (Glick, 1968), and a normal response to insulin hypoglycemia has been observed in 3 children with diabetes insipidus (Root *et al.*, 1967). The effect of glucose on vasopressin-induced secretion of GH has not been reported.

Miscellaneous Stress. Electroconvulsive therapy is often (Schalch, 1967; Takahashi *et al.*, 1967a), but not always (Glick *et al.*, 1965) followed by a rise in plasma growth hormone. The secretion of GH seems to be unaffected by premedication with sedatives (Takahashi *et al.*, 1967a) or with succinylcholine (Schalch, 1967; Takahashi *et al.*, 1967a). The level of GH is considerably less after electroconvulsive shock than after insulin-induced shock, although both are significant neural stresses.

Acute trauma (Schalch, 1967), arterial puncture (Copinschi *et al.*, 1967a), a visit to the dentist (Baylis *et al.*, 1968), and anticipation of insulin hypoglycemia (Greenwood and Landon, 1966a) have been associated with elevations of plasma growth hormone and explained as a manifestation of stress. A variety of stressors, including pain, noise, hemorrhage, and histamine, were effective in stimulating the secretion of monkey GH (Meyer and Knobil, 1967). On the other hand, the stress of medical school exams (Schalch, 1967) and myocardial infarction (Norman and Turter, 1968), did not increase GH secretion. Cold exposure, which is a potent stimulus to the secretion of GH in non-primates, was not effective in normal adult humans (Berg *et al.*, 1966), in ether anesthetized infants (Baum *et al.*, 1967), or in pentobarbital-anesthetized stumptail monkeys (Glick, 1968).

Neural Stimuli

Sleep. Quabbe, in his study of 24-hour patterns of GH secretion (Quabbe *et al.*, 1966), commented on increased nocturnal levels of GH and noticed that peaks often coincided with periods of deep sleep. We noted smaller elevations of GH in overnight studies (Roth *et al.*, 1967), but erroneously attributed them to late postprandial rebounds of plasma GH. Similarly elevated nocturnal levels of GH have been noted by others (Hunter and Rigal, 1966; Morris and Jorgensen, 1968). Several investigators (Honda, 1967; Takahashi *et al.*, 1967b; D. Parker *et al.*, 1968) have now clearly shown that large peaks of plasma GH are regularly observed with the onset of deep sleep as judged by electroencephalographic (EEG) patterns. Delay in the onset of sleep delays the peak, and splitting of a night's sleep into two portions results in a major peak with each entry into the deep sleep phase. The administration of chlorpromazine and phenobarbital did not affect the GH pattern in two subjects (Takahashi *et al.*, 1967b). The patterns of plasma GH induced by sleep changes are not correlated with blood glucose, plasma free fatty acids, or plasma insulin (Takahashi, *et al.*, 1967b; Quabbe *et al.*, 1966). Along somewhat similar lines, Meyer and Knobil (1967) reported that the arousal from pentobarbital anesthesia was regularly associated with acute elevations of plasma GH in monkeys, although our own observations have not confirmed the consistency of this finding.

Other.   In a series of experiments on the influence of feeding patterns on plasma GH (Glick and Goldsmith, 1968) it has become apparent that it is difficult, even in a non-stressed subject at bed rest, to keep GH secretion suppressed for more than a few hours. Neither oral feeding every 1/2 hour, nor continuous intravenous glucose, nor continuous glucose by nasogastric tube, nor intravenous glucose and amino acids have been able to keep GH secretion suppressed for an entire 24-hour period. Because of the observation (Marks *et al.*, 1967) that the GH secretory mechanism can accommodate itself to a given blood glucose level, continuous suppression was attempted by gradually increasing rates of glucose infusion over 24 hours. This regimen, too, was associated with "breakthrough" secretion of GH, as if some central nervous system mechanism were causing periodic bursts of GH secretion. The periodic bursts of GH secretion in normal subjects are unlike the fairly constant levels in acromegalic subjects (Hunter *et al.*, 1966a).

Stimuli Related to Protein Metabolism

Arginine and Other Amino Acids.   The observation that arginine and several other amino acids can acutely stimulate GH secretion (Knopf *et al.*, 1965; Merimee *et al.*, 1965) has provided the clinician with a useful tool for testing pituitary function. The mechanism of action of arginine is not clear, however, nor has it been proved that the effect of arginine represents a physiologic stimulus (Merimee and Rabinowitz, 1967).

The stimulation by arginine in adults seems to be partially sex-dependent, in that many men fail to respond unless they have been pretreated with estrogens (Merimee et al., 1966a, 1967). Although initial reports suggested that the GH secretion stimulated by arginine was not suppressible by glucose (Rabinowitz et al., 1966a), subsequent studies indicate that glucose can partially suppress arginine-stimulated GH release (Burday et al., 1968).

Protein Ingestion. Subsequent to the demonstration of arginine's ability to stimulate GH secretion, GH secretion was examined under more physiologic conditions of increasing plasma amino nitrogen by feeding of protein. The ingestion of 500 g of chicken liver (Knopf et al., 1966), 1 lb of tenderloin steak (Rabinowitz et al., 1966b) or 3.85 gm/kg of ham (Sukkar et al., 1967) is followed over the next 2 to 4 hours by a significant increase in plasma GH, though to levels not nearly as high as with arginine administration. Greenwood's group, however, reported rather variable results with protein ingestion (Baylis et al., 1968). The simultaneous administration of glucose blunts the GH response to protein (Rabinowitz et al., 1966b).

The protein ingestion data would seem to fit the classic role of GH in protein anabolism, and have been explained thus (Knopf et al., 1966; Rabinowitz et al., 1966b). Sukkar et al. (1967) emphasize the role of growth hormone in the control of free fatty acid mobilization, and see in protein-induced growth hormone release following insulin secretion a means for applying a brake on excessive inhibition of fat breakdown.

Protein Depletion. In striking contrast to the above data are those in children with kwashiorkor, who have, along with protein depletion, markedly elevated levels of plasma GH (Pimstone et al., 1966; Hadden, 1967). That this elevation of plasma GH is not merely the result of generalized starvation is evidenced by the failure of the plasma growth hormone to fall when a diet adequate in calories but deficient in proteins is administered. (Pimstone et al., 1968). Only with the administration of protein do growth hormone levels return toward normal. Although the plasma albumin and plasma aminogram are grossly abnormal in kwashiorkor, it is not clear what the specific trigger for growth hormone release in protein depletion is.

Miscellaneous Stimuli

Effects of Changes in Plasma Free Fatty Acids. Although growth hormone has profound effects on fat metabolism when administered to an experimental subject, there is relatively little information on the effects of variations in fat metabolism on plasma growth hormone. The oral ingestion of olive oil (Glick *et al.*, 1965), or of fat with heparin (Baylis *et al.*, 1968), does not alter plasma growth hormone. Baylis and his co-workers have also shown that the elevation of free fatty acids secondary to the administration of cream plus heparin before an insulin tolerance test does not suppress the growth hormone response to insulin hypoglycemia (Baylis *et al.*, 1968). These investigators also report that acute lowering of free fatty acid levels by insulin together with enough glucose to prevent hypoglycemia does not stimulate GH secretion.

The administration of nicotinic acid with its concomitant lowering of free fatty acids is followed 120 minutes later by a rise of plasma GH (Irie *et al.*, 1967b). The rise in GH can be prevented by the simultaneous administration of heparin, which prevents a fall in free fatty acids. During exercise, the lowering of free fatty acids by the administration of nicotinic acid results in prolongation of high GH levels (Hartog *et al.*, 1967). However, if free fatty acids do influence growth hormone secretion, as these reports suggest, their effects are relatively minor.

In evaluating the role of increased GH secretion on the rise of plasma free fatty acids produced by hypoglycemia, exercise, and the like, the usual time course of action of GH on free fatty acids must be taken into account. Several hours normally elapse between the administration of GH and the marked rise in plasma free fatty acids, making it most unlikely that GH secretion at times of acute carbohydrate need could be responsible for the acute fat mobilization. More recently, several experimental observations have more directly contradicted a major role for GH in acute fat mobilization. Plasma glycerol levels, which are a better index of fat mobilization than are free fatty acid levels, rise with exercise before GH levels rise (Hartog *et al.*, 1967). Furthermore, in Addisonian and adrenalectomized patients there was little free fatty acid response to 2-deoxy-D-glucose in spite of GH elevations that were at least normal (Grasso *et al.*, 1968). These data indicate that epinephrine secretion, which was absent in these patients, is more important for fat mobilization than is GH secretion. Similarly, propranolol administration to subjects during insulin hypoglycemia effectively blocks fat mobilization while causing GH secretion to be somewhat augmented (Abramson *et al.*, 1966). Propranolol similarly blocks the fat mobilization of exercise without impairing GH secretion (Troyer *et al.*, 1966). GH secretion may be important for longer-term fat mobilization, but its role in the immediate mobilization of fat seems open to serious question.

3'5' Cyclic Adenosine Monophosphate (3'5'-AMP).   3'5'-AMP has recently been proposed as a mediator in the action of several hormones. When administered in large doses to anesthetized monkeys it stimulates secretion of GH (Gagliardino and Martin, 1967), and its effect is blocked by dihydroergotamine. Levine (1969) has found that both 3'5'-AMP and its dibutyryl derivative, which enters cells more readily, are potent stimuli to both insulin and GH secretion in man. While the administration of 3'5'-AMP in the doses used is often associated with unpleasant side effects, the dibutyryl derivative is relatively free of such stress-inducing propensities. However, additional data regarding the effectiveness of other nucleotides are needed before the action of 3'5'-AMP can be regarded as specific.

Schofield (1967) reported that theophylline increased the release of GH from isolated bovine pituitary glands in vitro, a finding in accord with a role for 3'5'-AMP. However, the infusion of theophylline in humans was not associated with any change in plasma GH concentration (Blackard and Heidingsfelder, 1968).

Specificity of Stimuli to GH

The initial demonstration that a series of stimuli which increased GH secretion had in common a shortage of carbohydrate substrate for energy metabolism (Roth *et al.*, 1963b) led to the postulate that GH secretion was specifically stimulated by threats to the adequacy of the carbohydrate supply to the brain (Roth *et al.*, 1963b; Hunter and Greenwood, 1964; Glick *et al.*, 1965). Its secretion under such circumstances was said to lead to decreased utilization of glucose, increased breakdown of fat, and conservation of protein, all of which are teleologically useful. However, an increasing number of stimuli to GH secretion have been described which can be fitted into a "carbohydrate shortage" theory only by the most tortured reasoning. Therefore, it has been suggested that all stimuli associated with hypoglycemia are nonspecific stressors rather than specific metabolic stimuli (Meyer and Knobil, 1967; Müller *et al.*, 1967a). Parallelism between stimulation of GH and ACTH secretion has been cited as evidence for this nonspecificity (Meyer and Knobil, 1967; Müller *et al.*, 1967a). Dissociation between the secretion of GH and the secretion of ACTH and cortisol has repeatedly been reported, however. Situations in which this occurs include untreated Addison's disease (Frantz and Rabkin,

1964), metyrapone administration (Frantz and Rabkin, 1964), acute myocardial infarction (Norman and Turter, 1968), long-term corticosteroid treatment (Friedman and Greenwood, 1967), exercise plus glucose (Hunter *et al.*, 1965) and pyrogen administration (Kohler *et al.*, 1967; Kimball *et al.*, 1968). These data suggest that even if the response of GH were a "nonspecific stress response," its sensitivity and presumably the pathways by which it is mediated are different than those for ACTH.

A number of other experimental observations point strongly toward the existence of a specific glucose-sensitive growth hormone regulatory system. Growth hormone secretion is stimulated by nonstressful falls in blood glucose 3 to 5 hours after glucose ingestion, and after minute doses of insulin (Luft *et al.*, 1966; Greenwood *et al.*, 1966). Of particular pertinence is the elevation of GH without concomitant elevation of plasma cortisol in response to small doses of insulin (Greenwood *et al.*, 1966). The suppression by glucose of growth hormone secretion in the fasting state (Roth *et al.*, 1963b) and the partial suppression by glucose of the arginine-stimulated GH release (Burday *et al.*, 1968) also suggest specificity of response. The degree of specificity of suppression by glucose is highlighted by the ineffectiveness of fat ingestion and of protein ingestion as suppressors of GH during exercise (Hunter *et al.*, 1965). The effectiveness of minute amounts of intrahypothalamic glucose in the prevention of insulin-induced GH secretion in the presence of peripheral hypoglycemia (Blanco *et al.*, 1966) is best explained by the existence of specific intrahypothalamic glucoreceptors.

It is reasonable to conclude that stress, neural stimuli from higher brain centers, and other factors independent of glucose availability can also profoundly influence GH secretion. Multiplicity of independent control pathways for the secretion of a single hormone is not unusual; ACTH secretion is regulated independently by plasma cortisol levels, by stress, and by diurnal rhythm. Similarly, osmotic stimuli and volume stimuli act independently to control vasopressin secretion, but secretion of this hormone is also affected by "nonspecific" stresses. Thus, GH secretion may be regulated by a specific glucose-sensitive mechanism, by stress, by neural mechanisms, by protein needs, and perhaps by still other factors. It is too early to place into proper relative perspective all of the reported stimuli to GH secretion.

Suppressors of GH Secretion

Glucose. In normal individuals beyond infancy, the ingestion or infusion of glucose is followed promptly by a fall in plasma GH to almost undetectable levels. The duration of suppression is roughly correlated with the quantity of glucose administered (Hunter *et al.*, 1968). However, suppression does not persist for more than a few hours of continuous glucose administration. (Glick and Goldsmith, 1968).

The sensitivity of GH secretion to suppression is not present at birth (Cornblath *et al.*, 1965; Milner and Wright, 1966) but develops during the first few weeks of life. It has been suggested that the failure of the newborn to respond to hyperglycemia by a decrease in growth hormone secretion represents immaturity of the hypothalamus.

Corticosteroids. The chronic administration of large doses of corticosteroids suppresses the GH response to insulin hypoglycemia (Frantz and Rabkin, 1964; Hartog, *et al.*, 1964a; Friedman and Greenwood, 1967), but the response to arginine infusion was not suppressed in a series of patients treated with 200 mg/day of cortisone for 5 days (Merimee *et al.*, 1967). The effectiveness of corticosteroids as suppressors is related to the dosage used and to the duration of therapy. Long-term treatment with low doses of corticosteroids or the acute administration of large doses of corticosteroids are variably suppressive (Frantz and Rabkin, 1964), while intermittent therapy with corticosteroids has been associated with normal GH responsiveness (M. Martin *et al.*, 1968; Sadeghi-Nejad and Senior, 1968).

Patients with Cushing's syndrome are generally insensitive to the stimulatory effects of insulin (Frantz and Rabkin, 1964; Hartog *et al.*, 1964a; James *et al.*, 1968) or 2-deoxyglucose (Grasso *et al.*, 1968), but there is a report of a patient with Cushing's syndrome secondary to an adrenal adenoma with a very brisk GH response to insulin hypoglycemia (Cohen and Deller, 1966). Cessation of corticosteroid therapy is usually followed by restoration of GH responsiveness to normal (Greenwood and Landon, 1966b), but responsiveness may not return following adrenalectomy in patients with Cushing's syndrome secondary to bilateral adrenal hyperplasia (Greenwood and Landon, 1966b; James *et al.*, 1968). The persistent abnormality in GH secretion after reduction of plasma cortisol by adrenalectomy has led to the postulate that Cushing's disease secondary to adrenal hyperplasia is the result of a hypothalamic defect that also involves the GH secretory mechanism (James *et al.*, 1968). In contrast to the effects of corticosteroids, treatment with ACTH in therapeutically equivalent doses does not suppress, and may actually enhance, GH responsiveness to insulin hypoglycemia (Friedman and Greenwood, 1967).

Suppression of GH secretion may explain the growth retardation observed with chronic corticosteroid therapy of children. On the other hand, ACTH therapy, which does not suppress GH secretion, likewise does not suppress growth (Friedman and Greenwood, 1967). The existence of corticosteroid suppression of GH secretion has been challenged in the report of a study of asthmatic children, (Morris *et al.*, 1968a), and emphasis has been placed instead on peripheral antagonism by corticosteroids to GH as a cause of growth retardation (Morris *et al.*, 1968b). Peripheral antagonism as a mechanism for growth retardation is a reasonable contributing factor, but the authors' interpretation of the data on GH suppression by corticosteroids is open to question. Although they report that the mean GH levels with stimulation were similar in the corticosteroid and control groups, the distribution of values was different. In the normal group only 2 of 22 subjects had peaks of GH less than 18 mug/ml, whereas 11 of 23 corticosteroid-treated subjects failed to reach 18 mug/ml with insulin stimulation.

Patients with Addison's disease have been reported to have GH responses to insulin hypoglycemia which are higher (Luft, 1965) and particularly more sustained (Greenwood, 1966a; Wegienka *et al.*, 1967) than normal. The response to 2-deoxyglucose also may be more sustained (Grasso *et al.*, 1968). The prolonged elevation of GH in Addisonian patients may reflect absence of suppression by plasma cortisol or by free fatty acids which are poorly mobilized in these subjects (Grasso *et al.*, 1968).

Progestational Agents. When given in a high dose, medroxy-progesterone acetate can suppress the GH rise induced by insulin and possibly by arginine (Simon *et al.*, 1967). The suppression may be related in some way to the suppression of gonadotropin secretion, with "overlap" suppression of other pituitary functions.

GH Feedback. Although experiments on animals indicate that elevated levels of plasma GH exert a negative feedback on pituitary secretion of GH (see Chapter 6), there is little evidence for such an effect in humans. It has been reported, however, that individuals with elevated basal levels of hormones respond submaximally to stimuli (Marks *et al.*, 1965; Landon *et al.*, 1966; Green *et al.*, 1967; Frohman *et al.*, 1967b; Kaplan *et al.*, 1968). These data are compatible with the thesis that GH levels do exert a suppressive effect on the pituitary or hypothalamus in man.

Emotional Deprivation. Decreased secretion of GH in response to stimuli has been reported by several investigators in children with growth retardation associated with emotional deprivation. Such GH abnormalities were found in 6 of 10 children tested in one series (Powell *et al.*, 1967) and 2 of 9 in another (Kaplan *et al.*, 1968). Restoration of normality with respect to GH secretion occurs with change of environment. The importance of higher central nervous system centers in GH secretion is suggested by these data.

α-Adrenergic Blockade. Significant reduction of the GH response to insulin hypoglycemia can be accomplished by administration of phentolamine, an α-adrenergic blocking agent (Blackard and Heidingsfelder, 1968), although complete suppression is not achieved. β blockade with propanolol is associated with slightly augmented GH secretion. It also produces a more prolonged hypoglycemia and lower levels of plasma free fatty acids. No effect on resting GH levels was observed with the administration of either agent. These data suggest a modulating role for the sympathetic nervous system in the regulation of GH secretion.

Effects of Other Hormones

Estrogens. In the basal state, plasma GH levels are not much different in men and women, but women have higher levels of plasma GH than men in the ambulatory state (Unger *et al.*, 1965; Frantz and Rabkin, 1965; Garcia *et al.*, 1967). Multiple blood sampling during a 24-hour period under several different nutrient regimens revealed over-all plasma GH levels to be considerably higher in women than in men (Glick and Goldsmith, 1968). Women are considerably more responsive to arginine than are men (Merimee *et al.*, 1966a) and may be slightly more responsive to insulin (M. Parker *et al.*, 1967). The reported sex difference initially observed in response to vasopressin infusion (Greenwood and Landon, 1966a) has not been substantiated by further testing (Greenwood, 1967). An increase in GH levels in women has been reported during the postovulatory and premenstrual phases of the menstrual cycle (Frantz and Rabkin, 1965), and lower levels have been observed in postmenopausal women (Frantz and Rabkin, 1965).

The administration of estrogens to men increases their sensitivity to exercise (Frantz and Rabkin, 1965) and to arginine (Merimee *et al.*, 1966a). Similarly, the ingestion of oral contraceptives is associated with elevated levels of plasma GH (Garcia *et al.*, 1967; Spellacy *et al.*, 1967). The treatment of children with estrogens also increases their GH responsiveness to insulin and arginine (Kaplan *et al.*, 1968).

The explanation for the enhancing effect of estrogens on GH secretion is not readily apparent. The elevated levels are not the result of abnormalities in protein binding of GH, or in the degradation of plasma GH, nor is there evidence for the secretion of a non-GH immunologically cross-reacting material (Frantz and Rabkin, 1965). Substantial evidence does exist for a peripheral antagonism between estrogens and GH (McCullagh *et al.*, 1955; Mintz *et al.*, 1967; Josimovich *et al.*, 1967; Roth *et al.*, 1968; Schwartz *et al.*, 1967), and it may be that the net metabolic effect of estrogens and elevated levels of GH in women is equivalent to the lower levels of GH acting unopposed in men. Whatever mechanism senses the need for GH secretion might be stimulated to do so by estrogens because they, in effect, mimic the metabolic effects of a reduction of plasma GH.

Androgens. Few studies of the effect of androgens on GH secretion have been reported. In 3 patients, marked enhancement of the response to insulin was produced by testosterone therapy (Deller *et al.*, 1966; L. Martin *et al.*, 1968). A similar response was observed in 1 patient treated with human chorionic gonadotrophin (HCG) and in 1 subject after spontaneous sexual maturation (L. Martin *et al.*, 1968). Whether or not either the effect of estrogens or androgens on GH secretion plays any role in the stimulation of normal growth at puberty is purely speculative at this time.

Thyroid Hormones. Hypothyroidism is frequently, but not invariably, associated with decreased GH responsiveness to insulin or arginine (Sheikholislam *et al.*, 1966; Iwatsubo *et al.*, 1967; Brauman and Corvilain, 1968; MacGillivray *et al.*, 1968). The response is restored to normal with thyroid hormone therapy. Restoration of linear growth after thyroid administration may precede normalization of the GH response (MacGillivray *et al.*, 1968). Thyrotoxicosis may also be associated with dampened GH responsiveness, but short-term administration of tri-iodothyronine was not in the few cases tested (Burgess *et al.*, 1966).

Corticosteroids. The inhibitory effects of corticosteroids on GH secretion are discussed in detail above.

Epinephrine. With the first demonstration that acute hypoglycemia stimulates GH release the question arose as to the role of epinephrine in this release. The effect of epinephrine administration on GH secretion was tested with negative results (Roth *et al.*, 1963a). Other investigators, using small doses of epinephrine, have reported similarly negative results in humans (Rabinowitz *et al.*, 1966a; Schalch, 1967; Luft *et al.*, 1966), and, using higher doses, have obtained the same negative results in monkeys (Reichlin, 1968; Glick, 1968). With very high, clearly stressful, doses of epinephrine, significant elevations of plasma GH have been observed in monkeys (Meyer and Knobil, 1967; Gagliardino *et al.*, 1967).

It has been suggested (Blackard and Heidingsfelder, 1968) that cate-cholamines may stimulate GH secretion but that the stimulation might be masked by the hyperglycemia resulting from the administered cate-cholamines, and that the partial suppression of GH release produced by α-adrenergic blockade supports this thesis. However, an interesting case report of normal growth hormone responsiveness in a child with adrenal medullary failure (Hung and Migeon, 1968) argues against an important role for catecholamines in the usual GH response to insulin hypoglycemia.

Glucagon.   Glucagon administration has been reported to have no effect in normal subjects (Roth *et al.*, 1963a; Milner and Wright, 1967) but in a recent report was said to increase GH levels slightly in diabetic children (Drash *et al.*, 1968).

Effect of Age

The existence of augmented secretion of GH at times of most rapid growth during life is an attractive concept, but has thus far lacked firm experi-mental backing. The rapidity of turnover of secreted GH and the rapid fluctuations in plasma level render precise determinations of secretory rate difficult. Urinary GH levels have not been proved to parallel secretory rates in the judgment of most investigators (M. Parker *et al.*, 1962; Roth *et al.*, 1967; Girard and Greenwood, 1968) although some have reported a reasonable correlation between urinary GH and plasma levels of GH (Sakuma *et al.*, 1968). Therefore, no firm data exist on the secretory rate of GH at various ages, and estimates must be made on the basis of multiple plasma samples, an unsatisfactory alternative.

There is universal agreement that newborn infants have elevated levels of GH (Glick *et al.*, 1963; Cornblath *et al.*, 1965; Greenwood *et al.*, 1964a; Laron *et al.*, 1966a) and that GH levels during infancy, while lower than in the immediate newborn period, are higher than later in life. Results during childhood are not as clear, however. While some investi-gators report little difference between children and adults (Glick *et al.*, 1965; Irie and Sakuma, 1966), the results of other invesigators suggest that under varying situations the over-all level of plasma GH in children is higher than that in adults (Greenwood *et al.*, 1964b; Hunter and Rigal, 1966; Hunter *et al.*, 1967).

There is also a suggestion that GH levels might be somewhat lower prepuberally, corresponding to a period of relatively slow growth (Stimmler and Brown, 1967). However, Kaplan *et al.* (1968) could not confirm this finding.

In spite of GH levels throughout the day that may be higher than those of adults, the response of GH to insulin hypoglycemia and to arginine is less in children than in adults. (Kaplan *et al.*, 1968; Wolter *et al.*, 1969; Morris *et al.*, 1968a). While it is conceivable that the attenuated response to insulin may reflect the decreased response to stimuli observed when the initial level is high, it is more likely that the onset of puberty with attendant secretion of gonadal hormones enhances the response to insulin hypoglycemia and to arginine.

Plasma GH levels were measured in fetal plasma and found to be elevated as early as day 71 of gestation (Kaplan and Grumbach, 1967). The plasma GH of 3 anencephalic infants was in the low normal range in one series (Kaplan and Grumbach, 1967) and was very low in 2 other cases (Laron *et al.*, 1966a).

In the aged the GH response to insulin hypoglycemia is present but somewhat less than it is earlier in life (Laron *et al.*, 1966b).

GH and Growth

It has been suspected for many years that GH is not essential for growth at all periods of growth and development. The normal birth weight of hypopituitary and anencephalic infants suggests that intra-uterine growth is not GH-dependent. Confirmation of this view has come from studies of families with hereditary isolated GH deficiency. Infants with this defect may be normal in size at birth (Rimoin *et al.*, 1966).

That GH is essential for growth in childhood and adolescence seems well established. The good correlation between low plasma GH levels on stimulation, poor growth, and a good response to GH administration seems in full accord with the role of GH in normal growth. However, there have recently been a number of case reports that raise questions about the relationship. First there was the case report of gigantism with onset at age 17 in the presence of generalized hypopituitarism (Goldman *et al.*, 1963). No assays for GH were performed in this subject, and the authors assumed that plasma GH might be elevated. Similar cases were subsequently reported (Sarver *et al.*, 1964), again without measurement of plasma GH. However, two cases have now been reported in which there was no measurable plasma GH even after insulin hypoglycemia (Zimmerman *et al.*, 1967). This suggested the paradox of excessive growth in the absence of GH, but GH had not been measured during the period of rapid growth, and it conceivably could have been present at that time. Two groups of investigators have now reported several children with tumors of the pituitary region who had restoration of normal growth or supra-normal growth following removal of the tumors, in spite of unmeasurable levels of plasma GH even after stimulation (Holmes *et al.*, 1967; Kenny *et al.*, 1968). Unless it is postulated that GH levels below the threshold of measurement by highly sensitive immunoassays are adequate to support normal growth, one is led to conclude that normal childhood growth is possible under certain circumstances in the absence of GH.

The role of the acute secretion of GH over short-term periods or of the patterns of GH secretion in normal growth are unclear. It is interesting that GH, a substance with a half-life in the plasma of about ½ hour, should be effective in stimulating normal growth when given several times weekly.

Because of the conceptual difficulty of assigning so many different, and perhaps incompatible, roles to one hormone, the concept that GH might really be two hormones was recently revived (Levine and Luft, 1964). One of the two hormones was said to be the "true" growth hormone, and the other, it was suggested, affected lipid metabolism and was subject to acute fluctuations. It is of interest to note that a group of investigators has recently reported successful separation of GH into two such hormones (Trygstad and Fass, 1968). However, their prelimi-nary report suggests that the hormone with the most potent nitrogen-retaining effects was the one that fluctuated acutely in response to stimuli (Norman and Turter, 1968).

Hypothalamic Control of GH Secretion

It is now generally accepted that GH secretion is under the control of the hypothalamus. There have been several lines of evidence supporting this control mechanism in primates. An individual with the stalk of the pituitary gland sectioned was unable to respond to normal stimuli regu-lating GH secretion (Roth *et al.*, 1963a), and lesions of the hypothalamus in monkeys are associated with decreased GH responsiveness to various stimuli (Abrams *et al.*, 1966). Disease of the hypothalamus is often asso-ciated with diminished GH secretion (Rabkin and Frantz, 1966; Landon *et al.*, 1966; Krieger *et al.*, 1968), and occasionally with paradoxic hyper-secretion of GH in response to glucose (Beck *et al.*, 1966).

Sheep hypothalamic extracts stimulated GH release in monkeys even in the presence of hyperglycemia (Garcia and Geschwind, 1966), and crude extracts of porcine, ovine, and human median eminence were also effective in monkeys (Meyer and Knobil, 1968). However, Meyer and Knobil were not able to reproduce the results in monkeys using purified bovine or porcine growth hormone releasing factor (GRF). Until GRF is clearly identified and its structure determined conclusions regarding its effectiveness or lack of effectiveness must be kept in abeyance.

A variety of sedatives and tranquilizers are ineffective in blocking GH release following insulin hypoglycemia in man (Takahashi et al., 1967a). Chlorpromazine was similarly ineffective in the monkey (Glick, 1968). The peak of GH occurring with the onset of deep sleep is not suppressible by phenobarbital or chlorpromazine (Takahashi et al., 1967b). In monkeys, a combination of morphine and pentobarbital may be effective in suppressing release of GH under certain conditions (Knobil and Meyer, 1968).

GH Secretion in Various Clinical States

Hypersecretion of GH

The syndromes associated with hypersecretion of GH, acromegaly and gigantism, are readily diagnosed by radioimmunoassay. While GH levels as high as in acromegaly can be observed in normal individuals under appropriate stimulation, failure to suppress GH levels upon glucose administration is characteristic of acromegaly (Beck et al., 1965; Glick et al., 1965; Hartog et al., 1964b; Irie and Sakuma, 1966; Boden et al., 1968). Acromegalic subjects respond variably to insulin hypoglycemia or to 2-deoxy-D-glucose (Glick et al., 1965; Beck et al., 1965; Wegienka et al., 1967).

Many patients have persistently elevated GH levels after treatment with conventional X-ray therapy (Glick et al., 1965), although significant falls of plasma GH from pretherapy values do occur (Beck et al., 1965). The best results with conventional X-ray therapy have recently been reported in a careful study in which irradiation lowered plasma GH to about 60 per cent of pretreatment values. A few patients had a return of plasma GH to normal (Roth et al., 1968). The results with heavy particle irradiation have been better (Linfoot and Greenwood, 1965; Kjellberg et al., 1968), and the same has generally been true with yttrium implantation (Greenwood et al., 1965; Hartog et al., 1964b; Kaufman et al., 1966; Horwith et al.,1967). Total hypophysectomy produced excellent results. with 17 of 18 patients achieving normal levels in the largest series reported to date (Horwith et al., 1967). Very promising preliminary results have been reported using cryohypophysectomy (Lazarus *et al.*, 1966; Rand, 1966). This procedure seems to be more rapidly and consistently effective than X-ray therapy, heavy particle irradiation or yttrium implantation, and yet it does no produce the mortality and morbidity of surgical hypophysectomy. The results are fragmentary, however, and many more reports are needed for proper evaluation.

Hyposecretion of GH

Because low levels of GH are often present normally in the unstimulated state, a number of provocative procedures have been used for the diagnosis of hypopituitarism. The first of these was the insulin tolerance test (Roth *et al.*, 1963a), which has achieved wide usage and which remains the standard to which other procedures are compared. Arginine infusions have proved as effective in children, and they are safe and less discomforting (M. Parker *et al.*, 1967; Raiti *et al.*, 1967; Goodman *et al.*, 1968).

Some normal individuals will respond to one and not another of these tests without obvious cause (Raiti *et al.*, 1967; M. Parker *et al.*, 1967; Goodman *et al.*, 1968). It is therefore recommended that a diagnosis of hypopituitarism be based on a diminished secretion of GH in response to both tests. In an effort to simplify the test procedures, screening tests using multiple fasting blood samples (Frohman *et al.*, 1967b) or samples taken 3 to 4 hours after the ingestion of glucose (Hunter *et al.*, 1967; Stimmler *et al.*, 1967; Chen *et al.*, 1968) have been recommended. The separation between normal and abnormal is not always distinct, and there are individuals who cannot be satisfactorily classified (Kaplan *et al.*, 1968). Precise criteria for normality vary somewhat between different laboratories. In general, those patients who have decreased GH responses to stimulation tests respond best to administered GH (Melvin *et al.*, 1967; Kaplan *et al.*, 1968). A therapeutic trial of GH may be indicated in doubtful cases (Kaplan *et al.*, 1968).

In hypopituitarism and in hypothalamic disorders secretion of GH is depressed before that of the gonadotropins, thyrotropin, or ACTH (Landon *et al.*, 1966; Rabkin and Frantz, 1966; Frohman *et al.*, 1967a; Kohler *et al.*, 1967). However, in a small group of patients with hypothalamic disease, abnormalities of the circadian adrenal steroid rhythm were more common than disordered GH secretion (Krieger *et al.*, 1968).

A syndrome of isolated GH deficiency with abnormal growth and occasional symptomatic hypoglycemia has been described (Wilber and Odell, 1965; Rimoin *et al.*, 1966; Goodman *et al.*, 1968). Patients with this disorder, like those with generalized hypopituitarism, respond well to therapy with GH.

Diabetes Mellitus

The possible relationship between excessive secretion of GH and diabetes mellitus has intrigued investigators for several decades. Measurement of plasma GH in diabetic subjects does not support the hypothesis that diabetes is a disorder of GH secretion. Fasting levels of GH are relatively normal in diabetics (Glick et al., 1965), and their response to glucose tolerance testing (Yalow et al., 1965; Rosselin et al., 1967b) and to arginine infusion is normal (Rosselin et al., 1967b). Newborn infants of diabetic mothers either have normal levels of plasma GH or have lower levels than do infants of normal mothers (Roth et al., 1967; Laron et al., 1967). The early report of failure of diabetics to respond to arginine with a rise in GH (Merimee et al., 1966b) was probably due to the obesity of the group of maturity-onset diabetics studied (M. Parker et al., 1967; Burday et al., 1968). The effects of obesity on GH secretion are discussed below. Juvenile diabetics have been reported to have a normal GH response to glucose, tolbutamide, and arginine (M. Parker et al., 1968; Baker et al., 1967). One group of investigators has reported higher GH levels after arginine in juvenile diabetics than in normal controls (Drash et al., 1968), but the levels they reported for controls are significantly less than those of other investigators. Diabetics with retinopathy had no consistent abnormality of GH secretion, and improvement in the retinopathy following pituitary stalk secretion did not correlate well with alterations in GH levels (Powell et al., 1966). On the other hand, possibly because of their fluctuating blood sugars, diabetics may have elevated levels of GH more often than normal subjects (Glick et al., 1965; Powell et al., 1966; Service et al., 1968), particularly if the disease is under poor control.

An interesting observation has been made about the responsiveness of diabetics to falls in blood sugar late in the course of a glucose tolerance test. It was reported that in normal subjects plasma GH did not rise until the blood sugar had fallen below the initial level, whereas the diabetics had a rise in plasma GH while blood glucose was still above the fasting level (Hunter et al., 1966b). Confirmation of these data has not been published, and indeed others have reported that, in normal subjects, a fall in blood glucose from postabsorptive peaks without a fall below the fasting level can stimulate GH secretion (Roth et al., 1963b; Irie et al., 1967a; Hunter et al., 1968).

Several investigators have now reported that prediabetics, with glucose tolerance curves indistinguishable from normal controls, have a higher GH rebound than normals several hours after glucose ingestion (Unger et al., 1964; Levin and Recant, 1967; Boden et al., 1968). The consistency of the finding by three independent groups of investigators suggests that it is valid. On the other hand, there is no evidence that this apparent hypersecretion of GH is of clinical significance, or that it plays a significant role in the etiology of diabetes. These subjects have a significantly decreased plasma insulin level and as a result there may be significant, as yet undefined differences in energy metabolism, which may secondarily enhance GH secretion.

Obesity

Obese individuals respond sluggishly and variably to many of the stimuli which cause GH secretion. Prolonged fasting (Roth et al., 1963b; Beck et al., 1964; Schwarz et al., 1966; Henneman, 1967) insulin hypoglycemia (Beck et al., 1964; Lessof et al., 1966; Henneman, 1967), arginine infusion (Merimee et al., 1965; Copinschi et al., 1967b); Tchobroutsky et al., 1969a), 2 deoxy-D-glucose infusion (Wegienka et al., 1967), exercise (Lawrence, 1966), the late post-glucose period (Yalow et al., 1965; Tchobroutsky et al., 1969a), and tolbutamide administration (Lessof et al., 1966) are all associated with subnormal GH responses in obese individuals. Similarly, the spontaneous peaks of GH that occur during the night are diminished in obese subjects (Hunter et al., 1966a; Quabbe et al., 1966; Quabbe and Helge, 1967). Nevertheless there is no absolute deficiency in GH secretion in obesity, and GH secretion can be elicited by appropriately intense stimuli (Roth et al., 1963b; Yalow et al., 1965; Quabbe and Helge, 1967). There is a rough correlation between the degree of obesity and the magnitude of depression of GH secretion (Lessof et al., 1966). Few data are available concerning repeated testing of obese individuals after reduction of weight to the normal range; however, in 7 of 9 patients tested, significant weight reduction was associated with a return of GH secretion toward normal (Lessof et al., 1966).

We have no explanation for the sluggish response of the obese individual to stimuli that increase GH secretion. Whatever the role ascribed to increased GH secretion during fasting, the obese individual seems to suffer no ill effects as a result of deficient secretion of GH. Fat mobilization and nitrogen sparing would appear to proceed unimpaired.

Pregnancy and Lactation

During pregnancy the placenta secretes a hormone into the maternal circulation which is immunologically similar to but not identical with GH. This material has been called human placental lactogen or chorionic growth hormone—prolactin. It is present in enormous concentrations relative to GH levels during pregnancy and makes the measurement of GH itself difficult.

Although GH secretion does occur during pregnancy, the responsiveness to insulin has been reported to be less than that present in the nonpregnant state (Spellacy, 1967; Yen et al., 1967; Mintz et al., 1968). The responsiveness to arginine is said to be unimpaired (Tyson et al., 1968). In normal subjects there is a gradual return to normal insulin responsiveness in the first few postpartum weeks (Spellacy, 1967; Mintz et al., 1968); in 5 diabetic mothers the responsiveness returned considerably sooner (Mintz et al., 1968). The abnormal responses during pregnancy may reflect suppression of pituitary secretion of GH because of the elevated growth hormone-like human placental lactogen, or may be the result of any of a number of other hormonal and metabolic changes that occur during pregnancy.

GH levels are normally low during lactation (Garcia et al., 1967; Roth et al., 1968), at a time when bioassays indicate high prolactin levels (Roth et al., 1968), and are normal in patients with galactorrhea (Spellacy et al., 1968). Conversely, patients with acromegaly have high GH levels and low prolactin levels (Roth et al., 1968). The normal lactation observed in women with an isolated deficiency of GH (Rimoin et al., 1967a), provides further evidence that GH plays little role in lactation in humans.

Miscellaneous States

GH secretion has been studied in a variety of endocrine, genetic, and other general medical conditions. Gonadal dysgenesis has been studied by a number of investigators. The GH response to insulin hypoglycemia is uniformly normal (Greenwood, 1966b; Lindsten et al., 1967; Pfeiffer and Melani, 1967; Donaldson et al., 1968; Kaplan et al., 1968) but one group has reported that there is a paradoxical rise of GH in response to the intravenous administration of glucose (Lindsten et al., 1967). Unfortunately, the fasting levels of GH were unusually high because of an inadequate rest period before starting the infusion, and these results need to be confirmed under more ideal conditions. Estrogen treatment raises basal GH levels (Lindsten et al., 1967) and enhances the normal rise following insulin hypoglycemia (Kaplan et al., 1968) as well as the paradoxic rise after glucose (Lindsten et al., 1967), in these patients.

In both the pygmy (Rimoin et al., 1967b) and the cerebral giant (Hook and Reynolds, 1967; Stephenson et al., 1968), GH responsiveness is normal. A fascinating familial type of growth retardation, with elevated GH levels, a metabolic pattern of GH deficiency, and normal responsiveness to the administration of exogenous GH has been reported (Laron *et al.*, 1966c; Laron and Pertzlan, 1967). The syndrome has been attributed to a GH molecule immunologically similar to normal GH but biologically inactive. One similar case was reported by another group (Rimoin *et al.*, 1967b). Reports of additional cases are eagerly awaited.

Renal disease is not generally associated with abnormal levels of GH, but glucose may fail to suppress (Horton *et al.*, 1967; Tchobroutsky *et al.*, 1969b) or may even produce a paradoxical rise in GH levels (Samaan *et al.*, 1966a). Patients with liver disease have been reported to have elevated levels of GH associated with clinical hyperestrogenism, and the levels did not fall normally with glucose administration (Hernandez *et al.*, 1968). In women with breast cancer, two groups of investigators have reported normal responsiveness to insulin, but poor suppressibility by glucose with occasional paradoxic responses (Samaan *et al.*, 1966b; Greenwood *et al.*, 1969). Similar paradoxic responses to glucose were reported in acute intermittent porphyria (Perlroth *et al.*, 1967).

Steiner *et al.*, (1968) have reported a single patient with pulmonary osteoarthropathy, a lung tumor, and high levels of plasma GH who had a fall in GH levels and relief of his arthropathy with removal of the tumor. This suggests ectopic secretion of GH by the tumor, but, unfortunately, no measurements were made of the tumor content of GH or arteriovenous plasma GH differences across the tumor.

Studies in Nonprimates

Assay Problems

The application of radioimmunoassay to nonprimate GH, in particular to rat GH, has resulted in an array of disturbing and unexplained contradictory data. It had been hoped that the immunoassay and bioassay data would agree and that both would confirm some of the physiologic data obtained using the radioimmunoassay for primate GH. The resolution of the contradictory data is not at hand and a hard rethinking of each of the systems is clearly in order. The specificity and statistical analysis of the rat tibia assay, which has been the standard bioassay, has recently been questioned (Rodger *et al.*, 1967). Similarly, the assumption that the radioimmunoassay for rat GH is specific with regard to biological activitiy is by no means beyond question. For each new immunoassay, validation of results must be proved by comparison with "known" data. Fortunately with human GH there are a number of clinical disease states which aid in the validation of the immunoassay, but these aids do not exist for rat GH. In spite of careful studies of specificity by each group reporting rat GH radioimmunoassay data, (Schalch and Reichlin, 1966; Birge *et al.*, 1967a; Garcia and Geschwind, 1968), we cannot dismiss the possibility that the radioimmunoassay is not measuring what it purports to measure.

Bioassay Data

In general, the investigators using bioassay methods for GH have used pituitary depletion as an index of increased secretion of GH, although the same data might be interpreted as indicative of decreased synthesis of GH in the pituitary. With many of the stimuli evaluated, the reported depletion of the pituitary is so great that one should be able to detect the resulant increase in plasma GH even by bioassay. Concomitant measurement of plasma GH as well as pituitary GH in the rat by bioassay has recently been reported for the first time after the administration of growth hormone releasing factor (GRF), and levels of 4 μg/ml were observed in the peripheral blood (Sawano *et al.*, 1968). This level is perhaps 50 times as high as the highest level observed using immunoassay (Schalch and Reichlin, 1966; Garcia and Geschwind, 1968), and the discrepancy cries out for resolution.

It has been reported that insulin-induced hypoglycemia depletes hypothalamic GRF, increases plasma GRF (Katz *et al.*, 1967), and depletes pituitary GH (Müller *et al.*, 1967a). The insulin-induced depletion could be suppressed by reserpine, but the depletion induced by GRF could not be similarly suppressed (Müller *et al.*, 1967a). Subsequent studies by the same authors suggested that the effect of reserpine was due to its catecholamine-depleting action and that its effect could be prevented by a monoamine oxidase inhibitor (Müller *et al.*, 1967b). The authors suggested that brain amines might play a role as hypothalamic neurohumoral transmitters. On the other hand, some monoamine oxidase inhibitors have been reported to suppress GH production (Zor *et al.*, 1967).

Starvation depletes pituitary GH (Friedman and Reichlin, 1965) and GRF (Meites, 1964), but whereas the former group of investigators attributed the depletion to increased secretion of GH, Meites interpreted his results as suggesting decreased synthesis and release of GH. This divergence in interpretation illustrates the problem that arises when depletion data are the only ones available.

Several varieties of stress, including cold, high doses of vasopressin, epinephrine and urecholine, have been reported to deplete pituitary GH, but the administration of histamine or of formalin or laparotomy did not do so (Müller *et al.*, 1967a). Similarly, McCann's group found that a number of stresses "altered GH content," but the patterns were not clearly consistent (Krulich and McCann, 1966). Suckling has recently been reported to deplete pituitary GH (Grosvenor et al., 1968).

Extracts of the hypothalamus have been purified and examined carefully in order to isolate the specific GRF. The evidence is fairly strong for the existence of such a factor, which not only causes the secretion of GH but also its synthesis (Schally et al., 1968a). Progress in this area, and some of the controversial aspects of the chemistry of the factor, have recently been reviewed (Guillemin, 1967; Schally et al., 1968b). It has also been suggested that a GH inhibitory factor exists in the hypothalamus (Krulich et al., 1967).

Older rats are less sensitive to the injection of GRF (Krulich et al., 1965; Pecile et al., 1965) and their hypothalami contain considerably decreased amounts of GRF (Pecile et al., 1965). Yet transplanted pituitary glands from older animals can sustain growth as well as those from younger animals (Pecile et al., 1966).

Animals treated with GH or with corticosteroids do not release GH well when stimulated by insulin hypoglycemia (Müller and Pecile, 1966; Pecile and Müller, 1966b). On the basis of experimental observations on the effect of each of these suppressors on GRF and GH, Müller et al. (1967c) suggested that GH acts on the pituitary and that corticosteroids exert their effect on the hypothalamus.

Immunoassay Studies in the Rat and Mouse

The application of radioimmunoassay to the study of rat GH secretion has in certain cases confirmed bioassay data, but for the most part it has directly contradicted data that have been repeatedly observed with bioassay techniques. Particularly distressing has been the striking failure to observe either pituitary depletion of GH or increased plasma GH after insulin hypoglycemia (Daughaday et al., 1968; Garcia and Geschwind, 1968; Schalch and Reichlin, 1968). Indeed, pituitary GH has actually been reported in increase (Daughaday et al., 1968) and plasma GH may fall (Schalch and Reichlin, 1968). Similarly disturbing have been the findings with exposure to cold, which produces very marked depletion of bioassayable GH (Müller et al., 1967b) but singularly unimpressive changes when measured by radioimmunoassay. As mentioned earlier, the effects of cold on plasma levels of GH in humans and monkeys have also been unimpressive. Hypothalamic extracts have not induced a rise in immunoassayable plasma GH in the rat (Garcia and Geschwind, 1968; Schalch and Reichlin, 1968). Fasting was associated with a rise in plasma GH and a fall in pituitary GH in mice (Garcia and Geschwind,

1968), and GH given exogenously or supplied by a GH-producing tumor did suppress GH secretion by the pituitary gland (Daughaday *et al.*, 1968). Pituitary GH concentrations were observed to be increased during the first week of life and during puberty, were depressed by estrogens and by hypothyroidism, and were increased by androgens (Daughaday *et al.*, 1968). In contrast to the in vivo studies of Müller *et al.* (1967c), which suggested that suppression of GH secretion by corticosteroids takes place in the hypothalamus, in vitro observations using radioimmuno-assay demonstrated a direct effect on hemipituitaries in tissue culture (Birge *et al.*, 1967b). Dwarf mice have been show to lack GH in the pituitary or the plasma by radioimmunoassay (Garcia and Geschwind, 1968), confirming results obtained by biochemical and biological tests (Lewis *et al.*, 1965). Recently, hypothalamic lesions have been reported to decrease pituitary and plasma GH content in rats (Frohman and Bernardis, 1968). Animals with such lesions should be useful in research on GH secretion.

Immunoassay Studies in Other Nonprimates

In rabbits, fasting was followed by an elevation of plasma GH, and a small rise occurred with insulin hypoglycemia, but no rise followed the infusion of arginine, the administration of hypothalamic extracts, or the induction of massive bleeding (Garcia and Geschwind, 1968). In sheep there was no rise in plasma GH with fasting, but there was a rise with exposure to cold, with arginine infusion, and with the administration sheep median eminence extracts (Machlin *et al.*, 1968a). In pigs there was a rise of plasma GH with insulin hypoglycemia, with fasting, with rapid falls in blood glucose, and in response to stress. However, the responses were sluggish and, even in nonobese pigs, resembled those observed in human obesity (Machlin *et al.*, 1968b). Dwarf pigs had normal GH secretion (Machlin *et al.*, 1968b).

Summary

Growth hormone secretion is subject to rapid fluctuations in response to stimulation. Several of the reported stimuli are associated with an absolute, relative, actual, or impending shortage of carbohydrate substrate adequate to meet bodily energy requirements. Stresses of several kinds also stimulate GH secretion acutely. A controversy exists over whether or not the stimuli, which have in common a shortage of carbohydrate, operate specifically or merely as stressors. This reviewer feels that they act as specific stimuli which call forth a response useful to the organism in combating potential glucose deficiency in the brain. The central nervous system, particularly the hypothalamus but probably also higher centers, regulates GH secretion and its responsiveness, as suggested by the rise of plasma GH with deep sleep and the suppression observed in emotionally deprived children.

A number of other stimuli have been described, including amino acid infusion, protein ingestion, protein deprivation, and falling free fatty acid levels, but their significance in the over-all pattern of control of GH release is not as yet clear.

Glucose is a direct, immediate suppressor of GH secretion, presumably by its action on the hypothalamus. Other suppressors include hormonal agents and α-adrenergic blocking agents. Corticosteroids in large doses are particularly effective suppressors of GH secretion. Hypersecretion and hyposecretion of several endocrine glands modify GH secretion, but none of these glands seems to play a major regulatory role in pituitary GH secretion.

The evidence for acute secretion of GH has not diminished the importance of GH in its classic role as controller of growth. The precise relationship between the acute secretion of GH and the regulation of growth is not clear at present. However, except for some recently described exceptions, failure of GH to respond to stimuli is associated with growth retardation.

Except for the well-recognized syndromes of general and selective hypopituitarism and acromegaly, no evidence exists for any disease state caused by hyposecretion or hypersecretion of GH. However, abnormalities of GH secretion have been reported in a host of medical conditions, with no obvious consequences.

Whereas monkey GH secretion seems to be regulated by the same factors regulating human GH secretion, there have been serious discrepancies observed using a radioimmunoassay for rat GH. These discrepancies have been further compounded by contradictions between bioassay data and radioimmunoassay data. These differences need to be resolved before the data can be interpreted.

References

Abrams, R. L., M. L. Parker ,S. Blanco, S. Reichlin, and W. H. Daughaday (1966). Hypothalamic regulation of growth hormone secretion. *Endocrinology 78*, 605-13.

Abramson, E. A., R. A. Arky, and K. A. Woeber (1966). Effects of propranolol on the hormonal and metabolic responses to insulin-induced hypoglycemia. *Lancet ii*, 1386-88.

Arky, R. A., and N. Freinkel (1964). The response of plasma human growth hormone to insulin and ethanol-induced hypoglycemia in two patients with "isolated adrenocorticotropic defect." *Metabolism 13*, 547-50.

Baker, L. A., A. Root, R. Kay, and N. Haque (1967). Studies on metabolic homeostasis in juvenile diabetes mellitus. I. Role of growth hormone. *Proc. Soc. Ped. Res., 37th Ann. Mtg.*, April 28-29, Atlantic City, p. 64 (Abstract).

Baum, D., C. C. Gale, and D. M. Dillard (1967). Hyperglycemia with deep hypothermia: the roles of growth hormone and insulin. *Excerpta Medica, Int. Cong. Ser. 142*, 49.

Baylis, M., F. Greenwood, V. James, J. J. Jenkins, J. Landon, V. Marks, and E. Samols (1968). An examination of the central mechanism postulated to control growth hormone secretion in man. *Proc. Int. Symp. Growth Hormone*, Milan, Italy, September 11-13, 1967, Excerpta Medica, Amsterdam, pp. 89-104.

Beck, P., J. H. T. Koumans, C. A. Winterling, M. F. Stein, W. H. Daughaday, and D. M. Kipnis (1964). Studies of insulin and growth hormone secretion in human obesity. *J. Lab. Clin. Med. 64*, 654-67.

Beck, P., D. S. Schalch, M. L. Parker, D. M. Kipnis, and W. H. Daughaday (1965). Correlative studies of growth hormone and insulin plasma concentrations with metabolic abnormalities in acromegaly. *J. Lab. Clin. Med. 66*, 366-79.

Beck, P., M. L. Parker, and W. H. Daughaday (1966). Paradoxical hypersecretion of growth hormone in response to glucose. *J. Clin. Endocrinol. Metab. 26*, 463-69.

Berg, G. R., R. D. Utiger, D. S. Schalch, and S. Reichlin (1966). Effect of central cooling in man on pituitary-thyroid function and growth hormone secretion. *J. Appl. Physiol. 21*, 1791-94.

Birge, C. A., G. T. Peake, I. K. Mariz, and W. H. Daughaday (1967a). Radioimmunoassayable growth hormone in the rat pituitary gland: effects of age, sex, and hormonal state. *Endocrinology 81*, 195-204.

Birge, C. A., G. T. Peake, I. K. Mariz, and W. H. Haughaday (1967b). Effects of cortisol and diethylstilbestrol on growth hormone release by rat pituitary in vitro. *Proc. Soc. Exp. Biol. Med. 126*, 342-45.

Blackard, W. G., and S. A. Heidingsfelder (1968). Adrenergic receptor control mechanism for growth hormone secretion. *J. Clin. Invest. 47*, 1407-14.

Blanco, S., D. S. Schalch, and S. Reichlin (1966). Control of growth hormone secretion by glucoreceptors in the hypothalamic-pituitary unit. *Fed. Proc. 25*, 191 (Abstract).

Boden, G., J. S. Soeldner, R. E. Gleason, and A. Marble (1968). Elevated serum human growth hormone and decreased serum insulin in prediabetic males following intravenous tolbutamide and glucose. *J. Clin. Invest. 47*, 729-39.

Brauman, H., and J. Corvilain (1968). Growth hormone response to hypoglycemia in myxedema. *J. Clin. Endocrinol. Metab. 28*, 301-4.

Brostoff, J., V. H .T. James, and J. Landon (1968). Plasma corticosteroid and growth hormone response to lysine vasopressin in man. *J. Clin. Endocrinol. Metab. 28*, 511-18.

Burday, S. Z., P. H. Fine, and D. S. Schalch (1968). Growth hormone secretion in response to arginine infusion in normal and diabetic subjects: relationship to blood glucose levels. *J. Lab Clin. Med. 71*, 897-911.

Burgess, J. A., B. R. Smith, and T. J. Merimee (1966). Growth hormone in thyrotoxicosis: effect of insulin-induced hypoglycemia. *J. Clin. Endocrinol. Metab. 26*, 1257-60.

Cahill, G. F., Jr., M. G. Herrera, A. P. Morgan, J. S. Soeldner, J. Steinke, P. L. Levy, G. A. Reichard, Jr., and D. M. Kipnis (1966). Hormone-fuel inter-relationships during fasting. *J. Clin. Invest. 45*, 1751-69.

Chakmakjian, Z. H., and J. E. Bethune (1968). Stimulation of growth hormone secretion in man. *Clin. Res. 16*, 146 (Abstract).

Chen, R., A. Drash, and F. Kenny (1968). The oral glucose tolerance test as a diagnostic screening test for growth hormone deficiency. *Proc. Soc. Ped. Res., 38th Ann. Mtg.*, May 3-4, 1968, Atlantic City, p. 88 (Abstract).

Cohen, R. J., and J. J. Deller (1966). Growth hormone studies in Cushing's syndrome. *Am. J. Med. Sci. 252*, 451-57.

Copinschi, G., M. Hartog, J. M. Earll, and R. J. Havel (1967a). Effect of various blood sampling procedures on serum levels of immunoreactive human growth hormone. *Metabolism 16*, 402-9.

Copinschi, G., L. C. Wegienka, S. Hane, and P. H. Forsham (1967b). Effect of arginine on serum levels of insulin and growth hormone in obese subjects. *Metabolism 16*, 485-91.

Cornblath, M., M. L. Parker, S. H. Reisner, A. E. Forbes, and W. H. Daughaday (1965). Secretion and metabolism of growth hormone in premature and full-term infants. *J. Clin. Endocrinol. Metab. 25*, 209-18.

Daughaday, W. H., and M. L. Parker (1965). Human pituitary growth hormone. *Ann. Rev. Med. 16*, 47-66.

Daughaday, W. H., G. T. Peake, C. A. Birge, and I. K. Mariz (1968). The influence of endocrine factors on the concentration of growth hormone in the rat pituitary. *Proc. Int. Symp. Growth Hormone*, Milan, Italy, September 11-13, 1967, Excerpta Medica, Amsterdam, pp. 238-52.

Deller, J. J., D. C. Plunket, P. H. Forsham (1966). Growth hormone studies in growth retardation: therapeutic response to administration of androgen. *Calif. Med. 104*, 359-62.

Donaldson, C. L., L. C. Wegienka, D. Miller, and P. H. Forsham (1968). Growth hormone studies in Turner's syndrome. *J. Clin. Endrocrinol. Metab. 28*, 383-85.

Drash, A., J. B. Field, L. Y. Garces, F. M. Kenny, D. Mintz, and A. M. Vasquez (1968). Endogenous insulin and growth hormone response in children with newly diagnosed diabetes mellitus. *Ped. Res. 2*, 94-102.

Frantz, A. G., and M. T. Rabkin (1964). Human growth hormone: Clinical measurement, response to hypoglycemia and suppression by corticosteroids. *New Eng. J. Med. 271*, 1375-81.

Frantz, A. G., and M. T. Rabkin (1965). Effects of estrogen and sex difference on secretion of human growth hormone. *J. Clin. Endocrinol. Metab. 25*, 1470-80.

Freychet, P., G. Rosselin, R. Assan, J. Dolais, G. Tchobroutsky, and M. Derot (1967). Non-elevated growth hormone and glucagon fasting plasma levels in twelve cases of spontaneous hypoglycemia: stimulation by arginine infusion. *Proc. 6th Cong. Int. Diabetes Fed.*, Stockholm, Sweden, July 30-August 4, 1967, Excerpta Medica, Amsterdam, Abst. #416.

Friedman, M., and F. C. Greenwood (1967). The effects of prolonged ACTH or corticosteroid therapy in children on growth and on pituitary-adrenal and pituitary function. In *The Investigation of Hypothalamic-Pituitary-Adrenal Function* (V. H. T. James and J. Langdon, eds.), pp. 249-70. Cambridge University Press, London.

Friedman, R. C., and S. Reichlin (1965). Growth hormone content of the pituitary gland of starved rats. *Endocrinology 76*, 787-88.

Frohman, L. A., and L. L. Bernardis (1968). Growth hormone and insulin levels in weanling rats with ventromedial hypothalamic lesions. *Endocrinology 82*, 1125-32.

Frohman, L. A., E. S. Horton, and H. E. Lebovitz (1967a). Growth hormone releasing action of a pseudomonas endotoxin (Piromen). *Metabolism 16*, 57-67.

Frohman, L. A., T. Aceto, Jr., and M. H. MacGillivray (1967b). Studies of growth hormone secretion in children: normal, hypopituitary and constitutionally delayed. *J. Clin. Endocrinol. 27*, 1409-17.

Gagliardino, J. J., and J. M. Martin (1967). Mechanism of growth hormone secretion. Program of the Forty-Ninth Meeting of the Endocrine Society, p. 74.

Gagliardino, J. J., J. D. Bailey, and J. M. Martin (1967). Effect of vasopressin on serum-levels of human growth hormone. *Lancet i*, 1357-58.

Garcia, J. F., and I. I. Geschwind (1966). Increase in plasma growth hormone level in the monkey following the administration of sheep hypothalamic extracts. *Nature 211*, 372-74.

Garcia, J. F., and I. I. Geschwind (1968). Investigation of growth hormone secretion in selected mammalian species. *Proc. Int. Symp. Growth Hormone*, Milan, Italy, September 11-13, 1967, Excerpta Medica, Amsterdam, pp. 267-91.

Garcia, J. F., J. A. Linfoot, E. Manougian, J. L. Born, and J. H. Lawrence (1967). Plasma growth hormone studies in normal individuals and acromegalic patients. *J. Clin. Endocrinol. Metab. 27*, 1395-1402.

Girard, J., and F. C. Greenwood (1968). The absence of intact growth hormone in urine as judged by radioimmunoassay. *J. Endocrinol. 40*, 493-503.

Glick, S. M. (1968). Normal and abnormal secretion of growth hormone. *Ann. N.Y. Acad. Sci. 148*, 471-87.

Glick, S. M., and S. Goldsmith (1968). Secretion of human growth hormone. *Int. Symp. Growth Hormone*, Milan, Italy, September 11-13, 1967, Excerpta Medica, Amsterdam, pp. 84-88.

Glick, S. M., J. Roth, R. S. Yalow, and S. A. Berson (1963). Immunoassay of human growth hormone in plasma. *Nature 199*, 784-87.

Glick, S. M., J. Roth, R. S. Yalow, and S. A. Berson (1965). The regulation of growth hormone secretion. *Rec. Prog. Horm. Res. 21*, 241-83.

Goldman, J. K., G. F. Cahill, and G. W. Thorn (1963). Gigantism with hypopituitarism. *Am. J. Med. 34*, 407-16.

Goodman, H. G., M. M. Grumbach, and S. L. Kaplan (1968). Growth and growth hormone. II. A comparison of isolated growth hormone deficiency and multiple pituitary hormone deficiencies in 35 patients with idiopathic hypopituitary dwarfism. *New Eng. J. Med. 278*, 57-68.

Grasso, S. G., J. H. Karam, L. C. Wegienka, G. M. Grodsky, and P. H. Forsham (1968). Use of 2-deoxy-D-glucose in studying the mechanism of lipid mobilization. *J. Clin. Endocrinol. Metab. 28*, 535-42.

Green, O. C., R. Fefferman, S. Nair (1967). Plasma growth hormone levels in children with cystic fibrosis and short stature: unresponsiveness to hypoglycemia. *J. Clin. Endocrinol. Metab. 27*, 1059-61.

Greenwood, F. C. (1966a). Biological problems regarding hormonal surgery. *Int. Colloq. Endocrine Surg. Cancer*, Lyon, France, May 5-7.

Greenwood, F. C. (1966b). The clinical and physiological application of growth hormone assays. In *Immunological Properties of Protein Hormones* (F. Polvani and P. G. Crosignani, eds.), pp. 123-31, Academic Press, New York.

Greenwood, F. C. (1967). Growth hormone. In *Hormones in Blood* (C. H. Gray and A. L. Bacharach, eds.), pp. 195-231. Academic Press, London.

Greenwood, F. C., and J. Landon (1966a). Growth hormone secretion in response to stress in man. *Nature 210*, 540-41.

Greenwood, F. C., and J. Landon (1966b). Assessment of hypothalamic pituitary function in endocrine disease. *J. Clin. Path. 19*, 284-92.

Greenwood, F. C., W. M. Hunter, and A. Klopper (1964a). Assay of human growth hormone in pregnancy at parturition and in lactation. *Brit. Med. J. i*, 22-24.

Greenwood, F. C., W. M. Hunter, and V. J. Marrian (1964b). Growth hormone levels in children and adolescents. *Brit. Med. J. i*, 25-26.

Greenwood, F. C., H. J. Stewart, A. P. M. Forrest, and R. G. Wood (1965). Plasma growth hormone levels in untreated acromegaly and after radioactive implants into the pituitary. *Lancet ii*, 555-58.

Greenwood, F. C., J. Landon, and T. C. B. Stamp (1966). The plasma sugar, free fatty acid, cortisol, and growth hormone response to insulin. I. In control subjects. *J. Clin. Invest. 45*, 429-36.

Greenwood, F. C., V. H. T. James, B. F. Meggitt, J. D. Miller, and P. H. Taylor (1969). Pituitary function in breast cancer. Submitted for publication.

Grosvenor, C. E., L. Krulich, and S. M. McCann (1968). Depletion of pituitary concentration of growth hormone as a result of suckling in the lactating rat. *Endocrinology 82*, 617-19.

Guillemin, R. (1967). The adenohypophysis and its hypothalamic control. *Ann. Rev. Physiol. 29*, 313-48.

Hadden, D. R. (1967). The effect of growth hormone during protein deficiency in rats, and during subsequent refeeding. *Excerpta Medica, Int. Cong.*, Ser. *142*, 36.

Hartog, M., M. A. Gaafar, and R. Fraser (1964a). Effect of corticosteroids on serum growth hormone. *Lancet ii*, 376-78.

Hartog, M., M. A. Gaafar, B. Meisser, and R. Fraser (1964b). Immunoassay of serum growth hormone in acromegalic patients. *Brit. Med. J. ii*, 1229-32.

Hartog, M., R. J. Havel, G. Copinschi, J. M. Earll, and B. C. Ritchie (1967). The relationship between changes in serum levels of growth hormone and mobilisation of fat during exercise in man. *Quart. J. Exp. Physiol. 52*, 86-96.

Henneman, P. H. (1967). Plasma growth hormone during prolonged starvation in obesity. *Excerpta Medica, Int. Cong.*, Ser. *142*, 52.

Hernandez, A., E. Zorilla, and H. Gershberg (1968). Decreased insulin production, elevated growth hormone levels, and glucose intolerance in liver disease. *Diabetes 17*, 327 (Abstract).

Holmes, L. B., A. C. Frantz, J. S. Soeldner, and J. D. Crawford (1967). Growth in the absence of growth hormone. *Proc. Soc. Ped. Res.* April 28-29, Atlantic City, p. 68 (Abstract).

Honda, Y. (1967). Paper presented at the 16th Annual Meeting of the Japan EEG Society, October 18, 1967.

Hook, E. B., and J. W. Reynolds (1967). Cerebral gigantism: endocrinological and clinical observations of six patients including a congenital giant, concordant monozygotic twins, and a child who achieved adult gigantic size. *J. Pediat. 70*, 900-914.

Horton, E. S., C. Johnson, and H. E. Lebovitz (1967). Insulin and growth hormone response to intravenous glucose tolerance test in normal, diabetic, and uremic patients. *Clin. Res. 15*, 43 (Abstract).

Horwith, M., H. Demura, B. B. Saxena, R. E. Peterson, and B. S. Ray (1967). Plasma growth hormone concentration pre and post total surgical hypophysectomy. *Excerpta Medica, Int. Cong.*, Ser. *142*, 46.

Hung, W., and C. J. Migeon (1968). Hypoglycemia in a two year old boy with adrenocorticotrophic hormone (ACTH) deficiency (probably isolated) and adrenal medullary unresponsiveness to insulin-induced hypoglycemia. *J. Clin. Endocrinol. 28*, 146-52.

Hunter, W. M., and F. C. Greenwood (1964). Studies on the secretion of human pituitary growth hormone. *Brit. Med. J. i*, 804-7.

Hunter, W. M., and W. M. Rigal (1966). The diurnal pattern of plasma growth hormone concentration in children and adolescents. *J. Endocrinol. 34*, 147-53.

Hunter, W. M., C. C. Fonseka, and R. Passmore (1965). The role of growth hormone in the mobilization of fuel for muscular exercise. *Quart. J. Exp. Physiol. 50*, 406-16.

Hunter, W. M., J. A. R. Friend, and J. A. Strong (1966a). The diurnal pattern of plasma growth hormone concentration in adults. *J. Endocrinol. 34*, 139-46.

Hunter, W. M., B. F. Clarke, and L. J. P. Duncan (1966b). Plasma growth hormone after an overnight fast and following glucose loading in healthy and diabetic subjects. *Metabolism 15*, 596-607.

Hunter, W. M., J. Wolfsdorf, J. W. Farquhar, and W. M. Rigal (1967). Screening tests for growth hormone deficiency in dwarfism. *Lancet ii*, 1271-73.

Hunter, W. M., J. M. T. Willoughby, and J. A. Strong (1968). Plasma insulin and growth hormone during 22-hour fasts and after graded glucose loads in six healthy adults. *J. Endocrinol. 40*, 297-311.

Irie, M., and M. Sakuma (1966). Radioimmunoassay of human growth hormone. *Folia Endocrinologica Japonica 42*, 475-88.

Irie, M., M. Sauma, T. Tsushima, F. Matsuzaki, K. Shizume, and K. Nakao (1967a). Effect of acute glucose infusion on plasma concentration of human growth hormone. *Proc. Soc. Exp. Biol. Med. 125*, 1314-16.

Irie, M., M. Sakuma, T. Tsushima, K. Shizume, and K. Nakao (1967b). Effect of nicotinic acid administration on plasma growth hormone concentrations. *Proc. Soc. Exp. Biol. Med. 126*, 708-11.

Iwatsubo, H., O. Kiyohiko, Y. Okada, M. Fukachi, M. Miyai, H. Abe, and Y. Kumahara (1967). Human growth hormone secretion in primary hypothyroidism before and after treatment. *J. Clin. Endocrinol. Metab. 27*, 1751-54.

James, V. H. T., J. Landon, V. Wynn, and F. C. Greenwood (1968). A fundamental defect of adrenocortical control in Cushing's Disease. *J. Endocrinol. 40*, 15-28.

Josimovich, J. B., D. H. Mintz, and J. L. Finster (1967). Estrogenic inhibition of growth hormone-induced tibial epiphyseal growth in hypophysectomized rats. *Endocrinology 81*, 1428-30.

Kaplan, S. L., and M. M. Grumbach (1967). Growth hormone secretion in the human fetus and in anencephaly. *Ped. Res. i*, 308-9 (Abstract).

Kaplan, S. L., C. A. L. Abrams, J. J. Bell, F. A. Conte, and M. M. Grumbach (1968). Growth and Growth Hormone. *Ped. Res. ii*, 43-63.

Katz, S. H., A. P. S. Dhariwal, and S. M. McCann (1967). Effect of hypoglycemia on the content of pituitary growth hormone and hypothalamic growth hormone-releasing factor in the rat. *Endocrinology 81*, 333-39.

Kaufman, B., O. H. Pearson, C. N. Shealy, E. S. Chernak, N. Samaan, and J. P. Storaasli (1966). Transnasal-transsphenoidal yttrium-90 pituitary implantation in the therapy of acromegaly. *Radiology 86*, 915-20.

Kenny, F. M., A. Drash, L. Y. Garces, and A. Susen (1968). "Catch-up growth" despite hypopituitarism after craniopharyngioma removal. In *Proc. 78th Ann. Mtg. Am. Pediatric Soc.*, May 1-4, 1968, Atlantic City, p. 3 (Abstract).

Ketterer, H., D. Powell, and R. H. Unger (1966). Growth hormone response to surgical stress. *Clin. Res. 14*, 65.

Kimball, H. R., M. B. Lipsett, W. D. Odell, and S. M. Wolff (1968). Comparison of the effect of the pyrogens, etiocholanolone and bacterial endotoxin on plasma cortisol and growth hormone in man. *J. Clin. Endocrinol. Metab. 28*, 337-42.

Kjellberg, R. N., A. Shintani, A. G. Frantz, and B. Kliman (1968). Proton-beam therapy in acromegaly. *New Eng. J. Med. 278*, 690-95.

Knobil, E., and J. Hotchkiss (1964). Growth hormone. *Ann. Rev. Physiol. 26*, 47-74.

Knobil, E., and V. Meyer (1968). Observations on the secretion of growth hormone, and its blockade, in the Rhesus monkey. *Ann. N.Y. Acad. Sci. 148*, 459-70.

Knopf, R. F., J. W. Conn, S. S. Fajans, J. C. Floyd, E. M. Guntsche, and J. A. Rull (1965). Plasma growth hormone response to intravenous administration of amino acids. *J. Clin. Endocrinol. Metab. 25*, 1140-44.

Knopf, R. F., J. W. Conn, J. C. Floyd, Jr., S. S. Fajans, J. A. Rull, E. M. Guntsche, and C. A. Thiffault (1966). The normal endocrine response to ingestion of protein and infusions of amino acids: sequential secretion of insulin and growth hormone. *Trans. Ass. Am. Phys. 79*, 312-21.

Koh, C. S., J. Kohn, K. J. Catt, and H. G. Burger (1968). Lack of relation between plasma growth hormone levels and small decrements in blood sugar. *Lancet i*, 13-14.

Kohler, P. O., B .W. O'Malley, P. L. Rayford, M. B. Lipsett, and W. D. Odell (1967). Effect of pyrogen on blood levels of pituitary trophic hormones: observations of the usefulness of the growth hormone response in the detection of pituitary disease. *J. Clin. Endocrinol. Metab. 27*, 219-26.

Krieger, D. T., S. Glick, A. Silverberg, and H. P. Krieger (1968). Comparative study of tests of endocrine function in hypothalamic disease. *Clin. Res. 16*, 270 (Abstract).

Krulich, L., and S. M. McCann (1966). Influence of stress on the growth hormone content of the pituitary of the rat. *Proc. Soc. Exp. Biol. Med. 122*, 612-16.

Krulich, L., A. P. S. Dhariwal, and S. M. McCann (1965). Growth hormone-releasing activity of crude ovine hypothalamic extracts. *Proc. Soc. Exp. Biol. Med. 120*, 180-84.

Krulich, L., A. P. S. Dhariwal, and S. M. McCann (1967). Stimulatory and inhibitory hypothalamic factors regulating secretion of growth hormone. Program of the Forty-Ninth Meeting of the Endocrine Society, p. 87.

Landon, J., F. C. Greenwood, T. C. B. Stamp, and V. Wynn (1966). The plasma sugar, free fatty acid, cortisol, and growth hormone response to insulin, and the comparison of this procedure with other tests of pituitary and adrenal function. II In patients with hypothalamic or pituitary dysfunction or anorexia nervosa. *J. Clin. Invest. 45*, 437-49.

Laron, Z. and A. Pertzelan (1967). The syndrome of pituitary dwarfism with high serum concentration of growth hormone. *Acta. Endocr. (kbh) Suppl. 119*, 18 (Abstract).

Laron, Z., S. Mannheimer, A. Pertzelan, and M. Nitzan (1966a). Serum growth hormone concentration in full term infants. *Israel J. Med. Sci. 2*, 770-73.

Laron, Z., M. Doron, and B. Amikan (1966b). Growth hormone secretion in men and women over 70 years of age. *Proc. Int. Symp. Physical Activity and Aging, Tel Aviv*, p. 33 (Abstract).

Laron, Z., A. Pertzelan, and S. Mannheimer (1966c). Genetic pituitary dwarfism with high serum concentration of growth hormone: a new inborn error of metabolism? *Israel J. Med. Sci. 2*, 152-55.

Laron, Z., S. Mannheimer, M. Nitzan, and J. Goldman (1967). Growth hormone, glucose, and free fatty acid levels in mother and infant in normal, diabetic and toxaemic pregnancies. *Arch. Dis. Child. 42*, 24-28.

Lawrence, A. M. (1966). Marked elevation in plasma free fatty acids due to exercise in obese subjects. *J. Clin. Invest. 45*, 1035-36 (Abstract).

Lazarus, J., K. F. Bleasel, T. J. Connelley, and J. D. Young (1966). Serum growth hormone in acromegaly: effect of cyrogenic pituitary destruction. *Lancet ii*, 90-91.

Lessof, M. H., S. Mc. Young, and F. C. Greenwood (1966). Growth hormone secretion in obese subjects. *Guy's Hospital Reports 115*, 65-71.

Levin, M. E., and L. Recant (1967). Hormonal and biochemical studies in a diabetic family. *Ann. Int. Med. 66*, 69-76.

Levine, R. (1969). 3',5'-AMP, cellular mediator of insulin and growth hormone release in man. In *Proc. Int. Symp. Protein and Polypeptide Hormones*, Liège, May 19-25, 1968, Excerpta Medica, Amsterdam, Vol. 3, in press.

Levine, R., and R. Luft (1964). The relationship between the growth and diabeogenic effects of the so called growth hormone of the anterior pituitary. *Diabetes 13*, 651-55.

Lewis, U. J., E. V. Cheever, and W. P. Vanderlaan (1965). Studies on the growth hormone of normal and dwarf mice. *Endocrinology 76*, 210-15.

Lindsten, J., E. Cerasi, R. Luft, and G. Hultquist (1967). The occurrence of abnormal insulin and growth hormone responses to sustained hyperglycemia in a disease with sex chromosome aberrations (Turner's Syndrome). *Acta Endocrinologica 56*, 107-31.

Linfoot, J. A., and F. C. Greenwood (1965). Growth hormone in acromegaly: effect of heavy particle pituitary irradiation. *J. Clin. Endocrinol. Metab. 11*, 1515-18.

Luft, R. (1965). Human growth hormone and the control of blood glucose concentration. *Israel J. Med. Sci. 1*, 1277-83.

Luft, R., E. Cerasi, L. L. Madison, U. S. von Euler, L. Della Casa, and A. Roovete (1966). Effect of a small decrease in blood-glucose on plasma growth

hormone and urinary excretion of catecholamines in man. *Lancet ii*, 254-56.
MacGillivray, M. H., T. Aceto, Jr., and L. A. Frohman (1968). Plasma growth
    hormone responses and growth retardation of hypothyroidism. *Am. J. Dis.
    Child. 115*, 273-76.
Machlin, L. J., Y. Takahashi, M. Horino, F. Hertelendy, R. S. Gordon, and D.
    Kipnis (1968a). Regulation of growth hormone secretion in non-primate
    species. *Proc. Int. Symp. Growth Hormone*, Milan, Italy, September 11-13,
    1967, Excerpta Medica, Amsterdam, pp. 292-305.
Machlin, L. J., M. Horino, F. Hertelendy, and D. M. Kipnis (1968b). Plasma
    growth hormone and insulin levels in the pig. *Endocrinology 82*, 369-76.
Marks, V., N. Howorth, and F. C. Greenwood (1965). Plasma growth hormone
    levels in chronic starvation in man *Nature 208*, 686-87.
Marks, V., F. C. Greenwood, P. J. N. Howorth, and E. Samols (1967). Plasma
    growth hormone levels in spontaneous hypoglycemia. *J. Clin. Endocrinol.
    Metab. 27*, 523-28.
Martin, L. G., J. W. Clark, T. B. Connor (1968). Growth hormone secretion
    enhanced by androgens. *J. Clin. Endocrinol. Metab. 28*, 425-28.
Martin, M. M., F. Gaboardi, S. Raiti, and P. L. Calcagno (1968). Effect of inter-
    mitten steroid therapy on the response of plasma cortisol and growth hor-
    mone to insulin-induced hypoglycemia. *Proc. Soc. Ped. Res.*, 38th Ann.
    Mtg., May 3-4, 1968, p. 92 (Abstract).
McCann, S. M., A. P. S. Dhariwal, and J. C. Porter (1968). Regulation of the
    adenohypophysis. *Ann. Rev. Physiol. 30*, 589-640.
McCullagh, E. P., J. C. Beck, and C. A. Schaffenburg (1955). Control of diabetes
    and other features of acromegaly following treatment with estrogens. *Dia-
    betes 4*, 13-23.
Meites, J. (1964). Studies on the growth hormone stimulating factor of the hypo-
    thalamus. *Proc. 2nd Int. Cong. Endocrinol.*, London, Excerpta Medica,
    Amsterdam, pp. 522-29.
Melvin, K. E. W., A. D. Wright, M. Hartog, A.C. Antcliff, A. M. Copestake, and
    T. R. Fraser (1967). Acute metabolic response to human growth hormone
    in different types of dwarfism. *Brit. Med. J. i*, 196-99.
Merimee, T. J., and O. Rabinowitz (1967). Le profil metabolique après administra-
    tion d'arginine chez l'homme sain. *La Revue De Médecine 17*, 867-78.
Merimee, T. J., D. A. Lillicrap, and D. Rabinowitz (1965). Effect of arginine on
    serum levels of human growth hormone. *Lancet ii*, 668-70.
Merimee, T. J., J. A. Burgess, and D. Rabinowitz (1966a). Sex-determined varia-
    tion in serum insulin and growth hormone response to amino acid stimula-
    tion. *J. Clin. Endocrinol. Metab. 26*, 791-93.
Merimee, T. J., J. A. Burgess, and D. Rabinowitz (1966b). Arginine infusion in
    maturity-onset diabetes mellitus. *Lancet i*, 1300-1301.
Merimee, T. J., D. Rabinowitz, L. Riggs, J. A. Burgess, D. L. Rimoin, and V. A.
    McKusick (1967). Plasma growth hormone after arginine infusion: clinical
    experiences. *New Eng. J. Med. 276*, 434-39.
Meyer, V., and E. Knobil (1966). Stimulation of growth hormone secretion by
    vasopressin in the rhesus monkey. *Endocrinology 79*, 1016-18.
Meyer, V., and E. Knobil (1967). Growth hormone secretion in the unanesthe-
    tized rhesus monkey in response to noxious stimuli. *Endocrinology 80*,
    163-71.
Meyer, V., and E. Knobil (1968). Factors influencing the secretion of growth hor-

mone in the rhesus monkey. *Proc. Int. Symp. Growth Hormone*, Milan, Italy, September 11-13, 1967, Excerpta Medica, Amsterdam, pp. 226-37.

Milner, R. D. G., and A. D. Wright (1966). Blood glucose, plasma insulin and growth hormone response to hyperglycemia in the newborn. *Clin. Sci. 31*, 309-15.

Milner, R. D. G., and A. D. Wright (1967). Plasma glucose, non-esterified fatty acid, insulin and growth hormone response to glucagon in the newborn. *Clin. Sci. 32*, 249-55.

Mintz, D. H., J. L. Finster, and J. B. Josimovich (1967). Effect of estrogen therapy on carbohydrate metabolism in acromegaly. *J. Clin. Endocrinol. Metab. 27*, 1321-27.

Mintz, D. H., R. Stock, J. L. Finster, and A. L. Taylor (1968). The effect of normal and diabetic pregnancies on growth hormone responses to hypoglycemia. *Metabolism 17*, 54-61.

Morris, H. G., and J. R. Jorgensen (1968). Circadian pattern of plasma growth hormone concentration in children. *Clin. Res. 16*, 148 (Abstract).

Morris, H. G., J. R. Jorgensen, and S. A. Jenkins (1968a). Plasma growth hormone concentration in corticosteroid treated children. *J. Clin. Invest. 47*, 427-35.

Morris, H. G., J. R. Jorgensen, H. Elrick, and R. E. Goldsmith (1968b). Metabolic effects of human growth hormone in corticosteroid treated children. *J. Clin. Invest. 47*, 436-51.

Müller, E., and A. Pecile (1966). Influence of exogenous growth hormone on endogenous growth hormone release. *Proc. Soc. Exp. Biol. Med. 122*, 1289-91.

Müller, E. E., T. Saito, A. Arimura, and A. V. Schally (1967a). Hypoglycemia, stress and growth hormone release: blockade of growth hormone release by drugs acting on the central nervous system. *Endocrinology 80*, 109-17.

Müller, E. E., S. Sawano, A. Arimura, and A. V. Schally (1967b). Blockade of release of growth hormone by brain norepinephrine depletors. *Endocrinology 80*, 471-76.

Müller, E. E., S. Sawano, A. Arimura, and A. V. Schally (1967c). Mechanism of action of growth hormone in altering its own secretion rate: comparison with the action of dexamethasone. *Acta Endocrinologica 56*, 499-509.

Norman, N., and A. R. Turter (1968). Radioimmunoassay studies with human growth hormone and a pituitary lipid mobilizing factor. *Acta Endocrinologica 58*, 318-38.

Parker, D. C., J. W. Mace, R. W. Gotlin, and L. G. Rossman (1968). Nychthemeral variation of human growth hormone in plasma. *J. Clin. Invest. 47*, 76a (Abstract).

Parker, M. L., R. D. Utiger, and W. H. Daughaday (1962). Studies on human growth hormone: II The physiological disposition and metabolic fate of human growth hormone in man. *J. Clin. Invest. 41*, 262-68.

Parker, M. L., J. M. Hammond, and W. H. Daughaday (1967). The arginine provocation test: an aid in the diagnosis of hyposomatotropism. *J. Clin. Endocrinol. Metab. 27*, 1129-36.

Parker, M. L., R. S. Pildes, K. L. Chao, M. Cornblath, and D. M. Kipnis (1968). Juvenile diabetes mellitus, a deficiency in insulin. *Diabetes 17*, 27-32.

Pecile, A., and E. E. Müller (1966a). Control of growth hormone secretion. In *Neuroendocrinology* (L. Martini and W. F. Ganong, eds.), pp. 537-64. Academic Press, New York and London.

Pecile, A., and E. E. Müller (1966b). Suppressive action of corticosteroids on the secretion of growth hormone. *J. Endocrinol. 36*, 401-8.

Pecile, A., E. Müller, G. Falconi, and L. Martini (1965). Growth hormone releasing activity of hypothalamic extracts at different ages. *Endocrinology 77*, 241-46.

Pecile, A., E. Müller, and G. Falconi (1966). Endocrine function of pituitary transplants taken from rats of different ages. *Arch. Int. Pharmacodynamic Thérapie 159*, 434-41.

Perlroth, M. G., D. P. Tschudy, A. Waxman, and W. D. Odell (1967). Abnormalities of growth hormone regulation in acute intermittent porphyria. *Metabolism 16*, 87-90.

Pfeiffer, E. F., and F. Melani (1967). Menschliches Wachstumshormon: darstellung, bestimmung im blute und klinische bedeutung. In *Proc. 1st Int. Symp. Diabetes*, Mantua, Italy, June 1967.

Pimstone, B. L., W. Wittmann, J. D. L. Hansen, and P. Murray (1966). Growth hormone and kwashiorkor: role of protein in growth-hormone homeostasis. *Lancet ii*, 779-80.

Pimstone, B. L., G. Barbezat, J. D. L. Hansen, and P. Murray (1968). Studies on growth hormone secretion in protein-calorie malnutrition. *Am. J. Clin. Nutrit. 21*, 482-87.

Powell, E. D. U., A. G. Frantz, M. T. Rabkin, and R. A. Field (1966). Growth hormone in relation to diabetic retinopathy. *New Eng. J. Med. 275*, 922-25.

Powell, G. F., J. A. Brasel, S. Raiti, and R. M. Blizzard (1967). Emotional deprivation and growth retardation simulating idiopathic hypopituitarism. I Endocrinologic evaluation of the syndrome. *New Eng. J. Med. 276*, 1279-83.

Quabbe, H. J., and H. Helge (1967). Verhalten der STH-Sekretion bei der Fettsucht. *Verhandlungen der Deutschen Gesellschaft für innere Medizin 73 Kongress*, 389-94.

Quabbe, H. J., E. Schilling. and H. Helge (1966). Pattern of growth hormone secretion during a 24-hour fast in normal adults. *J. Clin. Endocrinol. Metab. 26*, 1173-77.

Rabinowitz, D., T. J. Merimee, J. A. Burgess, and L. Riggs (1966a). Growth hormone and insulin release after arginine: indifference to hyperglycemia and epinephrine. *J. Clin. Endocrinol. Metab. 26*, 1170-72.

Rabinowitz, D., T. J. Merimee, R. Maffezzoli, and J. A. Burgess (1966b). Patterns of hormonal release after glucose, protein, and glucose plus protein. *Lancet ii*, 454-57.

Rabkin, M. T., and A. G. Frantz (1966). Hypopituitarism: a study of growth hormone and other endocrine functions. *Ann. Int. Med. 64*, 1197-1207.

Raiti, S., W. T. Davis, and R. M. Blizzard (1967). A comparison of the effects of insulin hypoglycemia and arginine infusion on release of human growth hormone. *Lancet ii*, 1182-83.

Rand, R. W. (1966). Cyrosurgery of the pituitary in acromegaly. *Ann. Surg. 164*, 587-92.

Reichlin, S. (1966). Regulation of somatotrophic hormone secretion. In *The Pituitary Gland* (G. W. Harris and B. T. Donovan, eds.), *2*, pp. 270-98, University of California Press, Berkeley.

Reichlin, S. (1968). Hypothalamic control of growth hormone secretion and the response to stress. In *Endocrinology and Human Behavior* (R. Michael, ed.). Oxford University Press, London.

Rimoin, D. L., T. J. Merimee, and V. A. McKusick (1966). Growth hormone deficiency in man: an isolated, recessively inherited defect. *Science 152,* 1635-37.

Rimoin, D. L., G. B. Holtzman, T. J. Merimee, D. Rabinowitz, A. C. Barnes, and V. A. McKusick (1967a). Lactation without growth hormone. *Clin. Res. 15,* 265 (Abstract).

Rimoin, D. L., T. J. Merimee, D. Rabinowitz, V. A. McKusick, and L. L. Cavalli-Sforza (1967b). Growth hormone in African pygmies. *Lancet ii,* 523-26.

Rodger, N. W., J. C. Beck, R. Burgos, R. Guillemin (1967). Variability of response in the bioassay of ovine hypothalamic extracts from a somatotropin releasing factor. Program of the Forty-Ninth Meeting of the Endocrine Society, p. 88.

Root, A. W., R. L. Rosenfield, A. M. Bongiovanni, and W. R. Eberlein (1967). Plasma growth hormone response to insulin-induced hypoglycemia in children with retardation of growth. *Pediatrics 39,* 844-52.

Rosselin, G., R. Assan, P. Freychet, J. Doulais, and G. Tchobroutsky (1967a). Insuline, glucagon et hormone somatotrope plasmatiques dans cinq cas de tumeurs extra-pancréatiques hypoglycémiantes: revue de la litterature. *La Presse Medicals 75,* 1045-51.

Rosselin, G., G. Tchobroutsky, R. Assan, P. Freychet, and M. Derot (1967b). Delayed and/or low insulin secretion and non-elevated fasting growth hormone level in non-obese adult diabetic subjects with or without sulfonylurea therapy: relationship to recent organic pancreatic diabetes. In *Proc. 6th Cong. Int. Diabetes Fed.,* Stockholm, Sweden, July 30-August 4, 1967, Excerpta Medica, Amsterdam, Abstract #213.

Roth, J., S. M. Glick, R. S. Yalow, and S. A. Berson (1963a). Hypoglycemia: a potent stimulus to secretion of growth hormone. *Science 140,* 987-88.

Roth, J., S. M. Glick, R. S. Yallow, and S. A. Berson (1963b). Secretion of human growth hormone: physiologic and experimental modification. *Metabolism 12,* 577-79.

Roth, J., S. M. Glick, P. Cuatrecasas, and C. S. Hollander (1967). Acromegaly and other disorders of growth hormone secretion. *Ann. Int. Med. 66,* 760-88.

Roth, J., P. Gorden, and R. W. Bates (1968). Studies of growth hormone and prolactin in acromegaly. *Proc. Int. Symp. Growth Hormone,* Milan, Italy, September 11-13, 1967, Excerpta Medica Foundation, Amsterdam, pp. 124-28.

Russel, J. A. (1957), Effects of growth hormone on protein and carbohydrate metabolism. *Am. J. Clin. Nutrit. 5,* 404-16.

Sadeghi-Nejad, A., and B. Senior (1968). Pituitary-adrenal responsiveness and growth hormone levels following prolonged alternate day steroid therapy. *Proc. Am. Ped. Soc. 78th Ann. Mtg.,* May 1-4, 1968, Atlantic City, p. 61 (Abstract).

Sakuma, M., M. Irie, K. Shizume, T. Tsushima, and K. Nakao (1968). Measurement of urinary growth hormone by radioimmunoassay. *J. Clin. Endocrinol. Metab. 28,* 103-5.

Samaan, N., W. S. Cumming, J. W. Craig, and O. H. Pearson (1966a). Serum growth hormone and insulin levels in severe renal disease. *Diabetes 15*, 546 (Abstract).

Samaan, N., O. H. Pearson, D. Gonzalez, and O. Llerena (1966b). Paradoxical secretion of growth hormone in patients with breast cancer. *J.. Lab. Clin. Med. 68*, 1011 (Abstract).

Sarver, M. E., G. Sabeh, G. H. Fetterman, N. Wald, and T. S. Danowski (1964). Fractional hypopituitarism with giantism and normal sella turcica. *New Eng. J. Med. 271*, 1286-89.

Sawano, S., A. Arimura, C. Y. Bowers, T. W. Redding, and A. V. Schally (1968). Pituitary and plasma growth hormone concentration after administration of highly purified pig growth hormone-releasing factor. *Proc. Soc. Exp. Biol. Med. 127*, 1010-14.

Schalch, D. (1967). The influence of physical stress and exercise on growth hormone and insulin secretion in man. *J. Lab. Clin. Med. 69*, 256-69.

Schalch, D. S., and S. Reichlin (1966). Plasma growth hormone concentration in the rat determined by radioimmunoassay: influence of sex, pregnancy, lactation, anesthesia, hypophysectomy and extrasellar pituitary transplants. *Endocrinology 79*, 275-80.

Schalch, D. S., and S. Reichlin (1968). Stress and growth hormone release. *Proc. Int. Symp. Growth Hormone*, Milan, Italy, September 11-13, 1967, Excerpta Medica, Amsterdam, pp. 211-25.

Schally, A. V., S. Sawano, E. E. Müller, A. Arimura, C. Y. Bowers, T. W. Redding, and S. L. Steelman (1968a). Hypothalamic growth hormone releasing factor: purification and in vivo and in vitro studies. *Proc. Int. Symp. Growth Hormone*, Milan, Italy, September 11-13, 1967, Excerpta Medica, Amsterdam, pp. 185-203.

Schally, A. V., E. E. Müller, A. Arimura, T. Saito, S. Sawano, and C. Y. Bowers (1968b). Growth hormone releasing factor: physiological and biochemical studies with growth hormone releasing factor preparations of bovine and porcine origin. *Ann. N.Y. Acad. Sci. 148*, 372-88.

Schofield, J. G. (1967). Role of cyclic 3′,5′-adenosine monophosphate in the release of growth hormone in vitro. *Nature 215*, 1382-83.

Schwartz, E., E. Echemendia, M. Schiffer, and V. A. Panariello (1967). Mechanism of estrogenic action in acromegaly. *Excerpta Medica, Int. Cong. Ser. 142*, 47.

Schwarz, F., H. G. van Riet, and W. Shopman (1966). Serum growth hormone and energy supply in fasting obese patients. *Metabolism 15*, 194-205.

Service, F. S., G. D. Molnar, J. W. Rosevear, E. Ackerman, G. M. Cremer, V. Fatourechi, and K. E. Moxness (1968). Biochemical and hormonal profile of diabetic instability. *Diabetes 17*, 342.

Sheikholislam, B. M., H. E. Lebovitz, and R. S. Stempfel (1966). Growth hormone secretion in hypothyroidism. Program of the Forty-eighth Meeting of the Endocrine Society, p. 57.

Simon, S., M. S. Schiffer, S. M. Glick, and E. Schwartz (1967). Effect of medroxyprogesterone acetate upon stimulated release of growth hormone in men. *J. Clin. Endocrinol. Metab. 27*, 1633-36.

Spellacy, W. N. (1967). Anterior pituitary gland function in pregnancy: measurement of human growth hormone (HGH) and human placental lactogen (HPL). *Obstetrics and Gynecology 29*, 430 (Abstract).

Spellacy, W. N., K. L. Carlson, and S. L. Schade (1967). Human growth hormone levels in normal subjects receiving an oral contraceptive. *J.A.M.A.* 202, 451-54.

Spellacy, W. N., K. L. Carlson, S. L. Schade (1968). Human growth hormone studies in patients with galactorrhea (Ahumada–del Castillo syndrome). *Am. J. Obstet. and Gyn. 100*, 84-89.

Steiner, H., O. Dahlbach, and J. J. Waldenström (1968). Ectopic growth hormone production and osteoarthropathy in carcinoma of the bronchus. *Lancet ii*, 783-85.

Stephenson, J. N., R. C. Mellinger, and G. Mason (1968). Cerebral gigantism. *Pediatrics 41*, 130-38.

Stimmler, L., and G. A. Brown (1967). Growth hormone secretion provoked by insulin-induced hypoglycemia in children of short stature. *Arch. Dis. Child. 42*, 232-38.

Stimmler, L., R. G. McArthur, and G. A. Brown (1967). Plasma growth hormone in children of short stature following an oral glucose load. *Canadian Medical Association Journal 97*, 1159-61.

Sukkar, M. Y., W. M. Hunter, and R. Passmore (1967). Changes in plasma levels of insulin and growth hormone levels after a protein meal. *Lancet ii*, 1020-22.

Takahashi, K., S. Takahashi, Y. Honda, K. Shizume, M. Irie, M. Sakuma, and T. Tsushima (1967a). Secretion of human growth hormone during insulin coma and electroshock therapies. *Folia Psychiatrica et Neurologica Japonica 21*, 87-105.

Takahashi, V., M. L. Parker, W. H. Daughaday, and D. M. Kipnis (1967b). Growth Hormone, glucose and insulin in human plasma during sleep. *J. Lab. Clin. Med. 70*, 1021.

Tchobroutsky, G., G. Rosselin, R. Assan, P. Freychet, and M. Derot (1969a). Growth hormone secretion in obese subjects with and without diabetes: comparison with non-obese patients. *Proc. Int. Symp. Endocrinol.* Marseilles, in press.

Tchobroutsky, G., G. Rosselin, R. Assan, and M. Derot (1969b). Glucose intolerance in uremia. II Plasma growth hormone and glucagon values. Submitted for publication.

Troyer, W. G., Jr., S. J. Friedberg, E. S. Horton, and M. D. Bogdonoff (1966). The effect of β-receptor blockade upon the plasma free fatty acid and growth hormone response to exercise. *J. Clin. Invest. 45*, 1081 (Abstract).

Trygstad, O., and I. Foss (1968). The lipid-mobilizing effect of some pituitary gland preparations. IV. Subdivision of a human growth hormone preparation into a somatrophic and an adipokinetic-hypeglycemic agent. *Acta Endocrinologica 58*, 295-317.

Tyson, J. E., T. J. Merimee, and D. Rabinowitz (1968). Insulin and growth hormone release after arginine infusion during pregnancy. *Diabetes 17*, 347 (Abstract).

Unger, R. H. (1965). High growth-hormone levels in diabetic ketoacidosis. *J.A.M.A. 191*, 945-47.

Unger, R. H., M. D. Siperstein, L. L. Madison, A. M. Eisentraut, and N. Whissen (1964). Apparent growth hormone hyperresponsiveness in prediabetes. *J. Lab. Clin. Med. 64*, 1013 (Abstract).

Unger, R. H., A. M. Eisentraut, L. L. Madison, and M. D. Siperstein (1965). Fasting levels of growth hormone in men and women. *Nature 205*, 804.

Wegienka, L. C., G. M. Grodsky, J. H. Karam, S. G. Grasso, and P. H. Forsham (1967). Comparison of insulin and 2-deoxy-D-glucose-induced glucopenia as stimulators of growth hormone secretion. *Metabolism 16*, 245-56.

Wilber, J. F., and W. D. Odell (1965). Hypoglycemia associated with the isolated deficiency of growth hormone. *Metabolism 14*, 590-97.

Wolter, R., H. Loeb, and N. Brunet-Verhougstraeten (1969). Variations du taux de l'hormone de croissonce sérique en réponse à l'hypoglycémie chez l'enfant obèse. *Revue Médicale de Liège*, in press.

Yalow, R. S., S. M. Glick, J. Roth, and S. A. Berson (1965). Plasma insulin and growth hormone levels in obesity and diabetics. *Ann. N.Y. Acad. Sci. 131*, 357-73.

Yen, S. S. C., N. Samaan, and O. H. Pearson (1967). Growth hormone levels in pregnancy. *J. Clin. Endocrinol. Metab. 27*, 1341-47.

Zimmerman, T. S., M. G. White, W. H. Daughaday, and F. C. Goetz (1967). Hypopituitarism with normal or increased height. *Am. J. Med. 42*, 146-50.

Zor, U., J. Shore, D. Locker, and F. G. Sulman (1967). Metabolic effects of monoamine oxidase inhibitors on the rat pituitary. *J. Endocrinol. 39*, 1-6.

5
Extracellular Fluid Volume
and Vasopressin Secretion

LEONARD SHARE

Introduction

Sixty years ago, in 1909, Starling wrote that there are mechanisms in the body which "work together for the maintenance of an average quantity and composition of the internal media of the body." Since that time this view has been restated and reiterated by many prominent students of water and electrolyte metabolism. In the past ten to fifteen years, considerable progress has been made in providing a firm experimental basis for this hypothesis and in identifying many of the afferent and efferent mechanisms involved in the regulation of extracellular fluid volume and composition, a regulation which is dependent upon the control of the intake as well as the output of water and electrolytes. This chapter will deal with only one facet of this very complex homeostatic mechanism, the effect of changes in extracellular fluid volume on the plasma concentration of vasopressin.

Measurement of the Plasma Vasopressin Concentration

The precise chemical measurement of the concentration of vasopressin (antidiuretic hormone, ADH) in biological fluids is still not possible. All of the alternative approaches to this problem employed to date have inherent limitations. Some are particularly noteworthy for their lack of specificity and reliability. It is, then, pertinent at this point to review briefly the general principles involved in these alternative methods. One approach, followed particularly by earlier investigators, has been to use changes in urine flow in the experimental subject as an index of the changes in the concentration of vasopressin in the plasma. The lack of specificity of this approach is readily apparent; a change in the glomerular filtration rate, with no change in the plasma vasopressin concentration, could readily account for an observed change in urine flow. Even when changes in glomerular filtration rate are ruled out, account must also be taken of changes in solute excretion. A more sophisticated variant of this approach has been to use change in the free water clearance as an index of change in the circulating vasopressin level. This index is reasonably valid in situations in which arterial blood pressure, glomerular filtration rate, renal medullary blood flow and solute excretion are constant. These experimental restrictions, as well as the inability to quantitate the changes in the plasma vasopressin concentration and the inability to demonstrate changes in the plasma vasopressin concentration beyond that required to produce a maximal change in the free water clearance, render this technique less than satisfactory. Even when these restrictions have been met, one must always face the possibility that a change in the free water clearance is the result of an action by some hitherto unidentified factor.

The only satisfactory methods presently available for the routine determination of the plasma vasopressin concentration make use of the antidiuretic bioassay. This subject has been reviewed in detail recently (Sawyer, 1966; Share, 1967a). All the bioassays commonly in use are basically variations of the one introduced by Jeffers et al. (1942), involving the use of the hydrated, ethanol-anesthetized rat and the intravenous administration of standards and unknowns. Since, in the hands of most investigators, this assay is not sensitive enough for the measurement of resting plasma levels of vasopressin, techniques for extraction and concentration of the hormone are now commonly used. Most of these procedures are patterned after those described either by Weinstein et al. (1960) and Share (1961), or by Bisset et al. (1967). The former of these would seem to provide for greater specificity than the latter. Those methods which combine extraction procedures with a bioassay also have problems. Because of the large inherent error in the bioassay, small changes in the plasma vasopressin concentration are difficult to measure. The bioassay is tedious and sometimes capricious, so that the number of samples that can be assayed in a given period of time is limited. No one has as yet demonstrated, by the extraction and concentration techniques now in common use, the isolation of an antidiuretic substance which is not vasopressin, but one cannot rule out the possibility that such a substance may indeed be found under certain circumstances. Some investigators have attempted to guard against this possibility by showing that the antidiuretic material obtained in their experiments can be inactivated by agents such as thioglycollate or oxytocinase. All things considered, a method that incorporates extraction and bioassay procedures is clearly the method of choice at this time for the measurement of the concentration of vasopressin in plasma.

The development of radio-immunoassay techniques for the measurement of several polypeptide hormones has represented a major technological break-through. Although Permutt *et al.* (1966) have reported a radio-immunoassay for vasopressin, neither they nor others have reported the use of the radio-immunoassay for the routine measurement of the plasma vasopressin concentration. It is, however, reasonable to expect that this will be possible in the near future. Hopefully, such a procedure will make it possible to measure circulating levels of vasopressin with much greater precision than is now possible with the bioassay.

Index for Change in Rate of Vasopressin Secretion

Because of the complexity and relative inaccessability of the blood supply to the neurohypophysis, we cannot readily measure the rate of release of vasopressin *in vivo*. Most workers in this field make the tacit assumption that changes in the concentration of vasopressin in systemic plasma reflect changes in the rate of secretion of the hormone from the posterior pituitary. This assumption is probably reasonable when the changes in the vasopressin titer are rapid and large. In view of the short half-life of vasopressin in the circulation (1 to 2 minutes in the rat, 5 to 8 minutes in the dog, and 8 to 20 minutes in man; see Lauson, 1967) changes in the rate of removal of vasopressin from the circulation may contribute to changes in the plasma concentration of the hormone, particularly over long periods of time. However, the question of the physiological control of the metabolism of vasopressin has received little attention. Some investigators have hoped to obtain a better index of the rate of release of vasopressin by measuring its concentration in blood draining from the neurohypophysis, e.g. blood obtained from the internal jugular vein in the dog and cat and the external jugular vein in the rat and sheep. This approach is open to even greater error than when the blood for analysis is obtained from an artery, since in the venous situation the concentration of vasopressin can be influenced by the additional variable, change in cerebral blood flow.

Effect of Reduction in Extracellular Fluid Volume on Plasma Vasopressin Concentration

That hemorrhage can serve as a stimulus for an increase in the plasma vasopressin titer was first suggested by the work of Rydin and Verney

(1938). They showed that removal of as little as 58 ml of blood from a trained, conscious dog weighing 10 kg resulted in an inhibition of a water diuresis, although there was only a slight, transient fall in mean arterial blood pressure. Since that time a number of investigators have shown that this response is indeed due to an increase in the plasma vasopressin concentration. Ginsburg and Heller (1953) found an increase in the concentration of vasopressin in jugular vein blood in rats subjected to hemorrhage. This was confirmed by de Wied (1960), and similar findings were obtained in anesthetized dogs subjected to moderate or severe hemorrhage by Weinstein, Berne and Sachs (1960), Baratz and Ingraham (1960), and Bocanegra and Lauson (1961).

With the exception of the work of Rydin and Verney (1938), the degree of hemorrhage in these experiments was large and, where measured, involved a considerable reduction in arterial blood pressure. However, if vasopressin is a significant factor in the regulation of blood volume, then one would expect that relatively small changes in blood volume would be effective in inducing a change in the plasma concentration of this hormone. Such is indeed the case. Share (1961) produced a slow, progressive reduction in extracellular fluid volume in anesthetized dogs by peritoneal dialysis with a solution which had an electrolyte composition similar to that of extracellular fluid and which was made hypertonic with glucose. There was a progressive increase in the blood vasopressin titer as extracellular fluid volume fell, under circumstances in which mean arterial blood pressure and the plasma concentrations of sodium and potassium were unchanged. When blood volume was reduced only 9 per cent, there was a sixfold increase in the concentration of vasopressin in the blood. More recently, trained, conscious dogs (Henry et al., 1968) and anesthetized dogs (Share, unpublished observation) were subjected to successive bleedings of approximately 10 per cent of the blood volume, with a 5-minute interval between each bleeding. Although the responses of the unanesthetized dogs were quite variable, the threshold for an increase in the plasma vasopressin titer was a loss of 10 to 20 per cent of the blood volume. In the anesthetized dog (Fig. 5-1), a loss of approximately 10 per cent of the blood volume resulted in a more than doubling of the circulating vasopressin level, indicating that the threshold for the response in these animals was lower than this value. Thus, the reflex that results in an increase in the plasma vasopressin concentration in response to a reduction in blood volume is quite sensitive.

The magnitude of the response to hemorrhage can be quite large. In dogs anesthetized with sodium pentobarbital, rapid reduction of mean arterial blood pressure to 50 mm Hg by bleeding resulted within a few minutes in concentrations of vasopressin as high as 1100 μU/ml in arterial plasma (Sachs et al., 1967). In dogs anesthetized with chloralose and urethane and bled 8 ml/kg at 5-minute intervals, arterial plasma vasopressin concentrations as high as 600 μU/ml were observed after the dogs had been bled 40 ml/kg, and there was no indication that the response had reached a maximum (Share, unpublished observations).

The increase in the plasma vasopressin concentration that follows a reduction in blood volume is almost certainly due in large part to an increased rate of secretion of the hormone. Secretion rates of vasopressin in dogs have apparently been satisfactorily measured only twice (Weinstein et al., 1960). In these experiments, virtually all of the blood draining from the head was collected, and blood flow rates and arteriovenous concentration differences for vasopressin were measured. The peak secretion rates for vasopressin, reached within a few minutes after the dogs had been bled to a mean arterial pressure of 50 mm Hg, were 142 and 297 mU/min. The increase in the plasma vasopressin concentration in response to even a relatively small reduction in blood volume is so rapid and large (e.g. see Fig. 5-1) as to suggest that, under this circumstance also, the secretion rate of the hormone is increased. This view is supported by the experiments of Usami and Chien (1963), who measured the splanchnic extraction of vasopressin following hemorrhage. The splanchnic extraction ratio for vasopressin was 0.22, and appeared to be independent of the degree of hemorrhage. The rate of removal of vasopressin by the splanchnic viscera was reduced in proportion to the reduction in splanchnic blood flow. On the basis of these observations and the estimated total vasopressin plasma clearance, these investigators concluded that a reduction in the rate of removal of vasopressin from the plasma cannot account for the increased plasma vasopressin concentration in the early period following hemorrhage. Further support for the view that the initial increase in the plasma vasopressin concentration following hemorrhage is due largely to an increased release of vasopressin is found in experiments in which the known "volume receptors" were rendered inoperative (Share, 1967b). Anesthetized dogs, in which the vagi were sectioned and the carotid sinuses were perfused at a constant pressure, were bled 8 ml/kg body weight 4 times at 5-minute intervals. Hemorrhage of a total of 32 ml/kg, approximately 40 per cent of the blood volume, failed to produce a statistically significant increase in the vasopressin titer (Fig. 5-2).

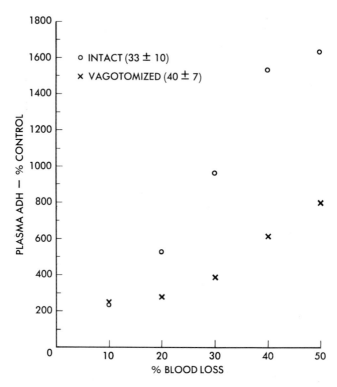

Figure 5-1   Effects of successive bleedings of 8 ml/kg body weight on the plasma vasopressin concentration in intact and vagotomized dogs. The dogs were bled at 5-minute intervals. Blood samples for the determination of vasopressin were taken 3 minutes after the midpoint of each hemorrhage. The plasma vasopressin concentration, on the ordinate, is expressed as per cent of the concentration of vasopressin in the plasma just prior to the first hemorrhage. The abscissa is the degree of blood loss, expressed as per cent of the initial blood volume, which was taken to be 8 per cent of the body weight. The figures in parentheses are the concentration of vasopressin in μU/ml plasma in the initial blood samples (means ± SE).

There have been no adequate studies directed to the question of whether the rate at which blood volume is reduced is a factor in determining the magnitude of the increase in the rate of secretion of vasopressin. Share (1961) produced a slow progressive reduction in extracellular fluid volume by subjecting dogs anesthetized with sodium pentobarbital to peritoneal dialysis with a hypertonic solution. Twenty minutes after the start of this procedure, when it was calculated that

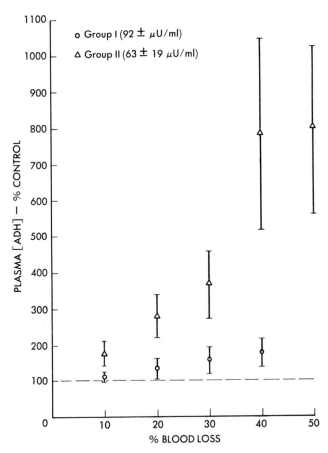

Figure 5-2   Effects of hemorrhage on the plasma vasopressin concentration in dogs which were vagotomized and in which the carotid sinuses were perfused at constant pressure via an external circuit. The plasma vasopressin concentration, on the ordinate, is expressed as per cent of the concentration of vasopressin in the plasma just prior to the first hemorrhage. The abscissa is the degree of blood loss, expressed as per cent of the initial blood volume, which was taken to be 8 per cent of the body weight. The lines extending above and below the symbols indicate ± SE. The figures in parentheses are the concentrations of vasopressin in μU/ml plasma in the initial blood samples (means ± SE). Group I, vagotomized dogs with carotid sinuses perfused at constant pressure, bled 8 ml/kg body weight at 5-minute intervals; blood samples for vasopressin determination 3 minutes after the midpoint of each hemorrhage. Group II, vagotomized dogs with carotid sinuses perfused via the external circuit for 25 minutes and then perfusion via the systemic circulation resumed prior to hemorrhage (modified from Share, 1967b).

blood volume was reduced by 9 per cent, the increment in the plasma vasopressin concentration was 86 μU/ml[1]. In intact dogs, sedated with morphine and anesthetized with a mixture of chloralose and urethane, hemorrhage of 8 ml/kg, approximately 10 per cent of the blood volume, over a period of 1 minute led to an increment in the plasma vasopressin concentration of 72 μU/ml[1] (Share, unpublished observations). These data may indicate that it is the absolute amount by which the blood volume is reduced, rather than the rate of reduction, which is of primary importance in determining the magnitude of the vasopressin release. However, in view of the dissimilarity of the two experimental procedures, this interpretation can be accepted only with considerable reservation.

With severe hemorrhage the initial high rate of release of vasopressin is not maintained. When anesthetized dogs were bled rapidly to a mean arterial pressure of 50 mm Hg, there was an initial, rapid increase in the secretion of vasopressin (Weinstein *et al.*, 1960) and in the plasma vasopressin concentration (Sachs *et al.*, 1967). Although the blood pressure was held at 50 mm Hg, the rate of release of vasopressin and the plasma vasopressin concentration fell off appreciably over a period of 30 minutes. The shed blood was returned to the dogs at this time, and 1 hour later the plasma vasopressin concentration had returned to control levels (Sachs *et al.*, 1967). At this time a second hemorrhage to a blood pressure of 50 mm Hg resulted in a much smaller increase in the plasma vasopressin concentration. This was apparently due to depletion of a readily releasable pool of vasopressin in the posterior pituitary. The effect of a small to moderate hemorrhage on the circulating level of vasopressin over a long period of time has not been studied. Leaf and Mamby (1952), however, have demonstrated an elevated concentration of antidiuretic material in the plasma of a dog 24 hours after reduction of extracellular fluid volume by peritoneal dialysis.

In the anesthetized dog, the increase in the plasma vasopressin concentration is proportional to the degree of blood loss over the very broad range, 10 to 50 per cent of the blood volume (Fig. 5-1, Share, unpublished observations). Similar findings have been obtained in the rat (Ginsburg and Heller, 1953). This was not the case in a series of experiments in unanesthetized dogs (Henry *et al.*, 1968). These dogs, which had chronically implanted catheters for blood sampling and the recording of pressures, were bled 9 ml/kg at 5-minute intervals.

1. The original figures have been corrected for incomplete recovery, and the figures taken from the peritoneal dialysis experiments have been corrected for the fact that blood rather than plasma was used for bioassay.

The increase in the plasma vasopressin titer was not necessarily proportional to the degree of hemorrhage. Although the dogs were well trained, and great pains were taken to prevent them from being disturbed during an experiment, it is possible that the relationship between the plasma vasopressin concentration and the reduction in blood volume, which is evident in the anesthetized animal, may have been obscured by fear or discomfort.

Effect of Increase in Extracellular Fluid Volume on Plasma Vasopressin Concentration

Although it is firmly established that a reduction in blood volume results in an elevated circulating plasma ADH level, the effects of an increase in extracellular fluid volume are uncertain. The reason for this uncertainty is in large part because in many experimental situations the plasma vasopressin concentration is low and close to the limit of sensitivity of most methods currently in use. The concentration of vasopressin in the plasma of the conscious, undisturbed dog with free access to water is of the order of 1 to 2 μU/ml (Share and Travis, unpublished observations). The situation is similar in humans. In anesthetized dogs, the plasma vasopressin concentration is higher, the degree depending upon the type of anesthetic and the nature and extent of any preliminary surgery. Thus, it is apt to be extremely difficult to demonstrate with any degree of confidence that a given procedure, e.g. expansion of the blood volume, induces a reduction in the plasma vasopressin titer. It is, then, not surprising that there is apparently only one report of the effect of expansion of the extracellular fluid volume on the plasma vasopressin level. Baratz and Ingraham (1960) increased blood volume an estimated 25 per cent by the intravenous infusion of 6 per cent dextran in isotonic saline. In 5 dogs the average concentration of antidiuretic activity in the plasma fell from 38 to 18 μU/ml, but this change was not statistically significant. These investigators concluded that when extracellular fluid volume is increased, "the volume receptor mechanism is not of great importance in the regulation of body fluid volume." The estimates of the plasma vasopressin concentration after the infusion of dextran are suspect, because the dextran in the untreated plasma which was assayed caused an anaphylactic reaction in the assay rats. The authors, however, felt that this did not interfere with the assay, since the reaction did not appear until after the urine collection period for the assay was completed.

The problem of the consequences of expansion of extracellular fluid volume has been the subject of a number of studies in which changes in renal handling of water in the experimental subject were used as an index of changes in the plasma vasopressin concentration. However, the results have been conflicting. Although the findings in many of these reports suggest that expansion of extracellular fluid volume results in a diuresis which appears to be the result of inhibition of vasopressin release (much of this earlier work has been reviewed by Smith, 1957, and by Strauss, 1957), these experiments were frequently complicated by increases in solute excretion, glomerular filtration rate, and renal plasma flow (e.g. see reports by Gilmore and Weisfeldt, 1965, and Pearce and Lichardus, 1967). In order to determine whether this diuresis was the result of a reduction in the plasma vasopressin concentration, some investigators have sought to inhibit the diuresis either by the administration of vasopressin or by procedures known to stimulate the endogenous release of vasopressin. Orloff and Blake (1951) found that the diuresis produced in unanesthetized dogs by the infusion of 25 per cent albumin in isotonic saline solution was prevented either by the simultaneous infusion of Pitressin or the prior administration of morphine. Similarly, Welt and Orloff (1951) reported that the diuresis produced in human subjects by the infusion of 4 per cent albumin in isotonic saline was prevented by the administration of a posterior pituitary preparation. On the other hand, Pearce (1968) found that exogenous vasopressin was without any apparent effect on the changes in urine flow rate or free water clearance in anesthetized dogs in which blood volume was increased by the infusion of an "artificial blood."

The effect of vagotomy on the diuresis resulting from expansion of the blood volume is also disputed. Section of the vagus nerves is known to increase the plasma vasopressin concentration (Share and Levy, 1962). Vagotomy results in a reduction in the diuresis produced by the infusion of homologous plasma (Atkins and Pearce, 1959) or an isotonic dextran-saline solution in the anesthetized dog (Gilmore and Weisfeldt, 1965). More recently, Pearce and Lichardus (1967) have found that vagotomy was without effect on the renal response to expansion of blood volume with an "artificial blood" in the anesthetized dog. They suggest that the earlier findings of Atkins and Pearce were due to inadequate controls and the possibility that the infused homologous plasma contained histamine.

A unique approach has been taken by Moses et al. (1967). These investigators have shown that in human subjects undergoing a sustained water diuresis, expansion of blood volume with 6 per cent dextran in isotonic saline raised the level of plasma osmolality at which an antidiuresis occurred in response to an osmotic stimulus. The studies do not prove that an increase in blood volume results in a reduction in the plasma vasopressin concentration. They do show, at the very least, that an increase in blood volume can decrease the sensitivity of the hypothalamo-neurohypophyseal system to stimuli which increase the rate of secretion of vasopressin.

The preponderance of the evidence seems to favor the concept that an increase in blood volume can result in a decrease in the circulating level of vasopressin, presumably as a result of a decreased secretion of the hormone. It is quite clear, however, that definitive proof must await the development of methods that permit the precise measurement of vasopressin at low plasma concentrations. The use of a change in renal function as an index of change in the plasma vasopressin concentration can be misleading, and studies employing this index must be interpreted with caution. The diuresis and natriuresis which result from expansion of extracellular fluid volume are complex phenomena, resulting from the interplay of such humoral agents as aldosterone, vasopressin, and the proposed "third factor," which affects sodium reabsorption in the proximal tubules. Changes in intrarenal hemodynamics may also be included.

Receptors that Can Function as Volume Receptors in the Control of Vasopressin Release

Is the increased release of vasopressin in response to hemorrhage the efferent limb of a reflex in which peripheral receptors are required? In order to attempt to answer this question, receptors that are believed to function as volume receptors were rendered inoperative in anesthetized dogs (Share, 1967b). To achieve this, the cervical vagi were cut, and the carotid sinuses were perfused at constant mean and pulse pressures via an external circuit. These animals were then bled 8 ml/kg at 5-minute intervals, and blood samples for the measurement of vasopressin were taken 3 minutes after each hemorrhage. The ability of these dogs to respond to hemorrhage with an increase in the plasma vasopressin concentration was virtually eliminated (Fig. 5-2). There appeared to be some tendency for the plasma vasopressin concentration to rise, but this effect was small and was not statistically significant. The impaired capacity of these dogs to respond to hemorrhage was not an artefact due to the surgical procedure. In one group of dogs, perfusion of the carotid sinuses by the systemic circulation was resumed after a period of perfusion via the external circuit. The response of these animals (Fig. 5-2) was similar to that seen in anesthetized, vagotomized dogs which were not subjected to surgical manipulation of the carotid sinuses (Fig. 5-1). Thus, in the dog, peripheral receptors are required for an increase in the secretion of vasopressin in response to hemorrhage. Further confirmation of this conclusion is found in the observation that in the vagotomized, carotid-denervated, anesthetized dog, a hemorrhage of 16 ml/kg was without effect on the plasma vasopressin concentration (Share, unpublished observations). Conflicting results have been obtained in the rat by Ginsburg and Brown (1956) and in the cat by Clark and Rocha e Silva (1967). These investigators have reported that vagotomy and denervation of the carotid sinuses did not abolish the increase in the plasma vasopressin concentration following hemorrhage, although the magnitude of the response was attenuated. However, the hemorrhage in these experiments was associated with very large reductions in arterial blood pressure. Therefore, their results may have been due to an impaired removal of vasopressin from the circulation. Alternatively, they may have been due to a reduced cerebral blood flow, since the blood samples for vasopressin determination were obtained from an external jugular vein in the rat and an internal jugular vein in the cat.

Do the "volume receptors" sense changes only in the blood volume, or in the interstitial fluid volume as well? Evidence obtained by Share (1962) suggests that it is the former. Extracellular fluid volume was decreased in dogs by peritoneal dialysis with a hypertonic solution. After 20 minutes, when the blood vasopressin concentration was increased sixfold, blood volume was preferentially re-expanded by the rapid infusion of an isotonic dextran-saline solution. The blood vasopressin level was returned almost to the control level. This reduction was greater than could be attributed to dilution of the circulating vasopressin. Consistent with these observations is the report by Orloff and Blake (1951) that the infusion of a hyperoncotic solution of plasma albumin in the conscious dog resulted in a diuresis. This procedure results in a reduction in interstitial fluid volume and an increase in blood volume. On the other hand, the infusion of hyperoncotic solutions of plasma albumin in normal man induced an antidiuresis (Goodyer et al., 1949; Welt and Orloff, 1951). This question may merit further study with methods which permit the direct measurement of the plasma vasopressin concentration.

Localization of the "volume receptors" in the cephalad portion of the body was suggested by the experiments of Strauss et al. (1951). These investigators showed that an infusion of isotonic saline was effective in producing a diuresis in the recumbent but not in the sitting human subject. The work of Henry and Gauer and their associates focused attention upon the intrathoracic vasculature. Positive pressure respiration, which decreases intrathoracic blood volume, results in an antidiuresis (Drury et al., 1947), while negative pressure respiration results in a diuresis (Gauer et al., 1954; Sieker et al., 1954). The concept that left atrial stretch receptors function as volume receptors in the control of vasopressin release emerged when Henry et al., (1956a) showed that distention of the left atrium in the anesthetized dog resulted in an increased urine flow. The afferent nerve fibers from these receptors are carried in the vagi (Henry and Pearce, 1956). Direct proof, by measurement of the plasma vasopressin concentration, that stimulation of these receptors by distention of the left atrium inhibits vasopressin release was obtained by Baïsset and Montastruc (1957) and by Share (1965). More recently, Johnson et al. (1967) have shown that a relatively small increase in left atrial pressure can result in a reduction in the circulating vasopressin level.

It is possible that the increased urine flow observed by Henry et al., (1956a) when they distended the left atrium was not due primarily to a reduction in the circulating vasopressin level. The increase in urine flow obtained in this manner is said not to be prevented by exogenous vasopressin (Ledsome et al., 1959; Lydtin and Hamilton, 1964), and is accompanied by increases in glomerular filtration rate, renal plasma flow, and solute excretion (Arndt et al., 1963). This illustrates some of the possible pitfalls in the use of changes in urine volume as an index of changes in the plasma vasopressin concentration. Henry et al., (1956a) concluded that receptors in the right atrium and pulmonary vessels are not concerned in the control of vasopressin secretion. However, this question should be reinvestigated with the direct measurement of plasma vasopressin levels.

A change in activity of receptors on the arterial side of the circulation can also lead to a change in the plasma vasopressin concentration. Share and Levy (1962) showed that occlusion of both common carotid arteries in the vagotomized dog resulted in an increase in the blood vasopressin titer; this maneuver was without effect when the vagi were intact. Occlusion above the junction of the thyroid and carotid arteries was as effective as occlusion below this point, and the response was abolished by prior denervation of the carotid sinus region. It was concluded that a reduction of pressure in the carotid sinuses results in a decreased activity of the carotid sinus baroreceptors, which in turn results in a decreased inhibition of the central neural mechanism controlling the release of vasopressin from the posterior pituitary. It was suggested that the failure to observe this response when the vagi were intact was due to an increased inhibitory activity from the aortic arch baroreceptors, stimulated by the increase in arterial blood pressure. The possibility that the hemodynamic consequences of carotid occlusion lead to an increased inhibitory activity from the left atrial stretch receptors, which also have afferent nerve fibers in the vagi, could not be excluded. The findings of Share and Levy were subsequently confirmed by Usami et al. (1962) and Chien et al. (1962). Natcheff et al. (1965), employing a qualitative antidiuretic assay, reported an increase in the antidiuretic activity of the plasma when the common carotid arteries were occluded in the unanesthetized dog with intact vagi.

In order to obtain more definitive proof that a reduction in activity of the carotid sinus baroreceptors results in an increase in the plasma vasopressin concentration, advantage was taken of the fact that these receptors can respond to changes in pulse pressure when mean pressure is held constant (Ead et al., 1952). The carotid sinuses of anesthetized dogs were perfused via an external circuit, with a normal mean pressure and a relatively large pulse pressure (Share and Levy, 1966a). Virtual elimination of the pulse pressure, while mean pressure was held constant, resulted in an increased plasma vasopressin level.

Perlmutt (1963) studied the effects of carotid occlusion, using changes in the free water clearance as an index of changes in the plasma vasopressin concentration. These experiments were done in dogs anesthetized with sodium pentobarbital, in which excretion of a dilute urine was induced by the prolonged infusion of an isotonic glucose solution. Occlusion of the common carotid arteries below but not above the junction with the thyroid arteries resulted in a decreased free water clearance; the vagi were intact. Perlmutt concluded that the carotid receptors involved in the reflex control of vasopressin release are located at the junction of the thyroid and carotid arteries, not in the carotid sinuses. The temporal aspects of these observations are unusual. The free water clearance was reduced only when the carotid arteries were occluded for 5 minutes; shorter or longer periods of occlusion were ineffective. There was also a long lag in the response. The onset of the reduction in urine flow did not occur until 5 to 15 minutes after the release of the occlusion, and in some experiments, the maximal effect did not occur until 1 hour later. In the experiments of Share and Levy (1962), the effect of carotid occlusion was extremely rapid. The plasma vasopressin concentration was more than doubled within 3 minutes after the onset of occlusion, and there was some indication that the vasopressin level was beginning to fall within 10 minutes. Whether or not the effects observed by Perlmutt were due to changes in the plasma vasopressin concentration cannot be stated in the absence of direct measurement of this parameter. On the other hand, the possibility cannot be ruled out that Perlmutt was dealing with a response which has a long delay, and which would have been missed in the short-term observations made by Share and Levy.

Mazer *et al.* (1962) have presented evidence for carotid receptors, other than carotid sinus baroreceptors, which may also play a role in the control of vasopressin release. Using a "cul de sac" preparation of the common carotid in the anesthetized dog, they found that reduction of pressure within either carotid resulted in an antidiuresis. These receptors, which are apparently innervated by the vagi, are distributed along the right common carotid artery from its origin to a point 3 cm below the thyrocarotid junction, and along the entire left common carotid. Evidence that this antidiuresis is due to an increase in the plasma level of vasopressin is provided by the following: reduction in pressure in the common carotids resulted in an increased antidiuretic activity in the plasma; the antidiuretic response was blocked by treatment of the dog with alcohol and by total hypophysectomy, but not by anterior hypophysectomy (Lemaire *et al.*, 1962). Unfortunately, the data given on the changes in the antidiuretic activity of the plasma were scanty, but these observations merit confirmation.

Do the baroreceptors of the aortic arch function in a manner analogous to the receptors of the carotid sinuses in the control of vasopressin secretion? Reasoning by analogy with respect to their similar roles in the regulation of arterial blood pressure, one would expect that they do. There is, however, little direct evidence. The observations that occlusion of the common carotid arteries is without effect on the plasma vasopressin concentration and that vagotomy per se results in an increase in the circulating level of this hormone (Share and Levy, 1962) are consistent with this position. The effects of vagotomy, however, must be due, at least in part, to a loss of activity from the atrial receptors.

An increase in activity of the carotid chemoreceptors also leads to a rise in the plasma vasopressin titer. This was shown by Share and Levy (1966b), who perfused an isolated carotid sinus in the anesthetized dog with deoxygenated blood. It is reasonable to assume that stimulation of these receptors by other means, e.g. an increase in blood pCO_2 or hydrogen ion concentration, will produce a similar effect. Once again reasoning by analogy, one may expect the chemoreceptors of the aortic bodies to respond in a similar fashion. An increased chemoreceptor activity may have contributed to the effects of carotid occlusion on vasopressin release, since this maneuver results in stimulation of the chemoreceptors (Chungcharoen et al., 1952; Landgren and Neil, 1951a; von Euler and Liljestrand, 1943). However, Share and Levy (1966b) concluded that this chemoreceptor reflex is of little importance in the control of vasopressin release, although it may contribute to the increased release of vasopressin with severe hemorrhage. Under these conditions the chemoreceptors are stimulated (Landgren and Neil, 1951b).

Relative Roles of Atrial and Arterial Receptors in the Control of Vasopressin Release

In the dog there are two groups of receptors that are primarily involved in the reflex release of vasopressin in response to a reduction in blood volume: receptors with afferent nerve fibers in the vagi, and baroreceptors in the carotid sinuses. The former group includes left atrial stretch receptors, possibly receptors in the other chambers of the heart and pulmonary vessels, and probably the aortic arch baroreceptors. How do these receptors interact in response to a change in blood volume? The discussion of this problem is facilitated by an approach taken by Henry et al. (1956b) and Gauer and Henry (1963). These investigators contend that, with respect to changes in blood volume, the capacitance vessels, pulmonary vessels, the right heart, and the left atrium behave as a unit. This is the low-pressure system as contrasted to the high-pressure system, i.e. the arterial tree. They further state that, in view of the volume-elasticity properties of these two systems, small to moderate changes in blood volume result in changes in pressure in the low-pressure system, when changes in the arterial system are minor. "Hence, biological receptors, possibly receptors in the other chambers of the heart and low-pressure system could from a physical point of view record the 'fullness of the blood stream'" (Gauer and Henry, 1963). The available evidence supports this view. Much of this evidence derives from attempts to determine the nature of the effective stimulus for a change in vasopressin release when blood volume is changed.

It is quite clear that a change in mean arterial pressure is not an essential stimulus for a change in vasopressin release following reduction in blood volume. In the experiments made by Share (1961) in which extracellular fluid volume was reduced by peritoneal dialysis with a hypertonic solution, the blood vasopressin titer was markedly increased prior to any change in mean arterial pressure. When unanesthetized dogs were bled 10 per cent of the blood volume at 5-minute intervals, the threshold for the increase in the plasma vasopressin concentration was a reduction in blood volume of 10 to 20 per cent (Henry et al., 1968). This degree of hemorrhage, however, was without effect on mean arterial blood pressure. When this same protocol was applied to dogs anesthetized with morphine and a mixture of chloralose and urethane (Share, unpublished observations), a blood loss of 10 per cent of the blood volume resulted in a more than doubling in the plasma vasopressin concentration, but mean arterial blood pressure did not fall until blood volume was reduced by 40 per cent. A contrary view was taken by Ginsburg and Brown (1956), who concluded on the basis of experiments in the rat that hemorrhage was not an effective stimulus for vasopressin secretion until there was a marked reduction in mean arterial blood pressure. However, this finding may have been due to the poor sensitivity of their assay procedure; the minimal detectable plasma vasopressin concentration in these experiments appeared to be approximately 100 µU/ml. Beleslin et al. (1967) supported the position taken by Ginsburg and Brown, but their experiments were not designed to test this point, in that they bled their cats a volume sufficient to produce an abrupt fall in arterial blood pressure of 80 to 120 mm Hg. Their conclusion that the effective stimulus is the fall in mean arterial blood pressure is largely based on one experiment in a cat. Hemorrhage resulted in a very large increase in the plasma vasopressin concentration, which then fell spontaneously without return of the shed blood, as mean arterial blood pressure returned to control levels. Sachs et al. (1967) have shown that the former phenomenon is the result of depletion of a readily releasable pool of vasopressin in the posterior pituitary. Furthermore, in other experiments, Beleslin et al. (1967) reported that in the first 5 to 20 minutes after hemorrhage, a continued rise in the circulating vasopressin level was associated with a spontaneous rise in mean arterial blood pressure.

It also appears that a reduction in arterial pulse pressure may not be the effective stimulus for the increased release of vasopressin produced by small to moderate hemorrhage, but the evidence here is not as definitive as one would like. Although small to moderate hemorrhage can result in a reduction in arterial pulse pressure (e.g. Henry et al., 1968), there is reason to believe that the magnitude of this change may not be sufficient to affect the rate of release of vasopressin. In vagotomized dogs which were anesthetized with morphine and a mixture of chloralose and urethane, a reduction in carotid sinus pulse pressure from 35 ± 3 to 9 ± 3 mm Hg (mean $\pm$ SE, 7 observations) had little or no effect on either systemic arterial pressure or the plasma vasopressin level (Share and Levy, unpublished observations). In other experiments in anesthetized dogs a reduction in blood volume of 10 per cent, which exceeded the threshold for an increase in the plasma vasopressin concentration, was not accompanied by a fall in arterial pulse pressure (Share, unpublished observations).

Further evidence against a reduction in pulse pressure as the effective stimulus for the increased secretion of vasopressin with small to moderate reduction in blood volume is provided by the work of Gupta *et al.* (1966), who recorded changes in afferent impulse activity from aortic arch baroreceptors in dogs subjected to graded, serial hemorrhage. With each bleeding the number of impulses per cardiac cycle decreased, due to the reduction in pulse pressure, but this tended to be offset by an increase in heart rate. Thus, when blood volume had been reduced 20 per cent, the firing rate for these receptors, calculated as number of impulses per unit time, was still 94 per cent of the control rate.

If an increase in blood volume does decrease vasopressin secretion (see above), it seems unlikely that the effect is mediated via changes in arterial blood pressure. Thus, Gupta *et al.* (1966) have shown that when the blood volume in dogs anesthetized with morphine and chloralose was increased by increments of 10 per cent at 5-minute intervals, mean arterial pressure was unchanged after a total increase in blood volume of 30 per cent. No data for changes in arterial pulse pressure were given, but the firing rate of aortic arch baroreceptors had increased only 12 per cent.

That a change in atrial pressure can serve as the effective stimulus for the change in vasopressin release when blood volume is changed is seen in the observations that central venous pressure varies in proportion to a change in blood volume over a range of at least plus or minus 30 per cent (Henry *et al.*, 1956b; Gupta *et al.*, 1966; Henry *et al.*, 1968). Furthermore, Gupta *et al.* (1966) showed that the firing rate of atrial type B receptors was also proportional to changes in blood volume over this range. Finally, Arndt (1966) reported that there is a linear relationship between change in atrial pressure and change in blood volume and between change in circumference of the atria and change in atrial pressure.

Thus, in the normal animal, it may be that, as blood volume is changed, the first receptors to sense this change are located in the low-pressure vascular system, as suggested by Henry and Gauer. However, the ability of the animal deprived of these receptors to respond to hemorrhage with an increase in the plasma vasopressin concentration is not greatly impaired. The effects of graded, serial hemorrhage were compared in intact dogs and in dogs which had been vagotomized, a procedure which denervates the receptors of the aortic arch as well as those of the atria (Fig. 5-1; Share, unpublished observations). With a loss of approximately 10 per cent of the blood volume, there was no significant difference in the increase in the plasma vasopressin concentration between the two groups. With more severe hemorrhage, the vasopressin level rose to a lesser extent in the vagotomized dogs. Clark and Rocha e Silva (1967) have also reported that the stimulation of the release of vasopressin by hemorrhage was impaired in the cat by vagotomy.

Feedback Control of Vasopressin Secretion

Is there closed-loop feedback control of the release of vasopressin from the neurohypophysis? In the sense that there is rapid negative feedback control, mediated by a humoral component, as is the case with the adenohypophyseal-adrenocortical system, the answer is no. There is no evidence that vasopressin stimulates the release of some other humoral factor that would act centrally to inhibit the further release of vasopressin. Nor is there any reason to believe that vasopressin itself can act in this fashion. On the contrary, vasopressin, when added to the incubation medium, stimulated the rate of release of the hormone from the isolated posterior pituitary (Sachs and Haller, 1968). The secretion of vasopressin is subject to negative feedback control in the sense that, as the disturbance in volume or composition of the extracellular fluid which originally triggered the release of vasopressin is corrected, the activity of the appropriate receptors and, presumably, the secretion rate of vasopressin will also return to normal. However, correction of disturbances in volume and composition tend to be slow, so that there may be a long delay in this type of "feedback inhibition" of vasopressin release. The absence of any immediate feedback inhibition of vasopressin release may, at least in part, explain the very high plasma concentrations of vasopressin that can be achieved with a reduction in blood volume.

On the other hand, negative feedback control of vasopressin release during a reduction in blood volume may result from the effects on the mechanism which controls the release of vasopressin of other hormones secreted at an increased rate during blood loss. Thus, it has been postulated that the catecholamines inhibit vasopressin release. O'Connor and Verney (1945) reported that the intravenous administration of epinephrine prevented the inhibition of a water diuresis which otherwise results from emotional stimulation in the conscious dog. Abrahams and Pickford (1956) reported that the inhibition of a water diuresis in the unanesthetized dog by the intracarotid administration of acetylcholine could be prevented by the prior intracarotid injection of epinephrine. It is not certain whether these effects were due to a direct central action of the epinephrine or to an indirect inhibition of vasopressin release via an increased activity of the arterial baroreceptors, resulting from the pressor action of the catecholamines. Share and Levy (1966b) bled anesthetized dogs to keep mean arterial blood pressure constant, while infusing norepinephrine intravenously at rates of 2 and 5 µgm/minute over a period of 2 minutes. The plasma vasopressin concentration did not rise, although the volume bled, a mean of 114 ml at the low rate of norepinephrine infusion and 176 ml at the high rate, should have been sufficient to stimulate an increased release of the hormone. Here, too, the action of the catecholamine was not necessarily the direct inhibition of vasopressin secretion. These dogs were vagotomized, and the norepinephrine may very well have prevented a reduction in the activity of the carotid sinus baroreceptors while the dogs were being bled. Thus, the proposal that the catecholamines inhibit vasopressin release by a direct central action remains conjectural.

It has been suggested that the glucocorticoids can inhibit the release of vasopressin by a direct central action. An extensive but inconclusive literature suggesting a neurohypophyseal-adrenal interrelationship will not be reviewed here. However, support for this proposition is found in the work of Ahmed et al. (1967) and Aubry et al. (1965). The former investigators reported that in patients with adrenal insufficiency there is an elevated plasma vasopressin concentration, which can be reduced acutely by the administration of one hundred mg of cortisone. The latter group of workers found that the injection of over 50 mg of cortisol elevates the osmotic threshold for the inhibition of a water diuresis in human subjects. On the other hand, Kleeman et al. (1964) reported that adrenal insufficiency is not associated with an increase in the circulating vasopressin level. More recently, however, Share and Travis (unpublished observations) have shown that in dogs with adrenal insufficiency the plasma vasopressin concentration does rise, but that this response can be prevented by giving the dogs supplemental salt. Thus, the rise in the plasma vasopressin concentration in adrenal insufficiency does not appear to be due to the direct lack of an inhibitory action of adrenal steroid on the central mechanism which controls the release of vasopressin, but to reduction in blood volume or arterial blood pressure. That an increase in the plasma vasopressin level in adrenal insufficiency is a consequence of a reduction in extracellular fluid volume was suggested earlier by Gill et al. (1962). Furthermore, Share and Travis, after an acute intravenous administration of 100 mg of cortisol, were unable to show any effect on the plasma vasopressin concentration in their dogs with adrenal insufficiency. However, the failure to confirm this aspect of the report of Ahmed et al. (1967) may have been due either to a species difference or to sampling the blood for vasopressin at an inappropriate time. There are two other factors which must be taken into consideration in reviewing the work of Ahmed *et al.* (1967) and Aubry *et al.* (1965). First, the very large doses of glucocorticoid used by these workers suggest the possibility that the effects which they observed were pharmacological rather than physiological. Second, the effects which they observed may have been the result of an increase in blood volume due to the acute effects of the glucocorticoid. Share and Travis (unpublished observations) found a significant reduction in the hematocrit one hour after the intravenous injection of 100 mg of cortisol hemisuccinate in dogs in adrenal insufficiency. Thus, the effects of adrenal steroids on the secretion of vasopressin also remain to be clarified.

Both catecholamines and glucocorticoids are secreted at increased rates following hemorrhage. If it is correct that either of these agents can inhibit vasopressin release under physiological circumstances, then they may function to limit the increase in vasopressin secretion when blood volume is reduced.

Physiological Role of Vasopressin Released in Response to Reduction in Blood Volume

Does the increased secretion of vasopressin in response to a reduction in blood volume represent primarily an emergency measure, or does this response play a physiological role in the day-to-day functioning of the individual? If the latter is the case, the response must be sensitive, i.e. the reflex release of vasopressin must be stimulated by relatively small changes in blood volume. This would appear to be the case, although it is difficult to determine the threshold for the response because of the lack of precision of current bioassay procedures. In the anesthetized dog (Share, 1961 and unpublished observations) and under certain circumstances in the unanesthetized dog (Henry, 1968) the threshold is a reduction in blood volume of less than 10 per cent. Furthermore, the stimulus may be a redistribution of the blood volume rather than a reduction in total circulating blood volume, as occurs, for example, when a human subject changes from the recumbent to the erect position. Evidence that a redistribution of blood volume can serve as an effective stimulus for vasopressin secretion has been obtained by Rogge *et al.* (1967). They have shown that a reduction in thoracic blood volume produced by centrifugation results in an increase in the blood vasopressin concentration in the normal human subject.

There is certainly no question that an increase in the osmotic pressure of the extracellular fluid per se is a stimulus for an increased release of vasopressin. However, dehydration results in a reduction in the volume of the extracellular fluid as well as an increase in its osmotic pressure. Thus, for example, to what extent does a reduction in extracellular fluid volume contribute to the increase in the plasma vasopressin concentration that occurs in humans who are deprived of fluid overnight (Yoshida et al., 1963)? This is a difficult question to answer, but it is certainly not unreasonable to infer that the two stimuli of volume and osmolarity function in at least an additive fashion, if not synergistically.

With severe hemorrhage, the concentration of vasopressin in the plasma may be high enough for this hormone to function as a pressor agent and thus aid in the maintenance of arterial blood pressure. That even lower levels of vasopressin may function in the maintenance of arterial blood pressure is suggested by the report of Bartelstone and Nasmyth (1965). These investigators presented evidence that vasopressin at low, non-pressor concentrations potentiates the pressor response to catecholamines. Finally, Frieden and Keller (1954) reported that diabetes insipidus impaired the ability of the dog to maintain blood pressure during hemorrhage, and that this deficit was corrected by the acute administration of sub-pressor doses of Pitressin.

Summary

An attempt to summarize the concepts and notions which have been discussed here is presented in Fig. 5-3. There are essentially three feedback loops. One, by virtue of the effects of vasopressin on the reabsorption of water by the kidney, affects the osmolality of the plasma, which is sensed by the osmoreceptors. A second loop acts via changes in blood volume, by virtue of the effects of vasopressin and aldosterone on the renal handling of water and salt. Changes in blood volume are sensed by receptors in the low-pressure and arterial systems, in a manner which is determined by the relationships between the pressures in these systems and blood volume. The third loop acts via changes in arterial pressure that result from changes in arteriolar tone. These changes are mediated by the sympathetic nervous system, circulating catecholamine levels, and perhaps the plasma vasopressin concentration. The possibility that the glucocorticoids and catecholamines may act upon the mechanism controlling vasopressin release is also indicated.

Fig. 5-3 is clearly an oversimplification. The systems that control the

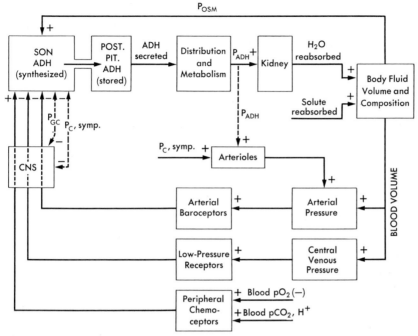

Figure 5-3 Summary of the control of vasopressin secretion in the context of the regulation of blood volume. SON, supraoptic nucleus; post. pit., posterior pituitary; CNS, central nervous system; symp., sympathetic nervous system; P_{ADH}, plasma vasopressin concentration; P_{OSM}, plasma osmolality; P_{GC}, plasma glucocorticoid concentration; P_C, plasma catecholamine concentration; +, increase or stimulation; −, decrease or inhibition. Dotted arrows indicate questionable functions or unknown pathways.

release of renin from the kidney, and through it the secretion of aldosterone by the adrenal, the release of ACTH from the anterior pituitary, and through it the secretion of glucocorticoids by the adrenal, the sympathetic nervous system, and through it the dynamic events of the cardiovascular system, all respond to changes in extracellular fluid volume. All these systems, as well as the system which controls the release of vasopressin, must interact, and their actions must be integrated in order to provide for the regulation of extracellular fluid volume and pressure and flow in the cardiovascular system. No attempt has been made to portray this very complex homeostatic regulatory mechanism. In addition, stimuli that affect vasopressin secretion, but that do not play a major role in the regulation of blood volume, e.g. emotion, pain, and surgical stress, have been omitted. Even that portion of the system which is shown is oversimplified. The afferent inputs from the peripheral receptors to the hypothalamus are shown "passing through" the central nervous system. Little is known of the pathways between the initial way-station, the nucleus solitarius, and the supraoptic nucleus. All inputs are shown terminating upon the supraoptic nucleus, but are there factors of physiological importance that can act directly upon the nerve endings in the posterior lobe to modify the releasing mechanism for vasopressin? Finally, Figure 5-3 suffers badly from a complete lack of quantitation of the stimuli and responses shown there. Obtaining these quantitative data will require the development of more precise methods for the measurement of the concentration of vasopressin in plasma. In any event, future research can profitably be directed toward the study of the interaction of the systems that regulate the volume and composition of the extracellular fluid, particularly at the level of the central nervous system.

References

Abrahams, V. C., and M. Pickford (1956).   Observations on a central antagonism between adrenaline and acetylcholine.   *J. Physiol. 131*, 712-18.

Ahmed, A. B. J., B. C. George, C. Gonzalez-Auvert, and J. F. Dingman (1967). Increased plasma arginine vasopressin in clinical adrenocortical insufficiency and its inhibition by glucosteroids.   *J. Clin. Invest. 46*, 111-23.

Arndt, J. O. (1966).   Die Beziehungen zwischchen Umfang Vorhöfe und Vorhof-drucken bei Volumenänderungen an narkotisierten Katzen.   *Pflügers Arch. ges. Physiol. 292*, 343-55.

Arndt, J. O., H. Reineck, and O. H. Gauer (1963).   Ausscheidungsfunktion und Hämodynamik der Nieren bei Dehnung des linken Vorhofes am narkotisierten Hund.   *Pflügers Arch. ges. Physiol. 277*, 1-15.

Atkins, E. L., and J. W. Pearce (1959).   Mechanisms of the renal response to plasma volume expansion.   *Can. J. Biochem. Physiol. 37*, 91-102.

Aubry, R. H., H. R. Nankin, A. M. Moses, and D. H. P. Streeten (1965).   Measurement of the osmotic threshold for vasopressin release in human subjects, and its modification by cortisol.   *J. Clin. Endocrinol. Metab. 25*, 1481-92.

Baïsset, A., and P. Montastruc (1957).   Polyurie par distension auriculaire chez le chien; rôle de l'hormone antidiurétique.   *J. Physiol. (Paris) 49*, 33-36.

Baratz, R. A., and R. C. Ingraham (1960).   Renal hemodynamics and antidiuretic hormone release associated with volume regulation.   *Am. J. Physiol. 198*, 565-70.

Bartelstone, H. J., and P. A. Nasmyth (1965).   Vasopressin potentiation of catecholamine actions in dog, rat, cat, and rat aortic strip.   *Am. J. Physiol. 208*, 754-62.

Beleslin, D., G. W. Bisset, J. Haldar, and R. L. Polak (1967).   The release of vasopressin without oxytocin in response to haemorrhage.   *Proc. Roy. Soc. B 166*, 443-58.

Bisset, G. W., S. M. Hilton, and A. M. Poisner (1967). Hypothalamic pathways for independent release of vasopressin and oxytocin. *Proc. Roy. Soc. B 166*, 423-58.

Bocanegra, M., and H. D. Lauson (1961). Ultrafilterability of endogenous antidiuretic hormone from plasma of dogs. *Am. J. Physiol. 200*, 486-92.

Chien, S., B. Peric, and S. Usami (1962). The reflex nature of release of antidiuretic hormone upon common carotid occlusion in vagotomized dogs. *Proc. Soc. Exp. Biol. Med. 111*, 193-96.

Chungcharoen, D., M. de Burgh Daly, E. Neil, and A. Schweitzer (1952). The effect of carotid occlusion upon the intrasinusal pressure with special reference to vascular communications between the carotid and vertebral circulations in the dog, cat and rabbit. *J. Physiol. (London) 117*, 56-76.

Clark, B. J., and M. Rocha e Silva, Jr. (1967). An afferent pathway for the selective release of vasopressin in response to carotid occlusion and haemorrhage in the cat. *J. Physiol. (London) 191*, 529-42.

De Wied, D. (1960). A simple automatic and sensitive method for the assay of antidiuretic hormone with notes on the antidiuretic potency of plasma under different experimental conditions. *Acta Physiol. Pharmacol. Neerl. 9*, 69-81.

Drury, D. R., J. P. Henry, and J. Goodman (1947). The effects of continuous pressure breathing on kidney function. *J. Clin. Invest. 26*, 945-51.

Ead, H. W., J. H. Green, and E. Neil (1952). A comparison of the effects of pulsatile and non-pulsatile blood flow through the carotid sinus on the reflexogenic activity of the sinus baroreceptors in the cat. *J. Physiol. (London) 118*, 509-19.

von Euler, U. S., and G. Liljestrand (1943). The role of the chemoreceptors of the sinus region for the occlusion test in the cat. *Acta Physiol. Scand. 6*, 319-23.

Frieden, J., and A. D. Keller (1954). Decreased resistance to hemorrhage in neurohypophysectomized dogs. *Circulation Res. 2*, 214-20.

Gauer, O. H., and J. P. Henry (1963). Circulatory basis of fluid volume control. *Physiol. Rev. 43*, 423-81.

Gauer, O. H., J. P. Henry, H. O. Sieker, and W. E. Wendt (1954). The effect of negative pressure breathing on urine flow. *J. Clin. Invest. 33*, 287-96.

Gill, J. R., Jr., D. S. Gann, and F. C. Bartter (1962). Restoration of water diuresis in Addisonian patients by expansion of the volume of extracellular fluid. *J. Clin. Invest. 41*, 1078-85.

Gilmore, J. P., and M. L. Weisfeldt (1965). Contribution of intravascular receptors to the renal responses following intravascular expansion. *Circulation Res. 17*, 144-54.

Ginsburg, M., and L. M. Brown (1956). Effect of anaesthetics and haemorrhage on the release of neurohypophysial antidiuretic hormone. *Brit. J. Pharmacol. 11*, 236-44.

Ginsburg, M., and H. Heller (1953). Antidiuretic activity in blood obtained from various parts of the cardiovascular system. *J. Endocrin. 9*, 274-82.

Goodyer, A. V. N., E. R. Peterson, and A. S. Relman (1949). Some effects of albumin infusions on renal function and electrolyte excretion in normal man. *J. Appl. Physiol. 1*, 671-82.

Gupta, P. D., J. P. Henry, R. Sinclair, and R. von Baumgarten (1966). Responses of atrial and aortic baroreceptors to nonhypotensive hemorrhage and to transfusion. *Am. J. Physiol. 211*, 1429-37.

Henry, J. P., and J. W. Pearce (1956). The possible role of cardiac atrial stretch receptors in the induction of changes in urine flow. *J. Physiol. (London)* *131*, 572-85.

Henry, J. P., O. H. Gauer, and J. L. Reeves (1956a). Evidence of the atrial location of receptors influencing urine flow. *Circulation Res.* *4*, 85-90.

Henry, J. P., O. H. Gauer, and H. O. Sieker (1956b). The effect of moderate changes in blood volume on left and right atrial pressures. *Circulation Res.* *4*, 91-94.

Henry, J. P., P. D. Gupta, J. P. Meehan, R. Sinclair, and L. Share (1968). The role of afferents from the low-pressure system in the release of antidiuretic hormone during non-hypotensive hemorrhage. *Can. J. Physiol. Pharmacol.* *46*, 287-95.

Jeffers, W. A., M. M. Livezey, and J. H. Austin (1942). A method for demonstrating an antidiuretic action of minute amounts of Pitressin: statistical analysis of results. *Proc. Soc. Exp. Biol. Med.* *50*, 184-88.

Johnson, J. A., W. W. Moore, and W. E. Segar (1967). The relationship between left atrial pressure and plasma ADH levels in the dog. *The Physiologist 10*, 213.

Kleeman, C. R., J. W. Czaczkes, and R. Cutler (1964). Mechanisms of impaired water excretion in adrenal and pituitary insufficiency. IV. Antidiuretic hormone in primary and secondary adrenal insufficiency. *J. Clin. Invest. 43*, 1641-48.

Landgren, S., and E. Neil (1951a). The contribution of carotid chemoreceptor mechanisms to the rise of blood pressure caused by carotid occlusion. *Acta Physiol. Scand. 23*, 152-57.

Landgren, S., and E. Neil (1951b). Chemoreceptor impulse activity following hemorrhage. *Acta Physiol. Scand. 23*, 158-67.

Lauson, H. D. (1967). Metabolism of antidiuretic hormones. *Am. J. Med. 42*, 713-44.

Leaf, A., and A. R. Mamby (1952). An antidiuretic mechanism not regulated by extracellular fluid tonicity. *J. Clin. Invest. 31*, 60-71.

Ledsome, J. R., R. J. Linden, and W. J. O'Connor (1961). The mechanisms by which distention of the left atrium produces diuresis in anaesthetized dogs. *J. Physiol. (London) 159*, 87-100.

Lemaire, R., A. Mazer, C. Labouche, and J. Allegrini (1962). Mécanisme de l'oligurie déclenchée par l'hypopression intracarotidienne. *Comptes Rend. Soc. Biol. 156*, 340-42.

Lydtin, H., and W. F. Hamilton (1964). Effect of acute changes in left atrial pressure on urine flow in unanesthetized dogs. *Am. J. Physiol. 207*, 530-36.

Mazer, A., J. Allegrini, and R. Lemaire (1962). Localisation des zones vasosensibles carotidiennes responsables de la sécrétion de l'hormone antidiurétique chez le chien. *Comptes Rend. Soc. Biol. 156*, 718-21.

Moses, A. M., M. Miller, and D. H. P. Streeten (1967). Quantitative influence of blood volume expansion on the osmotic threshold for vasopressin release. *J. Clin. Endocrinol. Metab. 27*, 655-62.

Natcheff, N., B. Piryova, and T. Bratanova (1965). Effet de la compression carotidienne bilaterale sur la sécrétion de l'hormone antidiurétique chez le chien en expérimentation chronique. *J. Physiol. (Paris) 57*, 337-42.

O'Connor, W. J., and E. B. Verney (1945). The effect of increased activity of the sympathetic system in the inhibition of water-diuresis by emotional stress. *Quart. J. Exp. Physiol. 33*, 77-90.

Orloff, J., and W. D. Blake (1951). Effects of concentrated salt-poor albumin on metabolism of water and electrolytes in dogs. *Am. J. Physiol. 164*, 167-74.

Pearce, J. W. (1968). The renal response to volume expansion. *Can. J. Physiol. Pharmacol. 46*, 305-13.

Pearce, J. W., and B. Lichardus (1967). Effects of vagotomy and renal denervation on renal response to blood volume expansion. *Can. J. Physiol. Pharmacol. 45*, 689-703.

Perlmutt, J. H. (1963). Reflex antidiuresis after occlusion of common carotid arteries in hydrated dogs. *Am. J. Physiol. 204*, 197-201.

Permutt, M. A., C. W. Parker, and R. D. Utiger (1966). Immunochemical studies with lysine vasopressin. *Endocrinology 78*, 809-14.

Rogge, J. D., W. W. Moore, W. E. Segar, and A. F. Fasola (1967). Effect of +G$_z$ and +G$_x$ acceleration on peripheral venous ADH levels in humans. *J. Appl. Physiol. 23*, 870-73.

Rydin, H., and E. B. Verney (1938). The inhibition of water-diuresis by emotional stress and muscular exercise. *Quart. J. Exp. Physiol. 27*, 343-74.

Sachs, H., and E. W. Haller (1968). Further studies on the capacity of the neurohypophysis to release vasopressin. *Endocrinology 83*, 251-62.

Sachs, H., L. Share, J. Osinchak, and A. Carpi (1967). Capacity of the neurohypophysis to release vasopressin. *Endocrinology 81*, 755-70.

Sawyer, W. H. (1966). Biological assays for neurohypophysial principles in tissues and in blood. In *The Pituitary Gland* (G. W. Harris and B. T. Donovan, eds.), *3*, pp. 288-306. University of California Press, Berkeley.

Share, L. (1961). Acute reduction in extracellular fluid volume and the concentration of antidiuretic hormone in blood. *Endocrinology 69*, 925-33.

Share, L. (1962). Vascular volume and blood level of antidiuretic hormone. *Am. J. Physiol. 202*, 791-94.

Share, L. (1965). Effects of carotid occlusion and left atrial distention on plasma vasopressin titer. *Am. J. Physiol. 208*, 219-23.

Share, L. (1967a). Vasopressin, its bioassay and the physiological control of its release. *Am. J. Med. 42*, 701-12.

Share, L. (1967b). Role of peripheral receptors in the increased release of vasopressin in response to hemorrhage. *Endocrinology 81*, 1140-46.

Share, L., and M. N. Levy (1962). Cardiovascular receptors and blood titer of antidiuretic hormone. *Am. J. Physiol. 203*, 425-28.

Share, L., and M. N. Levy (1966a). Carotid sinus pulse pressure, a determinant of plasma antidiuretic hormone concentration. *Am. J. Physiol. 211*, 721-24.

Share, L., and M. N. Levy (1966b). Effect of carotid chemoreceptor stimulation on plasma antidiuretic hormone titer. *Am. J. Physiol. 210*, 157-61.

Sieker, H. O., O. H. Gauer, and J. P. Henry (1954). The effect of continuous negative pressure breathing on water and electrolyte excretion by the human kidney. *J. Clin. Invest. 33*, 572-77.

Smith, H. W. (1957). Salt and water volume receptors. *Am. J. Med. 23*, 623-52.

Starling, E. H. (1909). *The Fluids of the Body*. W. T. Keener and Co., Chicago.

Strauss, M. B. (1957). *Body Water in Man*. Little, Brown and Co., Boston.

Strauss, M. B., R. K. Davis, J. D. Rosenbaum, and E. C. Rossmeisl (1951). "Water diuresis" produced during recumbency by the intravenous infusion of isotonic saline solution. *J. Clin. Invest. 30*, 862-95.

Usami, S., and S. Chien (1963). Role of hepatic blood flow in regulating plasma concentration of antidiuretic hormone after hemorrhage. *Proc. Soc. Exp. Biol. Med. 113*, 606-9.

Usami, S., B. Peric, and S. Chien (1962). Release of antidiuretic hormone due to common carotid occlusion and its relation with vagus nerve. *Proc. Soc. Exp. Biol. Med. 111*, 189-93.

Weinstein, H., R. M. Berne, and H. Sachs (1960). Vasopressin in blood: effect of hemorrhage. *Endocrinology 66*, 712-18.

Welt, L. G., and J. Orloff (1951). The effects of an increase in plasma volume on the metabolism and excretion of water and electrolytes by normal subjects. *J. Clin. Invest. 30*, 751-61.

Yoshida, S., K. Motohashi, H. Ibayashi, and S. Okinaka (1963). Method for the assay of antidiuretic hormone in plasma with a note on the antidiuretic titer of human plasma. *J. Lab. Clin. Med. 62*, 279-85.

6

"Short" Feedback Mechanisms in the Control of Anterior Pituitary Function

M. MOTTA, F. FRASCHINI, and L. MARTINI

Introduction

It is now well established that the pituitary gland is regulated by two different types of feedback mechanisms. The first, which might be called the "classic" feedback system, was discovered several years ago; in this system the controlling (inhibiting or activating) signals are the hormones produced by the peripheral target glands (adrenal cortex, gonads, thyroid). The second was discovered more recently and is usually referred to as the "short," "auto," or "internal" feedback mechanism; in this system the controlling signals are the pituitary hormones themselves. A physiological role for "short" feedback mechanisms has been suggested for all the hormones manufactured in the anterior and intermediate lobes of the pituitary gland. It is relevant that "short" systems are involved in the control of the secretion of Prolactin, Growth Hormone (GH), and the Melanocyte Stimulating Hormones, α-MSH and β-MSH, pituitary principles which do not have peripheral target glands, and which consequently are not regulated by traditional feedback mechanisms.

The receptors sensitive to the signals of the "classic" feedback mechanisms are localized either in the brain (mainly in the median eminence of the hypothalamus) or in the anterior pituitary (Mangili et al., 1966; Mess and Martini, 1968). Those sensitive to "short" feedback messages are mainly located in the brain; intrapituitary receptors for this type of signal have not been conclusively demonstrated so far.

The existence of "short" feedback loops and the participation of the central nervous system (CNS) in their operation has been proved by

211

different techniques. It has been shown, for instance, that the implantation of minute amounts of certain pituitary hormones in the CNS results in an inhibition of the anterior pituitary gland. In some instances, the systemic administration of an exogenous pituitary hormone to animals deprived of the target glands for that hormone has been shown to modify, simultaneously, the secretion of the hormone and the production of its hypothalamic releasing factor. In addition, hypophysectomy has been reported to alter hypothalamic stores of some releasing factors and to make them appear in the general circulation. There is other evidence that pituitary hormones act directly on the brain; some of them exert activating or inhibiting effects on the electrical activity of the CNS which are independent of the effects on their peripheral target glands. Pituitary hormones also exert direct behavioral and neuropharmacological effects, modify brain histology, and influence several biochemical processes which take place in the CNS (see Chapter 3).

How can one visualize a mechanism through which, under physiological conditions, pituitary hormones may reach the brain and modify its functions? One possibility is that pituitary hormones are transported to the median eminence and to other brain structures through the general circulation. The other possibility is transport up the pituitary stalk. Török (1954, 1964) and Jazdowska and Dobrowolski (1965) have demonstrated a vascular system passing from the posterior surface of the anterior pituitary gland to the capillary complex of the median eminence; this vascular system might be a route through which the pituitary could dispatch hormonal information directly to its hypothalamic controller. Several pituitary hormones have been isolated from the basal hypothalamus, where this particular vascular system terminates (Guillemin et al., 1962, 1963; Schally et al., 1962; Jacobowitz et al., 1963; De La Lastra and Croxatto, 1964; Tramezzani and Voloschin, 1965; Croxatto et al., 1966; Johnson and Nelson, 1966).

"Short" Feedback Control of Adrenocorticotropin Secretion

The hypothesis that adrenocorticotropin (ACTH) might influence its own secretion by a direct feedback on structures in the CNS has recently gained considerable support. Stressful stimuli induce a greater secretion of ACTH in adrenalectomized rats if the initial plasma level of the hormone is low rather than high, suggesting that high levels of circulating ACTH reduce the reactivity of the hypothalamic-pituitary axis (Hodges and Vernikos, 1958; 1959). Chronic treatment of adrenalectomized animals with exogenous ACTH increases pituitary ACTH stores, the increase being proportional to the dose of the hormone administered (Kitay et al., 1959; Isobe, 1967). Exogenous ACTH, when given in sufficient amounts, is also able to block the fall of pituitary ACTH usually induced by stress in adrenalectomized rats (Kitay et al., 1959). The presence of ACTH-secreting pituitary tumors prevents the increase in plasma and pituitary ACTH that usually occurs after adrenalectomy (Vernikos-Danellis and Trigg, 1967). Stress-induced increases in plasma ACTH in adrenalectomized animals bearing tumors of this type are not as great as those found in adrenalectomized rats without tumors (Vernikos-Danellis and Trigg, 1967). High plasma levels of ACTH apparently interfere particularly with the release of the hormone; its synthesis is not reduced and may even be stimulated, as shown by the fact that exogenous ACTH increases pituitary ACTH stores even when given concurrently with dexamethasone (Isobe, 1967). When given alone this synthetic corticoid reduces the synthesis of ACTH (Holub et al., 1959; Mangili et al., 1966).

A recent study of ACTH-induced inhibition of stress responses has provided new support for the hypothesis that this hormone may directly intervene in the control of its own secretion. Dallman and Yates (1968) have evaluated the effects of chronic ACTH pretreatment in normal rats on the acute secretion of ACTH induced by several types of stresses. Stimuli were applied 24 hours after the last injection of ACTH, at a time when plasma corticosterone levels had returned to normal but the adrenal remained hypertrophied. Stresses such as noise and ether were partially inhibited by ACTH pretreatment, while others (scald, laparotomy, etc.) were not. Similar results were reported in guinea pigs by Yudaev (1966). The conclusion from these studies was that ACTH can block stress-induced increases in ACTH secretion; however, the inhibition seems to depend on the type of the stimulus.

Dallman and Yates (1968) and Yudaev (1966) postulated a direct effect of ACTH on the brain. However, when exogenous corticoids are administered, stress responses remain blocked for several hours after plasma corticoid levels have returned to normal (Gavazzi et al., 1962; Smelik, 1963); presumably this occurs because corticoids remain bound to their brain receptors (Henkin et al., 1967). Therefore the inhibition of stress responses reported by Yudaev (1966) and by Dallman and Yates (1968) might be the consequence of the accumulation in the brain of endogenous corticoids. In order to overcome this argument, Dallman and Yates (1968) have studied the inhibitory effects of pretreatment with ACTH in normal animals in which the receptors for the "classic" steroid feedback mechanism had theoretically been completely saturated by the administration of dexamethasone. They found, in confirmation of Mangili *et al.* (1965), that histamine and laparotomy activated ACTH release even in the presence of high doses of dexamethasone, but that the stimulating activity of these stresses was inhibited if dexamethasone-treated animals were also given ACTH. Dallman and Yates (1968) concluded that the hypothalamic-pituitary-adrenal axis normally receives two types of inputs: one which is corticosteroid-sensitive and can be saturated by dexamethasone; and one which is corticosteroid-insensitive but can be blocked by treatment with ACTH.

Where are the receptors that respond to ACTH? The "in vitro" data by Fand *et al.* (1966) suggest that the pituitary itself may respond to changing levels of ACTH. These investigators observed an increased "basophilism" (which presumably indicates an increased intracellular storage of ACTH) when exogenous ACTH was added to the incubation medium of cultures of human pituitaries. However, the bulk of the available evidence suggests that the brain, and in particular the hypothalamus, contains the most important receptor areas for the "short" feedback effect of ACTH. In a pioneer work, Halász and Szentágothai (1960) implanted anterior pituitary tissue in the infundibular recess of the third ventricle of the rat, and found a depressing effect of such implants on adrenal function. Motta *et al.* (1965) implanted solid ACTH into several areas of the brain and the pituitary of normal male rats. The animals were then subjected to a mild environmental stress. ACTH proved effective in depressing blood corticosterone levels and in inhibiting the response to the mild stress, but only when placed in the median eminence region; implants of ACTH in the frontal cerebral cortex or the pituitary were completely ineffective, as were implants of luteinizing hormone (LH) in the median eminence. These results have been interpreted as indicating that the receptors for the "short" feedback effect of ACTH are mainly located in the basal hypothalamus, and particularly in the median eminence. Exactly the same degree of inhibition was observed when either a crude or a synthetic ACTH preparation (β 1-24 corticotropin) was implanted in the median eminence. These results provide one of the few demonstrations so far available that a "short" feedback effect can be obtained with a hormone absolutely devoid of contamination. Since β 1-24 corticotropin has complete ACTH activity (Desaulles and Rittel, 1968), the data also suggest that the feedback effect is a property of ACTH as such; however, this conclusion cannot be accepted until results are collected on the effects of shorter fragments of the ACTH molecule on ACTH secretion. These studies are particularly important in view of evidence indicating that the same behavioral phenomena can be induced by a whole family of short peptides derived from either ACTH or MSH (see Chapter 3). The latter hormone has a close chemical relationship to ACTH (Novales, 1967). Davidson *et al.* (1968) have recently reported that ACTH implants in the median eminence do not reduce "basal" levels of corticosterone in normal male rats and do not inhibit the response of the pituitary-adrenal axis to a strong stimulus (ether anesthesia). There is not necessarily any discrepancy between these results and those of Motta *et al.* (1965), since the latter investigators never evaluated the effects of ACTH implants in animals under resting conditions or exposed to major stresses.

The role of the hypothalamus in the "short" feedback effect of ACTH has been assessed in other ways. Adrenalectomy is known to increase the concentration of the Corticotropin Releasing Factor (CRF) in the hypothalamus (Vernikos-Danellis, 1965; Bagul, 1967; Motta *et al.*, 1968a). A further increase in CRF content is obtained if hypophysectomy is added to adrenalectomy (Motta *et al.*, 1968a). Since CRF also appears in the circulation after hypophysectomy (Schapiro *et al.*, 1958; Eik-Nes and Brizzee, 1958; Brodish and Long, 1962), these results suggest that the elimination of the inhibiting feedback signal normally provided by ACTH activates the synthesis as well as the release of its hypothalamic mediator (Motta *et al.*, 1968a). Treatment of adrenalecto-mized-hypophysectomized animals with exogenous ACTH reduces CRF stores to the level found following adrenalectomy alone; but even high doses of ACTH will not reduce the hypothalamic content of CRF to pre-adrenalectomy levels (Motta *et al.*, 1968a). This suggests that CRF is under a dual feedback control via corticoids and ACTH. A similar conclusion has been reached by Chowers *et al.* (1967); they have demonstrated that, in the rat, intrahypothalamic implants of dexametha-sone cause a reduction of adrenal weight, as well as a significant decrease of CRF in the median eminence and of ACTH in the pituitary. Implants of dexamethasone in the anterior pituitary also cause a reduction of adrenal weight and a decrease of ACTH stores. However, CRF in the median eminence is considerably increased. It appears, therefore, that CRF stores are lowered by the direct effect of corticoids applied to the hypothalamus, and enhanced by the reduced plasma and pituitary ACTH levels brought about by intrapituitary placements of dexamethasone.

Support for a hypothalamic site of action of the feedback effect of ACTH also comes from histological studies. Treatment of adrenalecto-mized rats with ACTH has been reported to result in marked changes in the nuclear size and in chromatolysis in several hypothalamic nuclei

(Castor *et al.*, 1951; Mühlen and Ockenfels, 1968), as well as in an increased storage of neurosecretory material (Peczely, 1966).

Evidence has now accumulated showing that ACTH exerts neuropharmacological, behavioral, and electrophysiological effects. Woodbury and Vernadakis (1967) have found that ACTH is able to antagonize the effect exerted by adrenal steroids on electroshock seizure threshold. Wasserman *et al.* (1965) have reported that ACTH reduces the threshold to minimal electroshock seizures in normal as well as in adrenalectomized rats. Tonkikh (1960), Milcu *et al.* (1964), and Op de Coul (1966) have observed that the administration of ACTH to normal cats is followed, after a phase of excitation, by a long period of drowsiness. Since cortisone or cortisol did not produce the same effects, they were believed to be due to a direct action of ACTH on the brain. Klein and Livingstone (1950) and Millichap and Jones (1964) observed impressive clinical and electroencephalographic (EEG) improvements following ACTH medication in children who had suffered for years from epilepsy refractory to other types of therapy. Adrenal steroids did not produce the same effects in these patients, so a direct neural effect of ACTH was again postulated. Administration of ACTH to patients with Addison's disease or congenital adrenal hyperplasia in whom there is deficient cortisol synthesis was accompanied by severe EEG alterations. These reverted to normal after corticosteroid treatment (Milcu *et al.*, 1964). An activation of the EEG following ACTH administration was also reported in normal, hypophysectomized and adrenalectomized rats by Torda and Wolff (1952).

The experiments of de Wied and his associates showing that ACTH and related peptides exert complex effects on behavior are summarized in Chapter 3. Others have shown that crude, purified, and synthetic ACTH preparations induce stretching and yawning motions in dogs, cats, rabbits, and rats when injected intracisternally. This property is shared by shorter peptides having only part of the aminoacid sequence (1 to 10; 4 to 10; etc.) of ACTH or of MSH (Ferrari *et al.*, 1957; 1961; 1963; Ferrari, 1958; Gessa *et al.*, 1966; 1967; Nikolov, 1967). The receptors for the effect are apparently located in the hypothalamus, as indicated by the results of intracerebral injections of synthetic β 1-24 corticotropin (Ferrari *et al.*, 1966). It is interesting that vasopressin, which, when given intracisternally, is a potent stimulus for ACTH release (Martini, 1966a), mimics the behavioral effects of ACTH (Nikolov, 1967).

Impressive data on the effects of ACTH on the CNS have been provided by recent electrophysiological studies. Aleksanyan (1967) has found that hypophysectomy increases the electrical activity of the hypothalamus of the frog. The absence of ACTH, a major principle secreted by the anterior lobe of amphibia (Barker Jørgensen and Larsen, 1967), may be responsible for the activation of the hypothalamus. In agreement with these data, Kawakami et al. (1966) have shown in the rabbit that the electrical activity of median eminence neurons is depressed by increased plasma levels of ACTH. The same neurons are activated by a decrease in blood adrenal steroid levels. This is another piece of evidence indicating that the median eminence is usually under the dual control of ACTH and corticoids. When corticoids are lacking (for instance, following adrenalectomy) the median eminence is activated, so that more ACTH is secreted. However, the increase in plasma levels of ACTH inhibits the median eminence and limits the hypersecretion of ACTH. The inhibitory effect of ACTH on median eminence neurons has been confirmed by Sawyer (personal communication, 1968), who has shown in addition that ACTH, when administered to adrenalectomized rats, enhances the electrical activity of the lateral hypothalamus (see Chapter 7).

Apparently the influence of ACTH on brain electrical phenomena is not limited to the hypothalamus. ACTH activates the septum, the somatomotor cortex (Korányi et al., 1966) and the thalamus (Monnier, 1953) in normal and in adrenalectomized rats. The electrical activity of the midbrain reticular formation and the amygdaloid nuclei in rabbits is also enhanced by ACTH (Kawakami et al., 1966); this is certainly a direct effect of the hormone, since adrenal steroids have an opposite action. By contrast, the activity of the hippocampus and some other areas of the limbic system is depressed by high ACTH levels and is stimulated by an increase of plasma corticoids (Kawakami et al., 1966). It is not known yet whether the extrahypothalamic structures whose electrical activity is modified by ACTH also operate as feedback receptors for the "short" feedback effect of ACTH. Studies in this area are needed.

The existence of a "negative" feedback effect of ACTH on its own secretion has potential clinical implications. For instance, if the "short" feedback effect of ACTH is present in humans, one might expect that the administration of ACTH to patients on long-term corticoid therapy would result in a further depression of the reactivity of the hypothalamic-pituitary axis. A few clinical data have appeared which indicate this to be the case. ACTH has been shown to restore adrenal size and responsiveness in steroid-treated patients (Sandberg et al., 1957); yet, despite ACTH treatment, the adrenals of these patients revert to the hypofunctional state as soon as ACTH is discontinued (Liddle et al., 1959). In addition, subjects pretreated with ACTH for three days, and tested with either metyrapone or vasopressin immediately after discontinuation of ACTH administration, show a decreased endogenous release of ACTH (Plager and Cushman, 1962; Sussman *et al.*, 1965).

"Short" Feedback Control of Melanocyte Stimulating Hormone Secretion

There are a few data which indicate that a "short" feedback mechanism is also involved in the regulation of MSH secretion. (The term "MSH" is used here to refer to MSH activity without specifying whether α-MSH or β-MSH is responsible for it.) Kastin and Schally (1967) have shown in the rat that the injection of natural and synthetic preparations of α-MSH and β-MSH cause a significant increase in the MSH content of the pituitaries of the treated animals. The increase is proportional to the dose of MSH injected. These data may indicate either that MSH release has been inhibited or that its synthesis has been enhanced by the presence of high plasma levels of the hormone.

Although the possibility of a direct effect of MSH on the pituitary gland has not been experimentally disproved, a transhypothalamic mechanism appears more logical. It has been clearly established that the hypothalamus is involved in the control of MSH secretion (Kastin and Ross, 1965; Taleisnik and Orias, 1965; Schally and Kastin, 1966). Moreover, MSH-like substances have been found in the brain (Ralph and Peyton, 1966; Guillemin *et al.*, 1962), and the brain also contains an enzyme able to split this hormone (Long *et al.*, 1961). As in the case of ACTH, evidence for an action of MSH on the nervous system is provided by electrophysiological data (Guillemin and Krivoy, 1960; Krivoy and Guillemin, 1961) and behavioral data (Ferrari *et al.*, 1963). (See also Chapter 3.)

It is interesting that an increase of pituitary MSH stores in the rat can also be obtained by injecting ACTH. This appears to be an extra-adrenal effect of the hormone, since corticoids do not have the same property. The intrinsic MSH activity possessed by ACTH (Novales, 1967) is insufficient to explain this action. It is not known whether shorter peptides having parts of the amino-acid sequences of MSH or of ACTH would exert the same type of effect. All the data indicating that MSH may regulate its own rate of synthesis and release have been obtained in mammals, and in mammals MSH has no clearly established function. Obviously, it would be important to know whether a similar control mechanism exists in amphibia, in which MSH plays a major role in the control of skin pigmentation (Novales, 1967).

"Short" Feedback Control of Gonadotropin Secretion

"Short" Feedback Control of Luteinizing Hormone Secretion

The existence of a "short" feedback mechanism for the control of LH secretion was proposed by Sawyer and Kawakami (1959) and by Kawakami and Sawyer (1959) on the basis of the observation that, in estrogen-primed ovariectomized rabbits, the EEG was influenced by exogenous gonadotropins or by the endogenous gonadotropins released by coitus. This pioneer idea has since been validated by a good deal of convincing evidence.

Dávid et al. (1966), Corbin and Cohen (1966), and Corbin (1966a) have found that placement of small amounts of LH in the median eminence of normal or castrated rats of both sexes results in a decrease of pituitary and plasma LH levels. A small decline in pituitary LH following placement of LH in the median eminence of castrated females has also been observed in McCann's laboratory (quoted by McCann et al., 1968a). However, in these studies, no consistent effects on plasma LH were observed. When LH was implanted in the median eminence of normal adult female rats (Corbin and Cohen, 1966), vaginal cycles became irregular and there was a predominance of metestrous-diestrous smears. Histological examination of the ovaries revealed the presence of a few corpora lutea, indicating that ovulation was not completely blocked. However, only one out of nine implanted females became pregnant when exposed to a fertile male, and this female delivered two dead fetuses. The secretion of Follicle Stimulating Hormone (FSH) was apparently unaffected, as evidenced by the normal growth of ovarian follicles (Corbin and Cohen, 1966). All these data suggest that the median eminence contains receptors sensitive to changing levels of LH. When these receptors are activated, LH secretion is inhibited. Implants of FSH and of ACTH in the median eminence did not modify LH secretion, illustrating the specificity of the inhibiting effect of LH on its production (Dávid et al., 1966; Corbin and Cohen, 1966; Corbin, 1966a). Implants of LH in the amygdala were also ineffective (Corbin and Cohen, 1966).

Implants of LH in the median eminence also suppress LH secretion in immature (prepuberal) animals. Ojeda and Ramirez (1969) have recently shown that placement of LH in the median eminence of immature female rats induces a delay in the opening of the vagina (retarded puberty) and a marked atrophy of the ovaries and of the uteri. A reduction in the number of corpora lutea was also observed after puberty had occurred, and vaginal smears indicated a state of prolonged diestrus. As in the experiments performed in adults, the secretion of FSH was not impaired by LH implants. The atrophic ovaries of the experimental animals were rich in large follicles, similar to those found in constant-estrous animals (Barraclough, 1967). Rats with LH implanted in other hypothalamic areas, or directly in the adenohypophysis, were normal, indicating that the median eminence is the major receptor site for the "short" feedback effect of LH.

Additional support for the existence of a "short" mechanism regulating LH secretion has been provided by Szontágh et al. (1962) and Szontágh and Uhlarik (1964), who reported a reduction of pituitary stores of LH and changes in PAS-positive "gonadotropic" cells in intact and castrated mature female rats treated chronically with exogenous gonadotropins. However, "castration cells" did not disappear, even when high doses were administered. Unfortunately, the physiological significance of these experiments is uncertain, because only gonadotropins of nonpituitary origin were used. Similar effects of "pregnancy" gonadotropins [Pregnant Mare Serum (PMS) and Human Chorionic Gonadotropin (HCG)] and of LH on pituitary and plasma LH levels have been reported by McCann et al. (1960; 1968a), Novella et al. (1964), Gay and Bogdanove (1966), Rennels and O'Steen (1967) and Lawton and Schwartz (1968).

The participation of the hypothalamus in the "short" feedback effect of LH is also indicated by the observation that hypophysectomy, which eliminates the inhibiting signal provided by LH, apparently induces hypersecretion of LH Releasing Factor (LRF). LRF activitiy may become detectable in the plasma of hypophysectomized animals (Nallar and McCann, 1965; Frankel et al., 1965; Pelletier, 1965), and exogenous LH reduces this circulating LRF activity (McCann et al., 1968a, 1968b). Indirect evidence that LH suppresses LRF synthesis is provided by the experiments of Ramirez and Sawyer (1965). These investigators observed that the LRF content of the hypothalamus of the rat declines during the day of proestrous and reaches its lowest levels during early estrus. Since there is considerable evidence for high circulating levels of LH during proestrus, well before the time at which LRF stores are maximally reduced (Everett, 1956; Schwartz and Bartosik, 1962; Ramirez and McCann, 1964), Ramirez and Sawyer (1965) proposed that circulating LH curtails the synthesis of LRF. A somewhat similar conclusion was reached by Chowers and McCann (1965). They observed that estrogen implants in the pituitary produce a marked elevation in hypothalamic LRF content while similar implants in the median eminence reduce LRF stores. They have explained these data by postulating that LRF is regulated by two independent inhibiting signals, estrogen and

LH. In rats with estrogen implants in the pituitary, plasma LH is low because of the direct effect of the steroid on the hypophysis. This causes a secondary fall in the output of endogenous estrogen, and the elimination of the "negative" feedback effects of estrogen and of LH brings about an increased production of LRF. The postulated dual mechanism for the control of LRF could explain why castration does not induce the expected increase in the hypothalamic stores of this factor (Chowers and McCann, 1965; Piacsek and Meites, 1966), and why systemic injections of estrogen do not reduce it (Chowers and McCann, 1965).

The electrophysiological approach to the study of the effects of gonadotropins on brain function, originally used by Sawyer and Kawakami (1959) and Kawakami and Sawyer (1959), has recently been revived with the more sophisticated techniques now available (mainly the recording of "unit" firing patterns). A number of interesting facts have come to light. Ramirez and his colleagues (1966, 1967) have observed that, in female rats under light urethane anesthesia, intravenous LH reduces the firing rates of basal hypothalamic neurons. This effect appears to be specific, since it is independent of major EEG changes. It is not induced by FSH, by boiled or denatured LH, or by several chemical or physical stimuli.

Terasawa and Sawyer (1968) have been able to define more precisely the type of the responses evoked by the injection of LH. The hormone activates the neurons of the arcuate region and inhibits those of the anterior hypothalamus-medial preoptic area. Other hypothalamic zones are apparently insensitive to LH. If the modifications in firing rates of hypothalamic cells induced by LH are electrical concomitants of changes in the synthesis and release of LRF, it appears remarkable that opposite electrical patterns have been recorded in the two areas in which LRF is synthesized (Mess et al., 1967; Martini et al., 1968a). These two areas control the "basal" and the "cyclic" release of LH, respectively (Barraclough, 1967). Different responses to LH in different parts of the hypothalamus have also been reported in cats by Kawakami and Saito (1967). Their studies also indicate that the levels of circulating estrogen play a major role in directing the type of the response to LH. They found that the neurons of the arcuate nucleus increase their firing rates when LH is administered during estrus; only a minor activation was found in anestrous animals. In the cat, the anterior hypothalamus is not inhibited by LH. On the contrary, there are neurons in this area which increase their discharge rates following LH administration. A long-lasting decrease in the firing rates of neurons in the ventromedial nucleus follows LH administration, both in estrous and anestrous animals. One peculiarity of the effect of LH on brain electrical activity is that it normally has a long latency (Kawakami and Sawyer, 1959; Kawakami and Saito, 1967; Terasawa and Sawyer, 1968). The shortest latency (10 seconds to 10 minutes) was reported by Ramirez et al. (1966, 1967). Several hypotheses have been put forward to explain this phenomenon. One holds that LH must be converted into a metabolite of smaller molecular size in order to pass through the blood-brain barrier. However, recent experiments using both biological and radioimmunological techniques, indicate that gonadotropins cross the blood-brain barrier very easily (Bagshawe et al., 1968). Therefore it appears more probable that the latency is an intrinsic property of LH-sensitive neurons.

A new method for evaluating the effects of pituitary hormones on the brain, and particularly on the hypothalamus, has been recently introduced by Moguilevsky (1967). This author has observed that the oxygen consumption of hypothalamic tissue cultured "in vitro" is increased when LH is added to the medium. Since respiration is spontaneously enhanced in hypothalami taken just after ovulation, this author has postulated that the increase might be the metabolic consequence of the ovulatory release of LH.

The preceding discussion has been concerned with "short" feedback effects in mammalian species. A discussion of the "short" feedback mechanisms that control gonadotropin secretion in birds may be found in a paper by Kobayashi and Farner (1966).

"Short" Feedback Control of Follicle Stimulating Hormone Secretion

Two types of "short" feedback mechanisms have been identified for the control of FSH secretion. One, which is very similar to those described for ACTH, MSH, and LH in previous sections of this chapter, is of the "negative" type, and has been found only in adult animals. The other is of the "positive" type, and appears to be a peculiarity of immature animals. This "positive" "short" feedback mechanism may play a major role at the time of puberty. One common feature of the two "short" feedback systems is that they do not act directly on the pituitary gland but need the mediation of CNS structures.

Corbin (1966b) and Corbin and Story (1967) have reported that, in normal adult female rats, median eminence implants of FSH are effective in lowering pituitary FSH stores and the hypothalamic concentration of the FSH Releasing Factor (FSHRF). The estrous cycles of the median-eminence-implanted rats were erratic, with predominantly diestrous smears. Their ovaries contained many degenerate and primordial follicles, a result which indicates that blood levels of FSH were reduced. Corpora lutea were present, so ovulation was not completely blocked. The effect of FSH appeared to be specific; median eminence implants of LH were without significant effects on pituitary FSH and on hypothalamic FSHRF. Negative results were obtained with implants of FSH in the amygdala. Inhibition of FSH secretion following placement of FSH in the median eminence has also been reported by Arai and Gorski (1968), who studied the influence of brain implants of FSH and of other gonadotropins on the appearance of ovarian compensatory hypertrophy. Since this hypertrophy is an FSH-dependent phenomenon (Flerkó, 1966), its inhibition normally indicates that FSH release has been blocked. In their experiments, Arai and Gorski (1968) used androgen-sterilized female rats (Barraclough, 1967). These animals appear well suited to test possible inhibitors of FSH secretion because, although their ability to synthesize and release LH is much reduced (Martini, 1966b; Barraclough, 1967; Martini et al., 1968b), they have normal stores of FSH and of FSHRF (Martini et al., 1968b) and are able to release them following unilateral ovariectomy (Gorski and Barraclough, 1962; Swanson and Van der Werff ten Bosch, 1964). In these animals, the implantation of FSH or of PMS (a "pregnancy" gonadotropin with FSH-like activity) in the region of the median eminence markedly inhibited the ovarian compensatory hypertrophy. Vaginal smears were unaltered and remained in the constant estrous pattern characteristic of androgen-sterilized animals. Uterine and hypophyseal weights were not altered, indicating that the secretion of LH (and consequently of estrogen) was not inhibited by FSH implants. The inhibition of compensatory hypertrophy appears to be specifically induced by FSH and FSH-like materials, since hypothalamic implants of ACTH, LH, HCG, and thyrotropin (TSH) had no demonstrable effects. FSH implants in the anterior pituitary, the amygdala and the cerebral cortex did not influence the secretion of FSH.

Another type of approach for the study of the "short" feedback effect of FSH was adopted by Martini's group. Fraschini et al. (1968) studied the effects of the administration of exogenous FSH on the pituitary stores of FSH and on the hypothalamic content of FSHRF in castrated adult male rats. FSH was measured according to the assay of Steelman and Pohley (1953) and FSHRF using the "pituitary depletion method" described by Dávid et al. (1965). The data summarized in Fig. 6–1 indicate that treatment with exogenous FSH results in a significant drop of pituitary stores of FSH and of the hypothalamic content of FSHRF. The data shown in the figure also suggest that the inhibitory signal

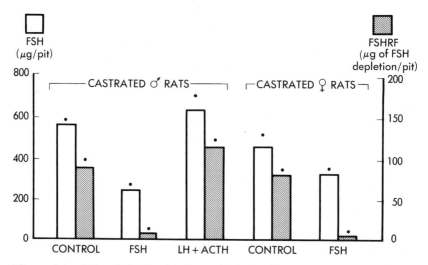

Figure 6-1   "Short" feedback effect of FSH. Effect of systemic administration of FSH on pituitary FSH content and on hypothalamic FSHRF stores in castrated male and female rats.

provided by FSH is specific; it has been impossible to duplicate its effects by injecting ACTH and LH into the castrated animals. Since recent data indicate that there are sex differences in the "classic" feedback mechanism which controls the secretion of FSH,[1] it was decided to investigate whether the administration of FSH to adult female rats had different effects from those previously reported in males. Using an experimental design similar to that of Fraschini *et al.* (1968), it was found that the administration of FSH (20 µg/day for 5 days of NIH-FSH-S-3) to adult castrated female rats brought about a reduction in pituitary FSH and hypothalamic FSHRF content which was similar to that induced in castrated males (Motta, 1969). (See Fig. 6-1.) Since it has been assumed (Fraschini *et al.*, 1968; Motta, 1969) that a reduction of FSH and of FSHRF stores reflects a reduced synthesis and release of both

---

1. Male rats normally have much lower quantities of FSHRF in the hypothalamus and much higher levels of FSH in the pituitary than female rats. Castration produces a very large increase of FSHRF in males and only a minor one in females. Moreover, the response of FSHRF to sex steroids is different in the two sexes: in females, estrogen and progesterone inhibit its synthesis and release, while testosterone is inactive; in males, testosterone and estrogen, but not progesterone, suppress FSHRF synthesis and release (Martini *et al.*, 1968a).

these principles, the data have been interpreted as supporting the view that the "short" mechanism controlling the secretion of FSH in adult animals is of the "negative" type. The assumption of a parallelism between stores and rates of secretion appears acceptable when dealing with FSH and FSHRF. Evidence for this includes the following: (1) castration, which increases the release of both FSHRF and FSH, also increases their stores (Martini *et al.*, 1968a, 1968c); (2) treatment with sex steroids, which certainly suppresses the release of both principles, reduces their levels in the hypothalamus and in the pituitary (Martini *et al.*, 1968a, 1968c); and (3) the enhanced release of FSHRF induced in female rats by exposure to constant light (Piacsek and Meites, 1967) is accompanied by an increase of the storage of this factor at the hypothalamic level (Negro-Vilar *et al.*, 1968a).

The demonstration that an artificial increase in FSH in the general circulation reduced hypothalamic FSHRF content led to a study of the influence of eliminating endogenous FSH on the secretion of FSHRF. Different groups of adult male rats were subjected to castration, hypophysectomy, or castration followed by hypophysectomy. Their hypothalamic stores of FSHRF were then evaluated utilizing the "in vivo" procedure of Dávid *et al.* (1965). Three weeks following castration a significant

Figure 6-2   Effect of castration (Cx), hypophysectomy (Hypox) and castration plus hypophysectomy (Cx + Hypox) on hypothalamic FSHRF stores and on seminal vesicles and prostate weight in male rats.

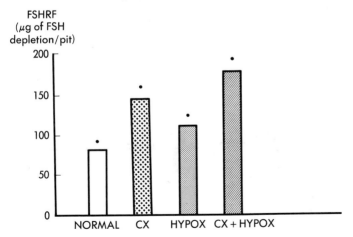

FSHRF
(μg of FSH
depletion/pit)

204.0 ± 10.3   8.5 ± 0.3   70.0 ± 3.4   10.8 ± 0.4   Seminal vesicles (mg/100g b.w.)
70.0 ± 2.7   2.8 ± 0.2   25.8 ± 0.9   3.4 ± 0.3   Prostates (mg/100g b.w.)

increase in the amounts of FSHRF stored in the hypothalamus was observed (Fig. 6-2). One week following hypophysectomy a slight, but insignificant, increase of FSHRF was detected. It is uncertain whether this small increase was due to the elimination of the "short" signal or to the reduction of testosterone secretion brought about by hypophysectomy, but the latter appears a likely explanation since all testosterone-dependent structures (prostates and seminal vesicles) were atrophied in this group of rats. In the animals subjected to the removal of the pituitary and the testes, hypothalamic FSHRF stores reached a level well above that observed following the elimination of either gland alone (Motta, 1969). These data indicate that the effects of castration and of hypophysectomy are additive. It is also clear that in castrated animals FSHRF stores do not reach the high levels found following castration plus hypophysectomy because of the "short" "negative" feedback signal provided by FSH. The fact that the elimination of the "short" feedback signal increases release as well as synthesis of FSHRF is documented by the observation that, after hypophysectomy, FSHRF appears in the peripheral plasma of male rats (Saito et al., 1967; Negro-Vilar et al., 1968b). It is interesting that FSHRF has never been reported in the plasma of hypophysectomized females, but more data are needed on this point before definitive conclusions can be drawn. Treatment of hypophysectomized animals with exogenous FSH has made FSHRF disappear from the blood in one experiment (Corbin, personal communication, 1968); however, this result has not been observed by others (Saito et al., 1967).

As stated at the beginning of this section, the "short" feedback effect of FSH in immature animals appears to be completely different from that present in adults. Before puberty, FSH seems to exert a "positive" effect on its own secretion. The hypothalamic area which contains the receptors for this "positive" effect is much larger than that sensitive to the inhibiting action of FSH. Engelhardt and Diepen (1957) reported an increase in uterine weight a few days after the implantation, near the arcuate nuclei, of a dose of PMS which was ineffective on systemic administration. Ojeda and Ramirez (1969) have shown that the implantation of FSH in a rather large area of the basal medial hypothalamus of prepuberal female rats induces precocious puberty. The ovaries of these animals had a normal weight and contained a large number of corpora lutea. Uterine and pituitary weights were increased, indicating high levels of circulating estrogen. Ojeda and Ramirez (1969) have suggested that in prepuberal females FSH exerts an activating effect on its own secretion. The FSH, in synergism with endogenous LH, activates the release of estrogens and these stimulate the release of additional amounts of LH through their typical "positive" feedback effect (Motta *et al.*, 1968b). However, another explanation might be offered. FSH could act as a "positive" feedback agent on FSH and LH secretion simultaneously. An activation of LH secretion by FSH would not be surprising since there is other evidence that FSH-like materials modify the secretion of LH (Szontágh *et al.*, 1962; Szontágh and Uhlarik, 1964).

The electrophysiological evidence in favor of an effect of FSH on the brain is not as substantial as that for LH. Kawakami and Sawyer (1959) showed that the injection of FSH-like materials induces a positive EEG after-reaction in castrated male and female rabbits. The administration of pituitary FSH was followed by sleep spindles. Kawakami and Terasawa (1967) have shown that FSH has an inhibitory effect on hypothalamic potentials evoked by stimulation of the amygdala. On the other hand, Ramirez *et al.* (1967) did not find any effect of FSH on "unit" recordings from the hypothalamus of female rats.

Moguilevsky and his colleagues have obtained evidence indicating that FSH may directly modify the activity of the hypothalamus. They have shown that in male rats castration depresses the oxygen consumption of this region of the brain. The administration of testosterone to gonadec-tomized rats prevents this decrease. However, testosterone is ineffective when added to hypothalamic tissue "in vitro" (Moguilevsky, 1966; Moguilevsky *et al.*, 1967). Therefore, Moguilevsky *et al.* argue that the decreased metabolism of the hypothalamus of castrated rats is not directly due to the lack of sex hormones. Since gonadectomy results in a marked increase in FSH secretion, and this increase is prevented by the administration of testosterone (Flerkó, 1966), the suggestion has been put forward that FSH might be the hormone responsible for the depression in oxygen consumption induced by castration. Consequently the effects of FSH added "in vitro" to fragments of hypothalamic tissue have been studied (Moguilevsky *et al.*, 1967); it has been found that this hormone produces a decrease in hypothalamic oxygen consumption. However, the hypothesis that the metabolic modifications are related to the effects of FSH on the synthesis and the release of FSHRF (Moguilevsky, 1967) remains to be proved. In view of the observation by Ojeda and Ramirez (1969) that in prepuberal animals FSH exerts a "positive" rather than a "negative" feedback effect on FSH secretion, it is interesting that Moguilevsky and Rubinstein (1967) have found that in prepuberal animals FSH stimulates rather than inhibits the respiration of hypothalamic tissue.

Several other studies suggest an effect of FSH on the brain. It is known that castration increases the content (Stefano and Donoso, 1967; Donoso *et al.*, 1967) as well as the turnover (Anton-Tay and Wurtman, 1968) of norepinephrine in the hypothalamus. Since the removal of the pituitary gland does not modify the turnover of hypothalamic norepinephrine, Anton-Tay and Wurtman (1968) have suggested that the effect of castration might depend on the hypersecretion of pituitary gonadotropins. Unfortunately, they have not yet determined whether the administration of pure LH or FSH to castrated animals further increases the turnover of brain catecholamines. However, the data are particularly interesting in view of the observations which indicate that monoamines may play an important role in the control of the secretion of gonadotropin releasing factors (Coppola *et al.*, 1965; Lippman *et al.*, 1967; Coppola, 1968).

"Short" Feedback Control of Prolactin Secretion

Evidence for a "short" feedback mechanism that plays a role in the control of prolactin secretion has been published in recent years. These studies have provided the first sure demonstration of a feedback regulation of the secretion of this hormone. In species such as the rat, in which prolactin acts as luteotropin (LTH) and facilitates the secretion of progesterone, it could be argued that a form of "classic" feedback control of prolactin secretion exists; in these species progesterone is believed by some investigators to exert a peculiar type of "positive" feedback effect on the release of luteotropic principles from the anterior pituitary (Rothchild, 1960). However, in other species prolactin does not have peripheral target endocrine glands, and cannot normally be controlled by a "classic" feedback (Meites, 1966).

The first approach that has been used to test whether prolactin influences its own secretion has been that of transplanting prolactin-secreting pituitary tumors into host animals. It has been shown that all tumors secreting prolactin depress prolactin stores in the pituitary of the host animals. Pituitary prolactin content was measured either by disc electrophoresis, a method which provides only semiquantitative evaluations (MacLeod and Smith, 1966; MacLeod *et al.*, 1966a; 1968) or by biological assays, the pigeon crop sac method (Chen *et al.*, 1967). Chen and his coworkers have reported, in addition, that the hypothalamic factor that controls prolactin secretion (Prolactin Inhibiting Factor, or PIF) is significantly increased in rats bearing prolactin-secreting tumors. This suggests that prolactin stores in the anterior pituitary are reduced because of increased PIF secretion. Since no one of the tumors used produced only prolactin, it is difficult to accept the conclusion that their effects on pituitary prolactin stores were due only to the presence of large amounts of this hormone in the blood (Meites and Nicoll, 1966). Fortunately, two recent papers have shown that a conspicuous drop in prolactin stores can be induced also by injecting pure prolactin into normal female rats (Sinha and Tucker, 1968), or by placing homografts of pituitary glands underneath the kidney capsule of ovariectomized rats (Welsch et al., 1968). These grafts are known to secrete increased amounts of prolactin and very little ACTH, LH, FSH, thyrotropin, and growth hormone (Meites, 1966).

The approach of implanting hormones into the brain has also been used for studying the "short" feedback control of prolactin secretion. Clemens and Meites (1968) have shown that implants of prolactin in the median eminence of mature intact or ovariectomized rats enhance the hypothalamic content of PIF and reduce the pituitary concentration of prolactin. The same implants also produce a decreased release of the hormone into the blood, as shown by marked mammary gland atrophy and reduced numbers of corpora lutea. It is interesting that rats implanted with prolactin in the median eminence were cycling regularly, i.e. had a normal release of both FSH and LH. It is relevant that implants of prolactin increase the concentration of PIF, while the implants of all other pituitary hormones decrease the hypothalamic concentrations of their respective releasing factors (see previous sections of this chapter). The observed increase in PIF argues against the possibility that the reduction of the other releasing factors might be due to a nonspecific "lesion effect."

Median eminence implants of prolactin apparently are able to inhibit the secretion of this hormone when its production is enhanced by particular conditions such as lactation and pseudopregnancy. Prolactin implants significantly reduce the length of pseudopregnancy induced by mechanical stimulation of the cervix. They also inhibit the formation of deciduomata after uterine traumatization in pseudopregnant animals. LH or FSH do not duplicate these effects of prolactin (Chen et al., 1968). Clemens et al. (1968) have shown that implants of prolactin in the median eminence of postpartum rats profoundly inhibit lactation, as judged by the reduction of the weight gained by the litter. These implants also reduce mammary gland weight, and make the corpora lutea of lactation regress. Lactating rats with median eminence implants of prolactin come into estrus and begin to cycle regularly. The simultaneous implantation of prolactin and ACTH results in an even greater impairment of lactation and in a larger reduction in mammary gland weight.

Grosvenor et al. (1965) have reported the only data that might be interpreted as inconsistent with the possibility that prolactin inhibits its own secretion. They have found that subcutaneous injections of large amounts of prolactin fail to influence the fall in pituitary prolactin concentration induced by the combined effect of nursing and of the stress of laparotomy plus bleeding. It is possible that the doses of prolactin administered by Grosvenor and his colleagues were not large enough to counteract the marked stimulating effect of the two stimuli used simultaneously.

"Short" Feedback Control of Growth Hormone Secretion

Evidence that GH may inhibit its own secretion is accumulating rapidly. The lack of a "classic" feedback mechanism for the control of this hormone makes it reasonable to postulate that a "short" feedback might play a relatively important role in its regulation. As in the case of prolactin and of MSH, the study of the "short" mechanism controlling GH secretion is facilitated by the fact that this hormone does not stimulate the secretion of any specific peripheral target gland. Consequently, the effects of the administration of exogenous GH can be studied in normal animals.

A biphasic alteration in pituitary GH content has been reported in rats treated with large doses of exogenous (bovine or ovine) GH. GH content is unmodified 30 minutes following the administration of the hormone (Müller et al., 1967a; Sawano et al., 1967), increased 6 hours later (Müller and Pecile, 1966) and significantly elevated 24 hours later (Krulich and McCann, 1966a). GH stores return to normal after 5 days of treatment (Krulich and McCann, 1966a), but when treatment is continued for a few more days, pituitary GH content becomes depressed (Krulich and McCann, 1966a). Pituitary GH content is also reduced in animals bearing tumors that secrete GH either alone or in combination with prolactin and ACTH (MacLeod et al., 1966a; 1968). This is not surprising since Tashjian et al. (1968) have shown that the GH produced by these tumors is indistinguishable from normal rat pituitary GH in a number of chemical and immunological tests.

Like other pituitary hormones, GH also appears to inhibit its own secretion when this is increased by exogenous stimuli; insulin hypoglycemia, a potent stimulus for GH release (Roth et al., 1963), has been shown to result in a smaller decrease in pituitary GH stores in animals pretreated with GH (Müller and Pecile, 1966).

These studies do not indicate whether the inhibitory effect of GH is exerted directly on the pituitary or mediated via the hypothalamus. Several pieces of evidence support the latter view. Katz et al. (1967)

have found that, in the rat, GH implants in the median eminence and adjacent hypothalamic areas cause a significant reduction in pituitary growth hormone concentration. This effect was not obtained with prolactin implants (Clemens and Meites, 1968), a point of interest because of the numerous interrelationships between the metabolic effects of prolactin and GH (Beck *et al.*, 1964). The appearance of GH Releasing Factor (GHRF) activity in the plasma of animals after hypophysectomy (Müller *et al.*, 1967b) also supports the view that GH acts on the hypothalamus. This finding has been recently confirmed by Falconi and Rossi (1967), using an elegant parabiosis technique. Since the concentration of GHRF in the hypothalamus of hypophysectomized rats is similar to that found in intact animals (Falconi *et al.*, 1966), it appears that hypophysectomy stimulates the synthesis as well as the release of GHRF. However, the possibility that GH also feeds back at the pituitary level cannot be excluded at the present time. It has been reported that exogenous GH inhibits the decrease in pituitary GH content normally induced in the rat by the intracarotid administration of crude or purified GHRF (Sawano *et al.*, 1967; Müller *et al.*, 1967a, 1967b).It has also been observed that the administration of high doses of exogenous GH does not modify plasma levels of GHRF in hypophysectomized rats (Müller *et al.*, 1967a, 1967b).

One possible interpretation of the seemingly conflicting data summarized in the preceding paragraph might be that GH present in the systemic circulation is unable to reach its receptor area in the hypothalamus because it does not cross the blood-brain barrier. In support of this hypothesis one might point out that exogenous GH given systemically has never been reported to alter electrical phenomena in the brain. Obviously, endogenous GH could reach the hypothalamus via the reverse flow which is believed to occur in the pituitary portal vessels.

Katz *et al.* (1968) have demonstrated an impaired release of GH following insulin or arginine administration during the last trimester of human pregnancy and in the postpartum period. Since pituitary GH and the placental "GH-prolactin" have similar chemical, immunological, and biological properties (Catt *et al.*, 1967), these observations may indicate that the placental principle feeds back on the hypothalamic-pituitary axis to inhibit GH secretion.

"Short" Feedback Control of Thyrotropin Secretion

Until recently, very little information was available on "short" feedback mechanisms controlling TSH secretion. Some preliminary but inconclusive data were presented by Knigge in 1964. He showed that, in 3 cats out of 18, the infusion of small amounts of TSH into the anterior ventral hypothalamus resulted in a brief inhibition of thyroid ^{131}I release. These data, which might indicate that TSH induces an inhibition of TSH release when placed in the hypothalamus, have not been confirmed.

Support for the possibility that TSH secretion might be controlled by a "short" mechanism has been provided by Motta and co-workers (1969). They have studied pituitary TSH content, plasma TSH levels and the hypothalamic concentration of the TSH Releasing Factor (TRF) in the following groups of adult male rats: (1) normal; (2) thyroidectomized for 1 month; (3) thyroidectomized for 1 month and given thyroxine (T4) subcutaneously (10 µg/rat per day) for the last 16 days; and (4) thyroidectomized and given TSH (500 mU/100 gm of body weight of NIH-TSH-B4) for the last 16 days. Animals were killed 24 hours after the last treatment. Pituitary and plasma TSH were measured using McKenzie's procedure (1958) as modified by Yamazaki et al. (1963). Hypothalamic TRF was evaluated by the "pituitary depletion method" recently developed by Mess et al. (1969).

The data from the experiments are summarized in Fig. 6-3. In agreement with previous findings (see Reichlin, 1966, for references), there is a drop in the TSH content of the pituitary following thyroidectomy. Treatment with T4 reduces pituitary TSH further, but not significantly. TSH does not modify pituitary TSH levels in thyroidectomized rats. Thyroidectomy is not followed by any modification of TRF stores in the hypothalamus, a result which is not in agreement with a previous report by Sinha and Meites (1966). These investigators adopted similar experimental conditions, but they used an "in vitro" method for measuring TRF. In the experiments of Motta et al. (1969), treatment with T4 was without significant effects on hypothalamic TRF; this is in agreement with earlier results (Sinha and Meites, 1966). On the other hand, treatment with TSH led to a very significant drop in hypothalamic TRF content.

As expected, a significant increase in plasma TSH levels was found following thyroidectomy (see Reichlin, 1966, for references). A further increase was observed in animals thyroidectomized and given TSH, while plasma TSH was practically zero in animals thyroidectomized and given T4.

The data obtained with T4 provide an additional proof of the fact that thyroid hormones block the synthesis and the release of TSH by acting directly at the pituitary level (see von Euler and Holmgren, 1956, and Reichlin, 1966, for references). Those obtained with TSH have been

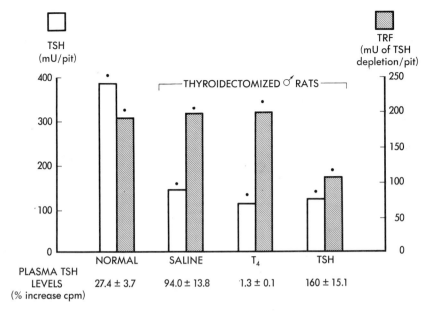

Figure 6-3   Effect of thyroidectomy and of treatment with thyroxine (T4) and TSH on pituitary and plasma levels of TSH and on hypothalamic TRF stores in male rats. Plasma TSH levels are expressed as the per cent increase in blood radioactivity induced in recipient rats prepared according to McKenzie's (1958) procedure by the intravenous administration of 1 ml of plasma of the experimental animals.

tentatively interpreted as indicating that TSH exerts a "short" "positive" feedback effect on the release of TRF. This explains why, in thyroidectomized animals treated with TSH, the levels of TRF in the hypothalamus are low; the increased output of TRF would induce an activation of TSH release, resulting in low levels of TSH in the pituitary and high levels of the hormone in the plasma. It is believed that the increase of plasma TSH observed in thyroidectomized animals treated with exogenous TSH reflects stimulation of release of endogenous TSH, rather than the persistence of the exogenous hormone in the blood. This assumption is based on: (1) the short half-life of exogenous TSH injected into normal or thyroidectomized rats in doses comparable to those used by Motta *et al.* (1969) (D'Angelo, 1951; Bakke and Lawrence, 1962) and (2) the observation that, in thyroidectomized animals given the same dose of exogenous TSH, the levels of plasma TSH are not related to the time elapsed between the last injection of the hormone and the sacrifice of the animal. It has been observed, for instance, that plasma TSH is not higher in animals killed 2 hours after the last treatment than in animals sacrificed 24 hours later (Motta *et al.*, 1969, results not reported in Fig. 6-3). A peak of plasma TSH soon after the administration of TSH is what one would expect if the exogenous hormone were contributing significantly to plasma TSH levels. If this interpretation is correct, these experiments would provide the first demonstration of the existence of a "positive" feedback effect exerted by a pituitary hormone in adult animals. As previously mentioned, a "short" "positive" feedback effect of FSH has been described in immature animals by Ojeda and Ramirez (1969).

Indirect support for a "positive" feedback effect of TSH on the hypothalamus has been provided by the studies of Akada (1959) and Atech (1964). These investigators reported histological signs of activation in hypothalamic neurons following TSH administration. Milcu *et al.* (1964) reported an increase in hypothalamic potentials after injections of TSH into thyroidectomized cats. Moreover, TSH may be recovered from the basal hypothalamus, and its concentration in this region appears to be independent of circulating TSH titers (Bakke and Lawrence, 1967; Bakke *et al.*, 1968) and inversely related to the pituitary levels of TSH (Bakke and Lawrence, 1966).

Earlier data indicate that a peculiar type of a "positive" feedback effect may be exerted by TSH in amphibia. In the tadpoles of several anuran species, the differentiation of the median eminence is dependent upon the presence of thyroid hormones (Etkin, 1963; 1967), but exogenous T4 does not induce differentiation of the median eminence in animals deprived of the adenohypophysis. This suggests that a pituitary factor (possibly TSH) released under the influence of T4 is involved in the differentiation process (Etkin, 1964; 1967). The studies also indicate that the effect of the pituitary factor on the maturation of the median eminence is exerted at the local level and that the factor does not enter the general circulation. Hypophysectomized tadpoles in parabiosis with normal partners do not develop a median eminence following the administration of T4, even though they metamorphose simultaneously with their normal parabiotic partners (Etkin, 1964; 1967).

Hypothalamic Releasing Factors in Peripheral Blood

The appearance of a number of hypothalamic releasing factors in the peripheral circulation following the removal of the pituitary gland from the sella turcica has been mentioned in several sections of this chapter.

The hypothalamic origin of the releasing factors present in the blood is demonstrated by their disappearance following lesions in the median eminence (Brodish and Long, 1962; Nallar and McCann, 1965) or interruption of the circulation to the head (Müller *et al.*, 1967b). The presence of releasing factors in the plasma of hypophysectomized animals is evidence that the "short" feedback mechanisms operate through the CNS. Presumably, the elimination of inhibiting messages originating in the anterior pituitary permits the increased production of the hypothalamic principles, and when their concentration in the hypothalamus reaches a threshold level, they are released into the general circulation. In the case of pituitary hormones having a peripheral target gland, the appearance of releasing factors in the plasma is obviously not due only to the elimination of the "short" feedback signal; the reduced release of the secretory products of the peripheral target glands also contributes.

One of the most interesting problems in this area is the time relationship between hypophysectomy and the appearance of releasing factors in the peripheral circulation. Brodish and Long (1962) were able to detect CRF in plasma 1 to 4 days after hypophysectomy, whereas Nallar and McCann (1965) did not find any LRF activity until 2 to 3 months after the operation. FSHRF was not detected in the plasma of male rats hypophysectomized 10 days previously, but it appeared 1 to 2 months later (Saito *et al.*, 1967; Negro-Villar *et al.*, 1968b). GHRF activity was not observed until approximately three months following ablation of the pituitary gland (Müller *et al.*, 1967b; Falconi and Rossi, 1967). The rapid appearance of CRF in the circulation apparently rules out the possibility that a new "neurohemal structure" (Bern and Knowles, 1966) must be organized (Stutinski, 1951; Billenstien and Leveque, 1955; Sathyanesan and Gorbman, 1965; Monroe, 1967) in order to permit the passage of releasing factors into the blood. The alternative explanation is that the threshold for the activation of the synthesis and release of each releasing factor is different. The secretion of some of them is apparently increased as soon as the inhibiting signals are eliminated while others react more slowly. The hypothesis that there is a threshold level for the activation of the secretion of releasing factors is supported by the observation that two different subthreshold stimuli may sum to cause their release. Krulich and McCann (1966b) have shown that GHRF is not present in the plasma of animals hypophysectomized for 1 week, or in the plasma of normal animals during insulin-induced hypoglycemia, However, GHRF becomes detectable if hypoglycemia is induced in rats hypophysectomized for 1 week.

Apparently, a prolonged overstimulation of the hypothalamus induced by the simultaneous absence of "short" and "long" inhibitors brings about exhaustion of the cells synthesizing the releasing factors. Saito *et al.* (1967) have shown that FSHRF is not detectable in peripheral plasma 40 days following the removal of both the pituitary and the gonads, while it is present 2 months after hypophysectomy alone.

It has been claimed that releasing factors are present in blood only if the pituitary gland is absent. This statement is not completely correct, since there is considerable evidence that pituitary transplants far from the sella turcica are activated by circulating releasing factors. Heterotopically transplanted pituitaries in hypophysectomized rats can secrete ACTH (Kendall *et al.*, 1966; Purves and Sirett, 1967), gonadotropins (Davidson and Smith, 1967), GH (Hertz, 1959), and TSH (Purves *et al.*, 1966). These transplants become inactive if lesions are placed in the median eminence, which confirms the idea that the activating principles come from the hypothalamus (Beddow and McCann, 1968). Pituitary hormones secreted by transplanted glands presumably do not exert much inhibiting "short" feedback effect on the secretion of hypothalamic releasing factors. Their concentration in plasma is rather low. However, the major way "short" signals reach the brain may be via that part of the portal vessels in which the blood flows upward from the pituitary to the median eminence (Török, 1954, 1964).

Specificity of "Short" Feedback Receptors

It is obviously important to know whether the receptors for the "short" feedback effect of pituitary hormones respond to more than one hormone. The bulk of the evidence summarized in the preceding sections of this chapter supports the thesis of a specificity of "short" feedback responses. However, there are a few reports that suggest that some cross-reactions occur.

A pituitary tumor that secretes prolactin and GH but no TSH or ACTH has been shown to inhibit thyroid function. It also reduces the number of "thyrotropic cells" and the concentration of TSH in the anterior pituitary gland of the rat (MacLeod *et al.*, 1966b; MacLeod and Abad, 1968). Prolactin seems to be the hormone responsible for this inhibition of TSH secretion, since a tumor secreting only GH did not have the same effect (MacLeod *et al.*, 1968). In pigeons and in certain urodeles, the administration of prolactin exerts an antigonadal effect. Since regressive changes are observed in the pituitaries of treated animals, it has been suggested that prolactin inhibits the secretion of FSH (Riddle and Bates, 1933; Bates et al., 1937; Mazzi et al., 1966, 1967; Mazzi and Vellano, 1968). Exogenous prolactin may also inhibit the secretion of ACTH (Sinha and Tucker, 1968).

Human growth hormone causes a prompt fall in cortisol secretion when administered to patients with Cushing's syndrome due to hypersecretion of ACTH. The response to metyrapone is also decreased, suggesting that GH can inhibit the excessive secretion of ACTH found in these patients (Schteingart and Conn, 1968).

There is also some evidence of "positive" cross-reactions. Friedman and Stimmler (1966) have observed that, in children, ACTH enhances fasting GH levels and the response of GH to insulin-induced hypoglycemia. Since GH secretion is depressed in steroid-treated patients (Hartog et al., 1964), this peculiar effect of ACTH does not appear to be adrenally mediated. Board (1968) has reported a rise in plasma GH in anovulatory women treated with HCG.

Effect of Pituitary Hormones on Pituitary Weight

Certain pituitary hormones have been shown to reduce the weight of the pituitary gland by an action that appears to be independent of the peripheral target glands. Implants of ACTH in the median eminence of mature male rats have been shown to reduce pituitary weight very rapidly (Motta et al., 1965). Reduced pituitary weight after systemic administration of ACTH to adrenalectomized rats was also reported by Eriksson (1959) and by Gemzell and Heijkenskjöld (1957). LH, when placed in the median eminence of normal or castrated animals, does not have any effect on pituitary weight (Motta et al., 1965; Dávid et al., 1966; Corbin and Cohen, 1966; Corbin, 1966a, 1966b; Corbin and Story, 1967; Arai and Gorski, 1968), unless it is left "in situ" for a very long time (Ojeda and Ramirez, 1969). Systemic administration of LH-like materials also fails to alter pituitary weight (Szóntagh et al., 1962; Adams and Leathem, 1966). Five days following placement of FSH in the median eminence of castrated animals pituitary weight is reduced (Dávid et al., 1966; Corbin, 1966a), but it is unmodified in normal rats (Corbin and Story, 1967) or androgen-sterilized rats (Arai and Gorski, 1968). Clemens and Meites (1968) have found that median eminence implants of prolactin reduce pituitary weight in both normal and ovariectomized rats. Pituitary homografts secreting large amounts of prolactin (Welsch et al., 1968) and systemic administration of the hormone have the same effect (Bates et al., 1964; Sinha and Tucker, 1968). GH implants in the median eminence and in adjacent hypothalamic areas cause pituitary atrophy (Katz et al., 1967), and pituitary weight is reduced in animals with transplanted pituitary tumors that secrete GH (Milkovic et al., 1964; MacLeod and Smith, 1966; MacLeod et al., 1966a, 1966b, 1968; Chen et al., 1967). In the animals with tumors the only histological abnormality in the pituitary was a reduction in the number of acidophils. A similar reduction was reported by Koneff et al. (1949) following injection of exogenous GH. The relevance of these effects on pituitary weight to "short" feedback mechanisms remains to be ascertained.

"Ultra-Short" Feedback Control of the Secretion of Hypothalamic Releasing Factors

It is clear that the concentration of the releasing factors in the hypothalamus can be modified by changes in the level of the hormones produced either in the peripheral target glands or in the anterior pituitary. Motta and Hyyppa (1969) have recently explored the possibility that the synthesis, storage, and release of releasing factors might also be influenced by changes of their titers in the general circulation. In pilot experiments, a crude hypothalamic extract containing FSHRF was injected. Two groups of male rats that had been castrated for 3 weeks and hypophysectomized for 1 week were used. One of these groups was injected subcutaneously with an extract of rat hypothalamus (1 ME/rat per day, for 5 days); the other was treated in a similar way with saline solution. Animals were killed 3 hours after the last injection. Normal controls were also studied. The content of FSHRF in the hypothalami of the different groups of animals was measured by the "pituitary depletion method" described by Dávid et al. (1965).

Fig. 6-4 shows that the treatment with the hypothalamic extract brings back to normal the elevated hypothalamic stores of FSHRF typical of castrated hypophysectomized rats. This result is not due to contamination of the hypothalamic extract with FSH; the extract was assayed by the Steelman and Pohley procedure (1953), and this hormone was not detected. It is difficult, of course, to establish whether this reduction of stores is due to inhibition of the synthesis of FSHRF or to stimulation of its release. However, it appears that brain elements may exist which are sensitive to changing levels of releasing factors.

The possibility that hypothalamic products may influence hypothalamic function is supported by data in the literature. Two well-known polypep-

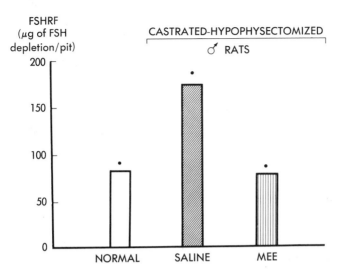

Figure 6-4   Effect of treatment with median eminence extracts (MEE) on hypothalamic FSHRF stores in castrated-hypophysectomized male rats.

tides of hypothalamic origin, oxytocin and vasopressin, apparently exert such effects. The administration of both these principles to normal animals is said to reduce the activity of the neurosecretory cells of the paraventricular and of the supraoptic nuclei (Mietkiewski and Kozik, 1965; Orf, 1966) and to increase the amount of Gomori-positive material in the median eminence (de Wied *et al.*, 1964; Orf, 1966). A considerable inactivation of acid phosphatase in the anterior hypothalamus has been reported following treatment with vasopressin (Hiroshige *et al.*, 1966). Vasopressin treatment also abolishes the histological abnormalities found in rats with a hereditary type of diabetes insipidus (Sokol and Valtin, 1965; Orkand and Palay, 1967). Of course, these changes in hypothalamic histology may be secondary to the effects of posterior pituitary hormones on water and electrolyte balance. More direct evidence for a local effect is the observation that oxytocin induces natriuresis when injected into the third ventricle (Chan and Sawyer, 1968). There is also electrophysiological evidence that vasopressin and oxytocin directly activate or inhibit brain potentials. Neural structures sensitive to both posterior pituitary hormones have been described in the basal hypothalamus (Kawakami and Sawyer, 1959; Kawakami and Saito, 1967; Kawakami and Teresawa, 1967), in the reticular activating system (Kawakami *et al.*, 1964), and in the hippocampus (Kawakami and Teresawa, 1967).

Conclusions

The evidence summarized in this chapter suggests that all the hormones manufactured in the anterior and intermediate lobes of the pituitary gland are capable of affecting their own rate of secretion through a "short" feedback mechanism. The hypothalamus has been shown to be the primary point of attack of all "short" signals, with the possible exception of GH. As in the case of "classic" feedback systems, both "negative" (inhibiting) or "positive" (activating) "short" feedback loops have been described. The hypothesis that "short" mechanisms play a more general role than "long" ones may be put forward, since "short" loops have been shown to control the secretion of those hormones that do not have a peripheral target gland and that consequently cannot be regulated by target gland secretion.

Much more work is obviously still needed in this field. One area which deserves attention is the possible interplay and reciprocal importance of "long" and "short" feedback mechanisms during the physiological development of major neuroendocrine events. Puberty, ovulation, and pregnancy all need to be studied. High priority should also be given to the exploration of extrahypothalamic areas for the possible presence of receptors sensitive to "short" feedback messages. Finally, the study of the biochemical processes taking place in the brain which are influenced by pituitary hormones should not be neglected. The study of these reactions should lead eventually to elucidation of the intimate mechanism of action of "short" feedback signals.

Acknowledgments

The experimental work that was performed in the authors' laboratory and described in this chapter was supported by funds of the Department of Pharmacology of the University of Milan and by the following grants: R/00088 of the World Health Organization, Geneva, Switzerland; AM 10119-01 -02 -03 of the National Institutes of Health, Bethesda, Maryland; M 64-64, M 65-118, M 66-121 of the Population Council, New York; and 67-530 of the Ford Foundation, New York. Gifts of FSH and TSH were made by the National Institutes of Health, Bethesda, Maryland. All such support is gratefully acknowledged.

References

Adams, W. C., and J. H. Leathem (1966). Interaction of gonadal and thyroid control of pituitary hypertrophy. *J. Endocrinol. 35*, 421-22.

Akada, J. (1959). *Endocrinol. Jap. 6*, 233-45. Quoted by S. M. Milcu, M. Demetrescu, and A. Nicolescu-Catargi (1964) in *Rev. Roum. Endocrinol. 1*, 297-306.

Aleksanyan, Z. A. (1967). Role of the pituitary in generation of the slow electrical activity of the hypothalamus in the frog. *Bull. Exp. Biol. Med. (U.S.S.R.) 62*, 854-56.

Anton-Tay, F., and R. J. Wurtman (1968). Norepinephrine: turnover in rat brains after gonadectomy. *Science 159*, 1245.

Arai, Y., and R. A. Gorski (1968). Inhibition of ovarian compensatory hypertrophy by hypothalamic implantation of gonadotrophin in androgen-sterilized rats: evidence for "internal" feedback. *Endocrinology 82*, 871-73.

Atech, Y. L. (1964). Action de l'hormone thyréotrope hypophysaire sur des neurones des centres sympathiques de la région hypothalamique du rat normal et thyroïdectomisé. *C.R. Soc. Biol. (Paris) 158*, 1691-93.

Bagshawe, K. D., A. H. Orr, and A. G. J. Rushworth (1968). Relationship between concentrations of human chorionic gonadotrophin in plasma and cerebrospinal fluid. *Nature 217*, 950-51.

Bagul, C. D. (1967). Corticotrophin releasing factor. *Diss. Abst. 27-B*, 3650-51.

Bakke, J. L., and N. L. Lawrence (1962). Disappearance rate and distribution of exogenous thyrotropin in the rat. *Endocrinology 71*, 43-56.

Bakke, J. L., and N. L. Lawrence (1966). Thyrotropin (TSH) in the rat hypothalamus. *Program of the Forty-eighth Meeting of the Endocrine Society*, p. 89.

Bakke, J. L., and N. L. Lawrence (1967). Thyrotropin (TSH) in the rat stalk-median eminence. *Neuroendocrinology 2*, 315-25.

Bakke, J. L., N. L. Lawrence, and E. Schönbaum (1968). Chronic effects of triiodothyronine on thyrotrophin levels in thyroidectomized rats. *Acta Endocrinol. 57*, 142-48.

Barker Jørgensen, C., and L. O. Larsen (1967). Neuroendocrine mechanisms in lower vertebrates. In *Neuroendocrinology* (L. Martini and W. F. Ganong, eds.), *2*, pp. 485-528. Academic Press, New York.

Barraclough, C. A. (1967). Modifications in reproductive function after exposure to hormones during the prenatal and early postnatal period. In *Neuroendocrinology* (L. Martini and W. F. Ganong, eds.), *2*, pp. 61-99. Academic Press, New York.

Bates, R. W., O. Riddle, and E. L. Lahr (1937). The mechanism of the antigonad action of prolactin in adult pigeons. *Am. J. Physiol. 119*, 610-14.

Bates, R. W., S. Milkovic, and M. M. Garrison (1964). Effects of prolactin, growth hormone and ACTH, alone and in combination, upon weights and adrenal function in normal rats. *Endocrinology 74*, 714-23.

Beck, J. C., A. Gonda, M. A. Hamid, R. O. Morgen, D. Rubinstein, and E. E. McGarry (1964). Some metabolic changes induced by primate growth hormone and purified ovine prolactin. *Metabolism 13*, 1108-34.

Beddow, D., and S. M. McCann (1968). In preparation. Quoted by S. M. McCann, A. P. S. Dhariwal, and J. C. Porter (1968) in *Ann. Rev. Physiol. 30*, 589-640.

Bern, H. A., and F. G. W. Knowles (1966). Neurosecretion. In *Neuroendocrinology* (L. Martini and W. F. Ganong, eds.), *1*, pp. 139-86. Academic Press, New York.

Billenstien, D. C., and T. F. Leveque (1955). The reorganization of the neurohypophysial stalk following hypophysectomy in the rat. *Endocrinology 56*, 704-17.

Board, J. A. (1968). Levels of plasma human growth hormone during administration of human menopausal gonadotropin and human chorionic gonadotropin. *Obstet. Gynec. 31*, 116-18.

Brodish, A., and C. N. H. Long (1962). ACTH-releasing hypothalamic neurohumor in peripheral blood. *Endocrinology 71*, 298-306.

Castor, C. W., B. L. Baker, D. J. Ingle, and C. H. Li (1951). Effect of treatment with ACTH or cortisone on anatomy of the brain. *Proc. Soc. Exp. Biol. Med. 76*, 353-57.

Catt, K. J., B. Moffat, and H. D. Niall (1967). Human growth hormone and placental lactogen: structural similarity. *Science 157*, 321.

Chan, W. Y., and W. H. Sawyer (1968). Intracranial action of oxytocin on sodium excretion by conscious dogs. *Proc. Soc. Exp. Biol. Med. 127*, 267-70.

Chen, C. L., H. Minaguchi, and J. Meites (1967). Effects of transplanted pituitary tumors on host pituitary prolactin secretion. *Proc. Soc. Exp. Biol. Med. 126*, 317-20.

Chen, C. L., J. L. Voogt, and J. Meites (1968). Effect of median eminence implants of prolactin, LH and FSH on luteal function in the rat. *Fed. Proc. 27*, 269.

Chowers, I., and S. M. McCann (1965). Content of luteinizing hormone-releasing factor and luteinizing hormone during the estrous cycle and after changes in gonadal steroid titers. *Endocrinology 76*, 700-708.

Chowers, I., N. Conforti, and S. Feldman (1967). Effects of corticosteroids on hypothalamic corticotropin releasing factor and pituitary ACTH content. *Neuroendocrinology 2*, 193-99.

Clemens, J. A., and J. Meites (1968). Inhibition by hypothalamic prolactin implants of prolactin secretion, mammary growth and luteal function. *Endocrinology 82*, 878-81.

Clemens, J. A., M. Sar, and J. Meites (1968). Inhibition of lactation by median eminence implant of prolactin and ACTH. *Fed. Proc. 27*, 269.

Coppola, J. A. (1968). The apparent involvement of the sympathetic nervous system in the gonadotrophin secretion of female rats. *J. Reprod. Fert.*, suppl. *4*, 35-45.

Coppola, J. A., R. G. Leonardi, W. Lippman, J. W. Perrine, and I. Ringler (1965). Induction of pseudopregnancy in rats by depletors of endogenous catecholamines. *Endocrinology 77*, 485-90.

Corbin, A. (1966a). Pituitary and plasma LH of ovariectomized rats with median eminence implants of LH. *Endocrinology 78*, 893-96.

Corbin, A. (1966b). The "internal" feedback mechanism: effect of median eminence (ME) implants of FSH on pituitary FSH and on stalk-median eminence (SME) FSH-RF. *Excerpta Medica, Int. Cong. Ser. III*, 194.

Corbin, A. (1968). Personal communication.

Corbin, A., and A. I. Cohen (1966). Effect of median eminence implants of LH on pituitary LH of female rats. *Endocrinology 78*, 41-46.

Corbin, A., and J. C. Story (1967). "Internal" feedback mechanism: response of pituitary FSH and of stalk-median eminence follicle stimulating hormone-releasing factor to median eminence implants of FSH. *Endocrinology 80*, 1006-12.

Croxatto, H., J. Arrau, and H. Croxatto (1966). Luteinizing hormone-like activity in human median eminence extracts. *Nature 204*, 584-85.

Dallman, M. F., and F. E. Yates (1968). Anatomical and functional mapping of central neural input and feedback pathways of the adrenocortical system. *Mem. Soc. Endocrinol. 17*, 39-72.

D'Angelo, S. A. (1951). Disappearance rate of exogenous thyrotrophin from the blood of normal and hypophysectomized rats. *Endocrinology 48*, 249-56.

Dávid, M. A., F. Fraschini, and L. Martini (1965). An in vivo method for evaluating the hypothalamic follicle stimulating hormone releasing factor. *Experientia 21*, 483-84.

Dávid, M. A., F. Fraschini, and L. Martini (1966). Control of LH secretion: role of a "short" feedback mechanism. *Endocrinology 78*, 55-60.

Davidson, J. M., and E. R. Smith (1967). Testosterone feedback in the control of somatic and behavioral aspects of male reproduction. In *Hormonal Steroids* (L. Martini, F. Fraschini, and M. Motta, eds.), pp. 805-13. Excerpta Medica, Amsterdam.

Davidson, J. M., L. E. Jones, and S. Levine (1968). Feedback regulation of adrenocorticotropin secretion in "basal" and "stress" conditions: acute and chronic effects of intrahypothalamic corticoid implantation. *Endocrinology 82*, 655-63.

De La Lastra, M., and H. Croxatto (1964). Ovarian ascorbic acid depleting activity in human brain extracts. *Nature 204*, 583-84.

Desaulles, P. A., and W. Rittel (1968). Adrenocorticotrophic activity of synthetic peptide sequences related to ACTH. *Mem. Soc. Endocrinol. 17*, 125-37.

De Wied, D., P. G. Smelik, J. Moll. and P. R. Bouman (1964). On the mechanism of ACTH release. In *Major Problems in Neuroendocrinology* (E. Bajusz and G. Jasmin, eds.), pp. 156-76. S. Karger, Basel.

Donoso, A. O., F. J. E. Stefano, A. M. Biscardi, and J. Cukier (1967). Effects of castration on hypothalamic catecholamines. *Am. J. Physiol. 212*, 732-39.

Eik-Nes, K. B., and K. R. Brizzee (1958). Some aspects of corticotrophin secretion in the trained dog. I. The presence of corticotrophin releasing factor in the blood stream of dogs shortly after hypophysectomy. *Acta Endocrinol. (Kbh) 29*, 219-23.

Engelhardt, F., and R. Diepen (1957). Über die Wirkung von Gonadotropinen nach gezielter intracerebral Instillation bei der Ratte. In *V Symposium der Deutschen Gesellschaft für Endokrinologie* (H. Nowakowski, ed.), pp. 246-68. Springer-Verlag, Berlin.

Eriksson, O. (1959). Anterior pituitary structural changes in adrenalectomized male albino rats following ACTH administration. *Acta Pathol. Microbiol. Scand. 47*, 9-20.

Etkin, W. (1963). The metamorphosis-activating system of the frog. *Science 139*, 810-14.

Etkin, W. (1964). Developmental dependence of the median eminence upon the epithelial pituitary. *Am. Zool. 4*, 392-93.

Etkin, W. (1967). Relation of the pars intermedia to the hypothalamus. In *Neuroendocrinology* (L. Martini and W. F. Ganong, eds.), *2*, pp. 261-82. Academic Press, New York.

Everett, J. W. (1956). The time of release of ovulating hormone from the rat hypophysis. *Endocrinology 59*, 580-85.

Falconi, G., and G. L. Rossi (1967). The growth hormone-releasing activity of hypophysectomized rats measured by means of parabiosis. *Excerpta Medica, Int. Cong. Ser. 142*, 32.

Falconi, G., E. Müller, and A. Pecile (1966). Maintenance of Growth Hormone Releasing activity in the hypothalamus of long-term hypophysectomized rats. *Experientia 22*, 333-35.

Fand, S. B., C. W. Ehmann, and J. R. Anderson (1966). Aspects of ACTH release indicated by histochemical studies of human anterior pituitary in organ culture. *Program of the Forty-eighth Meeting of the Endocrine Society,* p. 60.

Ferrari, W. (1958). Behavioral changes in animals after intracisternal injection with adrenocorticotrophic hormone and melanocyte-stimulating hormone. *Nature 181*, 925-26.

Ferrari, W., E. Floris, and F. Paulesu (1957). Su di una particolare imponente sintomatologia prodotta nel cane dall'ACTH iniettato nella "cisterna magna." *Arch. Int. Pharmacodyn. 110*, 410-22.

Ferrari, W., G. L. Gessa, and L. Vargiu (1961). Stretching activity in dogs intracisternally injected with a synthetic melanocyte-stimulating hexapeptide. *Experientia 17*, 90.

Ferrari, W., G. L. Gessa, and L. Vargiu (1963). Behavioral effects induced by intracisternally injected ACTH and MSH. *Ann. N. Y. Acad. Sci. 104*, 330-45.

Ferrari, W., G. L. Gessa, L. Vargiu, F. Crabai, and M. Pisano (1966). Localizzazione della zona cerebrale responsabile della sintomatologia da iniezione endoliquorale di peptidi con attività ACTH e MSH simili. *Boll. Soc. ital. Biol. sper. 42*, 1154-57.

Flerkó, B. (1966). Control of gonadotropin secretion in the female. In *Neuroendocrinology* (L. Martini and W. F. Ganong, eds.), *1*, pp. 613-68. Academic Press, New York.

Frankel, A. I., W. R. Gibson, J. W. Graber, D. M. Nelson, L. E. Reichert, Jr., and A. V. Nalbandov (1965). An ovarian ascorbic acid depleting factor in the plasma of adenohypophysectomized cockerels. *Endocrinology 77*, 651-57.

Fraschini, F., M. Motta, and L. Martini (1968). A "short" feedback mechanism controlling FSH secretion. *Experientia 24*, 270-71.

Friedman, M., and L. Stimmler (1966). Effect of the corticotrophin on growth-hormone secretion in response to insulin-induced hypoglycemia in children. *Lancet ii*, 944-45.

Gavazzi, G., G. Mangili, L. Martini, and A. Pecile (1962). Action de la dexaméthasone sur les taux plasmatiques de corticostérone chez le rat. *Actualité Endocr. 3*, 169-72.

Gay, V. L., and E. M. Bogdanove (1966). Effects of cyonin treatment on pituitary LH concentration in immature female rats. *Endocrinology 78*, 1268-70.

Gemzell, C. A., and F. Heijkenskjöld (1957). Effect of corticotropin on the content of corticotropin in the pituitary gland of adrenalectomized rats. *Acta Endocrinol. (Kbh) 24*, 249-54.

Gessa, G. L., L. Vargiu, and W. Ferrari (1966). Stretchings and yawnings induced by adrenocorticotrophic hormone. *Nature 211*, 426-27.

Gessa, G. L., M. Pisano, L. Vargiu, F. Crabai, and W. Ferrari (1967). Stretching and yawning movements after intercerebral injection of ACTH. *Rev. Can. Biol. 26*, 229-32.

Gorski, R. A., and C. A. Barraclough (1962). Studies on hypothalamic regulation of FSH secretion in the androgen-sterilized female rat. *Proc. Soc. Exp. Biol. Med. 110*, 298-300.

Grosvenor, C. E., S. M. McCann, and R. Nallar (1965). Inhibition of nursing-induced and stress-induced fall in pituitary prolactin in lactating rats by injection of acid extracts of bovine hypothalamus. *Endocrinology 76*, 883-89.

Guillemin, R., and W. A. Krivoy (1960). L'hormone mélanophorétique β-MSH joue-t-elle un rôle dans les fonctions du système nerveux central chez les mammifères supérieurs? *C. R. Acad. Sci. (Paris) 250*, 1117-19.

Guillemin, R., A. V. Schally, H. S. Lipscomb, R. N. Andersen, and J. M. Long (1962). On the presence in hog hypothalamus of β-corticotropin releasing-factor, α and β-melanocyte stimulating hormones, adrenocorticotropin, lysine-vasopressin and oxytocin. *Endocrinology 70*, 471-77.

Guillemin, R., M. Jutisz, and E. Sakiz (1963). Purification partielle d'un facteur hypothalamique (LRF) stimulant la sécrétion de l'hormone hypophysaire de luteinization (LH). *C. R. Acad. Sci. (Paris) 256*, 504-7.

Halász, B., and J. Szentágothai (1960). Control of adrenocorticotrophic function by direct influence of pituitary substance on the hypothalamus. *Acta Morphol. Acad. Sci. Hung. 9*, 251-61.

Hartog, M., M. A. Gaafar, and R. Fraser (1964). Effect of corticosteroids on serum growth hormone. *Lancet ii*, 376-78.

Henkin, R. I., M. D. Walker, A. B. Harlan, and A. G. T. Casper (1967). Dynamics of transport of cortisol from peripheral blood into cerebrospinal fluid (CSF), central and peripheral nervous system and other tissues of the cat. *Program of the Forty-ninth Meeting of the Endocrine Society*, p. 92.

Hertz, R. (1959). Growth in the hypophysectomized rat sustained by pituitary grafts. *Endocrinology 65*, 926-931.

Hiroshige, T., T. Nakatsugawa, Y. Matsuoka, and S. Itoh (1966). Acid phosphatase activity of the rat pituitary and hypothalamus in relation to secretory activity. *Jap. J. Physiol. 16*, 94-102.

Hodges, J. R., and J. Vernikos (1958). Influence of circulating adrenocorticotrophin on the pituitary adrenocorticophic response to stress in the adrenalectomized rats. *Nature 182*, 725.

Hodges, J. R., and J. Vernikos (1959). Circulating corticotrophin in normal and adrenalectomized rats after stress. *Acta Endocrinol. (Kbh) 30*, 188-96.

Holub, D. A., J. I. Kitay, and J. W. Jailer (1959). Effects of exogenous adrenocorticotropic hormone (ACTH) upon pituitary ACTH concentration after prolonged cortisone treatment and stress. *J. Clin. Invest. 38*, 291-98.

Isobe, K. (1967). Relationship between the blood corticotrophin level and synthesis or release of pituitary corticotrophin. *Folia Endocr. Jap. 43*, 592-606.

Jacobowitz, D., B. H. Marks, and J. Vernikos-Danellis (1963). Effect of acute stress on the pituitary gland: uptake of serine-1-C^{14} into ACTH. *Endocrinology 72*, 592-97.

Jazdowska, B., and W. Dobrowolski (1965). Vascularization of the hypophysis in sheep. *Endokr. Pol. 16*, 269-82.

Johnson, D. C., and D. M. Nelson (1966). Amount of luteinizing hormone activity in extracts of sheep hypothalamus. *Endocrinology 78*, 901-3.

Kastin, A. J., and G. T. Ross (1965). Melanocyte-stimulating hormone activity in pituitaries of frogs with hypothalamic lesions. *Endocrinology 77*, 45-48.

Kastin, A. J., and A. V. Schally (1967). Autoregulation of release of melanocyte stimulating hormone from the rat pituitary. *Nature 213*, 1238-40.

Katz, H. P., M. M. Grumbach, and S. L. Kaplan (1968). Serum growth hormone (SGH) response to arginine stimulation in the postpartum period. *Excerpta Medica, Int. Cong. Ser. 157*, 17.

Katz, S., M. Molitch, and S. M. McCann (1967). Feedback of hypothalamic growth hormone (GH) implants upon the anterior pituitary (AP). *Program of the Forty-ninth Meeting of the Endocrine Society*, p. 86.

Kawakami, M., and H. Saito (1967). Unit activity in the hypothalamus of the cat: effect of genital stimuli, luteinizing hormone and oxytocin. *Jap. J. Physiol. 17*, 466-86.

Kawakami, M., and C. H. Sawyer (1959). Induction of behavioral and electro-encephalographic changes in the rabbit by hormone administration or brain stimulation. *Endocrinology 65*, 631-43.

Kawakami, M., and E. Terasawa (1967). Differential control of sex hormone and oxytocin upon evoked potentials in the hypothalamus and midbrain reticular formation. *Jap. J. Physiol. 17*, 65-93.

Kawakami, M., E. Terasawa, and J. Kawachi (1964). Studies on the oxytocin sensitive component in the reticular activating system. *Jap. J. Physiol. 14*, 104-21.

Kawakami, M., T. Koshino, and Y. Hattori (1966). Changes in EEG of the hypothalamus and lymbic system after administration of ACTH, SU-4885 and ACH in rabbits with special reference to neurohumoral feedback regulation of pituitary-adrenal system. *Jap. J. Physiol. 16*, 551-69.

Kendall, J. W., A. K. Stott, C. Allen, and M. A. Greer (1966). Evidence for ACTH secretion and ACTH supressibility in hypophysectomized rats with multiple heterotopic pituitaries. *Endocrinology 78*, 533-37.

Kitay, J. I., D. A. Holub, and J. W. Jailer (1959). Inhibition of pituitary ACTH release: an extra-adrenal action of exogenous ACTH. *Endocrinology 64*, 475-82.

Klein, R., and S. Livingstone (1950). The effect of adrenocorticotrophic hormone in epilepsy. *J. Pediat. 37*, 733-42.

Knigge, K. M. (1964). Neural regulation of TSH secretion: effect of diencephalic lesions and intracerebral injection of thyroxin and thyrotropin upon thyroid activity in the cat. In *Major Problems in Neuroendocrinology* (E. Bajusz and G. Jasmin, eds.), pp. 261-85. S. Karger, Basel.

Kobayashi, H., and D. S. Farner (1966). Evidence of a negative feedback on photoperiodically induced gonadal development in the white-crowned sparrow "Zonotrichia leukophrys gambelii." *Gen. Comp. Endocrinol. 6*, 443-52.

Koneff, A. A., R .O. Scow, M. E. Simpson, C. H. Li, and H. M. Evans (1949).

Response by the rat thyro-parathyroidectomized at birth to GH and to thyroxine given separately or in combination. II. Histological changes in the pituitary. *Anat. Rec. 104*, 465-73.

Korányi, L., E. Endröczi, and F. Tárnok (1966). Sexual behavior in the course of avoidance conditioning in male rabbits. *Neuroendocrinology 1*, 144-57.

Krivoy, W. A., and R. Guillemin (1961). On a possible role of β-melanocyte stimulating hormone (β-MSH) in the central nervous system of the mammalia: an effect of β-MSH in the spinal cord of the cat. *Endocrinology 69*, 170-75.

Krulich, L., and S. M. McCann (1966a). Influence of GH on content of GH in the pituitaries of normal rats. *Proc. Soc. Exp. Biol. Med. 121*, 1114-17.

Krulich, L., and S. M. McCann (1966b). Evidence for the presence of growth-hormone-releasing factor in blood in hypoglycemic, hypophysectomized rats. *Proc. Soc. Exp. Biol. Med. 122*, 668-71.

Lawton, I. E., and N. B. Schwartz (1968). A circadian rhythm of luteinizing hormone secretion in ovariectomized rats. *Am. J. Physiol. 214*, 213-17.

Liddle, G. W., H. L. Estep, J. W. Kendall, Jr., W. C. Williams, Jr., and A. W. Townes (1959). Clinical application of a new test of pituitary reserve. *J. Clin. Endocr. Metab. 19*, 875-94.

Lippmann, W., R. Leonardi, J. Ball., and J. A. Coppola (1967). Relationship between hypothalamic catecholamines and gonadotrophin secretion in rats. *J. Pharmacol. Exp. Therap. 156*, 258-66.

Long, J. M., W. A. Krivoy, and R. Guillemin (1961). On a possible role of β-melanocyte stimulating hormone (β-MSH) in the central nervous system of the mammalia: enzymatic inactivation "in vitro" of β-MSH by brain tissue. *Endocrinology 69*, 176-81.

MacLeod, R. M., and A. Abad (1968). Thyroid inhibition of rats bearing transplantable, hormone-producing pituitary tumors. *Proc. Soc. Exp. Biol. Med. 128*, 120-25.

MacLeod, R. M., and M. C. Smith (1966). Inhibition of pituitary function by prolactin-secreting tumors. *Program of the Forty-eighth Meeting of the Endocrine Society*, p. 119.

MacLeod, R. M., M. C. Smith and G. W. De Witt (1966a). Hormonal properties of transplanted pituitary tumors and their relation to the pituitary gland. *Endocrinology 79*, 1149-56.

MacLeod, R. M., M. B. Bass, E. P. Buxton, J. N. Dent, and D. G. Benson, Jr. (1966b). Suppression of thyroid function by pituitary tumor MtTW5. *Endocrinology 78*, 267-76.

MacLeod, R. M., G. W. De Witt, and M. C. Smith (1968). Suppression of pituitary gland hormone content by pituitary tumor hormones. *Endocrinology 82*, 889-94.

Mangili, G., M. Motta, W. Muciaccia, and L. Martini (1965). Midbrain stress and ACTH secretion. *Europ. Rev. Endocrinol. 1*, 247-53.

Mangili, G., M. Motta, and L. Martini (1966). Control of adrenocorticotropic hormone secretion. In *Neuroendocrinology* (L. Martini and W. F. Ganong, eds.), *1*, pp. 297-370. Academic Press, New York.

Martini, L. (1966a). Neurohypophysis and anterior pituitary activity. In *The Pituitary Gland* (G. W. Harris and B. T. Donovan, eds.), *3*, pp. 535-77. Butterworths, London.

Martini, L., A. Carraro, F. Caviezel, and M. Fochi (1968b). Factors affecting *Behavior* (R. A. Gorski and R. E. Whalen, eds.), *3*, pp. 207-14. University of California Press, Berkeley.

Martini, L., F. Fraschini, and M. Motta (1968a). Neural control of anterior pituitary functions. *Recent Prog. Hormone Res. 24*, 439-96.

Martini, L., A. Carraro, F. Caviezel, and M. Fochi (1968b). Factors affecting hypothalamic functions: the pharmacology of puberty. In *Pharmacology of Reproduction* (E. Diczfalusy, ed.), pp. 13-30. Pergamon Press, Oxford.

Martini, L., F. Fraschini, and M. Motta (1968c). Comments on "long" and "short" feedback loops. In *Endocrinology and Human Behaviour* (R. P. Michael, ed.), pp. 175-87. Springer, Berlin.

Mazzi, V., and C. Vellano (1968). The counterbalancing effect of follicle-stimulating hormone on the antigonadal activity of prolactin in the male newt *Triturus cristatus carnifex (Laur)*. *J. Endocrinol. 40*, 529-30.

Mazzi, V., A. Peyrot, M. R. Anzalone, and C. Toscano (1966). L'histophysiologie de l'adénohypophyse du Triton creté (*Triturus cristatus carnifex Laur.*). *Z. Zellforsch. 72*, 597-617.

Mazzi, V., C. Vellano, and C. Toscano (1967). Antigonadal effects of prolactin in adult male crested newt (*Triturus cristatus carnifex Laur.*). *Gen. Comp. Endocrinol. 8*, 320-24.

McCann, S. M., S. Taleisnik, and H. M. Friedman (1960). LH-releasing activity in hypothalamic extracts. *Proc. Soc. Exp. Biol. Med. 104*, 432-34.

McCann, S. M., A. P. S. Dhariwal, and J. C. Porter (1968a). Regulation of the adenohypophysis. *Ann. Rev. Physiol. 30*, 589-640.

McCann, S. M., S. Watanabe, D. B. Crighton, D. Beddow, and A. P. S. Dhariwal (1968b). The physiology and biochemistry of luteinizing hormone-releasing factor and follicle stimulating hormone-releasing factor. In *Pharmacology of Hormonal Polypeptides and Proteins* (N. Back, L. Martini, and R. Paoletti, eds.), pp. 112-22. Plenum Press, New York.

McKenzie, J. M. (1958). The bioassay of thyrotropin in serum. *Endocrinology 63*, 372-82.

Meites, J. (1966). Control of mammary growth and lactation. In *Neuroendocrinology* (L. Martini and W. F. Ganong, eds.), *1*, pp. 669-707. Academic Press, New York.

Meites, J., and C. S. Nicoll (1966). Adenohypophysis: prolactin. *Ann. Rev. Physiol. 28*, 57-88.

Mess, B., and L. Martini (1968). The central nervous system and the secretion of anterior pituitary trophic hormones. In *Recent Advances in Endocrinology* (W. H. T. James, ed.), pp. 1-49. J. and A. Churchill, London.

Mess., B., F. Fraschini, M. Motta, and L. Martini (1967). The topography of the neurons synthesizing the hypothalamic releasing factors. In *Hormonal Steroids* (L. Martini, F. Fraschini, and M. Motta, eds.), pp. 1004-13. Excerpta Medica, Amsterdam.

Mess, B., M. Motta, N. Sterescu, and L. Martini (1969). Studies on TSH-RF. *Experientia*, in press.

Mietkiewski, K., and M. Kozik (1965). Histochemistry of neurosecretion in the pituitary-hypothalamic system of guinea pigs after administration of pituitrin. *Polish Med. J. 4*, 1202-20.

Milcu, S. M., M. Demetrescu, and A. Nicolescu-Catargi (1964). The cortico-sub-cortical action of hypophyseal tropic hormones. *Rev. Roum. Endocrinol. 1*, 297-306.

Milkovic, S., M. M. Garrison, and R. W. Bates (1964). Study of the hormonal control of body and organ size in rats with mammotropic tumors. *Endocrinology 75*, 670-91.

Millichap, J. G., and J. D. Jones (1964). Acid-base, electrolyte, and amino-acid metabolism in children with petit mal. Etiologic significance and modification by anticonvulsant drugs and the ketogenic diet. *Epilepsia 5*, 239-47.

Moguilevsky, J. A. (1966). Effect of testosterone "in vitro" on the oxygen uptake of different hypothalamic areas. *Acta Physiol. Lat. Am. 16*, 353-56.

Moguilevsky, J. A. (1967). Efectos de las hormonas sexuales y gonadotrofinas sobre el metabolisma de distintas areas hipotalamicas. *Rev. Argent. Endocrinol. Metab. 13*, 25-34.

Moguilevsky, J. A., and L. Rubinstein (1967). Glycolytic and oxidative metabolism of hypothalamic areas in prepuberal and androgenized rats. *Neuroendocrinology 2*, 213-21.

Moguilevsky, J. A., O. Schiaffini, and C. Libertun (1967). Anaerobic metabolism of different parts of hypothalamus. Influence of castration. *Acta Physiol. Lat. Am. 17*, 55-59.

Monnier, M. (1953). *Rev. Méd. Suisse Romande 32*, 511-18. Quoted by S. M. Milcu, M. Demetrescu, and A. Nicolescu-Catargi (1964) in *Rev. Roum. Endocrinol. 1*, 297-306.

Monroe, B. G. (1967). Ultrastructural reorganization of the infundibular stem and median eminence following hypophysectomy in the rat. *Anat. Rec. 157*, 289.

Motta, M. (1969). The brain and the physiological interplay of "long" and "short" feedback systems. *Proc. 3rd Int. Cong. Endocrinol.* Excerpta Medica, Amsterdam, in press.

Motta, M., and M. Hyyppa (1969). "Ultra-short" feedback control of follicle stimulating hormone releasing factor (FSH-RF) secretion. *Endocrinology* (to be submitted).

Motta, M., G. Mangili, and L. Martini (1965). A "short" feedback loop in the control of ACTH secretion. *Endocrinology 77*, 392-95.

Motta, M., F. Fraschini, F. Piva, and L. Martini (1968a). Hypothalamic and extra-hypothalamic mechanisms controlling adrenocorticotrophin secretion. *Mem. Soc. Endocrinol. 17*, 3-18.

Motta, M., F. Fraschini, G. Giuliani, and L. Martini (1968b). The central nervous system, estrogen and puberty. *Endocrinology 83*, 1101-7.

Motta, M., N. Sterescu, F. Piva, and L. Martini (1969). A positive "short" feedback mechanism controling TSH secretion. *Endocrinology* (submitted for publication).

Mühlen, K., and H. Ockenfels (1968). Morphologische Veränderungen in Diencephalon und Telencephalon nach Störungen des Regelkreises Adenohypophyse-Nebennierinde. I. Ergebnisse bein Meerschweichen nach Verabreichung von naturlichen und synthetischen ACTH. *Z. Zellforsch. 85*, 124-44.

Müller, E. E., and A. Pecile (1966). Influence of exogenous GH on endogenous growth hormone release. *Proc. Soc. Exp. Biol. Med. 122*, 1289-91.

Müller, E. E., S. Sawano, A. Arimura, and A. V. Schally (1967a). Mechanism of action of growth hormone in altering its own secretion rate: comparison with the action of dexamethasone. *Acta Endocrinol. (Kbh) 56*, 499-509.

Müller, E. E., A. Arimura, T. Saito, and A. V. Schally (1967b). Growth hormone-releasing activity in plasma of normal and hypophysectomized rats. *Endocrinology 80*, 77-81.

Nallar, R., and S. M. McCann (1965). Luteinizing hormone-releasing activity in plasma of hypophysectomized rats. *Endocrinology 76*, 272-75.

Negro-Vilar, A., E. Dickerman, and J. Meites (1968a). Effects of continuous light on hypothalamic FSH-releasing factor and pituitary FSH levels in rats. *Proc. Soc. Exp. Biol. Med. 127*, 751-55.

Negro-Vilar, A., E. Dickerman, and J. Meites (1968b). FSH-releasing factor activity in plasma of rats after hypophysectomy and continuous light. *Endocrinology 82*, 939-44.

Nikolov, N. A. (1967). Changes in the higher nervous activity and behaviour of dogs following suboccipital introduction of ACTH. *Pharmacol. Toxicol. 30*, 528-30.

Novales, R. R. (1967). Melanocyte-stimulating hormone and the intermediate lobe of the pituitary: chemistry, effects, and mode of action. In *Neuroendocrinology* (L. Martini and W. F. Ganong, eds.), 2, pp. 241-59. Academic Press, New York.

Novella, M., J. Alloiteau, and P. Aschheim (1964). La ratte préparée selon la technique de Parlow convient-elle a l'étude d'une substance stimulant la décharge d'hormone lutéinisante par l'hypophyse? *C. R. Acad. Sci. (Paris) 259*, 1553-56.

Ojeda, S. R., and V. D. Ramirez (1969). Automatic control of LH and FSH secretion by short feedback circuits in immature rats. *Endocrinology, 84*, 786-97.

Op de Coul, A. A. W. (1966). The effect of ACTH and corticosteroids on the brain. *Psychiat. Neurol. Neurochir. 69*, 385-98.

Orf, G. (1966). Morphologische Betrachtungen des Zwischenhirn-Hypophysen-Systems beim Hund nach Zufuhr von Oxytocin und Vasopressin. *Acta Neuroveget. 28*, 508-31.

Orkand, P. M., and S. L. Palay (1967). Effects of treatment with exogenous vasopressin on the structural alterations in the hypothalamo-neurohypophysial system of rats with hereditary diabetes insipidus. *Anat. Rec. 157*, 295.

Peczely, P. (1966). Effect of ACTH on the hypothalamic neurosecretion of the pigeon (*Columba livia domestica L.*). *Acta Biol. Acad. Sci. Hung. 16*, 291-310.

Pelletier, J. (1965). Effet du plasma de brebis sur la décharge de LH chez la ratte. *C. R. Acad. Sci. (Paris) 260*, 5624-27.

Piacsek, B. E., and J. Meites (1966). Effects of castration and gonadal hormones on hypothalamic content of luteinizing hormone releasing factor (LRF). *Endocrinology 79*, 432-39.

Piacsek, B. E., and J. Meites (1967). Stimulation by light of gonadotropin release from transplanted pituitaries of hypophysectomized rats. *Neuroendocrinology 2*, 129-37.

Plager, J. E., and P. Cushman (1962). Suppression of the pituitary-ACTH response in man by administration of ACTH or cortisol. *J. Clin. Endocr. Metab. 22*, 147-54.

Purves, H. D., and N. E. Sirett (1967). Corticotrophin secretion by ectopic pituitary glands. *Endocrinology 80*, 962-68.

Purves, H. D., N. E. Sirett, and W. E. Griesbach (1966). Thyrotrophic hormone secretion from pituitary transplants in hypophysectomized rats. *Neuroendocrinology 1*, 276-92.

Ralph, C. L., and S. C. Peyton (1966). MSH-like substance in the brain of the frog, *Rana pipiens. Gen. Comp. Endocrinol.*, 7, 363-69.

Ramirez, V. D., and S. M. McCann (1964). Fluctuations in plasma luteinizing hormone concentrations during the estrous cycle of the rat. *Endocrinology 74*, 814-16.

Ramirez, V. D., and C. H. Sawyer (1965). Fluctuations in hypothalamic LH-RF (luteinizing hormone-releasing factor) during the rat estrous cycle. *Endocrinology 76*, 282-89.

Ramirez, V. D., D. I. Whitmoyer, B. R. Komisaruk, and C. H. Sawyer (1966). Effects of hormones and vaginal stimulation on EEG and hypothalamic activity in the rat. *Fed. Proc. 25*, 191.

Ramirez, V. D., B. R. Komisaruk, D. I. Whitmoyer, and C. H. Sawyer (1967). Effects of hormones and vaginal stimulation on the EEG and hypothalamic units in rats. *Am. J. Physiol. 212*, 1376-84.

Reichlin, S. (1966). Control of thyrotropic hormone secretion. In *Neuroendocrinology* (L. Martini and W. F. Ganong, eds.), *1*, pp. 445-536. Academic Press, New York.

Rennels, E. G., and W. K. O'Steen (1967). Alterations in LH and FSH content and weight of the anterior pituitary gland of immature female rats treated with PMS. *Endocrinology 80*, 82-88.

Riddle, O., and R. W. Bates (1933). Concerning anterior pituitary hormones. *Endocrinology 17*, 689-98.

Roth, J., S. M. Glick, R. S. Yalow, and S. A. Berson (1963). Hypoglycemia: a potent stimulus to secretion of growth hormone. *Science 140*, 987-88.

Rothchild, I. (1960). The corpus luteum-pituitary relationship: the lack of an inhibiting effect of progesterone on the secretion of pituitary luteotrophin. *Endocrinology 67*, 54-61.

Saito, T., S. Sawano, A. Arimura, and A. V. Schally (1967). Follicle-stimulating hormone-releasing activity in peripheral blood. *Endocrinology 81*, 1226-30.

Sandberg, A. A., K. Eik-Nes, C. J. Migeon, and G. F. Koepf (1957). Plasma 17-OHCS in hyperfunction, suppression and deficiency of adrenal cortical function. *J. Lab. Clin. Med. 50*, 286-96.

Sathyanesan, A. G., and A. Gorbman (1965). Typical and atypical regeneration and overgrowth of hypothalamo-hypophyseal neurosecretory tract after partial or complete hypophysectomy in the goldfish. *Gen. Comp. Endocrinol. 5*, 456-63.

Sawano, S., A. Arimura, C. Y. Bowers, and A. V. Schally (1967). Effects of CNS-depressants, dexamethasone and growth hormone on the response to growth-hormone-releasing factor. *Endocrinology 81*, 1410-12.

Sawyer, C. H. (1968). Personal communication.

Sawyer, C. H., and M. Kawakami (1959). Characteristics of behavioral and electrcencephalographic after-reactions to copulation and vaginal stimulation in the female rabbit. *Endocrinology 65*, 622-30.

Schally, A. V., and A. J. Kastin (1966). Purification of a bovine hypothalamic factor which elevates pituitary MSH levels in rats. *Endocrinology 79*, 768-72.

Schally, A. V., H. S. Lipscomb, J. M. Long, W. E. Dear, and R. Guillemin (1962). Chromatography and hormonal activities of dog hypothalamus. *Endocrinology 70*, 478-80.

Schapiro, S., J. Marmorston, and H. Sobel (1958). Steroid feedback mechanism. *Am. J. Physiol. 192*, 58-62.

Schteingart, D. E., and J. W. Conn (1968). Suppression of adrenal cortical function by human growth hormone (HGH) in Cushing's syndrome. *Excerpta Medica, Int. Cong. Ser. 157*, 176.

Schwartz, N. B., and D. Bartosik (1962). Changes in pituitary LH content during the rat estrous cycle. *Endocrinology 71*, 756-62.

Sinha, D. and J. Meites (1966). Effects of thyroidectomy and thyroxine on hypothalamic concentration of "thyrotropin releasing factor" and pituitary content of thyrotropin in rats. *Neuroendocrinology 1*, 4-14.

Sinha, Y. N., and H. A. Tucker (1968). Pituitary prolactin content and mammary development after chronic administration of prolactin. *Proc. Soc. Exp. Biol. Med. 128*, 84-88.

Smelik, P. G. (1963). Relation between blood level of corticoids and the inhibiting effect on the hypophyseal stress response. *Proc. Soc. Exp. Biol. Med. 113*, 616-19.

Sokol, H. W., and H. Valtin (1965). Morphology of the neurosecretory system in rats homozygous and heterozygous for hypothalamic diabetes insipidus (Brattleboro strain). *Endocrinology 77*, 692-700.

Steelman, S. L., and F. M. Pohley (1953). Assay of the follicle stimulating hormone based on the augmentation with human chorionic gonadotropin. *Endocrinology 53*, 604-16.

Stefano, F. J. E., and A. O. Donoso (1967). Norepinephrine levels in the rat hypothalamus during the estrous cycle. *Endocrinology 81*, 1405-6.

Stutinsky, F. (1951). Sur l'origine de la substance Gomori-positive du complexe hypothalamo-hypophysaire. *C. R. Soc. Biol. (Paris) 145*, 367-70.

Sussman, L., L. Librik, and G. W. Clayton (1965). Effect of prior ACTH administration on ACTH release in man. *Metabolism 14*, 583-89.

Swanson, H. E., and J. J. Van der Werff ten Bosch (1964). The "early-androgen" syndrome: its development and the response to hemi-spaying. *Acta Endocrinol. (Kbh) 45*, 1-12.

Szontágh, F. E., and S. Uhlarik (1964). The possibility of a direct "internal" feedback in the control of pituitary gonadotrophin secretion. *J. Endocrinol. 29*, 203-4.

Szontágh, F. E., S. Uhlarik, and A. Jakobovits (1962). The effect of gonadotrophic hormones on the hypophysis of the rat. *Acta Endocrinol. (Kbh) 41*, 31-34.

Taleisnik, S., and R. Orias (1965). A melanocyte-stimulating hormone-releasing factor in hypothalamic extracts *Am. J. Physiol. 208*, 293-96.

Tashjian, A. H., Jr., Y. Yasumura, L. Levine, G. H. Sato, and M. L. Parker (1968). Establishment of clonal strains of rat pituitary tumor cells that secrete growth hormone. *Endocrinology 82*, 342-52.

Terasawa, E., and C. H. Sawyer (1968). Effects of luteinizing hormone (LH) on multiple unit activity in the rat hypothalamus. *Fed. Proc. 27*, 269.

Tonkikh, A. V. (1960). Neuro-hormonal factors in development of sleep. *Abst. 1st Int. Cong. Endocrinol.* (F. Fuchs, ed.), p. 59. Periodica, Copenhagen.

Torda, C., and H. G. Wolff (1952). Effects of various concentrations of adrenocorticotrophic hormone on electrical activity of brain and on sensitivity to convulsion-inducing agents. *Am. J. Physiol. 168*, 406-13.

Török, B. (1954). Lebendbeobachtung des Hypophysenkreislaufes an Hunden. *Acta Morph. Acad. Sci. Hung. 4*, 83-89.

Török, B. (1964). Structure of the vascular connections of the hypothalamohypophysial region. *Acta Anat. 59*, 84-89.

Tramezzani, J. H., and L. M. Voloschin (1965). Gonadotropic activity in hypothalamic extracts. *Experientia 21*, 69-70.

Vernikos-Danellis, J. (1965). Effect of stress, adrenalectomy, hypophysectomy and hydrocortisone on the corticotrophin-releasing activity of rat median eminence. *Endocrinology 76*, 122-126.

Vernikos-Danellis, J., and L. N. Trigg (1967). Feedback mechanisms regulating pituitary ACTH secretion in rats bearing transplantable pituitary tumors. *Endocrinology 80*, 345-50.

von Euler, C., and B. Holmgren (1956). The thyroxine "receptor" of the thyroidpituitary system. *J. Physiol. (London) 131*, 125-36.

Wasserman, M. J., N. R. Belton, and J. G. Millichap (1965). Effect of corticotropin (ACTH) on experimental seizures. *Neurology 15*, 1136-41.

Welsch, C. W., A. Negro-Vilar, and J. Meites (1968). Effects of pituitary homografts on host pituitary prolactin and hypothalamic PIF levels. *Neuroendocrinology 3*, 238-45.

Woodbury, D. M., and A. Vernadakis (1967). Influence of hormones on brain activity. In *Neuroendocrinology* (L. Martini and W. F. Ganong, eds.), *2*, pp. 335-75. Academic Press, New York.

Yamazaki, E., E. Sakiz, and R. Guillemin (1963). An "in vivo" bioassay for TSH-releasing factor (TRF). *Experientia 19*, 480-81.

Yudaev, N. A. (1966). Effects of corticosteroids and ACTH on the hypophysealadrenocortical system. *Fed. Proc. 25*, 1023-28 T.

7
Hypothalamic Unit Activity Related to Control of the Pituitary Gland

CARLOS BEYER and CHARLES H. SAWYER

Introduction

During the past 15 years electrophysiological techniques have been employed widely to investigate hypothalamic function. The studies have focused on the following themes: (1) electrophysiological characteristics of hypothalamic neurons; (2) effects of internal environmental changes on hypothalamic activity; (3) electrical correlates of functions integrated at the hypothalamic level, and (4) analysis of the afferent input to the hypothalamus and of the spatial organization of hypothalamic functions. Input projections have been re-analyzed recently in "unit" studies by Sawa *et al.* (1959), Tsubokawa and Sutin (1963), Stuart *et al.* (1964), Dafny *et al.* (1965), Dafny and Feldman (1967), Egger (1967), and Dreifuss *et al.* (1968) and will not be considered further here.

Several different electrical recording techniques have been used to study hypothalamic neuronal activity: direct current (DC) changes, electroencephalograms (EEG), evoked potentials, single units, and multi-unit background activity. Methodological details can be found in the book by Bures *et al.* (1967). One of the earliest attempts to correlate hypothalamic electrical activity with pituitary secretion was that of von Euler (1953), who succeeded in recording slow potential changes in the supraoptic region under conditions conducive to the secretion of antidiuretic hormone from the neurohypophysis. The DC change was interpreted as being due to the summation of slow potential changes from osmoreceptors or neurons activated by specific osmoreceptors (see below, under Neurohypophysis). This technique has subsequently been little used, probably because of our limited knowledge of the origin and functional meaning of hypothalamic DC potentials.

Slow waves of the EEG represent the algebraic sum of an enormous number of synaptic potentials (Morrell, 1967) originating in the large population of cells recorded with a macroelectrode (tip more than 100 μ in diameter). The analysis of EEG activity in terms of neuronal function is extremely difficult, particularly in an anatomically complex region like the hypothalamus. For example, it is practically impossible to decide whether a given EEG pattern is a correlate of neuronal excitation or inhibition in the recorded area. Moreover, it is difficult to determine the source of EEG changes, since the macroelectrode readily records distant activity. In spite of these drawbacks the EEG technique has been useful in establishing meaningful correlations between endocrine functions and distinct patterns of electrical activity in discrete hypothalamic areas. In fact, our basic knowledge of the action of hormones on brain mechanisms has so far been largely acquired by experiments employing EEG as the index of brain activity.

It is known that a brief stimulus (electric shock, click, flash, etc.) given to an animal elicits a synchronous volley of impulses that can provoke what is known as an "evoked potential" (Chang, 1959) in brain areas having neural connections with the stimulated structure (skin, eye, etc.). The evoked potential technique has been a useful tool in the analysis of anatomical and functional characteristics of the afferent input to the hypothalamus. With the application of this technique it was possible to demonstrate that afferent messages from many different sensory modalities converge and interact at the hypothalamus. Moreover, our understanding of the mechanism of action of several chemicals and humoral agents on hypothalamic activity is based partly on the use of the evoked potential technique (Feldman et al., 1959). As in the case of EEG activity, the source of the evoked potentials is difficult to establish, particularly when using monopolar recording. An interpretation of hypothalamic evoked potentials, relating their origin to unit activity, is discussed in a paper by Rudomin et al. (1965).

In comparison with results obtained by the methods mentioned above, the origin and nature of electrical phenomena recorded with the unit activity technique are easy to interpret since there is no doubt that they represent action potentials generated by neurons located close to the recording microelectrode (Morrell, 1967). Therefore, unit activity recording has become the method of choice for the location and study of hypothalamic cells specifically sensitive to diverse internal and external environmental changes (Vincent et al., 1967; Findlay and Hayward, 1968).

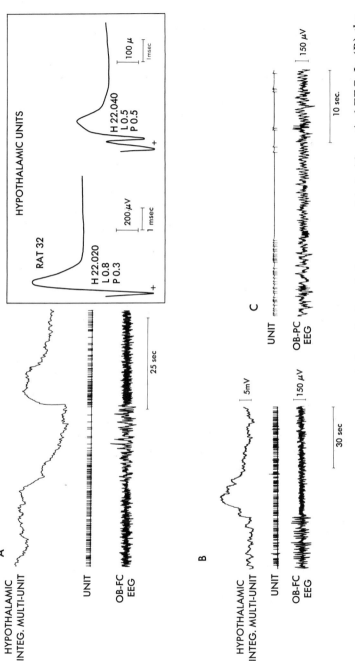

Figure 7-1 Single unit and adjacent multi-unit records from the hypothalamus correlated with cortical EEG. In (B) the unit firing rate is unchanged during spontaneous arousal, although the adjacent neuronal population is activated. In (A) temporally parallel changes in single- and multi-unit activities and cortical EEG are seen. In (C) a marked depression of unit activity occurs during "spontaneous EEG arousal": multi-unit activity was not recorded. OB, olfactory bulb; FC, frontal cortex; PC, parietal cortex.   (From Komisaruk et al., 1967.)   Insert: Tracings of typical hypothalamic units from the oscilloscope screen.   (From Ramirez et al., 1967.)

There are, nevertheless, certain limitations in the use of this technique for neuroendocrine studies. One of these is that the size of the sample studied is necessarily very small when compared with the total population of cells related to a given function. Moreover, large cells generating large action potentials are usually selected for recording. This bias may seriously affect neuroendocrine studies since it appears that the neurons directly related to the control of the adenohypophysis are rather small (parvocellular system of neurons, Szentágothai, 1964) and therefore rarely recorded as single units.

Recently, we (Beyer *et al.*, 1967) have introduced the so-called multi-unit background activity technique in the study of neuroendocrine phenomena. This method (Schlag and Balvin, 1963) permits the simultaneous recording of activity in a discrete number of cells with a large microelectrode (25 to 50 μ diameter). With this technique it has been possible to record activity in such regions as the tuber and median eminence, structures in which it is difficult to register single-unit activity. It is possible to combine single-unit and multi-unit recording (Komisaruk *et al.*, 1967) with closely adjacent large and small microelectrodes (Fig. 7-1).

In this chapter we are concerned with the discharge, facilitation, and inhibition of hypothalamic neurons closely related to neurohypophyseal and adenohypophyseal function. Space does not permit consideration of hypothalamic unit studies concerned only indirectly with neuroendocrine activity, such as investigations of the regulation of body temperature (reviewed by Hammel, 1968), feeding (reviewed by Oomura *et al.*, 1967), and sleep (reviewed by Jouvet, 1967). There are undoubtedly interactions between nervous mechanisms controlling these functions and processes regulating the secretion of pituitary hormones, including the thyrotrophic hormone (Andersson *et al.*, 1963) and growth hormone (Reichlin, 1966a). A few studies on the hypothalamus and control of sexual behavior will be mentioned in connection with unit recordings relative to pituitary gonadotrophic function.

Unit Activity and the Neurohypophysis

It is well established that neurons of the supraoptic (SO) and paraventricular (PV) nuclei synthesize neurohypophyseal hormones (oxytocin and vasopressin or ADH). Since these cells share characteristics of both neurons and secretory cells it is of interest to know if they have distinctive electrophysiological properties. Cross and Green (1959), who were the first to record with microelectrodes from single hypothalamic neurosecretory cells (SO neurons), noted that their action potentials were similar in shape, though generally smaller, than those recorded from other brain areas. These observations have since been confirmed by many other workers (Tolkunov, 1962; Brooks *et al.,* 1962; Koizumi *et al.,* 1964; Joynt, 1964). Neurosecretory cells from the SO and PV nuclei show a slowly firing "spontaneous" activity in the absence of any apparent stimulation. Koizumi *et al.* (1964) found in the cat under chloralose that neurons within or close to the SO nucleus displayed very slow rates of discharge (0.1 to 5 spikes per second), while so-called sensory neurons fired at a much faster rate. Similarly, PV neurons showed a slow rate of discharge (usually 2 to 6 spikes per second) that rarely exceeded 10 spikes per second (Brooks *et al.,* 1966). The physiological meaning of this spontaneous discharge is not known though it might be related to the tonic production or release of neurohypophyseal hormones.

The Search for Osmoreceptors

The brilliant experiments of Verney (1947) revealed that an increase in osmolarity of brain blood, produced by the intracarotid injection of hypertonic saline, elicits ADH release from the neurohypophysis. This crucial observation suggested the possible existence of specialized brain cells sensitive to osmotic pressure changes. By ligating various branches of the internal carotid artery in the dog, Verney concluded that the osmoreceptors lay in the anterior hypothalamus, and he suggested that the SO neurons might be involved in this function.

Electrophysiological techniques have been widely used in attempts to localize the osmoreceptors. Thus, von Euler (1953) was able to record slow potential changes (DC changes) rather differentially in the supraoptic area of the cat after intracarotid injections of hypertonic solutions. This not only suggested the existence of cells specifically sensitive to alterations in blood tonicity, but also indicated that these cells produced a generator receptor potential similar to that of peripheral receptors.

Ten years ago Cross and Green (1959) recorded the activity of single cells in the anterior hypothalamus of the rabbit under urethane anesthesia and found that intracarotid injections of hypertonic solutions (NaCl, glucose) affected the spontaneous rate of discharge of many neurons. Both excitatory and inhibitory responses were obtained. It was of great interest that the responsive cells were not isolated in a particular nucleus or nuclei, though most of the 71 osmosensitive neurons recorded lay close to the supraoptic (Fig. 7-2) or paraventricular nuclei. Inhibitory

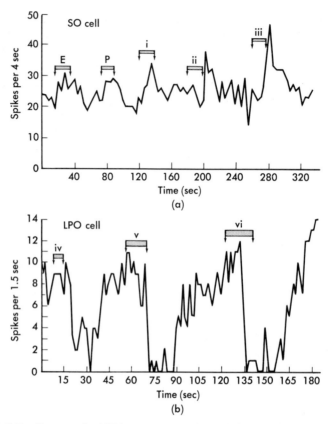

Figure 7-2   Supraoptic (SO) neuron accelerated by tactile (E and P) and osmotic stimuli of increasing intensity (i, ii, and iii), and lateral preoptic (LPO) neuron inhibited by osmotic stimuli (iv, v, vi) of increasing duration of intracarotid injection of 9 per cent NaCl. (From Cross and Green, 1959.)

responses predominated in PV neurons, a surprising finding, since Holland *et al.* (1959a) had shown that hypertonic injections stimulated the release of oxytocin and milk ejection in the rabbit. According to Cross and Green (1959) the hypothalamic neurons that responded to osmotic stimuli were highly specific, since they were generally unaffected by tactile, auditory, or visual stimulation.

Subsequently, Brooks *et al.* (1962, 1966) and Koizumi *et al.* (1964) have carefully studied the effects of osmotic and other stimuli on unit activity in the supraoptic region of the anesthetized cat (pentobarbital, chloralose, chloralose-urethane). They confirmed that intracarotid injections of hypertonic solutions alter the firing rate of SO neurons.

Excitatory responses were most common, but they also found patterns of inhibition and biphasic responses, i.e. inhibition followed by acceleration. Injections of distilled water generally inhibited the firing of supraoptic cells. Surprisingly, the discharge rate of SO neurons was also strongly influenced by somatic stimuli: excitation of either the posterior tibial nerve or the gastrocnemius nerve caused changes in the firing rate of a majority of osmosensitive cells. The responses to either hypertonic solutions or nerve stimulation were independent of changes in blood pressure. These results are consistent with reports that electrical stimulation of somatic nerves can elicit ADH release (Mills and Wang, 1964).

More recently, Joynt (1964) has studied the effects of changes in blood osmolarity on SO neurons approached transorally in the cat immobilized with Flaxedil. Eighty-five cells out of 108 tested responded to intracarotid injections of hypertonic solutions with changes in firing frequency (79 excitatory, 6 inhibitory). Osmosensitive neurons appeared to be very specific; only one neuron also responded to pain, another to sound, and two to light. Most of the osmosensitive neurons were outside the SO nucleus in the anterior and lateral hypothalamic regions.

Brooks et al. (1966) have also studied the effects of osmotic and other stimuli on the neuronal activity of the paraventricular nucleus in normal and postpartum cats. Of the PV neurons tested in normal cats 74 per cent were osmosensitive, though the increase in firing rate was not as dramatic as that observed in SO neurons. Inhibitory responses were rarely seen in these subjects, but in postpartum cats 17 per cent of the PV neurons gave inhibitory responses and only 58 per cent facilitatory responses to the injection of hypertonic solutions. The inhibitory responses could also be produced by nonosmotic changes such as the injection of cold solutions, and it was thought that they were secondary to the activation of "sensory afferents in or near the blood vessels." The PV neurons were considerably less responsive to stimulation of skin or afferent nerves from the leg muscles than were the neurons of the SO nucleus.

These data raise questions about the definition of "osmoreceptor." As pointed out by von Euler (1953), the cell should not be considered a receptor unless it is specifically excited by a particular stimulus and not by any other. Cross and Green (1959) and Joynt (1964) have found osmosensitive cells to be practically specific for osmotic changes but Brooks et al. (1966) have reported that most osmosensitive cells also respond to somatic stimulation. Perhaps the term "osmoreceptor" should be restricted to those neurons which are activated exclusively by osmotic stimulation.

There is no doubt that fibers arising from the SO and PV neurons constitute the "final common pathway" for the release of neurohypophyseal hormones in response to osmotic stimulation. Direct evidence for this concept has been provided by Ishikawa *et al.* (1966b), who succeeded in recording action potentials from the infundibular stalk in the cat and found that hypertonic solutions increased the traffic of impulses through this structure. On the basis of electrophysiological studies, however, there is no certainty concerning the location of primary osmosensitive neurons. In our opinion the criterion of considering a cell an osmoreceptor because it increases its firing rate only in response to injections of hypertonic solutions is inadequate. Changes in unit firing rate after osmotic stimulation might be due to neurogenic activation of osmoreceptors located elsewhere in the brain. Moreover, injections of hypertonic solutions induce a variety of central and peripheral effects, such as EEG arousal and changes in blood pressure (Holland *et al.*, 1959b), which may in turn diffusely excite a large number of neurons. Surprisingly, in the earlier unit papers EEG activity was not monitored; in these studies it is practically impossible to decide whether the observed changes in neuronal firing were caused specifically by stimulation of the area from which the units were recorded or from more general alterations in brain excitability.

There are data, however, which do suggest that primary osmosensitive neurons are located in the anterior hypothalamus. Sundsten and Sawyer (1961) induced milk ejection (indicative of oxytocin release) in rabbits with hypothalamic islands (all of the forebrain and the diencephalon other than the hypothalamus had been removed by suction) by intracarotid injections of hypertonic solutions. Furthermore, Suda *et al.* (1963) and Ishikawa *et al.* (1966a) have found that osmotic stimulation accelerated the firing of SO neurons in cats with hypothalamic islands. Bard and Macht (1958) had previously shown that chronic cats with hypothalamic islands maintained a reasonable water balance.

Osmotically altered EEG changes in the hypothalamus of the dog and rabbit were traced to the olfactory bulb in which they were maintained after surgical isolation of the bulb (Sundsten and Sawyer, 1959, 1961). In our UCLA laboratory, Freedman (1963) found that intracarotid injections of hypertonic solutions increased the unit firing rate of olfactory bulb neurons in the rabbit; the response persisted after surgical isolation of the olfactory bulb, indicating that osmoreceptor elements exist in this structure. Moyano and Brooks (1968) have recently confirmed these findings in the anesthetized cat and have demonstrated that electrical stimulation of the olfactory bulb increased the firing rate of hypothalamic cells in or near the ipsilateral supraoptic nucleus; thus there appear to be secondary osmoreceptor sites in the brain. Since the release of neurohypophyseal hormones can be induced by osmotic stimulation in animals with functionally isolated hypothalami, the role of the secondary osmosensitive neurons is not clear. Perhaps they can modulate the activity of the osmosensitive hypothalamic cells. There is evidence that other neurons widely scattered throughout the forebrain are influenced by variations in blood tonicity. Thus Wayner (1967) working with nonanesthetized female rats recorded clear increases in unit activity in many areas of the brain, including the hypothalamus, habenula, and limbic cortex, following injections of strong hypertonic solutions. These may or may not represent the presence of extrahypothalamic osmoreceptor elements; they may be more closely related to functions such as thirst than to the control of neurohypophyseal secretion.

Reflexogenous Release of Oxytocin and Vasopressin

It is established that the suckling or milking stimulus during lactation elicits oxytocin release (Cross, 1966). Electrical stimulation of the nipples fails to alter the firing rate of SO and PV neurons (Cross and

Figure 7-3 Effects of distention of the uterus on paraventricular nucleus neuron activity in 10 second intervals (bar graph) and mammary duct pressure (upper right). Left: unit discharges; A, control; B and C, during; and D, after uterine distension caused by inflating a balloon inside the uterine cavity with water. (From Brooks *et al.*, 1966.)

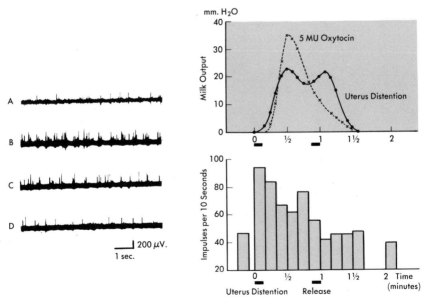

Green, 1959). On the other hand, Brooks *et al.* (1966) found in the postpartum cat under chloralose that gentle intermittent suction applied with a vacuum pump increased the firing rate of 80 per cent of the PV neurons tested. It had no effect in 17 per cent, and decreased the rate in none of the neurons. Most interestingly, a rise in intramammary pressure indicative of oxytocin release accompanied the unit changes in the PV nucleus. Similar effects on unit activation and the milk ejection response were obtained by distending the uterus, the Ferguson (1941) reflex activation of oxytocin release (Fig. 7-3). More recently, Ishikawa (1966b) found that stimulation of the nipples and uterine distension also increased activity in the SO-hypophyseal tract. These results indicate that oxytocin release from the neurohypophysis and the resultant increase in intramammary pressure is associated with an increase in the frequency of impulses generated in the PV and possibly the SO neurons. The importance of these observations can hardly be overemphasized since they represent the first demonstration of a definite correlation between unit activity and the secretion of a pituitary hormone.

Extrahypothalamic Influences on Hypothalamic Units and Neurohypophyseal Function

Electrical stimulation experiments have revealed both excitatory and inhibitory influences impinging on neurohypophyseal function from several regions of the brain. Stimulation of the cerebellum and of several forebrain areas influenced the spontaneous discharge of both SO and PV neurons. According to Koizumi *et al.* (1964), excitation of the anterior part of the cingulate gyrus accelerated 63 per cent of the "osmosensitive" neurons tested within or near the SO nucleus; stimulation of the cingulate gyrus in the cat and the dog induced release of oxytocin and vasopressin. Predominantly excitatory responses were obtained by stimulation of the motor cortex or prefrontal area, but chemical or electrical stimulation of the posterior lobe of the cerebellum inhibited 60 per cent of the SO neurons examined. Stimulation of the reticular formation produced variable results on unit activity of the SO nucleus in the cat (Suda *et al.*, 1963). Conversely, deafferenting the hypothalamus by producing a hypothalamic island caused enhanced spontaneous activity and responsivity in SO neurons (Suda *et al.*, 1963). Whereas decortication or elimination of the ipsilateral caudate nucleus did not modify the firing frequency of SO neurons, a transection separating the midbrain from the diencephalon markedly increased SO activity. Therefore it was concluded that the mesencephalic tegmentum exerts an inhibitory influence on SO activity. PV neurons are less dramatically influenced by stimulation of other parts of the brain, including the cerebellum. They are more excited by stimulation of the nipples and postpartum uterus than are SO neurons. These differences may be related to the fact that PV neurons appear to secrete predominantly oxytocin, while SO neurons are mainly related to the production of ADH (Farrell *et al.*, 1968).

Effects of Autonomic Agents

Microelectrode studies have yielded important data on the synaptic organization of the hypothalamo-neurohypophyseal system. It has been known since the work of Pickford (1947) that intrahypothalamic injections of acetylcholine elicit the release of neurohypophyseal hormones, suggesting that cholinergic synapses activate SO and PV neurons. Therefore it was of interest to find that the intracarotid administration of acetylcholine increased the firing rate of most SO and PV neurons (Brooks *et al.*, 1962, 1966; Joynt, 1966, Koizumi *et al.*, 1964; Ishikawa *et al.*, 1966a). Interestingly, all PV neurons that were reflexly excited by the suckling stimulus or uterine distension were also accelerated by acetylcholine. These effects were independent of changes in blood pressure. On the other hand, the effects of epinephrine and norepinephrine on unit activity in the SO nucleus are not completely clear; Brooks *et al.* (1962) reported activation of some neurons in the cat under pentobarbital, but in a subsequent paper Koizumi *et al.* (1964) found that intracarotid injections of 2 to 20 μg of epinephrine inhibited the firing of SO neurons. This last result is consistent with the general idea that the release of neurohypophyseal hormones is inhibited by adrenergic impulses.

Further Characteristics of Neurosecretory Neurons and their Processes

All of the observations on hypothalamic neurons described above were made with extracellular recording methods, i.e. with microelectrodes located outside the cell. In the goldfish Kandel (1964) succeeded in recording intracellularly from neurosecretory preoptic cells (the forerunner in fish of the SO and PV nuclei in mammals) and found that their potentials differed from those recorded in neighboring nonsecretory cells. The potentials of the preoptic neurons were characterized by their long duration (3.5 msec) and in most cases by a biphasic hyperpolarizing afterpotential: the first phase, brief and small, and the second, longer lasting and larger. Nonsecretory cells produced action potentials that were invariably followed by depolarizing afterpotentials. Kandel noted that these preoptic cells fired with a low frequency (2 to 8 spikes per second) and that this was determined in part by the long duration of their hyperpolarizing afterpotential. In contrast, the neighboring nonsecretory cells tended to fire in high frequency bursts. Whether mammalian neurosecretory cells have these characteristics remains to be determined by intracellular recording techniques.

Electrophysiological characteristics of hypothalamic neurosecretory fibers have been studied in the pituitary stalk. Taking advantage of the long pituitary stalk of the goosefish *Lophius piscatorius,* Potter and Loewenstein (1955) succeeded in recording action potentials from neurosecretory fibers. They found that these axons conducted normal action potentials at a slow speed (0.5 m/sec). In the preoptic hypophyseal tract of the goldfish Kandel measured the conduction velocity of fibers by stimulating the pituitary gland and recording from preoptic cells antidromically: the fibers conducted at 0.46 m/sec, a value similar to that obtained by Potter and Loewenstein. Somewhat higher values have been found recently in mammalian supraoptico-hypophyseal fibers (0.6 to 1.4 m/sec) by Ishikawa *et al.* (1966b), a velocity comparable to that of mammalian "C" fibers.

Kandel (1964) found that excitation of the hypophyseal stalk at subthreshold intensity to activate the neuron antidromically resulted in the production of an inhibitory postsynaptic potential (IPSP) in preoptic neurons of the goldfish. This indicated that in this system recurrent axons exist which connect with inhibitory internuncial cells. Moreover repetitive stimulation of the tract inhibited the spontaneous activity of preoptic neurons. The possible existence of recurrent axons establishing synaptic contacts with excitatory and intercalary neurons is suggested by the observations of Suda *et al.* (1963) in the cat. They found that low-frequency stimulation of the pituitary stalk (2 per second) considerably increased the firing frequency of SO neurons. An alternative explanation is that the hypophyseal stalk contains afferent fibers to the hypothalamus, as suggested by Cajal (1955).

Effects of Neurohypophyseal Hormones on Hypothalamic Electrical Activity

In the conscious, freely moving rabbit, vasopressin has been reported to induce sleep-like EEG activity (Faure, 1957; Kawakami and Sawyer, 1959a) and EEG arousal (Capon, 1960). Beyer *et al.* (1967) studied the effect of vasopressin on diencephalic background activity of the rabbit and the rat under urethane. In the rat, background activity in both the thalamus and hypothalamus was clearly depressed, and EEG spindles appeared simultaneously in the cerebral cortex. Further analysis suggested that these effects were secondary to the rise in blood pressure caused by vasopressin and evoked by activation of carotid baroreceptors which in turn produced EEG synchronization by acting on the lower brainstem (EEG synchronizing mechanism). In the rabbit, vasopressin usually increased hypothalamic background activity and activated the EEG.

In the unanesthetized rabbit, Kawakami and Sawyer (1959a) found that oxytocin could induce the sleep-like EEG afterreaction. In the rat under urethane anesthesia, oxytocin was generally ineffective in altering hypothalamic unit activity unless it induced a rise in blood pressure (Beyer *et al.,* 1967). However, in the cat, Kawakami and Saito (1967) have described various patterns of neuronal response to oxytocin, depending on the area recorded and the endocrine state. In anestrous cats there was an increase in firing rate of most anterior and lateral hypothalamic cells, but a decrease or inhibition in ventromedial hypothalamic (VMH) neurons. In contrast, estrous cats responded to oxytocin with a clearly decreased unit firing in lateral hypothalamic cells but no change in unit activity in anterior hypothalamus or VMH. The cells responsive to oxytocin were apparently specific since they did not respond to osmotic stimuli or LH injections. The functional significance of oxytocin-sensitive neurons is not clear, but there are suggestions that the concentration of oxytocin in blood may influence oxytocin release (Folley, 1959) or synthesis (Fendler and Telegdy, 1962).

Unit Activity and the Adenohypophysis

Hypothalamic control of the release of adenohypophyseal hormones involves more complex processes than regulation of neurohypophyseal secretion. The adenohypophysis produces several hormones within specialized cells of a gland which is physically separated from its controlling neurons by a vascular channel, the hypophyseal portal system. This humoral link is, largely, at least, a one-way conduit for transfer of information from hypothalamic neurons to pituitary cells, but there is evidence, summarized by Szentágothai *et al.* (1968), that small channels may convey data back from the effector gland cell to influence its "motor" neuron. Whether the pituitary cells utilize this anatomical route or the systemic circulation, there is considerable evidence (see Chapter 6) that "internal" or "short-loop" feedback circuits to the hypothalamus are functional. Electrophysiological support for this concept is given below.

Multiple external feedback circuits involving hormones of the target organs (e.g. adrenal, thyroid, gonads) condition the chemical environment and influence the reactivity of hypothalamic cells as well as neurons in other parts of the brain and glandular cells in the adenohypophysis itself. The hypothalamic neurons controlling a particular releasing factor and thereby its trophic hormone and target organ are not confined within specific nuclei as are the neurosecretory neurons of the neurohypophyseal system. There is, however, a topographical distribution of these neurons revealed by stereotaxic stimulation, lesion, and hormone-implant experiments (Sawyer et al., 1966; Mess et al., 1967; Watanabe and McCann, 1968). The local implantation results demonstrate that neurons in a specific site are directly sensitive to the action of a particular target organ hormone. With gonadal steroids it is possible to activate independently the discrete populations of hypothalamic neurons controlling sexual behavior and pituitary gonad function (Sawyer, 1967a, b).

The hypothalamic neurons controlling adenohypophyseal secretion are subjected to neural influences as well as to the humoral influences mentioned above. Activation of peripheral receptors can elicit reflexly the release of pituitary tropins, e.g. TSH in response to cold (Reichlin, 1966b), and ACTH following painful stimulation (Fortier, 1966). The best known example of this phenomenon is reflexogenous discharge of gonadotropins leading to ovulation following coitus or vaginal stimulation in certain species including the cat and the rabbit and under specialized conditions in the rat (Everett, 1964). Several attempts have been made to correlate patterns of electrical activity in the brain with adenohypophyseal secretion, using vaginal stimulation as the trigger.

Changes in Hypothalamic Electrical Activity Induced by Vaginal Stimulation

Using naturally estrous and estrogen-treated cats, Porter et al. (1957) recorded high amplitude spiking EEG changes in the anterior and lateral hypothalamus during and after vaginal stimulation. Barraclough (1960) reported similar electrical changes in the lateral hypothalamus of the proestrous rat, but not in the anestrous animal. Unanesthetized, unrestrained rabbits with permanently implanted electrodes responded to coitus or vaginal stimulation with a peculiar sleep-like EEG afterreaction (Sawyer and Kawakami, 1959). The response included a characteristic 8-cycles-per-second hypersynchronous rhythm predominating in limbic areas and the hypothalamus, a pattern now recognized as paradoxical sleep (Jouvet, 1967). Since the EEG afterreaction to coitus appears several minutes after reflexogenous discharge of LH has begun, it is unlikely that the response represents a neural correlate of pituitary activation. More probably, the EEG afterreaction is induced or facilitated by the release of pituitary hormones acting back on the brain. This idea, proposed by Sawyer and Kawakami (1959), is supported by the finding that the EEG afterreaction can be induced in ovariectomized estrogen-primed rabbits by the administration of LH, prolactin, oxytocin, and vasopressin (all of the hormones normally released postcoitally in the female rabbit), and by recent observations that the EEG afterreaction is seldom encountered in the hypophysectomized rabbit (Spies and Sawyer, unpublished).

Effects of Estrogen and Progesterone on Hypothalamic Unit Activity

Cross and his colleagues were the first to study the effects of ovarian steroids on unit activity in the hypothalamus. In the rat under urethane anesthesia, Barraclough and Cross (1963) studied the responsivity of lateral hypothalamic neurons to various stimuli during the different phases of the estrous cycle. The neurons were most responsive to olfactory stimuli during proestrus. Cold and painful stimuli accelerated the firing rates of fewer neurons during estrus than in other stages of the cycle. Conversely, more neurons were inhibited in firing rate by these stimuli (cold and pain) during estrus than in proestrus and diestrus. Similarly, the percentage of neurons inhibited by cervical probing (vaginal stimulation) was greater in estrus and proestrus than in diestrus, and the estrous females had the lowest percentage of excitatory responses. Urethane was a happy choice of anesthetic in these experiments, since light dosages do not block hypothalamopituitary activation of ovulation in the rat (Haller and Barraclough, 1968; Terasawa and Sawyer, unpublished) and "sleep-wakefulness" changes can be monitored in the EEG (Ramirez et al., 1967).

In subsequent papers, Cross and his colleagues have specifically analyzed the effect of estrogen on the responsivity of hypothalamic neurons to somatic and genital stimulation. Lincoln (1967) compared the spontaneous neuronal activity of spayed rats and estrogen dominated animals, and found decreased activity in the lateral hypothalamus of the spayed rat. Cross and Findlay (Cross, 1964, 1965) found that the administration of estrogen (1 µg im) to diestrous rats significantly increased the proportion of lateral hypothalamic units inhibited by pain, cold, and cervical stimuli as compared with nontreated diestrous rats (Fig. 7-4). More recently, Lincoln and Cross (1967) studied the effects of peripheral stimuli on the discharge of hypothalamic, preoptic, and

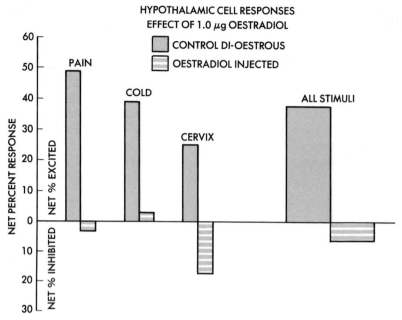

Figure 7-4   Histogram showing the effect of 1.0 µg estradiol in altering unit responses in the hypothalamus from a preponderance of excitatory effects to a preponderance of inhibitory effects. The stimuli used to produce the responses are indicated at the heads of the columns.   (From Cross, 1965, after Cross and Findlay.)

septal neurons in light-induced persistent-estrous rats, spayed rats, and spayed rats treated with estrogen. The lateral and anterior hypothalamic areas of the estrous groups showed significantly more inhibitory and fewer excitatory responses to pain, cold, and cervical stimuli than the spayed group. The results suggest that, in the estrogen-dominated rat, there is a drop in excitability of hypothalamic neurons to peripheral stimulation, an effect perhaps reflecting the negative feedback action of estrogen on hypothalamic pituitary function.

The effects of progesterone on unit activity have been given more thorough study than those of estrogen. In these experiments progesterone has usually been administered intravenously, dissolved in propylene glycol. Barraclough and Cross (1963) found that progesterone at a dosage of 40-400 µg intravenously blocked the excitatory response of lateral hypothalamic cells to cervical probing. The maximum depression of this response to vaginal stimulation was reached between 15 and 40 minutes and recovery was complete 1 hour after the injection of progesterone. Pain and cold were still effective in accelerating lateral hypothalamic neurons during this hour. Higher dosages (800 µg) suppressed the responses to all previously effective stimuli. No change in the spontaneous unit firing rate was reported following injection of progesterone. In the 7 to 11 day pseudopregnant rat, Cross and Silver (1965) found that the proportion of lateral hypothalamic neurons excited by cervical stimulation was only one-fourth of that previously observed in cyclic rats; under these conditions ovariectomy resulted in a striking fourfold increase in the number of responsive cells. Conversely, within 30 minutes after administration, progesterone inhibited most of the neurons previously responding to cervical stimulation. From these findings it was inferred that both exogenous and endogenous progesterone selectively depressed the response of lateral hypothalamic neurons to genital stimulation.

Ramirez *et al.* (1967) studied the effects of progesterone injections on the spontaneous discharge of thalamic and hypothalamic cells in the similarly anesthetized (urethane) rat. They observed that most units were depressed in their spontaneous firing range within 10 to 140 seconds following the injection of progesterone in propylene glycol (100 to 400 µg). However, these changes were clearly associated with the appearance of synchronization in the cortical EEG. Since all of the units affected had been previously observed to decelerate their discharge rates during EEG synchronization, it was suggested that the main effects of such injections of progesterone on hypothalamic unit activity were indirect and nonspecific. Beyer *et al.* (1967) recorded hypothalamic background activity in the rat under urethane and found that drops in background activity were generally related to EEG spindling; any treatment, including injections of progesterone, which elicited EEG synchronization in this particular preparation (rat under urethane), tended to diminish neuronal activity. Moreover, it was found that any stimulus provoking a rise in blood pressure (vasopressin, adrenalin, vaginal stimulation, etc.) tended to synchronize the EEG, probably acting through carotid baroreceptors. Progesterone in propylene glycol was found to raise the blood pressure (as previously reported by Cession *et al.,* 1966), and it is therefore possible that baroreceptor mechanisms are involved in the effects on brain activity described above. Obviously this does not rule out a direct action of progesterone on brain neurons.

More recently, Komisaruk *et al.* (1967) have studied the actions of progesterone on both hypothalamic background and unit activity. In rats under urethane, progesterone in propylene glycol induced a state of profound and long-lasting sleep-like EEG. The firing rates of 80 per cent of the units tested were suppressed simultaneously with the onset of

EEG synchrony. Single- and multi-unit activities that were depressed by progesterone could still be activated by arousing stimuli, including vaginal probing, but the arousal response was lesser in magnitude and duration for the animal under the influence of progesterone. This finding might explain the lack of responsivity of lateral hypothalamic units in the progestin-treated rats reported by Cross and Silver (1966).

From these apparently conflicting results it seems that some discrepancies exist concerning the effect of progesterone on hypothalamic unit activity as well as its mechanism of action. Our results suggest that intravenous injections of progesterone in propylene glycol depress diencephalic units indirectly through a generalized action on brain excitability associated with spindle sleep. On the other hand, Cross and his colleagues (Cross and Silver, 1966) maintain that progesterone selectively suppresses the response of hypothalamic cells to vaginal stimulation. A possible explanation for these differences is that, while his group has explored mainly the lateral hypothalamic area, the California group has recorded preferentially from the medial part of the hypothalamus. It should be mentioned that the striking effects of progesterone on unit activity in the urethane-anesthetized rat are not produced with equivalent dosages of the steroid in other species (rabbit, cat). Clearly, further studies must be done to clarify the mechanism of progesterone's action at the hypothalamus.

Recently Terasawa and Sawyer (unpublished) have been studying the effects of progesterone (1-2 mg subcutaneously in oil in the estrogen-treated ovariectomized rat) on multi-unit background activity in the arcuate nucleus and median eminence. The initial response is activation if the progesterone is injected in the morning and depression if it is injected after the onset of the "critical period"; there appears to be a diurnal variation in responsiveness of these neurons to the steroid. The over-all response to progesterone injected in the morning is triphasic; over the next 10 to 12 hours there is activation, then depression, and then activation. The afternoon response involves only the last two phases, i.e. depression followed by activation of multi-unit activity.

Unit recording techniques have recently been applied to the study of the responsivity of hypothalamic cells to vaginal stimulation with and without estrogen in the unanesthetized cat and rabbit. Kawakami and Saito (1967) reported that vaginal probing in the ovariectomized estrogen-treated cat (under Flaxedil) elicits hypothalamic firing patterns in which certain cells are inhibited during probing and activated for several minutes thereafter, while others are activated initially and inhibited during the subsequent period of synchronized EEG pattern

(Fig. 7-5). In nontreated spayed cats an initial rise during vaginal stimulation was also observed, but in no case was the inhibitory after-effect noted. The increased firing rates during stimulation were nonspecific, since pinching or stroking the skin also elicited them, but the rebound phenomena observed after cessation of vaginal stimulation in the estrous cat never appeared after somatic stimulation. Similar results have recently been obtained in the immobilized unanesthetized rabbit (Kawakami, personal communication).

In a comparable study, Alcaraz et al. (1969) have recently analyzed in the unanesthetized cat the effects of estrogen administration on the pattern of responsivity of anterior and medial hypothalamic cells to various stimuli (tactile, auditory, visual, and vaginal probing). Ovariectomy reduced considerably the number of excitatory responses, particularly to the cervical stimulus, whereas estrogen administration to the spayed cat reduced the proportion of inhibitory responses to all stimulus modalities. These results are in sharp contrast to those obtained in the rat (Lincoln and Cross, 1967). Since the anterior hypothalamus is related to the expression of sexual behavior in the female cat (Sawyer, 1960), it was tentatively proposed by Alcaraz et al. that the acceleration

Figure 7-5   Effects on unit discharges per second in the ventromedial hypothalamus and on the EEG in the frontal cortex (FC) of the estrogen-treated ovariectomized cat after stimulation of the vaginal cervix with a glass rod. (From Kawakami and Saito, 1967.)

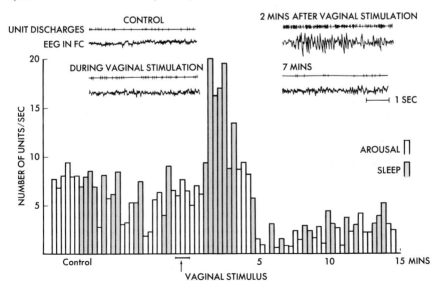

of anterior hypothalamic cell firing by vaginal stimulation in the estrous cat might reflect activation of the neural substrate related to sexual behavior. In these experiments it has not been possible to differentiate direct from indirect actions of estrogen on hypothalamic neurons. A direct effect on anterior hypothalamic cells is suggested from the estrogen implantation experiments of Sawyer (1963) and Michael (1966).

Quite recently, Faure et al. (1967) have made "chronic" recordings of unit activity in the hypothalamus of the fully conscious rabbit, searching for electrophysiological correlates of LH release. Vaginal probing produced a dramatic increase of unit activity in the premammillary region, with a peak of activity between 2 and 15 minutes after stimulation. Simultaneously, neurons in the dorsomedial-ventromedial region slowed in their discharge frequency. It is interesting that the neuronal changes were independent of the state of vigilance of the animal. Faure et al. interpreted the activation observed in premammillary neurons as perhaps related to the secretion of luteinizing hormone releasing factor (LRF) into the portal system.

Effects of Adrenal Steroids on Hypothalamic Unit Activity

Adrenocortical steroid hormones affect the excitability of the brain. Feldman et al. (1961) reported that intravenous administration of cortisol succinate increased the amplitude of evoked potentials in the brain stem within a few minutes. Moreover, cortisol provoked localized seizure discharges in the anterolateral hypothalamus (Feldman and Davidson, 1966). Whether adrenal steroid control of ACTH secretion is exerted primarily on the brain or directly on the pituitary gland is a controversial question (Smelik and Sawyer, 1962; Davidson and Feldman, 1963; De Wied, 1964).

The problem of the existence of hypothalamic cells sensitive to adrenocortical steroids has been approached with recording techniques employing multiple-microelectrodes by Slusher et al. (1966). They found, in unanesthetized cats, that the intravenous injection of 25 mg of cortisol produced significant alterations in the firing rate of most diencephalic cells within 10 minutes, and that the effect usually persisted from 20 to 60 minutes. Although most of the units were recorded from the dorsal and posterior hypothalamus, responsive neurons were also found in the zona incerta and mesencephalic-diencephalic junctions, suggesting a wide distribution of neurons sensitive to corticoids. In other experiments these investigators tested the effects of intracerebral injections of minute amounts of cortisol. They found that injections into the mesencephalon altered the firing rate of nearly all the diencephalic units recorded, usually 20 to 45 minutes after intracerebral administration. Interestingly, units located in the central mesodiencephalic zone were not affected. Injection of cortisol into the dorsal or lateral parts of the hypothalamus accelerated or decelerated the firing rates of many mesencephalic cells within 10 minutes of injection.

An even more direct approach to the question of specificity of steroid action on hypothalamic cells has recently been made by Ruf and Steiner (1967), using the rat under chloralose-urethane anesthesia. With microelectrophoretic techniques, these workers infused extremely small amounts of dexamethasone into the vicinity of single neurons. While this synthetic steroid consistently failed to influence the activity of neurons in the cortex, hippocampus, or thalamus, a marked depression of firing rate was observed in some mesencephalic and hypothalamic neurons (15 out of 115 neurons). The hypothalamic cells were inhibited almost instantaneously (Fig. 7–6) and mesencephalic units after a short delay. The inhibition of firing outlasted the microinfusion by only 20 to 30 seconds, after which the control rate was gradually re-established. The responsive cells were localized in a fairly circumscribed area in the periventricular gray of the hypothalamus and mesencephalic central gray. Ruf and Steiner speculated that these neurons might have the following functions: control of corticotropin releasing factor (CRF) secretion by a negative feedback action of adrenocortical hormones, or a monitoring device measuring the blood concentrations of adrenal steroids.

Feldman and Dafny (1966) have studied the action of intravenous injections of cortisol on both the spontaneous activity of anterior hypothalamic cells and their responsiveness to light, sound, and sciatic stimulation. In 10 out of 14 cells tested there was a clear increase in spontaneous firing rate between 450 and 730 seconds after cortisol injection. Of 11 neurons subjected to peripheral stimulation, 5 responded with acceleration and 2 with inhibition. When tested 12 to 20 minutes after cortisol injection, the 5 cells previously excited by sensory stimulation responded with a clear inhibition to the test stimuli. The 2 cells originally inhibited showed a still greater degree of inhibition following cortisol administration. The investigators interpreted their results as indicating that the hormone changed the responsiveness of hypothalamic cells to incoming peripheral impulses, but an alternative explanation might be that cortisol facilitates inhibitory connections to these cells.

In their study of the effects of ACTH on the multi-unit background activity of the diencephalon (to be reported below), Sawyer et al.

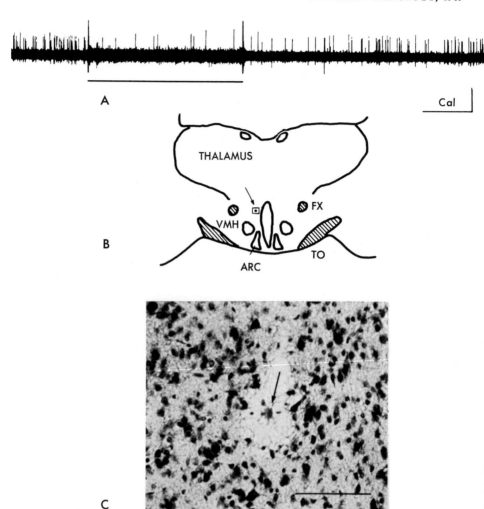

Figure 7-6 Inhibition of the spontaneous firing of a single neuron in the
anterior hypothalamus by microelectrophoresis (————) of dexamethasone.
Calibration (Cal): horizontal bar, 10 seconds; vertical bar, 0.3 mv. (B) Gross
localization of recording point (arrow) from which response shown in (A) was
obtained. (C) Microscopic localization of the electrode tip (arrow) by means
of fast green technique.   (From Ruf and Steiner, 1967.)

(1968) noted that in rats with intact adrenals ACTH depressed the
background activity in the zona incerta, a response that could be
duplicated with dexamethasone but not with ACTH in the

adrenalectomized rat. This response showed a latency of about 30 minutes; the interval to the point of maximal depression was about 90 minutes, followed by recovery. Dexamethasone also elevated the background activity of certain regions in the thalamus, but in the hypothalamus the response was either no change or depression of multi-unit activity.

Direct Actions of Pituitary Tropic Hormones on Hypothalamic Unit Activity

The suggestion of Sawyer and Kawakami (1961) and others (see Chapter 6), that the tropic hormones of the adenohypophysis may exert short-loop or internal feedback effects on the brain, has been mentioned earlier. A few studies have been made of the effects of these pituitary hormones on hypothalamic unit activity. In the preceding section reference was made to a study of the effects of ACTH and dexamethasone on multi-unit background activity. ACTH injections (2 U) produced an elevation in background activity in the arcuate nucleus (Fig. 7-7), and drops in background activity were observed in the basolateral thalamus, zona incerta, and entopeduncular nucleus (Sawyer et al. 1968). The

Figure 7-7 Short latency increase in multi-unit activity produced by ACTH in the arcuate nucleus of the rat hypothalamus (ARH). In the medial forebrain bundle (MFB) there is no change. (From Sawyer et al., 1968.)

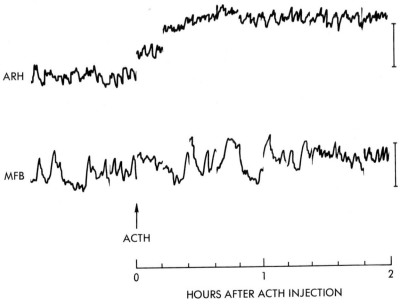

HOURS AFTER ACTH INJECTION

excitatory responses recorded in the arcuate nucleus after ACTH administration were also evoked in the adrenalectomized rat indicating that there might be a direct action of this hormone on arcuate cells. Thus the electrophysiological changes elicited by ACTH suggest that this hormone may exert an initially positive feedback action on the neurons controlling its secretion.

Kawakami and Sawyer (unpublished observations) have found that FSH administration to ovariectomized rats under urethane anesthesia elicits a long latency rise in multi-unit background activity of the arcuate nucleus and the ventral part of the ventromedial nucleus. This result may reflect the feedback action of this hormone on the hypothalamus proposed by some workers (see Chapter 6).

The effects of LH have received more attention than those of the other pituitary tropins on hypothalamic unit activity. In the rat under urethane anesthesia, Ramirez et al. (1967) have observed many units influenced by intravenous injections of LH. They distinguished between nonspecific units, in which the alterations elicited by LH were clearly correlated with widespread EEG changes, and specific units, in which the LH effects were totally independent of EEG activity. The specific units recorded from the base of the ventromedial nucleus responded to LH administration with a marked slowing in their discharge rates. The latency of onset of this depression in firing rate ranged from 10 seconds to 10 minutes, and the duration of the effect was from 3 minutes to 30 minutes. The responses appeared to be highly specific, since they were not duplicated by saline, vasopressin, boiled LH, or peripheral stimuli.

In the unanesthetized cat under Flaxedil, Kawakami and Saito (1967) also noted an inhibition of firing of neurons in the ventromedial nucleus following intravenous injection of LH. However, in the cat the depressed activity showed a correlation with cortical EEG activity and did not appear specific but rather linked with more general changes in brain excitability. Moreover, in the arcuate nucleus of the cat the LH injections produced a clear increase in the frequency discharge after a latency of 10 to 15 minutes, and the effect was independent of EEG changes. According to Kawakami these findings suggest that the arcuate nucleus and median eminence act in a reciprocal manner with the ventromedial nucleus in the control of gonadotrophin secretion. Ramirez et al. (1967) did not record from the arcuate nucleus in their study.

Recently, Terasawa and Sawyer (1968, and unpublished) have investigated the effects of LH on the background activity of the arcuate nucleus and medial preoptic area in the rat under urethane anesthesia. Intravenous injections of LH (20 to 40 μg) gradually increased the

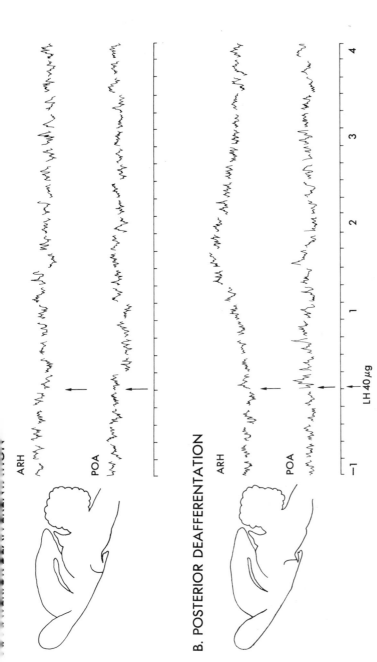

Figure 7-8   Effects of hypothalamic "deafferentation" on the multi-unit response to intravenous injections of LH. Separation from the preoptic region by a frontal cut (A) eliminates the response to LH in the arcuate nucleus (ARH), but a posterior cut (B) leaves the response intact. (From Terasawa and Sawyer, *Am. J. Physiol.*, in press, 1969.

background activity of the arcuate nucleus to a peak aproximately an hour and a half after injection. Conversely, the medial preoptic background activity was slightly depressed after LH injection; although opposite in direction, the time courses of these effects were similar in the two areas. The response to LH appeared to be specific, since no clear changes were observed in other diencephalic regions or in the EEG, and boiled LH was without effect. To test the possibility of a causal relationship between the activities in arcuate and preoptic regions, a semicircular cut with a small stereotaxic knife was made to separate the two areas: the "frontal cut" of Halász and Gorski (1967), which blocks cyclic ovulation. This lesion (anterior deafferentation) prevented the excitatory effect of LH on arcuate cells (Fig. 7-8). This result suggests that the increase in background activity observed in the arcuate nucleus after LH administration is synaptically mediated and is dependent on connections with rostral forebrain areas (anterior hypothalamus or medial preoptic region), areas controlling the cyclic release of LH in the rat (Everett, 1961).

Conclusion

The application of unit recording techniques to the analysis of neuroendocrine phenomena is still in its incipient stages. However, the field is expanding so rapidly that we are confident that this review will be outdated within a few months.

Two important concepts emerge from the studies discussed in the preceding pages: (1) patterns of hypothalamic neural activity can be correlated with pituitary secretion, and (2) various hormones, including the pituitary trophins, influence the basal level of activity and the responsivity of hypothalamic neurons. Although these results could be anticipated from data obtained by other techniques, they represent a starting point for a deeper analysis of hypothalamic functions.

It can be foreseen that certain lines of investigation on hypothalamic unit activity will receive special attention in future years. We will briefly deal with those we consider particularly promising for the advancement of knowledge on hypothalamic-pituitary interrelationships.

Statistical analysis of neuronal firing patterns. Until now most investigators have analyzed hypothalamic unit activity in terms of discharge frequency. However, as Burns (1967) has recently commented, mean frequency discharge is an aspect of neural behavior that is unlikely to be of great physiological importance. Analysis of the patterns of unit firing will probably be more useful in elucidating relations between neuronal activity and pituitary secretion. Statistical and computing techniques for analyzing the temporal distribution of neuronal discharge are now available, and they are expected to be used increasingly in future years.

Polygraphic recording associated with unit activity studies. It is known that the firing patterns of most hypothalamic neurons follow generalized changes of brain excitability. Moreover, fluctuations in blood pressure and other autonomic variables have been found to affect hypothalamic unit activity (Frazier *et al.,* 1965; Beyer *et al.,* 1967). Therefore, in order to know whether a given stimulus activates or inhibits hypothalamic cells specifically, it is absolutely necessary to monitor the electrical activity of other parts of the brain, and desirable to record other indicators of autonomic tone, such as the electrocardiogram and blood pressure. Therefore, the use of polygraphic methods is essential in future unit activity studies if meaningful information is to be obtained.

Unit activity recording in freely moving nonanesthetized animals. Unit activity studies related to neuroendocrine phenomena have generally been performed in anesthetized animals. This is a serious drawback, particularly in studies attempting to correlate electrophysiological phenomena with pituitary activation, since most anesthetics depress pituitary secretion. A promising line of research still under development is the recording of unit activity in freely moving conscious animals. When perfected this technique will permit examination of hypothalamic neuronal activity under normal conditions of pituitary activation (coitus, suckling, etc.).

Intracellular recording of hypothalamic neurons. To our knowledge, unit activity in the mammalian hypothalamus has been studied exclusively with extracellular microelectrodes. This technique gives little information about the synaptic events that precede neuronal firing. Such information would be useful for a better understanding of the mechanism of action of hormones and internal environmental changes on hypothalamic neurons. Unfortunately, intracellular recording in mammalian hypothalamic cells is technically difficult due to the small size of most hypothalamic cells and the pulsating movements of the mammalian hypothalamus associated with heart beat and respiration. However, further attempts should be made in this direction in the future.

Acknowledgments

Original work presented in this paper was supported by grants from the National Institutes of Health (NB 01162 and AM 08468) and the Ford Foundation. The assistance of the UCLA Brain Information Service is gratefully acknowledged (NINDB contract 43-66-59) and special thanks are due to Miss S. Elise Wilkins for bibliographic and secretarial help.

References

Alcaraz, M., M. Sales, C. Beyer, and C. Guzmán-Flores (1969). Effect of estrogen on the activity of hypothalamic and mesencephalic neurons in the cat. *Brain Res.*, in press.

Andersson, B., L. Ekman, C. C. Gale, and J. W. Sundsten (1963). Control of thyrotrophic hormone (TSH) secretion by the "heat loss center." *Acta Physiol. Scand. 59*, 12-33.

Bard, P., and M. B. Macht (1958). The behavior of chronically decerebrate cats. In Ciba Foundation Symposium: *Neurological Basis of Behavior* (G. E. W. Wolstenholme and C. M. O'Connor, eds.), pp. 55-75. Little, Brown and Co., Boston.

Barraclough, C. A. (1960). Hypothalamic activation associated with stimulation of the vaginal cervix of proestrous rats. *Anat. Rec. 136*, 159.

Barraclough, C. A., and B. A. Cross (1963). Unit activity in the hypothalamus of the cyclic female rat: Effect of genital stimuli and progesterone. *J. Endocrinol. 26*, 339-59.

Beyer, C., V. D. Ramirez, D. I. Whitmoyer, and C. H. Sawyer (1967). Effects of hormones on the electrical activity of the brain in the rat and rabbit. *Exp. Neurol. 18*, 313-26.

Brooks, C. McC., J. Ushiyama, and G. Lange (1962). Reactions of neurons in or near the supraoptic nuclei. *Am. J. Physiol. 202*, 487-90.

Brooks, C. McC., T. Ishikawa, K. Koizumi, and H.-H. Lu (1966). Activity of neurones in the paraventricular nucleus of the hypothalamus and its control. *J. Physiol. (London) 182*, 217-31.

Bures, J., M. Petran, and J. Zachar (1967). *Electrophysiological methods in biological research*. 3rd Ed. Academic Press, New York.

Burns, B. D. (1968). *The Uncertain Nervous System*. E. Arnold, London.

Cajal, S. Rámon y (1909). *Histologie du système nerveux de l'homme et des vertébres*. Vol. 2, p. 190. Consejo Superior de Investigaciones Cientificas, Madrid.

Capon, A. (1960). Analyse de l'effet d'éveil exercé par l'adrénaline et d'autres amines sympathicomimétiques sur l'électrocorticogramme du lapin non narcotisé. *Arch. Int. Pharmacodyn. 127*, 141-62.

Cession, G., A. Cession-Fossion, and R. Limet (1966). Action de la progestérone sur trois agents endogènes à action hypertensive. *Comp. Rend. Soc. Biol. 159*, 1864-66.

Chang, H. T. (1959). The evoked potentials. In *Handbook of Physiology, Sec. 1, Neurohypophysiology* (H. W. Magoun, J. Field, and V. E. Hall, eds.), *1*, pp. 299-313. American Physiological Society, Washington.

Cross, B. A. (1964). The hypothalamus in mammalian homeostasis. *Symp. Soc. Exp. Biol. 18*, 157-93.

Cross, B. A. (1965). Electrical recording techniques in the study of hypothalamic control of gonadotrophin secretion. *Proc. 2nd Int. Cong. Endocrinol., Excerpta Medica, Int. Cong.* Ser. *83*, pp. 513-16.

Cross, B. A. (1966). Neural control of oxytocin secretion. In *Neuroendocrinology* (L. Martini and W. F. Ganong, eds.), *1*, pp. 217-59. Academic Press, New York.

Cross, B. A., and J. D. Green (1959). Activity of single neurones in the hypothalamus: effect of osmotic and other stimuli. *J. Physiol. (London) 148*, 554-69.

Cross, B. A., and J. I. Kitay (1967). Unit activity in diencephalic islands. *Exp. Neurol. 19*, 316-30.

Cross, B. A., and I. A. Silver (1965). Effect of luteal hormone on the behaviour of hypothalamic neurones in pseudopregnant rats. *J. Endocrinol. 31*, 251-63.

Cross, B. A., and I. A. Silver (1966). Electrophysiological studies on the hypothalamus. *Brit. Med. Bull. 22*, 254-60.

Dafny, N., and S. Feldman (1967). Effects of caudate nucleus stimulation and lesions on single cell activity in the anterior hypothalamus. *Electroenceph. Clin. Neurophysiol. 23*, 546-57.

Dafny, N., E. Bental, and S. Feldman (1965). Effect of sensory stimuli on single unit activity in the posterior hypothalamus. *Electroenceph. Clin. Neurophysiol. 19*, 256-63.

Davidson, J. M., and S. Feldman (1963). Cerebral involvement in the inhibition of ACTH secretion by hydrocortisone. *Endocrinology 72*, 936-46.

De Wied, D. (1964). The site of the blocking action of dexamethasone on stress-induced pituitary ACTH release. *J. Endocrinol. 29*, 29-37.

Dreifuss, J. J., and J. T. Murphy (1968). Convergence of impulses upon single hypothalamic neurons. *Brain Res. 8*, 167-76.

Dreifuss, J. J., J. T. Murphy, and P. Gloor (1968). Contrasting effects of two identified amygdaloid efferent pathways on single hypothalamic neurons. *J. Neurophysiol. 31*, 237-48.

Egger, M. D. (1967). Responses of hypothalamic neurons to electrical stimulation in the amygdala and the hypothalamus. *Electroenceph. Clin. Neurophysiol. 23*, 6-15.

Everett, J. W. (1961). The mammalian female reproductive cycle and its controlling mechanisms. In *Sex and Internal Secretions*, 3rd Ed. (W. C. Young, ed.), pp. 497-555. Williams and Wilkins, Baltimore.

Everett, J. W. (1964). Central neural control of reproductive functions of the adenohypophysis. *Physiol. Rev. 44*, 373-431.

Farrell, G., L. F. Fabre, and E. W. Rauschkolb (1968). The neurohypophysis. *Ann. Rev. Physiol. 30*, 557-88.

Faure, J. (1957). Participation du rhinencéphale à la régularisation hormonale. *Rev. Path. Gen. 57*, No. 690, 1029-53; No. 691, 1263-83; No. 692, 1445-64.

Faure, J. M., J. D. Vincent, Cl. Bensche, B. Favarel-Garrigues, and B. Dufy (1967). Activités élémentaires dans l'hypothalamus au cours de l'ovulation chez la Lapine chronique. *J. Physiol. (Paris). 59*, 405.

Feldman, S., and N. Dafny (1966). Effect of hydrocortisone on single cell activity in the anterior hypothalamus. *Israel J. Med. Sci. 2*, 621-23.

Feldman, S., and J. M. Davidson (1966). Effect of hydrocortisone on electrical activity, arousal thresholds and evoked potentials in the brains of chronically implanted rabbits. *J. Neurol. Sci. 3*, 462-72.

Feldman, S., C. S. Van der Heide, and R. W. Porter (1959). Evoked potentials in the hypothalamus. *Am. J. Physiol. 196*, 1163-67.

Feldman, S., J. C. Todt, and R. W. Porter (1961). Effect of adrenocortical hormones on evoked potentials in the brain stem. *Neurology 11*, 109-15.

Fendler, K., and G. Telegdy (1962). Effect of oxytocin and vasopressin treatment on the oxytocic activity of the posterior pituitary in the rat. *Acta Physiol. Hung. 22*, 59-63.

Ferguson, J. K. W. (1941). A study of the motility of the intact uterus at term. *Surg. Gynecol. Obstet. 73*, 359-66.

Findlay, A. L. R., and J. N. Hayward (1968). Hypothalamic single unit activity during sleep and arousal in the rabbit. *Proc. XXIV Int. Cong. Physiol. Sci., 7*, p. 134.

Folley, J. S. (1959). In *Comparative Endocrinology* (A. Gorbman, ed.), p. 144. J. Wiley and Sons, New York.

Fortier, C. (1966). Nervous control of ACTH secretion. In *The Pituitary Gland* (G. W. Harris, and B. T. Donovan, eds.), 2, pp. 195-234. Butterworths, London.

Frazier, D. T., C. Taquini, L. L. Boyarsky, and M. F. Wilson (1965). Hypothalamic unit response to increases in arterial blood pressure. *Proc. Soc. Exp. Biol. Med. 120*, 450-54.

Freedman, S. (1963). Effects of osmotic stimuli on unit activity in the rabbit olfactory bulb. *Anat. Rec. 145*, 229-30.

Halász, B., and R. A. Gorski (1967). Gonadotrophic hormone secretion in female rats after partial or total interruption of neural afferents to the medial basal hypothalamus. *Endocrinology 80*, 608-22.

Haller, E. W., and C. A. Barraclough (1968). Urethane and progesterone-induced alterations in hypothalamic regulation of ovulation. *Fed. Proc. 27*, 270.

Hammel, H. T. (1968). Regulation of internal body temperature. *Ann. Rev. Physiol. 30*, 641-710.

Holland, R. C., B. A. Cross, and C. H. Sawyer (1959a). EEG correlates of osmotic activation of the neurohypophyseal milk-ejection mechanism. *Am. J. Physiol. 196*, 796-802.

Holland, R. C., J. W. Sundsten, and C. H. Sawyer (1959b). Effects of intracarotid injections of hypertonic solutions on arterial pressure in the rabbit. *Circulation Res. 7*, 712-20.

Ishikawa, T., K. Koizumi, and C. McC. Brooks (1966a). Activity of supraoptic nucleus neurons of the hypothalamus. *Neurology 16*, 101-6.

Ishikawa, T., K. Koizumi, and C. McC. Brooks (1966b). Electrical activity recorded from the pituitary stalk of the cat. *Am. J. Physiol. 210*, 427-31.

Jouvet, M. (1967). Neurophysiology of the states of sleep. *Physiol. Rev. 47*, 117-77.

Joynt, R. J. (1964). Functional significance of osmosensitive units in the anterior hypothalamus. *Neurology 14*, 584-90.

Joynt, R. J. (1966). Verney's concept of the osmoreceptor. *Arch. Neurol. 14*, 331-44.

Kandel, E. R. (1964). Electrical properties of hypothalamic neuroendocrine cells. *J. Gen. Physiol. 47*, 691-717.

Kawakami, M., and H. Saito (1967). Unit activity in the hypothalamus of the cat: effect of genital stimuli, luteinizing hormone and oxytocin. *Jap. J. Physiol. 17*, 466-86.

Kawakami, M., and C. H. Sawyer (1959). Induction of behavioral and electro-encephalographic changes in the rabbit by hormone administration or brain stimulation. *Endocrinology 65*, 631-43.

Koizumi, K., T. Ishikawa, and C. McC. Brooks (1964). Control of activity of neurons in the supraoptic nucleus. *J. Neurophysiol. 27*, 878-92.

Komisaruk, B. R., P. G. McDonald, D. I. Whitmoyer, and C. H. Sawyer (1967). Effects of progesterone and sensory stimulation on EEG and neuronal activity in the rat. *Exp. Neurol. 19*, 494-507.

Lincoln, D. W. (1967). Unit activity in the hypothalamus, septum and preoptic area of the rat: characteristics of spontaneous activity and the effect of oestrogen. *J. Endocrinol. 37*, 177-89.

Lincoln, D. W., and B. A. Cross (1967). Effect of oestrogen on the responsiveness of neurones in the hypothalamus, septum and preoptic area of rats with light-induced persistent oestrus. *J. Endocrinol. 37*, 191-203.

Mess, B., F. Fraschini, M. Motta, and L. Martini (1967). The topography of the neurons synthesizing the hypothalamic releasing factors. In *Proc. 2nd Int. Cong. Hormonal Steroids* (L. Martini, F. Fraschini, and M. Motta, eds.), *Excerpta Medica, Int. Cong. Ser. 132*, 1004-13.

Michael, R. P. (1965). Oestrogens in the central nervous system. *Brit. Med. Bull. 21*, 87-90.

Mills, E., and S. C. Wang (1964). Liberation of antidiuretic hormone: location of ascending pathways. *Am. J. Physiol. 207*, 1399-1404.

Morrell, F. (1967). Electrical signs of sensory coding. In *The Neurosciences* (G. C. Quarton, Y. Melnechuck, and F. O. Schmitt, eds.), pp. 452-69. The Rockefeller University Press, New York.

Moyano, H. F., and C. McC. Brooks (1968). Unit and E.E.G. osmosensitive responses in cat's olfactory bulb. *Fed. Proc. 27*, 320.

Oomura, Y., H. Ooyama, T. Yamamoto, F. Naka, N. Kobayashi, and T. Ono. (1967). Neuronal mechanism of feeding. *Prog. in Brain Res. 27*, 1-33.

Pickford, M. (1947). The action of acetylcholine in the supraoptic nucleus of the chloralosed dog. *J. Physiol. (London) 106*, 264-70.

Porter, R. W., E. B. Cavanaugh, B. V. Critchlow, and C. H. Sawyer (1957). Localized changes in electrical activity of the hypothalamus in estrous cats following vaginal stimulation. *Am. J. Physiol. 189*, 145-51.

Potter, D. D., and W. R. Loewenstein (1955). Electrical activity on neurosecretory cells. *Am. J. Physiol. 183*, 652.

Ramirez, V. D., B. R. Komisaruk, D. I. Whitmoyer, and C. H. Sawyer (1967). Effects of hormones and vaginal stimulation on the EEG and hypothalamic units in rats. *Am. J. Physiol. 212*, 1376-84.

Reichlin, S. (1966a). Regulation of somatotrophic hormone secretion. In *The Pituitary Gland* (G. W. Harris and B. T. Donovan, eds.), *II*, pp. 270-98. Butterworths, London.

Reichlin, S. (1966b). Control of thyrotropic hormone secretion. In *Neuroendocrinology* (L. Martini and W. F. Ganong, eds.), *I*, pp. 445-536. Academic Press, New York.

Rudomin, P., A Malliani, and A. Zanchetti (1965). Microelectrode recording of slow wave and unit responses to afferent stimuli in the hypothalamus of the cat. *Arch. Ital. Biol. 103*, 90-118.

Ruf, K., and F. A. Steiner (1967). Steroid-sensitive single neurons in rat hypothalamus and midbrain: identification by microelectrophoresis. *Science 156*, 667-69.

Sawa, M., N. Maruyama, T. Hanai, and S. Kaji (1959). Regulatory influence of amygdaloid nuclei upon the unitary activity in ventromedial nucleus of hypothalamus. *Folia Psychiat. Neurol. Jap. 13*, 235-56.

Sawyer, C. H. (1960). Reproductive behavior. In *Handbook of Physiology, Sec. I, Neurophysiology* (H. W. Magoun, J. Field, and V. E. Hall, eds.), *II*, pp. 1225-40. American Physiological Society, Washington.

Sawyer, C. H. (1963). Induction of estrus in the ovariectomized cat by local hypothalamic treatment with estrogen. *Anat. Rec. 145*, 280.

Sawyer, C. H. (1967a). Effects of hormonal steroids on certain mechanisms in the adult brain. *Proc. 2nd Int. Cong. on Hormonal Steroids, Excerpta Medica, Int. Cong. Ser. 132*, pp. 123-35.

Sawyer, C. H. (1967b). Some endocrine aspects of forebrain inhibition. *Brain Res. 6*, 48-59.

Sawyer, C. H., and M. Kawakami (1959). Characteristics of behavioral and electroencephalographic after-reactions to copulation and vaginal stimulation in the female rabbit. *Endocrinology 65*, 622-30.

Sawyer, C. H., and M. Kawakami (1961). Interactions between the central nervous system and hormones influencing ovulation. In *Control of Ovulation* (C. A. Villee, ed.), pp. 79-100. Pergamon Press, New York.

Sawyer, C. H., M. Kawakami, and S. Kanematsu (1966). Neuroendocrine aspects of reproduction. In *Endocrines and the Central Nervous System*, Chap. 4, *Res. Publ. Ass. Res. Nerv. Ment. Dis. 43*, 59-85.

Sawyer, C. H., M. Kawakami, B. Meyerson, D. I. Whitmoyer, and J. J. Lilley (1968). Effects of ACTH, dexamethasone and asphyxia on electrical activity of the rat hypothalamus. *Brain Res. 10*, 213-26.

Schlag, J., and R. Balvin (1963). Background activity in the cerebral cortex and reticular formation in relation with the electroencephalogram. *Exp. Neurol. 8*, 203-19.

Slusher, M. A., J. E. Hyde, and M. Laufer (1966). Effect of intracerebral hydrocortisone on unit activity of diencephalon and midbrain in cats. *J. Neurophysiol. 29*, 157-69.

Smelik, P. G., and C. H. Sawyer (1962). Effects of implantation of cortisol into the brain stem or pituitary gland on the adrenal response to stress in the rabbit. *Acta Endocrinol. 41*, 561-70.

Stuart, D. G., R. W. Porter, W. R. Adey, and Y. Kamikawa (1964). Hypothalamic unit activity. 1. Visceral and somatic influences. *Electroenceph. Clin. Neurophysiol. 16*, 237-47.

Suda, I., K. Koizumi, and C. McC. Brooks (1963). Study of unitary activity in the supraoptic nucleus of the hypothalamus. *Jap. J. Physiol. 13*, 374-85.

Sundsten, J. W., and C. H. Sawyer (1959). Electroencephalographic evidence of osmosensitive elements in olfactory bulb of dog brain. *Proc. Soc. Exp. Biol. Med. 101*, 524-27.

Sundsten, J. W., and C. H. Sawyer (1961). Osmotic activation of neurohypophysial hormone release in rabbits with hypothalamic islands. *Exp. Neurol.* *4*, 548-61.

Szentágothai, J. (1964). The parvicellular neurosecretory system. *Prog. in Brain Res. 5*, 135-46.

Szentágothai, J. (1968). Anatomical considerations. In *Hypothalamic Control of the Anterior Pituitary* (J. Szentágothai, B. Flerko, B. Mess, and B. Halász), Chap. II, pp. 22-103, 3rd Ed. Budapest Publishing House of the Hungarian Academy of Sciences.

Terasawa, E., and C. H. Sawyer (1968). Effects of luteinizing hormone (LH) on multiple unit activity in the rat hypothalamus. *Fed. Proc. 27*, 269.

Tolkunov, B. F. (1962). Bioelectrical activity of single neurons of the hypothalamus in short-term shifts of osmotic pressure in the systems of the internal carotid artery and portal vein of the liver. *Fiziol. Zh. SSSR. Sechenov 48*, 39-46 (in Russian).

Tsubokawa, T., and J. Sutin (1963). Mesencephalic influence upon the hypothalamic ventromedial nucleus. *Electroenceph. Clin. Neurophysiol. 15*, 804-10.

Verney, E. B. (1947). The antidiuretic hormone and the factors which determine its release. *Proc. Roy. Soc. B 135*, 25-106.

Vincent, J. D., O. Benoit, J. Scherrer, and J. M. Faure (1967). Activités élémentaires recueillies dans l'hypothalamus au cours de la vielle et du sommeil chez le Lapin chronique. *J. Physiol. (Paris) 59*, 527.

von Euler, C. (1953). A preliminary note on slow hypothalamic "osmo-potentials." *Acta Physiol. Scand. 29*, 133-36.

Watanabe, S., and S. M. McCann (1968). Localization of FSH-releasing factor in the hypothalamus and neurohypophysis as determined by *in vitro* assay. *Endocrinology 82*, 664-73.

Wayner, M. J. (1967). Hypothalamic and limbic system activation during salt arousal of drinking. *Psychon. Sci. 7*, 179-80.

8
The Role of the Sympathetic Nervous System in the Regulation of Sodium Excretion by the Kidney

JOHN R. GILL, JR.

Introduction

It is now apparent that many of the observed changes in the renal excretion of sodium cannot be explained adequately by changes in glomerular filtration rate or in the concentration of aldosterone in the blood (De-Wardener et al., 1961; Rector et al., 1964; Lindheimer et al., 1967). Many investigators are currently conducting an intensive search for other variables that control the tubular reabsorption of sodium. To date, important roles have been attributed to a natriuretic substance (Rector et al., 1968), and to physical factors, such as arterial pressure and oncotic pressure of the blood (Martino and Earley, 1967).

The sympathetic nervous system also appears to contribute importantly to the regulation of sodium excretion, and to do so directly through effects on the kidney and indirectly through the release of substances that also alter the renal excretion of sodium. This review presents the evidence on which the above suggestion is based.

Sympathetic Activity and Sodium Excretion

The kidney is extensively supplied with nerves. These have been traced along the arterial blood vessels to the afferent arterioles (Nilsson, 1965), to the efferent arterioles and to the venules (Christensen et al., 1951), and to the vasa recta (McKenna and Angelakos, 1968). At least three investigators have found evidence of a nerve supply to the tubules (Asfoury, 1951; Mitchell, 1951; Maillet, 1959). The renal nerves are thought to consist principally of sympathetic fibers. Electrical stimulation of the renal nerves produces changes in renal function which are qualitatively similar to those produced by infusion in the renal artery of the sympathetic neurotransmitter, norepinephrine (Kaplan et al., 1953; Barger et al., 1959; Zimmerman et al., 1964).

Early attempts to characterize the role of the renal nerves in the function of the kidney consisted of studies on the effects of unilateral renal denervation. In the anesthetized animal, the denervated kidney tended to have a higher blood flow and glomerular filtration rate and excreted more sodium than the contralateral innervated kidney(Kaplan et al., 1953; Berne, 1952; Surtshin et al., 1952). In most of the reported studies, the difference in glomerular filtration rates between the two kidneys was sufficient to explain the difference in sodium excretion. In fact, in one series of studies, when the renal artery of the denervated kidney was constricted, the glomerular filtration rate decreased to values comparable to those in the innervated kidney and the difference in sodium excretion between the two kidneys was abolished (Kamm and Levinsky, 1965).

In the studies in unanesthetized dogs, there was no essential difference in function between the innervated and the denervated kidneys (Surtshin et al., 1952; Berne, 1952; Surtshin and Hoeltzenbein, 1954). Generally, in the conscious unstressed dog, renal blood flow, glomerular filtration rate, and sodium excretion before and during infusion of saline were comparable in the two kidneys over a wide range of sodium excretion. Induction of anesthesia appears to increase sympathetic discharge to the innervated kidney, with a decrease in function of that kidney (Berne, 1952; Surtshin et al., 1952). This probably accounts for the difference in function of the two kidneys observed in those experiments carried out in anesthetized animals.

These observations have been interpreted as indicating that there is negligible sympathetic discharge to the canine kidney under normal circumstances. There is also evidence from studies in cats which is compatible with an absence of tonic discharge from the vasoconstrictor center to the renal vasculature under normal "resting" conditions. Thus, when the vasomotor center was freed from baroreceptor inhibition, blood flow through three vascular beds decreased, whereas blood flow through the kidney did not change (Folkow et al., 1961).

Generalized inhibition of sympathetic function produced by treatment with reserpine appears to decrease the natriuretic response to an infusion of saline in the anesthetized dog (Schrier et al., 1967). Mean arterial pressure was also lower in the reserpinized animals prior to and throughout the period of infusion, and this was cited as a possible explanation for the slower rate of sodium excretion.

Information on the presence or absence of sympathetic discharge to the kidney in the resting state is not available for man. Indeed, there is little information on the effect of renal denervation per se on renal function in man, as the denervation is usually the byproduct of renal transplantation. This makes it difficult to be certain which effects are attributable to the absence of renal nerves and which are attributable to transplantation (Bricker et al., 1956; Henderson et al., 1968).

More extensive impairment of sympathetic function in man as the result of autonomic insufficiency (Wagner, 1957) or treatment with a sympathetic blocking agent (Gill et al., 1964b) does not appear to alter sodium excretion in the resting state (Fig. 8-1). If one infuses saline in such patients, however, sodium excretion increases to a considerably greater extent than it does in normal subjects receiving a similar infusion (Fig. 8-1). In the patients with autonomic insufficiency, the exaggerated natriuresis was attributed to a greater than normal increase in glomerular filtration rate. As is apparent in Fig. 8-1, however, the greater rate of sodium excretion associated with sympathetic blockade in normal subjects was not dependent on a greater rate of glomerular filtration and occurred despite a lower mean arterial pressure. This suggests that the diminution in the renal tubular reabsorption of sodium which normally occurs with infusion of saline (Dirks et al., 1965) is greater in magnitude when sympathetic function is impaired. The reason for this apparent difference between dog and man is not clear.

Recently, it has been postulated that a natriuretic substance (Rector et al., 1968) as well as physical factors (decrease in plasma oncotic pressure, increase in mean arterial pressure, and renal vasodilatation) (Martino and Earley, 1967) are important determinants of the tubular response to infusion of saline. Some of these effects, such as renal vasodilatation or release of a natriuretic substance, which might occur in response to expansion of the intravascular volume with saline, may possibly be mediated by a decrease in sympathetic activity which also seems to occur (Frye and Braunwald, 1960). In the studies with sympathetic blockade, infusion of saline (Fig. 8-1) was associated with a consistent increase in cardiac output and a greater rate of renal blood flow (Gill and Mason, unpublished data). Whereas the effect of sympathetic blockade on renal hemodynamics could account for the greater rate of sodium excretion (Earley and Friedler, 1965), other possible effects of blockade (e.g. facilitation of the release of a natriuretic substance) cannot be excluded.

In subjects with sympathetic blockade, treatment with large doses of a sodium-retaining steroid decreased sodium excretion less effectively than it did when sympathetic function was intact (Fig. 8-2) (Gill *et al.*, 1964b). As in the case of saline infusion, the greater rate of sodium excretion was not dependent on a greater rate of glomerular filtration. This finding, together with the increased rate of potassium excretion,

Figure 8-1   Effect of an infusion of normal saline (2000 ml) on change in cardiac output (ΔCO), mean arterial pressure (MAP), mean clearance of para-amino-hippurate (C_{PAH}), mean clearance of inulin (C_{IN}) and mean sodium excretion ($U_{Na}V$) in normal subjects before (untreated) and again during treatment with guanethidine.

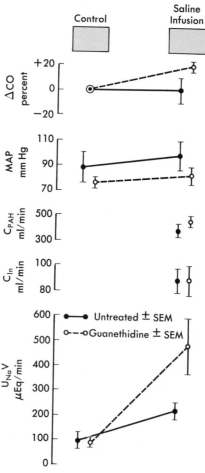

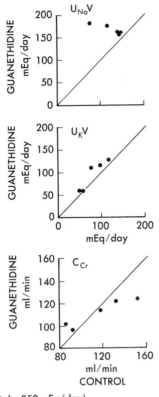

EFFECT OF GUANETHIDINE ON RESPONSE TO
TREATMENT WITH SODIUM-RETAINING STEROID

(Na intake 250 mEq/day)

Figure 8-2 A comparison of mean sodium excretion ($U_{Na}V$), mean potassium excretion (U_KV), and mean creatinine clearance (C_{cr}) in normal subjects during treatment with 2-methyl-9α-fluorohydrocortisone and guanethidine (guanethidine) for the days prior to "escape" with the mean values during treatment with 2-methyl-9α-fluorohydrocortisone alone (control) for a comparable number of days.

suggests that there is a decrease in sodium reabsorption in the proximal portions of the tubule with increased delivery to the distal sodium-for-potassium exchange site(s) (Fig. 8-2). Sympathetic blockade could produce such a decrease in the tubular reabsorption of sodium, and could augment sodium excretion after a very modest amount of sodium retention by facilitating renal vasodilatation, or the release of a natriuretic substance, or both.

Expansion of the volume of extracellular fluid with salt and water by intravenous infusion increases sodium excretion, whereas expansion by a high salt intake and treatment with sodium-retaining steroids leads to "escape" from the sodium-retaining effects of the steroid. Both procedures may possibly be accompanied by the release into the blood of a natriuretic substance which can lead to a decrease in the tubular reabsorption of sodium (Rector et al., 1968; Auld et al., 1968). The decrease in sympathetic activity associated with expansion of extracellular fluid and probably mediated by an increase in the effective circulating blood volume could contribute to the increased excretion of sodium in at least three ways.

(1) By vasodilatation of afferent arterioles to a greater extent than the efferent arterioles, it could increase the filtered load of sodium.

(2) By effects on the renal vasculature it could increase the volume of interstitial fluid and thus indirectly alter tubular transport processes, so as to decrease the tubular reabsorption of sodium (Earley and Friedler, 1966; Windhager, 1968).

(3) By mediation of the release of a natriuretic substance it could decrease the tubular reabsorption of sodium (Rector et al., 1968; Auld et al., 1968).

In support of the above concept of the role of decreased sympathetic activity in the natriuretic response is the finding that a comparable expansion of extracellular fluid produces a greater rate of renal blood flow (and possibly a greater or earlier release of a natriuretic substance) with a more rapid rate of sodium excretion when sympathetic activity is more completely depressed by treatment with a sympathetic blocking agent.

An increase in sympathetic discharge to the kidney in the dog, produced by stimulation of the renal nerves (Kaplan et al., 1953) or by infusion of norepinephrine in the renal artery (Barger et al., 1959), decreases sodium excretion and renal blood flow, and may or may not decrease glomerular filtration rate. A generalized increase in sympathetic activity can include both a release of norepinephrine into the circulation (Braunwald et al., 1964), and an increase in sympathetic nerve discharge to the kidney and to other areas of the body.

The application of blood pressure cuffs inflated to a pressure just below diastolic pressure to both thighs is a useful maneuver to decrease effective blood volume in man (Warren et al., 1945) and should lead to an increase in sympathetic activity through changes in baroreceptor activity. The results of studies in which cuffs were applied to normal subjects at 65 mm Hg for 40 minutes are presented in Fig. 8-3. The sequestration of blood in the legs was associated with an immediate decrease in sodium

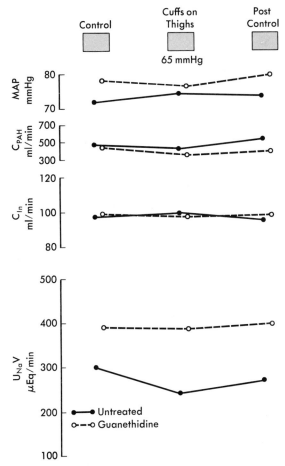

Figure 8-3   The effect of an application of blood pressure cuffs to both thighs on mean arterial pressure (MAP), mean clearance of para-amino-hippurate (C_{PAH}), mean clearance of inulin (C_{IN}) and mean sodium excretion ($U_{Na}V$) in three normal subjects before (untreated) and again during treatment with guanethidine. Values for "control" are the mean of the three 10-minute periods immediately preceding the application of the cuffs. The values for "cuffs on thighs" are the mean of the third and fourth 10-minute periods during which the cuffs were applied. Values for "post-control" are the mean of the first two 10-minute periods after release of the cuffs.

excretion, with the lowest value reached during the last 20 minutes of cuffing. The decrease in sodium excretion occurred without a decrease in mean arterial pressure or in glomerular filtration rate (Fig. 8-3), and was too rapid to be attributable to aldosterone (Barger *et al.*, 1959). When the study was repeated after blockade of the sympathetic nervous system by guanethidine, the sequestration of blood in the legs did not decrease the excretion of sodium despite a slight decrease in mean arterial pressure and in glomerular filtration rate (Fig. 8-3).

Figure 8-4   A comparison of mean sodium excretion ($U_{Na}V$), mean creatinine clearance (C_{cr}), and mean urinary aldosterone (Aldo) in normal subjects during 8 days of a low sodium intake (control) with the mean values during treatment with guanethidine for a comparable number of days of a low sodium intake (guanethidine).

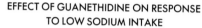

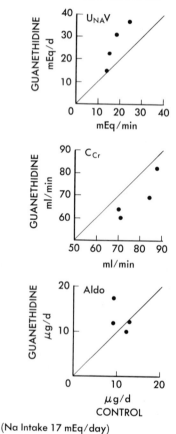

These findings suggest that, in man, a decrease in the effective circulating blood volume leads to a decrease in the renal excretion of sodium which is, in part, the consequence of an increase in the tubular reabsorption of sodium. The prevention of the decrease in sodium excretion by treatment with guanethidine suggests that it was mediated by increased activity of the sympathetic nervous system.

An abrupt decrease in dietary sodium is associated with a net loss of sodium from the body until urinary sodium reaches negligible values several days later. Evidence that the sympathetic nervous system is involved in the renal response is provided by the findings that a patient with autonomic insufficiency (Shear, 1963) and normal subjects with sympathetic blockade produced by guanethidine (Feb. 8-4; see also Gill and Bartter, 1966) excreted sodium at a greater than normal rate when dietary sodium was withheld. The production of aldosterone as estimated from the urinary excretion of aldosterone did not appear to be altered by treatment with guanethidine.

In subjects treated with guanethidine, sodium deprivation probably decreased effective circulating blood volume to a greater extent than did sequestration of blood in the legs. This would explain the greater decrease in mean arterial pressure (10 mm Hg versus 3 mm Hg) and in glomerular filtration rate (12 ml per minute versus 2 ml per minute) associated with sodium deprivation as opposed to sequestration of blood in the legs (Gill and Bartter, 1966). (See Figs. 8-3 and 8-4.) The decrease in arterial pressure and in glomerular filtration rate provide an explanation for the failure of sympathetic blockade to prevent the decrease in sodium excretion that occurred in response to sodium deprivation (Selkurt, 1951). When the intake of sodium is restricted in normal subjects, a greater decrease in sodium excretion occurs, and there is usually no decrease in arterial pressure or in glomerular filtration rate (Wiggins et al., 1951; Gill and Bartter, 1966). The decline in sodium excretion is probably the result of an increase in the tubular reabsorption of sodium mediated to a large extent by an increase in sympathetic activity.

To examine more critically the relationship between an increase in sympathetic activity and an increase in the renal reabsorption of sodium, it is necessary to increase sympathetic activity while avoiding other changes which could decrease the excretion of sodium. In the two types of study discussed above (the application of blood pressure cuffs to the thighs and the restriction of sodium intake), small decreases in renal perfusion pressure and in the filtered load of sodium tend to occur as the effective circulating blood volume decreases. Such changes, though small, could contribute to the decrease in the excretion of sodium (Selkurt, 1951).

In another series of studies, the effect on sodium excretion of an increase in sympathetic discharge to a kidney of a dog was determined during perfusion of that kidney by blood from a dog with an expanded effective circulating blood volume (Gill and Casper, 1969). Both the recipient and donor dogs were given desoxycorticosterone the day before and the day of the study to minimize the effect of changes in the secretion of aldosterone. When the femoral artery and vein of a donor dog were connected by tubing to the renal artery and vein of a kidney of a recipient dog so as to perfuse the kidney at arterial pressure, infusion of saline in the donor dog produced a natriuresis not only in the donor dog but also in the perfused kidney of the recipient dog (Fig. 8-5). An increase in sympathetic discharge to the perfused kidney with its renal nerves intact, produced by bleeding the recipient dog, did not affect natriuresis in the donor dog or glomerular filtration rate in the perfused kidney of the recipient dog (Fig. 8-5). Sodium excretion in the perfused kidney, which probably still continued to receive natriuretic stimuli from the saline-loaded donor dog, decreased in response to hemorrhage; presumably this was mediated by an increase in sympathetic nerve discharge. The results indicate that an increase in renal sympathetic nerve discharge can markedly increase the tubular reabsorption of sodium in a kidney even when that kidney is protected from an increase in circulating catecholamines and while it is exposed to factors which tend to decrease the tubular reabsorption of sodium.

Figure 8-5   A comparison of mean sodium excretion ($U_{Na}V$) in a kidney of the donor dog and of mean clearance of inulin (C_{IN}) and mean sodium excretion ($U_{Na}V$) in a perfused kidney of the recipient dog during infusion of saline in the donor dog (control), with mean values during infusion of saline in the donor dog plus bleeding of the recipient dog (bleeding).

EFFECT OF BLEEDING RECIPIENT DOG ON DONOR DOG AND PERFUSED KIDNEY
OF RECIPIENT DOG

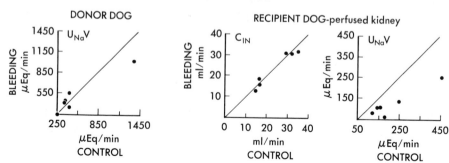

Thus, contraction of the volume of extracellular fluid produced by restriction of the intake of salt or water, or by losses from the body in the case of bleeding, decreases sodium excretion. Since a similar response is also observed when a portion of extracellular fluid is sequestered in the limbs, it seems quite likely that the increase in sympathetic activity associated with contraction of the volume of extracellular fluid is mediated by a decrease in the effective circulating blood volume. The importance of the increase in sympathetic activity in the conservation of extracellular fluid is demonstrated by the finding that the kidneys cannot limit the losses of salt and water normally when disease or treatment with a sympathetic blocking agent prevents an increase in sympathetic activity.

There are at least three ways by which an increase in sympathetic activity could decrease the excretion of sodium. First, it could constrict the afferent arteriole to a greater extent than the efferent arteriole. This decreases the filtered load of sodium (Zimmerman et al., 1964). Second, it could increase the tubular reabsorption of sodium by direct or indirect effects on the tubular transport processes (Windhager, 1968). Since effects of sympathetic activity on tubular transport processes can occur in the absence of changes in glomerular filtration rate, it is likely that the two effects are mediated either by different sympathetic nerve fibers, or by different degrees of discharge of the same fibers. Third, it could increase the release of renin from the juxtaglomerular apparatus (Vander, 1967; Wagermark et al., 1968). This increases the production of angiotensin and the secretion of aldosterone (Carpenter et al., 1961; Slater et al., 1963), each of which can decrease the renal excretion of sodium (Gill et al., 1964a; Barger et al., 1959).

A growing body of evidence indicates that increased sympathetic activity is present in some of the disease states characterized by excessive retention of sodium and formation of edema. Greater than normal amounts of catecholamines may be present in the urine of patients with nephrosis (Oliver et al., 1967) or congestive heart failure (Chidsey et al., 1965). In the latter disorder, increases in circulating norepinephrine (Chidsey et al., 1962) and in arterial and venous tone (Braunwald et al., 1966) have also been found. It has been postulated that teleologically, such increases in sympathetic activity represents an attempt by the organism to maintain the integrity of the circulation (Gaffney and Braunwald, 1963).

The probable basis for the increase in sympathetic activity in these two disease states is an absolute or relative decrease in effective circulating blood volume. In nephrosis, an absolute decrease in intravascular volume results from a decrease in plasma oncotic pressure, and is attributable to a failure of protein synthesis to keep pace with losses. In

EFFECT OF PENTOLINIUM ON RESPONSE TO SALINE INFUSION
OF DOGS WITH VENA CAVA CONSTRICTION

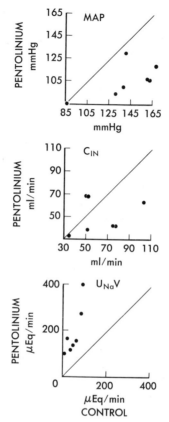

Figure 8-6   A comparison of mean arterial pressure (MAP), mean clearance of inulin (C_{IN}) and mean sodium excretion ($U_{Na}V$) during an infusion of saline (control) with mean values during an infusion of saline and pentolinium (pentolinium) in dogs with constriction of the thoracic inferior vena cava.

congestive heart failure although absolute intravascular volume may be normal or increased (Thomas and Bartter, 1961), there is a relative decrease in effective circulating blood volume. This results from the failure of the heart as a pump (Braunwald *et al.*, 1966) or from increased outflow of the blood from the arterial tree, as is the case with an arteriovenous fistula (Taylor *et al.*, 1968). Both the increase in sympathetic activity and the decrease in renal excretion of sodium tend to persist as long as the basic disorder prevents restoration of the effective circulating blood volume along with the increase in extracellular fluid volume. Evidence that the increase in sympathetic activity contributes to the increase in the renal reabsorption of sodium is provided by the finding that infusion of the alpha-adrenergic blocking agent dibenzyline into one renal artery increased the ipsilateral excretion of sodium in a dog with experimental congestive heart failure (Barger et al., 1959). A similar infusion into one renal artery of a normal dog had essentially no effect.

Constriction of the thoracic inferior vena cava in dogs produces edema and ascites (Davis et al., 1953) and prevents the decrease in proximal tubular reabsorption of sodium that usually occurs in response to an infusion of saline (Cirksena et al., 1966). In such dogs, generalized inpairment of sympathetic function produced by treatment with pentolinium increased the excretion of sodium (Gill et al., 1967) and partially restored the natriuretic response to an infusion of saline (Fig. 8-6). The increase in sodium excretion would probably have been greater if mean arterial pressure and glomerular filtration rate had not also decreased (Selkurt, 1951). The association of an increase in sodium excretion with a decrease in glomerular filtration rate suggests that ganglionic blockade led to a decrease in the tubular reabsorption of sodium.

The precise mechanism (or mechanisms) by which a sustained increase in sympathetic activity increases the tubular reabsorption of sodium remains to be clarified. It has been postulated that either a decrease in intracapillary pressure (Friedler et al., 1967) or an increase in oncotic pressure (Martino and Earley, 1967; Windhager, 1968) in the peritubular capillaries can increase the uptake of interstitial fluid and, in turn, increase the tubular reabsorption of sodium. An increase in sympathetic activity, through effects on the renal vasculature could produce either or both of these changes. A decrease in cortical blood flow has been observed in response to an increase in sympathetic discharge to the kidney (Barger, 1966). Such a change could conceivably increase the proportion of the total renal blood flow perfusing the juxtamedullary nephrons, which have longer loops of Henle and, presumably, a greater capacity to reabsorb sodium than those nephrons situated more superficially in the cortex. For the sake of completeness, one should also include the possibility that an increase in sympathetic activity can stimulate directly the tubular reabsorption of sodium. The circumstance and extent to which each of the above mechanisms operates in response to a given degree of sympathetic activity remain to be determined.

Apart from increasing the tubular reabsorption of sodium in any of the above ways, an increase in sympathetic activity can further augment the retention of sodium through its well-recognized ability to decrease the filtered load of sodium, and, through its effect on the renin-angiotensin system (Vander, 1967), to increase the secretion of aldosterone (Carpenter *et al.,* 1961; Slater *et al.,* 1963).

In a number of disease states, an expanded volume of extracellular fluid is associated with an increase in sympathetic activity and retention of sodium. As noted above, the sympathetic nervous system appears to contribute importantly to the decreased excretion of sodium. The presence of an increase in sympathetic activity despite an expanded volume of extracellular fluid and, at times, of blood as well, suggests that effective circulating blood volume, rather than absolute blood volume or extracellular fluid volume, is the more important determinant of sympathetic activity. Normally, effective circulating blood volume seems to change *pari passu* with changes in intravascular volume. As a result of disease, however, a change in intravascular volume may not be appreciated as such by the baroreceptor sensors which appraise the state of the circulation.

Conclusion

The sympathetic nervous system is uniquely adapted to monitor continuously changes in the circulation that occur as a result of changes in intravascular volume, and to respond rapidly to such changes in the circulation with appropriate changes in its activity. That such changes in sympathetic activity can exert an important effect on the renal excretion of sodium (and water) is supported by a growing body of evidence. An end result of the changes in sympathetic activity and of the corresponding changes in the rate of sodium excretion by the kidney appears to be the adjustment of the intravascular volume to the needs of the circulation. When, as a result of disease, the circulation is unable to function normally because of a reduced intravascular volume, or because a normal intravascular volume is no longer adequate, then an increase in sympathetic activity and a decrease in the excretion of sodium occur, and these changes tend to restore the function of the circulation to normal.

References

Asfoury, Z. M. (1951). Sympathectomy and the innervation of the kidney. *Brit. Med. J. 2,* 1304-6.
Auld, R. B., R. C. Lalone, and N. G. Levinsky (1968). Regulation of sodium

excretion during acute and chronic extracellular volume expansion in man. *J. Clin. Invest. 47*, 2a.

Barger, A. C. (1966). Renal hemodynamic factors in congestive heart failure. *Ann. New York Acad. Sci. 139*, 276-84.

Barger, A. C., F. P. Muldowney, and M. R. Liebowitz (1959). Role of the kidney in the pathogenesis of congestive heart failure. *Circulation 20*, 273-85.

Berne, R. M. (1952). Hemodynamics and sodium excretion of denervated kidney in anesthetized and unanesthetized dog. *Am. J. Physiol. 177*, 44-48.

Braunwald, E., D. C. Harrison, and C. A. Chidsey (1964). The heart as an endocrine organ. *Am. J. Med. 36*, 1-4.

Braunwald, E., C. A. Chidsey, P. E. Pool, E. H. Sonnenblick, J. Ross Jr., and J. W. Covell (1966). Congestive heart failure: biochemical and physiological considerations. *Ann. Int. Med. 64*, 904-41.

Bricker, N. S., W. R. Guild, J. B. Reardan, and J. P. Merrill (1956). Studies on the functional capacity of a denervated homotransplanted kidney in an identical twin with parallel observations in the donor. *J. Clin. Invest. 35*, 1364-80.

Carpenter, C. C. J., J. O. Davis, and C. R. Ayers (1961). Relation of renin, angiotensin II and experimental renal hypertension to aldosterone secretion. *J. Clin. Invest. 40*, 2026-42.

Chidsey, C. A., D. C. Harrison, and E. Braunwald (1962). Augmentation of the plasma norepinephrine response to exercise in patients with congestive heart failure. *New Eng. J. Med. 267*, 650-54.

Chidsey, C. A., E. Braunwald, and A. G. Morrow (1965). Catecholamine excretion and cardiac stores of norepinephrine in congestive heart failure. *Am. J. Med. 39*, 442-51.

Christensen, K., E. L. Lewis, and A. Kuntz (1951). Innervation of the renal blood vessels in the cat. *J. Comp. Neurol. 95*, 373-85.

Cirksena, W. J., J. H. Dirks, and R. W. Berliner (1966). Effect of thoracic cava obstruction on response of proximal tubule sodium reabsorption to saline infusion. *J. Clin. Invest. 45*, 179-86.

Davis, J. O., D. S. Howell, and J. L. Southworth (1953). Mechanisms of fluid and electrolyte retention in experimental preparations in dogs. III. Effect of adrenalectomy and subsequent desoxycorticosterone acetate administration on ascites formation. *Circulation Res. 1*, 260-70.

DeWardener, H. E., I. H. Mills, W. F. Clapham, and C. J. Hayter (1961). Studies on the efferent mechanism of sodium diuresis which follows the administration of intravenous saline in the dog. *Clin. Sci. 21*, 249-58.

Dirks, J. H., W. J. Cirksena, and R. W. Berliner (1965). The effect of saline infusion on sodium reabsorption by the proximal tubule of the dog. *J. Clin. Invest. 44*, 1160-70.

Earley, L. E., and R. M. Friedler (1965). Studies on the mechanism of natriuresis accompanying increased renal blood flow and its role in the renal response to extracellular volume expansion. *J. Clin. Invest. 44*, 1857-65.

Earley, L. E., and R. M. Friedler (1966). The effects of combined renal vasodilatation and pressor agents on renal hemodynamics and the tubular reabsorption of sodium. *J. Clin. Invest. 45*, 542-51.

Folkow, B., B. Johansson, and B. Lofving (1961). Aspects of functional differentiation of the sympatho-adrenergic control of the cardiovascular system. *Med. Exp. 4*, 321-28.

Friedler, R. M., L. J. Belleau, J. A. Martino, and L. E. Earley (1967). Hemo-
dynamically induced natriuresis in the presence of sodium retention resulting
from constriction of the thoracic inferior vena cava. *J. Lab. and Clin. Med.*
69, 565-83.

Frye, R. L., and E. Braunwald (1960). Studies on Starling's Law of the Heart.
I. The circulatory response to acute hypervolemia and its modification by
ganglionic blockade. *J. Clin. Invest. 39*, 1043-50.

Gaffney, T. E., and E. Braunwald (1963). Importance of the adrenergic nervous
system in the support of circulatory function in patients with congestive
heart failure. *Am. J. Med. 34*, 320-24.

Gill, J. R., Jr., and F. C. Bartter (1966). Adrenergic nervous system in sodium
metabolism. II. Effect of guanethidine on the renal response to sodium
deprivation in normal man. *New Eng. J. Med. 275*, 1466-71.

Gill, J. R., Jr., and A. G. T. Casper (1969). Role of the sympathetic nervous
system in the renal response to hemorrhage. *J. Clin. Invest. 48*, in press.

Gill, J. R., Jr., B. H. Barbour, J. D. H. Slater, and F. C. Bartter (1964a). Effect
of angiotensin II on urinary dilution in normal man. *Am. J. Physiol. 206*,
750-54.

Gill, J. R., Jr., D. T. Mason, and F. C. Bartter (1964b). Adrenergic nervous system in sodium metabolism: Effects of guanethidine and sodium-retaining
steroids in normal man. *J. Clin. Invest. 43*, 177-83.

Gill, J. R., Jr., A. A. Carr, L. E. Fleischmann, A. G. T. Casper, and F. C. Bartter
(1967). Effects of pentolinium on sodium excretion in dogs with constriction of the vena cava. *Am. J. Physiol. 212*, 191-96.

Henderson, L. W., K. D. Nolph, J. B. Puschett, and M. Goldberg (1968). Proximal
tubular malfunction as a mechanism for diuresis after renal homotrans-
plantation. *New Eng. J. Med. 278*, 467-78.

Kamm, D. E., and N. G. Levinsky (1965). The mechanism of denervation natriuresis. *J. Clin. Invest. 44*, 93-102.

Kaplan, S. A., C. D. West, and S. J. Fomon (1953). Effects of unilateral division
of splanchnic nerve on the renal excretion of electrolytes in unanesthetized
and anesthetized dogs: The mechanism of "crossed stimulation." *Am. J.*
Physiol. 175, 363-74.

Lindheimer, M. D., R. C. Lalone, and N. G. Levinsky (1967). Evidence that an
acute increase in glomerular filtration has little effect on sodium excretion
in the dog unless extracellular volume is expanded. *J. Clin. Invest. 46*,
256-65.

Maillet, M. (1959). Innervation sympathique du rein: Son role Trophique. *Acta*
Neuro. Veg. 20, 155-80.

Martino, J. A., and L. E. Earley (1967). Demonstration of a role of physical factors as determinants of the natriuretic response to volume expansion. *J.*
Clin. Invest. 46, 1963-78.

McKenna, O. C., and E. T. Angelakos (1968). Adrenergic innervation of the
canine kidney. *Circulation Res. 22*, 345-53.

Mitchell, G. A. G., (1951). The intrinsic renal nerves. *Acta Anat. 13*, 1-15.

Nilsson, O. (1965). The adrenergic innervation of the kidney. *Lab. Invest. 14*,
1392-95.

Oliver, W. J., R. C. Kelsch, and J. P. Chandler (1967). Demonstration of increased catecholamine excretion in the nephrotic syndrome. *Proc. Soc. Exp.*
Biol. 125, 1175-80.

Rector, F. C., Jr., G. van Giesen, F. Kiil, and D. W. Seldin (1964). Influence of expansion of extracellular fluid volume on tubular reabsorption of sodium independent of changes in glomerular filtration rate and aldosterone activity. *J. Clin. Invest. 43*, 341-48.

Rector, F. C., Jr., M. Martinez-MacDonado, N. A. Kurtzman, J. C. Sellman, Fred Oerther, and D. W. Seldin (1968). Demonstration of a hormonal inhibitor of proximal tubular reabsorption during expansion of extracellular volume with isotonic saline. *J. Clin. Invest. 47*, 761-73.

Schrier, R. W., K. M. McDonald, P. I. Jagger, and D. P. Lauler (1967). The role of the adrenergic nervous system in the renal response to acute extracellular fluid volume expansion. *Proc. Soc. Exp. Biol. 125*, 1157-62.

Selkurt, E. E. (1951). Effect of pulse pressure and mean arterial pressure modification on renal hemodynamics and electrolyte and water excretion. *Circulation 4*, 541-51.

Shear, L. (1963). Renal function and sodium metabolism in idiopathic orthostatic hypotension. *New Eng. J. Med. 268*, 347-52.

Slater, J. D. H., B. H. Barbour, H. H. Henderson, A. G. T. Casper, and F. C. Bartter (1963). Influence of the pituitary and the renin-angiotensin system on the secretion of aldosterone, cortisol and corticosterone. *J. Clin. Invest. 42*, 1504-20.

Surtshin, A., and J. Hoeltzenbein (1954). Excretion of sodium and water by the denervated canine kidney. *Am. J. Physiol. 177*, 44-48.

Surtshin, A., C. B. Mueller, and H. L. White (1952). Effects of acute changes in filtration rate on water and electrolyte excretion: Mechanism of denervation diuresis. *Am. J. Physiol. 177*, 194-200.

Taylor, R. R., J. W. Covell, and J. Ross, Jr. (1968). Left ventricular function in experimental aorta-caval fistula with circulatory congestion and fluid retention. *J. Clin. Invest. 47*, 1333-42.

Thomas, J. P., and F. C. Bartter (1961). Blood volume measurements in normal subjects and in patients with cirrhosis or cardiac disease. *Clin. Sci. 21*, 301-8.

Vander, A. J. (1967). Control of renin release. *Physiol. Rev. 47*, 359-82.

Wagermark, J., U. Ungerstedt, and A. Ljungqvist (1968). Sympathetic innervation of the juxtaglomerular cells of the kidney. *Circulation Res. 22*, 149-53.

Wagner, H. N. (1957). The influence of autonomic vasoregulatory reflexes on the rate of sodium and water excretion in man. *J. Clin. Invest. 36*, 1319-27.

Warren, J. V., E. S. Brannon, E. A. Stead, Jr., and A. J. Merrill (1945). The effect of venesection and pooling of blood in the extremities on the atrial pressure and cardiac output in normal subjects with observations on acute circulatory collapse in three instances. *J. Clin. Invest. 24*, 337.

Wiggins, W. S., C. H. Manry, R. H. Lyons, and R. F. Pitts (1951). Effect of salt loading and salt depletion on renal function and electrolyte excretion in man. *Circulation 3*, 275-81.

Windhager, E. E. (1968). Glomerulo-tubular balance of salt and water. *The Physiologist 11*, 103-14.

Zimmerman, B. G., F. M. Abboud, and J. W. Eckstein (1964). Effects of norepinephrine and angiotensin on total and venous resistance in the kidney. *Am. J. Physiol. 206*, 701-6.

9

The Endocrine Effects of Isolation of the Hypothalamus from the Rest of the Brain

BÉLA HALÁSZ

Introduction

Numerous experiments demonstrate the role of the central nervous system, and particularly the hypothalamus, in the control of anterior pituitary secretion. However, these findings do not indicate whether the observed effects are due to stimulation or destruction of nerve cells or of nerve tracts relaying information from other parts of the brain. The situation is particularly complicated if one deals with the medial basal hypothalamus. It has been demonstrated by several authors, first, that electrical stimulation of this area induces ovulation (Harris, 1948; Critchlow, 1958; Katsuki and Mizuta, 1958; Everett and Harp, 1960; Sawyer et al., 1960) and increases pituitary thyrotropic hormone (TSH) and adrenocorticotropic hormone (ACTH) secretion (Campbell et al., 1960; Shizume et al., 1962; de Groot and Harris, 1950; Porter, 1953, 1954; Anand and Dua, 1955; Katsuki et al., 1955; Endröczi et al., 1956; Mason, 1958; Endröczi and Lissák, 1960; Suzuki et al., 1960; Goldfien and Ganong, 1962); second, that destruction of the region causes a marked decrease in pituitary tropic hormone activity leading to target organ atrophy (Dey, 1941; Mess, 1952; Bogdanove and Halmi, 1953; Flerkó, 1953; McCann, 1953; Ganong et al., 1954; McCann and Sydnor, 1954; Davidson et al., 1960; and many others); and third, that extracts of the area stimulate or inhibit the release and probably also the synthesis of pituitary tropic hormones in vivo as well as in vitro (for references see McCann and Dhariwal, 1966). These findings indicate clearly that the

307

medial basal hypothalamus plays a key role in the control of pituitary secretion, but they do not show whether this region merely conveys the influence of other brain structures to the adenohypophysis, or whether it exerts a regulatory influence on the pituitary by itself. To study the functional capacity of the hypothalamus itself, hypothalamic island preparations have been very useful. In these preparations, there is no neural input to the island but the connections of the isolated region with the pituitary are left intact.

In the Department of Anatomy at the University Medical School of Pécs, we became interested in preparing islands of the medial basal

Figure 9-1   Schematic drawing of the location of the hypophysiotropic area (cross-hatched region).   ARC, arcuate nucleus; CA, anterior commissure; C CALL, corpus callosum; CHO, optic chiasm; CP, posterior commissure; DM, dorsomedial nucleus; FX, fornix; HL, lateral habenular nucleus; HM, medial habenular nucleus; LAHY, anterior lobe of hypophysis; LPHY, posterior lobe of hypophysis; MM, medial mammillary nucleus; NAH, anterior hypothalamic nucleus; PM, premammillary nucleus; PV, paraventricular nucleus; SCH, suprachiasmatic nucleus; SO, supraoptic nucleus; VM, ventromedial nucleus.   (From Halász et al., 1965.)

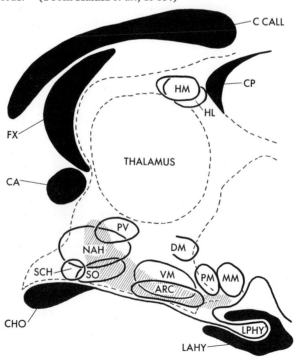

hypothalamic region. In previous experiments in which pituitary tissue was grafted into various regions of the brain, it was found that only the medial basal hypothalamus, and no other hypothalamic or extrahypothalamic area, was capable of maintaining the normal structure and function of the anterior lobe (Halász et al., 1962, 1963, 1965; Flament-Durand, 1965). Therefore, the medial basal hypothalamus was named the hypophysiotropic area (Halász et al., 1962). This suggests that the hypothalamic tropic and/or releasing substances essential for anterior lobe function are stored and possibly produced by the medial basal hypothalamus. The location and extent of the hypophysiotropic area is demonstrated in Fig. 9-1. The region extends laterally only 0.5 mm to 1.0 mm from the midline.

In order to obtain information about the functional capacity of the hypophysiotropic area itself, a special knife assembly was developed which permitted the interruption of all the neural connections of the area without altering its contact with the pituitary (Halász and Pupp, 1965). The present chapter is mainly a summary of the observations made with medial basal hypothalamic islands prepared in this fashion.

Techniques of Isolation

Two approaches have been used to make hypothalamic islands. One is surgical removal of the neighboring brain structures (Story et al., 1959; de Groot, 1962; Woods, 1962; Matsuda et al., 1963a,b; 1964; Wise et al., 1963). Animals with such islands require very intensive postoperative treatment, with special attention to food and water intake, body temperature, etc.

The other approach is simply cutting around the area one wants to isolate (Halász and Pupp, 1965). This procedure may be performed by means of a special knife assembly (Fig. 9-2) fixed in the holder of a stereotaxic instrument. Through a slot drilled in the calvarium, the knife is lowered into the brain and advanced to the base of the skull. By combining the turning of the knife with the movements of the carrier of the stereotaxic instrument, the medial basal hypothalamus can be cut around. The knife cut interrupts all neural connections of the medial basal hypothalamus, but leaves the area in contact with the pituitary by the unbroken pituitary stalk (Fig. 9-2). A series of frontal sections of the hypothalamus three weeks after such a cut are presented in Fig. 9-3. Since vascular regeneration occurs after the cut, it seems more appropriate to call these islands neural islands.

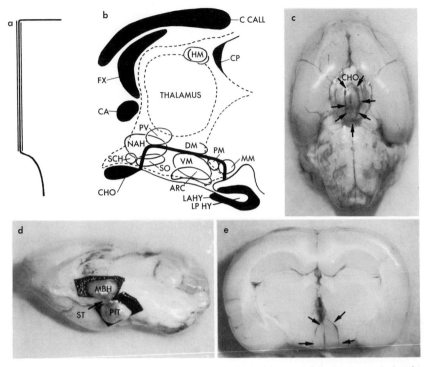

Figure 9-2   (a.) A schematic drawing of the knife assembly for hypothalamic deafferentation.
(b–e) Complete deafferentation of the medial basal hypothalamus.
(b) Sagittal schematic drawing of the experimental preparation. Knife cut indicated by the heavy line.
(c) Demonstration of the knife cut (arrows) as seen from the base of the brain.
(d) Midsagittal section of the rat's brain and the isolated medial basal hypothalamus (MBH)–pituitary (PIT) unit. This preparation was made immediately after deafferentation, by removing the left half of the brain except for the left half of the medial basal hypothalamus. The upper piece of black paper separates the deafferented region from the rest of the brain. The lower piece serves to delineate the pituitary gland with its intact stalk (ST).
(e) The extent of the deafferented region on a frontal section of the brain. Arrows indicate the cut. For abbreviations see caption of Figure 9-1. (Modified from Halász and Gorski, 1967.)

Neural islands of the whole hypothalamus can be prepared with the knife assembly shown in Fig. 9-2, or partial interruption of the neural connections of various hypothalamic or extrahypothalamic structures can be made if the size of the knife is changed. It should be pointed out that animals survive without any special treatment after isolation of the medial basal hypothalamus, but it is difficult to keep rats alive with whole hypothalamic islands. Deafferentation of the preoptic area also is associated with a high mortality.

Figure 9-3 A series of frontal sections of a rat hypothalamus 3 weeks after deafferentation. Arrows indicate the cut. AHL, lateral hypothalamic area; LM, lateral mammillary nucleus; ME, median eminence; PMD, dorsal premammillary nucleus; PMV, ventral premammillary nucleus; PVA, anterior periventricular nucleus; RCA, retrochiasmatic area; TO, optic tract; V III, third ventricle. For other abbreviations see caption of Figure 9-1. (From Halász and Pupp, 1965.)

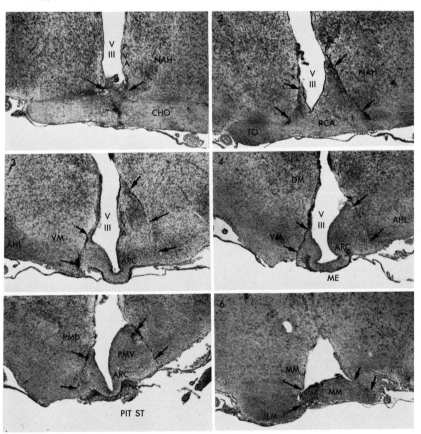

Hormone Secretion of the Anterior Pituitary after Hypothalamic Isolation

In this section the findings on pituitary ACTH, TSH, gonadotropic, and growth hormone (GH) secretion following isolation of the medial basal hypothalamus are summarized. Data on prolactin secretion are not available. There is also very little information about pituitary function in animals with whole hypothalamic islands.

It should be emphasized that in the absence of hypothalamic connections pituitary tissue becomes dedifferentiated and its hormone secretion (except prolactin) markedly reduced (Cutuly, 1941; Cheng et al., 1949; McDermott et al., 1950; Schweizer and Long, 1950; Fortier, 1951; Harris and Jacobsohn, 1952; Greer et al., 1953; Siperstein and Greer, 1956; Goldberg and Knobil, 1957; Nikitovitch-Winer and Everett, 1958, 1959; and several others). Animals bearing 10 heterotopic pituitary grafts have subnormal corticosterone secretion (Kendall et al., 1966), and the body growth of rats with as many as 30 pituitaries under the kidney capsule is still subnormal (Gittes and Kastin, 1966).

ACTH Secretion after Isolation

Basal Secretion. In the absence of major stress, neural isolation of the medial basal hypothalamus leads to increased basal ACTH secretion. As shown in Fig. 9-4, pituitary ACTH content is increased and plasma corticosterone levels are elevated four weeks following complete de-afferentation of the region (Halász et al., 1967b,c). Greer and Rockie (1968) have also found high resting levels of corticosterone in the peripheral plasma of rats with basal hypothalamic islands. Matsuda et al. (1963b) did not observe increased corticosteroid concentrations in rat plasma after isolation of the whole hypothalamus or the median eminence, but these preparations were made by brain removal. The discrepancy is probably due to the great difference in postsurgical condition of the animal preparations.

Pituitary ACTH content and corticosterone levels in the peripheral plasma are not increased after interruption of all posterior and lateral neural connections to the medial basal hypothalamus, but severance of the anterior connections of the region without cutting any other pathways (frontal cut, Figs. 9-4, 9-5) causes a rise in pituitary ACTH content similar to that which occurs after complete neural isolation. However, in contrast to the high levels of corticosterone seen following complete deafferentation, the frontal cut does not markedly influence basal corticos-

Figure 9-4   Adrenocorticotropic function in rats 4 weeks after partial or total deafferentation of the medial basal hypothalamus.   C, normal (sham-operated); CD, complete deafferentation; ID, incomplete deafferentation; FC, frontal cut.   The drawings at the top show, in schematic sagittal section, the type of deafferentation (heavy line) in the groups below.   AM, rats sacrificed at 9 a.m.; PM, sacrificed at 4 p.m.; I, weight of the adrenal removed first; II, weight of the second adrenal 30 days later; BEF., plasma corticosterone values before stress; AFT., 45 minutes after ether and surgical stress.   Vertical lines at the heads of columns indicate standard errors.   (Data from Halász et al., 1967b,c.)

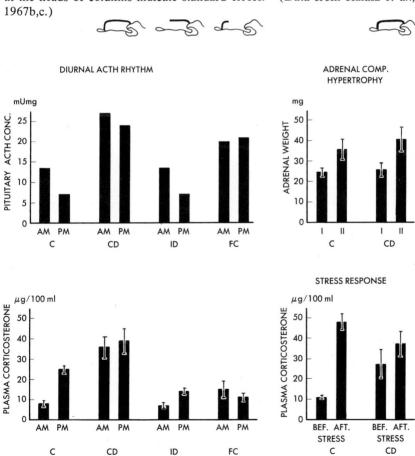

teroid secretion (Fig. 9-4). It appears that the frontal cut effectively separates ACTH synthesis and release, since hypophyseal ACTH is elevated while plasma corticosterone levels are relatively unchanged.

The significant increase in pituitary ACTH secretion after the interruption of the neural connections of the medial basal hypothalamus suggests that such deafferentation might eliminate an inhibitory influence on ACTH secretion. Inhibitory influences from various areas of the central

Figure 9-5   (a–c) Incomplete deafferentation of the medial basal hypothalamus interrupting bilateral, dorsal and posterior connections. (a) Schematic sagittal drawing of the experimental preparation. Heavy line indicates the cut. (b) Deafferentation as seen from the base of the brain. (c) Histology of the brain after deafferentation.
(d–f) Frontal cut interrupting anterior connections of the medial basal hypothalamus. (d) Schematic sagittal drawing of the experimental preparation. The knife cut is indicated by heavy line. (e) Frontal cut as seen from the base of the brain. (f) Frontal cut in horizontal section of the brain. Arrows indicate the knife cut.   PED, cerebral peduncle; TO, optic tract; V III, third ventricle. For other abbreviations see caption of Figure 9-1. (Modified from Halász and Gorski, 1967.)

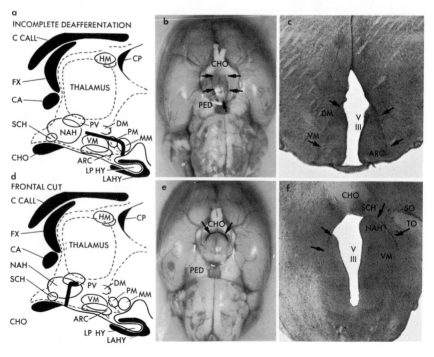

nervous system have been proposed (Porter, 1954; Newman et al., 1958; Slusher and Critchlow, 1959; Endröczi and Lissák, 1960; 1963; Suzuki et al., 1960; Slusher, 1961; Slusher and Hyde, 1961).

Egdahl has reported (1960) that adrenal cortical secretion is elevated in dogs after removal of the brain, including the entire hypothalamus. It is not clear what mechanism is responsible for the increased ACTH secretion in these dogs.

Diurnal ACTH Rhythm. In the rat, pituitary ACTH content is normally high in the morning and low in the afternoon, and plasma corticosterone level is low in the morning and elevated in the afternoon (Fig. 9-4). These fluctuations are not evident after neural isolation of the medial basal hypothalamus (Halász et al., 1967b,c; Palka et al., 1968). In our experiments both the pituitary ACTH content and the plasma corticosterone level were as high in the morning as in the afternoon. According to Palka et al. (1968), the AM plasma corticosterone values are consistently higher and the PM values consistently lower in the animals with complete deafferentation than they are in controls.

Studies in rats with partial deafferentation of the medial basal hypothalamus suggest that the afferent pathways necessary for the diurnal ACTH rhythm enter the hypothalamus anteriorly. We have demonstrated (Halász et al., 1967b,c) that the interruption of the dorsal, lateral, and posterior connections of the medial basal hypothalamus does not interfere with the diurnal variation in ACTH secretion, whereas section of the anterior afferents by a frontal cut causes a rise in ACTH synthesis and alters the diurnal ACTH rhythm (Fig. 9-4). Palka et al. (1968) have also reported that interruption of the anterior input to the medial basal hypothalamus abolishes the diurnal ACTH rhythm. Slusher (1964) reported that the anterior hypothalamic lesions destroying the periventricular zone and the arcuate nuclei were associated with inhibition of the normal ACTH rhythm. Galicich et al. (1965) showed that diurnal fluctuations in ACTH secretion persist in mice after suprathalamic brain ablation, whereas more extensive brain ablations, including the removal of the thalamus and hypothalamus, interfere with it.

Corticoid Feedback. Complete deafferentation of the medial basal hypothalamus does not alter the compensatory hypertrophy of the remaining adrenal that follows unilateral adrenalectomy (Fig. 9-4). The degree of hypertrophy is comparable to that noted in control rats (Halász et al., 1967b). Palka et al. (1968) have found that dexamethasone causes complete suppression of nonstress plasma corticosterone levels in animals in which the medial basal hypothalamus has been isolated.

Stress Response. Matsuda *et al.* (1964) reported that in rats with median eminence–pituitary islands, ether stress caused increased ACTH secretion. There was no response to traumatic stress in these animals. A normal response to ether stress was also oberved by Halász *et al.* (1967b), Palka *et al.* (1968), and Greer and Rockie (1968) in rats in which the medial basal hypothalamus had been isolated. In addition, Greer and Rockie have demonstrated that in such animals, the high plasma corticosterone levels induced by ether can be decreased to the basal level seen in intact rats by administering pentobarbital. Palka *et al.* (1968) have demonstrated a pituitary ACTH response to immobilization that is reduced but not abolished by complete deafferentation of the medial basal hypothalamus. Makara and Stark (1968) have observed that after interruption of the lateral and anterior connections of the medial basal hypothalamus there is a rise in plasma corticosterone levels following Escheria coli endotoxin administration, but no response to formalin stress, sound stress, or vibration.

There is evidence that (1) destruction of the medial basal hypothalamus blocks pituitary response to stress (de Groot and Harris, 1950; Hume and Wittenstein, 1950; McCann, 1953; Porter, 1953, 1954; Hume and Nelson, 1955; Laqueur *et al.*, 1955; Slusher, 1958) and adrenal compensatory hypertrophy (Ganong and Hume, 1954; Endröczi and Mess, 1955; Fulford and McCann, 1955); (2) corticosteroid-sensitive neural elements exist in the medial basal hypothalamus (Endröczi *et al.*, 1961, Smelik and Sawyer, 1962, 1964; Chowers *et al.*, 1963; Davidson and Feldman, 1963; Corbin *et al.*, 1965) and (3) stress, adrenalectomy, and cortisol treatment produce changes in corticotropin releasing activity of the medial basal hypothalamus (Vernikos-Danellis, 1965). In view of this evidence, the findings obtained in rats with hypothalamic islands suggest that the pituitary ACTH responses to ether stress, immobilization, and corticoid feedback are mediated through the medial basal hypothalamus. An alternative explanation of the observations in animals with hypothalamic islands is that the medial basal hypothalamus maintains the normal structure and responsiveness of the adenohypophysis and the stress response and the corticoid feedback are mediated, at least in part, directly by the anterior lobe. This possibility cannot be ruled out with certainty at present. The fact that neural isolation of the medial basal hypothalamus interferes with some stress responses whereas others remain intact suggests that various factors activate ACTH release by different mechanisms.

Gonadotropic Hormone Secretion after Isolation

Basal Secretion; Occurrence of Ovulation. In male rats, gonadotropic hormone secretion is fairly well maintained after the interruption of all neural connections of the medial basal hypothalamus (Halász and Pupp, 1965; Halász et al., 1967a). Testicular weight and histology are nearly normal; only a slight decrease in seminal vesicle weight was observed (Fig. 9-6). There is no gonadal atrophy in female rats (Fig. 9-6), but pituitary follicle-stimulating hormone (FSH) and luteinizing-hormone (LH) secretion appear to be seriously altered (Halász and Pupp, 1965; Halász and Gorski, 1967). Such animals are not able to ovulate (Fig. 9-7); their ovaries are usually polyfollicular and do not contain fresh corpora lutea. The vaginal smears indicate permanent estrus (for an explanation of the constant estrous syndrome see Flerkó, 1968). In some animals, only old corpora lutea were present in the ovary and these rats had diestrous smears. An explanation for the two different types of ovarian alterations cannot be offered, since no appreciable difference in the extent of the deafferented region was found.

Thus, interruption of the neural connections of the medial basal hypothalamus interferes with pituitary gonadotropic function in the female but not in the male. This difference is probably related to the fact that pituitary FSH and LH secretion is tonic in the male and cyclic in the female (For details see Flerkó, 1966). It therefore seems likely that the medial basal hypothalamus is responsible for tonic gonadotropic hormone secretion, while cyclic release depends on neural afferents to the area. If neural isolation of the medial basal hypothalamus is performed in immature female rats 22 days of age, there is precocious vaginal opening followed immediately by the onset of persistent vaginal estrus. These animals fail to ovulate and their ovaries contain large follicles but no corpora lutea (Ramaley and Gorski, 1967).

The medial basal hypothalamus of the frog, *Rana temporaria*, is capable of maintaing pituitary gonadotropic hormone secretion in the absence of neural afferents (Dierickx, 1966). In a large group of adult female and male specimens of *Rana temporaria* the pars ventralis of the tuber cinereum of the hypothalamus and the adjacent median eminence and pituitary were isolated from the rest of the brain. All animals with this operation showed normal gametogenesis, and there was seasonal development of the gonads and secondary sexual characteristics. In contrast, when all nervous pathways to the median eminence were interrupted without disturbing the normal blood supply of the median eminence and

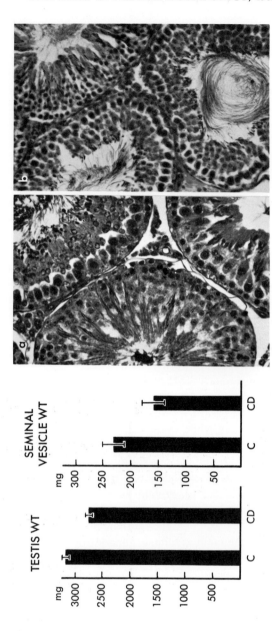

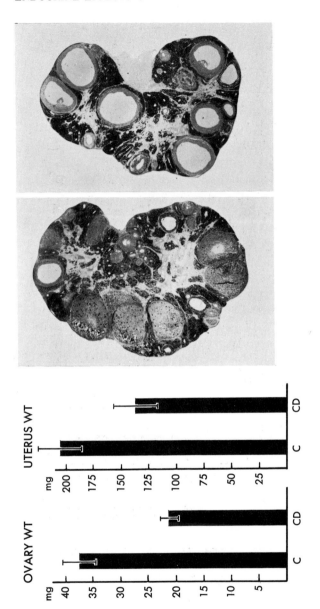

Figure 9-6 *Left*: Testis, seminal vesicle, ovary, and uterus weight in intact rats and in rats 3 weeks after neural isolation of the medial basal hypothalamus. C, intact; CD, rats with complete deafferentation. *Right*: The histological structure of the testes (above) and ovaries (below) in normal controls and in rats 3 weeks following complete deafferentation of the hypophysiotropic area. Testis: a, intact; b, neural isolation. Spermiogenesis was maintained in b. Ovary: c, intact; d, complete deafferentation, showing polyfollicular structure. (Testis and seminal vesicle weight data from Halász *et al.*, 1967a, all others from Halász and Pupp, 1965.)

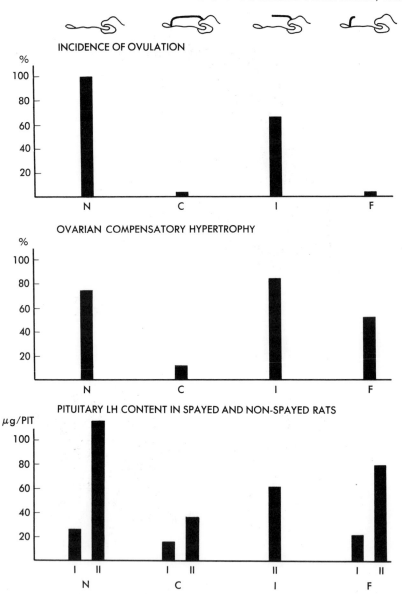

Figure 9-7   Occurrence of ovulation, ovarian compensatory hypertrophy, and pituitary LH response to castration in intact rats and in rats with partial or total deafferentation of the medial basal hypothalamus. Schematic drawings at the top indicate the type of deafferentation made in that group. N, normal; C, complete deafferentation; I, incomplete deafferentation; F, frontal cut; I, pituitary LH content in non-spayed rats; II, pituitary LH content in spayed rats.

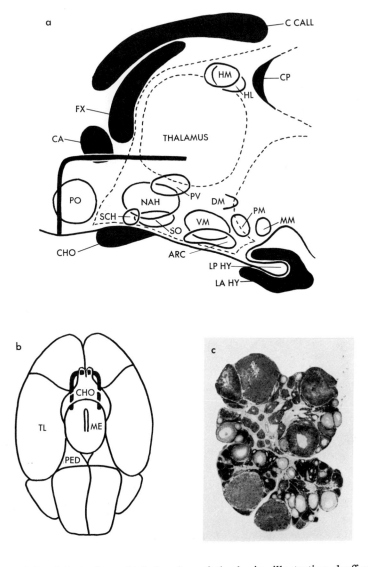

Figure 9-8   Schematic sagittal drawing of the brain, illustrating deafferentation of the preoptic area. PO, preoptic area. (b) The same cut as seen from the base of the brain. Heavy lines indicate the cut. ME, median eminence; PED, cerebral peduncle; TL, temporal lobe. (For other abbreviations see caption of Figure 9-1). (c) Histological structure of the ovary 4 days after preoptic deafferentation. The ovary contains fresh corpora lutea. Four ova were found in the oviduct of this rat.

hypophysis, gametogenesis and seasonal development of the gonads and the secondary sexual characteristics were absent.

Experiments in which partial deafferentation of the medial basal hypothalamic region was performed support the assumption that in higher vertebrates neural pathways to the medial basal hypothalamus are needed to induce the release of the ovulatory surge of LH from the pituitary. The available data indicate that, in rats, these afferents enter the medial basal hypothalamus anteriorly. It was found (Halász and Gorski, 1967) that if all except the anterior neural connections of the medial basal hypothalamic region were interrupted, ovulation occurred (Fig. 9-7). A frontal cut blocked ovulation in 100 per cent of the animals and produced the constant estrous syndrome. This latter finding has been corroborated by Tejasen and Everett (1967). Similar observations have been made by Ramaley and Gorski (1967), who performed hypothalamic deafferentation in 22-day-old female rats (see above). Studies in which the afferents to the medial basal hypothalamus were cut at various levels and to various extents (Halász and Gorski, 1967) suggest that the fibers of the afferent system concerned with ovulation are more widely dispersed in the preoptic region than they are near the median eminence. This agrees with the observations of Hillarp (1949) and Everett et al. (1964). By combining hypothalamic deafferentation with electrical stimulation, Tejasen and Everett (1967) have mapped these pathways in greater detail.

In recent studies in collaboration with Dr. Katalin Köves (unpublished observations), we investigated the question of where the critical afferents for ovulation actually come from. The anterior, lateral, and superior connections of the preoptic area were interrupted bilaterally in adult female rats (Fig. 9-8) and the occurrence of ovulation tested. It was extremely difficult to keep these animals alive. If the surgical procedure was performed in one step all the animals died within a few days. Therefore, deafferentation was carried out in two steps 7 to 10 days apart, performing only half the cut at one time. The mortality rate was still more than 90 per cent, but those animals which survived ovulated. Tubal ova were found in 6 of 10 rats with histologically verified deafferentation, and the ovaries of all 10 animals contained fresh corpora lutea (Fig. 9-8). However, the number of ova seen in the oviducts was less than in the controls, and the animals with preoptic isolation exhibited irregular sexual cycles. These findings indicate that the neurogenic stimulus causing the release of the luteinizing hormone releasing factor (LRF) in amounts necessary for ovulation comes, at least in part, from the preoptic area itself.

Feedback of Gonadal Hormones. The pituitaries of female rats with a neurally isolated medial basal hypothalamus respond to castration; pituitary LH content increases (Fig. 9-7) and castration cells are formed in the anterior pituitary (Halász and Gorski, 1967; Marić and Nikitov-itch-Winer, 1967). Since postcastration changes in the pituitary are abolished when the anterior lobe is disconnected from the hypothalamus by heterotopic transplantation (Hohlweg and Junkmann, 1932), this observation suggests that the medial basal hypothalamus is responsible for their occurrence. Data from several laboratories support the hypothesis that there are estrogen-sensitive structures in this region. Estrogen implants in the medial basal hypothalamus result in ovarian atrophy (Lisk, 1960; Davidson and Sawyer, 1961), prevent the formation of castration cells in the pituitary of the spayed rat (Lisk, 1963) and rabbit (Kanematsu and Sawyer, 1963), and inhibit the postcastration rise in pituitary and plasma LH (Ramirez *et al.*, 1964; Kanematsu and Sawyer, 1964). However, it is also possible that the medial basal hypothalamus simply maintains the normal structure and responsiveness of the pituitary to castration. A third possibility is that the pituitary response is partly mediated by the hypothalamus and partly by the pituitary itself. This possibility is supported by the observation that implants of estradiol in either the median eminence or the anterior pituitary prevent the postcastration rise of plasma LH (Ramirez *et al.*, 1964).

In contrast to the postcastration changes, there is no ovarian compensa-tory hypertrophy following the removal of one ovary (Fig. 9-7) when the neural connections of the medial basal hypothalamus are interrupted (Halász and Gorski, 1967). This seems to indicate that the neural structures responsible for the occurrence of ovarian compensatory hyper-trophy are located outside the medial basal hypothalamus. Such an assumption is consistent with the view that estrogen-sensitive neural elements occur in the anterior hypothalamic area and are involved in the negative feedback action of estrogens on the pituitary. This hypothesis was first advanced by Flerkó and Szentágothai (1957). Several observa-tions support it: first, individual neurons in the anterior hypothalamus accumulate estrogen (Michael, 1964), and the anterior hypothalamus shows a pattern of uptake and retention of estradiol-^{3}H which is similar to the pattern found in the uterus and vagina (Kato and Villee, 1967); second, rats with lesions between the optic chiasm and paraventricular nucleus show less inhibition of FSH secretion following estrogen treat-ment than do non-lesioned animals (Flerkó, 1957; Flerkó and Bárdos, 1960); and third, electrolytic lesions that destroy the suprachiasmatic and

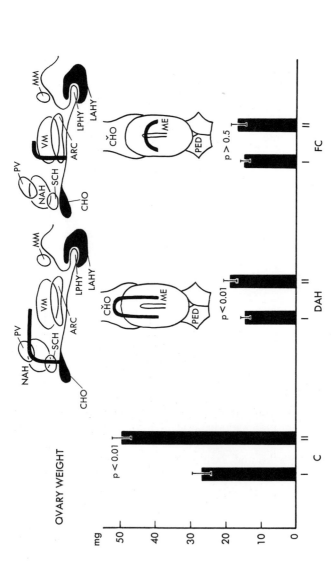

Figure 9-9 *Top:* Data on ovarian compensatory hypertrophy in control animals and in rats with two kinds of hypothalamic deafferentation. C, control; DAH, deafferentation of the medial basal and anterior hypothalamus; FC, frontal cut behind the anterior hypothalamus; I, weight of the ovary removed first; II, weight of the second ovary 30 days later. Vertical lines indicate standard error of mean. The drawings demonstrate the two kinds of deafferentation as seen in sagittal section of the hypothalamopituitary complex or from the base of the brain. Heavy lines indicate the cut. ME: median eminence; PED: cerebral peduncle (for other abbreviations see caption of Figure 9-1).

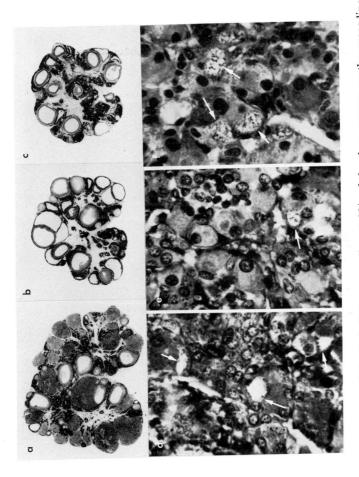

(a,b,c.) Histology of the ovaries (Scharlach R-hematoxylin, × 12) of the three groups on the preceding page. The ovaries in b and c are polyfollicular. (d,e,f.) Histology of the pituitaries of the three groups 30 days after the removal of the second ovary. Vacuolated basophile cells (castration cells) are present (arrows) in the anterior lobe of all three spayed groups (methylblueeosin, × 720; Köves and Halász, 1969).

anterior hypothalamic nuclei cause polyfollicular ovaries and constant vaginal cornification and at the same time interfere with the occurrence of ovarian compensatory hypertrophy (D'Angelo and Kravatz, 1960; Flerkó and Bárdos, 1961).

Recent experiments with hypothalamic deafferentation in female rats furnish further evidence for the assumption that the neurons of the ventral anterior hypothalamus are estrogen-sensitive and indispensable for the occurrence of ovarian compensatory hypertrophy (Köves and Halász, 1969). In these studies two kinds of intrahypothalamic operations were performed. In one group of animals the medial basal part of the anterior hypothalamus and the anterior hypothalamus immediately above it was deafferented anteriorly, superiorly, and laterally, leaving only the posterior connections of this area intact (Fig. 9-9). In other rats, a frontal cut of half-dome shape was made behind the anterior hypothalamus (Fig. 9-9). Ovarian compensatory hypertrophy occurred in rats with interruption of the neural connections of the ventral anterior hypothalamus. The magnitude of the response was greatly reduced, but the hypertrophy was statistically significant. However, no significant compensatory hypertrophy occurred in animals in which a frontal cut was made behind the anterior hypothalamus. In both groups the ovaries were polyfollicular. One month after the removal of the second ovary, castration cells were found in the pituitaries of both groups even when ovarian compensatory hypertrophy did not occur (Fig. 9-9).

The finding that deafferentation of the medial basal hypothalamus does not interfere with the pituitary gonadotropic response to castration but does block the response to unilateral ovariectomy, and that this latter reaction is evident in rats with neural isolation of the ventral anterior hypothalamus, seems to indicate that the sensitivity of the various hypothalamic structures to estrogen is not the same. It may be assumed that the neurons in the anterior hypothalamus are more sensitive, at least to a decrease in blood estrogen levels, than the more caudal elements of the medial basal hypothalamus-pituitary complex.

Data on pituitary gonadotropic function following isolation of the whole hypothalamus have been reported only in summary form, and detailed reports have not been published. According to Woods (1962), gonadotropin secretion persists in the rat but its pattern is disorganized after removal of cerebral cortex, basal ganglia, and dorsal thalamus and transection of the brainstem between the mammillary bodies and the pons. On the basis of vaginal smears, Woods has concluded that such animals seldom if ever secrete enough LH to produce ovulation. De Groot (1962) argued that a cyclic discharge of pituitary gonadotropins may be independent from telencephalic influence, but that isolation of the hypothalamus prevented pregnancy from occurring.

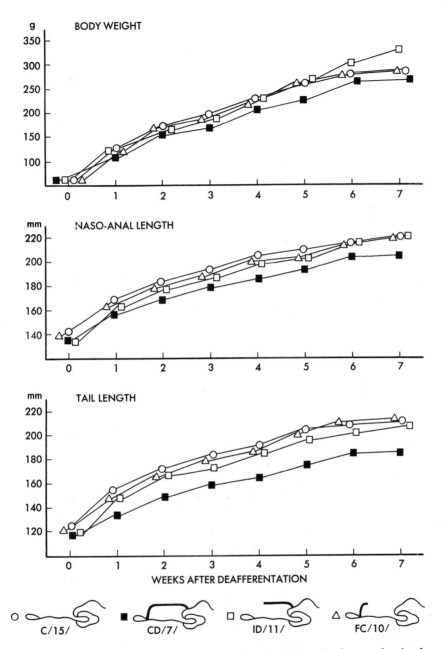

Figure 9-10   Mean body weight, naso-anal and tail length of control animals and of rats bearing different deafferentations of the medial basal hypothalamus. The schematic drawings of the hypothalamo-pituitary complex indicate the type of deafferentation (heavy line).   C, control; CD, complete deafferentation; ID, incomplete deafferentation; FC, frontal cut. The figures after the abbreviations are the number of animals in each group.   (From Halász, 1967.)

GH Secretion after Isolation

Basal Secretion. Young rats grow fairly well after neural isolation of the medial basal hypothalamus. As shown in Fig. 9-10, only a slight retardation in body growth occurs. Partial deafferentation of the same region does not interfere with body growth. Plasma growth hormone levels, determined by radioimmunoassay four weeks after isolation, were not different statistically from those in sham operated animals (Halász, 1967[1]). There is no information on whether or not the various stimuli that bring about acute changes in growth hormone secretion are effective in animals with hypothalamic islands.

TSH Secretion after Isolation

Basal Secretion. Basal TSH secretion appears to be only slightly impaired in animals with whole hypothalamic islands (Matsuda *et al.*, 1963a). As indicated by the thyroid epithelial cell height, ^{131}I uptake, biological half-life of thyroidal ^{131}I, and PBI tests (Fig. 9-11), complete deafferentation of the medial basal hypothalamus results in a moderate decrease in basal TSH activity. Interruption of the lateral, dorsal, and posterior connections of the area, or the severance of the anterior afferents at the level of the middle of the optic chiasm, does not cause appreciable changes in pituitary TSH release (Fig. 9-11; Halász *et al.*, 1967a). These latter findings seem to indicate that the neural afferents to the medial basal hypothalamus that affect basal TSH function are dispersed over a large area.

If a frontal cut of half-dome shape is made at the anterior end of the median eminence, pituitary TSH activity is markedly reduced (Fig. 9-11). A similar cut in the midlevel of the optic chiasm does not impair TSH secretion. These observations suggest that the region between the optic chiasm and the anterior level of the median eminence is essential for the maintenance of TSH secretion. This region is comparable to the "thyrotropic area" in which lesions depress thyroid function (for references see D'Angelo, 1963). Thyroidal radioiodine uptake is very low in rats with median eminence–pituitary islands, suggesting that basal TSH secretion is markedly reduced in such preparations (Matsuda *et al.*, 1963a).

---

1. This study was carried out in collaboration with Drs. D. Schalch and R. A. Gorski.

Response to Propylthiouracil. Isolation of the whole hypothalamus by brain ablation does not interfere with goiter formation following propylthiouracil administration (Matsuda *et al.*, 1963a). Propylthiouracil treatment (0.15 per cent in food for 14 days) induces an increase in TSH activity in rats with partial or total deafferentation of the medial basal hypothalamus (Halász *et al.*, 1967a). However, the pituitary TSH response to propylthiouracil varies considerably, depending on the type of neural isolation. Interruption of the lateral, dorsal, and posterior connections of the region (Fig. 9-5), or interruption of the anterior pathways at the midlevel of the optic chiasm (anterior frontal cut, Fig. 9-11), does not alter the propylthiouracil effect. In contrast, the response is only moderate after complete deafferentation, and very slight in animals with a frontal cut at the anterior level of the median eminence (Fig. 9-11). There is no thiouracil-induced thyroid hypertrophy in rats with a median eminence–pituitary island (Matsuda *et al.*, 1963a). The question of whether or not animals with an isolated medial basal hypothalamus are able to respond to cold with increased TSH secretion has not been studied as yet.

Two Levels in the Neural Control of the Anterior Pituitary

Neural isolation of the medial basal hypothalamus alters some pituitary functions, but does not interfere with others. After such isolation, basal secretion of tropic hormones is generally fairly well maintained, but mechanisms such as those responsible for the induction of ovulation and diurnal variation in ACTH secretion are disturbed. These data suggest that there are two levels of neural control of the anterior lobe, one in the medial basal hypothalamus, and a second in the neural structures located outside this region.

The Medial Basal Hypothalamus

The medial basal hypothalamus appears to be responsible for the production of the releasing factors and inhibiting factors that pass via the portal vessels to regulate anterior pituitary secretion. This concept was originally based on the finding that only the medial basal hypothalamus (the hypophysiotropic area), is able to maintain normal structure and function of the grafted anterior pituitary (Halász *et al.*, 1962, 1963, 1965; Flament-Durand, 1965). This concept is consistent with the data showing that corticotropin releasing factor (CRF; Vernikos-Danellis, 1964), LRF (McCann, 1962), and follicle-stimulating hormone releasing factor (FSHRF; Watanabe and McCann, 1968) are localized almost

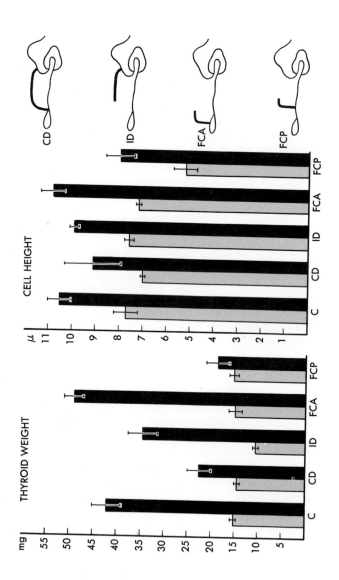

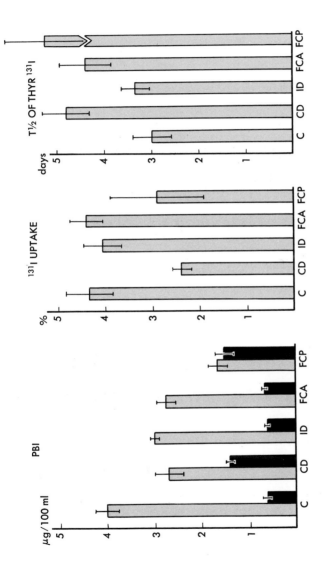

Figure 9-11 Thyroid function in rats with partial or total deafferentation of the medial basal hypothalamus. C, normal; CD, complete deafferentation; ID, incomplete deafferentation; FCA, anterior frontal cut; FCP, posterior frontal cut. Drawings at upper right indicate, in schematic sagittal section, the type of deafferentation (heavy line). Gray columns, rats on normal diet; black columns, rats treated with propylthiouracil. Vertical lines at tops of columns show standard errors. (Data from Halász et al., 1967a.)

exclusively in the medial basal hypothalamus. It is also in accord with morphological findings. The region includes the arcuate nuclei, the ventral part of the anterior periventricular nuclei, the medial part of the retrochiasmatic region, and the median eminence. The axons of the nuclei run in a ventral or ventromedial direction, and form the pathway called the tuberohypophyseal tract (Laruelle, 1934; Spatz, 1951; Nowakowski, 1951) or tuberoinfundibular tract (Szentágothai, 1962, 1964). The fibers of this tract terminate mainly in the superficial layer of the median eminence and in the proximal part of the pituitary stalk. A small number of the nerve fibers end on the capillary loops in the median eminence. The superficial layer of the median eminence is composed of nerve terminals of the tuberoinfundibular tract intermingled with ependymal and glial processes and end feet (for details see Szentágothai, 1962). The ultrastructure of the median eminence is also reviewed in detail in Chapter 1. Fuxe (1964) showed that the medial basal hypothalamic nuclei and the superficial zone of the median eminence contain relatively large amounts of monoamines. The functional significance of this mono-aminergic system in the hypothalamic control of the anterior pituitary is discussed in Chapter 2.

Are there separate regions inside the medial basal hypothalamus that produce the various releasing factors? This question was studied by Mess *et al.* (1966). They lesioned three different hypothalamic regions in rats, (the suprachiasmatic area, the region of the paraventricular nuclei, and the area of the arcuate and ventromedial nuclei) and measured the content of the various releasing factors in the medial basal hypothalamus. After destruction of the suprachiasmatic, arcuate and ventromedial regions, the LRF content of the extracts was decreased. Electrolytic lesions in the paraventricular region resulted in a decrease in FSHRF content. Thyro-tropin releasing factor (TRF) content of the extracts was decreased after all three kinds of lesions. No appreciable changes in CRF content were observed with any of the lesions. These findings seem to suggest that LRF and FSHRF production are limited to the suprachiasmatic and paraven-tricular regions, respectively, whereas the whole hypophysiotropic area is involved in TRF production. A diffuse representation of TRF production has also been proposed by D'Angelo *et al.*, (1964). The data of Guillemin *et al.* (1965) indicate that TRF is present in the whole hypothalamus. As shown in Fig. 9-11, TSH secretion is fairly well maintained in animals with a frontal cut at the level of the suprachiasmatic nuclei, but is seriously altered if a similar cut is made at the anterior end of the median eminence.

Several pieces of evidence support the view that CRF production is restricted to the median eminence. Only lesions of the median eminence region have been reported to cause adrenal atrophy (Bogdanove and Halmi, 1953; McCann, 1953; McCann and Brobeck, 1954; McCann and Sydnor, 1954; Greer and Ervin, 1956; Koibuchi, 1958; Slusher, 1958; Fortier and de Groot, 1964). CRF activity is concentrated in the median eminence region, while the hypothalamus without the median eminence area shows a negligible CRF activity (Vernikos-Danellis, 1964). ACTH secretion of pituitary grafts is maintained at a higher level if the graft is in contact with the median eminence. Compensatory adrenal hypertrophy is present if the graft is in contact with the vascular system of the median eminence, but fails to occur if the graft is not in contact (Halász et al., 1965). In the animals with hypothalamic islands the median eminence proper and pituitary stalk appear to be sufficient for the maintenance of ACTH secretion (Halász et al., 1967b). Porter (1968) has shown that ACTH secretion decreases only if the lower end of the pituitary stalk is cut. The elements in the median eminence and the pituitary stalk that produce CRF are unknown, although it is possible that the special kind of glial and ependymal elements in this region are involved (Leveque and Hofkin, 1961; Löfgren, 1961; Vigh et al., 1963).

The data obtained in animals with a neurally isolated medial basal hypothalamus also suggests that this area does not need the influence of other nervous structures to produce and release releasing and inhibiting factors. Thus it may be concluded that the medial basal hypothalamus is not merely the final step in the hypothalamic control of the anterior pituitary, which only transforms and forwards the influence of other nervous structures to the anterior lobe, but that this area represents a separate level in the hypothalamic control of the adenohypophysis. Generally speaking, it appears that the structure of the pituitary gland as well as basal secretion of the tropic hormones is maintained to a great extent by the area.

Is the basic functional level of the medial basal hypothalamus independent of the internal environment? It seems likely that the functional level of the region is influenced in a feedback fashion by the hormonal levels in the blood. This is indicated by the finding that, after neural isolation of the region, unilateral adrenalectomy is followed by the compensatory hypertrophy of the remaining adrenal, gonadectomy results in increased pituitary LH secretion and formation of castration cells in the anterior lobe, and thiouracil treatment causes a significant rise in TSH secretion. These pituitary responses are altered if the anterior lobe is disconnected from the hypothalamus. Estrogens, androgens, and corticosteroids placed in the medial basal hypothalamus cause marked decreases in pituitary tropic hormone secretion; for references and detailed discussion of the feedback mechanisms the reader is referred to the reviews of Davidson (1966), Flerkó (1966), Mangili et al. (1966), and Reichlin (1966). Substances such as ether and pentobarbital (Greer and Rockie, 1968) may also act at this level.

On the other hand, it is clear that this hypothalamic region is insufficient by itself to sustain hormone secretion of the anterior lobe at a normal level. This is evident from the observation that in the animals with an isolated medial basal hypothalamus, ovulation is blocked, basal ACTH secretion is elevated, diurnal ACTH rhythm fails, basal TSH and growth hormone secretion are slightly reduced, and the TSH response to propylthiouracil is subnormal. It may be assumed that all the pituitary functions that fail or are disturbed after the neural isolation of the medial basal hypothalamus are maintained by a second control level.

The Neural Regulatory Structures Located Outside the Medial Basal Hypothalamus

The neural structures outside the medial basal hypothalamus that participate in the control of the anterior lobe constitute, collectively, the second control level. These structures include several hypothalamic nuclei (anterior, ventromedial, etc.) and extrahypothalamic regions (whole limbic system and all its primary and secondary connections, reticular formation, cortex, etc.).

The first control level is probably a "closed system," in the sense that although its inputs are multiple, it has a single output channel, the tuberoinfundibular tract and its nerve endings in the surface zone of the median eminence. It appears to be involved primarily with the discharge into the portal circulation of the releasing factors. Conversely, the hypothalamic and the nonhypothalamic parts of the second control level are an "open system," with a wealth of other connections. This makes the study of this level difficult.

There is ample evidence that the elements of the second level exert stimulatory as well as inhibitory influences on tropic hormone secretion. The neurogenic stimulus causing the ovulatory surge of LH probably arises from the preoptic area, although other areas appear to be involved as well. The diurnal ACTH rhythm also depends on the second control level. The structures involved are not settled, but at least one part of the neural pathway involved in this mechanism enters the medial basal hypothalamus anteriorly.

Does the second control level act via the medial basal hypothalamus or directly on the pituitary? At present, the second alternative cannot be completely excluded. The nerve cells of the medial basal hypothalamus end around the capillary loops and in the surface zone of the median eminence (Szentágothai, 1962, 1964), but it is not known whether the median eminence also contains endings of axons coming from outside the medial basal hypothalamus.

Summary and Conclusion

Isolation of hypothalamic structures from the rest of the brain seems to be a useful approach for studying the functional significance and functional capacity of the hypothalamus in the control of the adenohypophysis. Experiments with island preparations have revealed that after the interruption of all neural connections of the medial ventral hypothalamus, basal secretion of pituitary tropic hormones is fairly well maintained but anterior lobe function is not normal. Atrophy of the target organs does not occur, adrenal compensatory hypertrophy develops following unilateral adrenalectomy, there is a pituitary ACTH response to ether stress, prophylthiouracil induces thyroid hypertrophy, LH content of the anterior lobe increases, castration cells are formed in the pituitary after gonadectomy, and only a slight retardation in body growth occurs. However, the animals do not ovulate, the diurnal rhythm in ACTH secretion is absent, and TSH and growth hormone secretion are abnormal. The afferents responsible for ovulation and at least part of those responsible for the maintenance of the ACTH rhythm have been shown to enter the medial basal hypothalamus anteriorly.

These observations suggest that there are two levels in the neural control of the anterior pituitary. One level is in the medial basal hypothalamus. It seems likely that this region stores or produces the hypothalamic releasing and inhibiting substances that regulate anterior pituitary secretion. The area appears to be able to produce and release these substances in the absence of neural afferents, and is probably responsible by itself for the maintenance of the basal secretion of the anterior lobe hormones. The feedback action of the peripheral hormones and the action of some other substances appear to be exerted on this region. The other level is in neural structures located outside the medial basal hypothalamus. This level exerts stimulatory as well as inhibitory effects on the adenohypophysis, and probably acts via the medial basal hypothalamus. The ovulatory surge of LH from the anterior lobe is triggered, at least in part, from the preoptic area.

References

Anand, B. K., and S. Dua (1955). Hypothalamic involvement in the pituitary adrenocortical response. *J. Physiol. (London) 127*, 153-56.

Bogdanove, E. M., and N. S. Halmi (1953). Effects of hypothalamic lesions and subsequent propylthiouracil treatment on pituitary structure and function in the rat. *Endocrinology 53*, 274-92.

Campbell, H. J., R. George, and G. W. Harris (1960). The acute effects of injection of thyrotrophic hormone or of electrical stimulation of the hypothalamus on the thyroid activity. *J. Physiol. (London) 152*, 527-44.

Cheng, C. P., G. Sayers, L. S. Goodman, and C. A. Swinyard (1949). Discharge of ACTH from transplanted pituitary tissue. *Am. J. Physiol. 159*, 426-32.

Chowers, I., S. Feldman, and J. M. Davidson (1963). Effects of intrahypothalamic crystalline steroids on acute ACTH secretion. *Am. J. Physiol. 205*, 671-73.

Corbin, A., G. Mangili, M. Motta, and L. Martini (1965). Effect of hypothalamic and mesencephalic steroid implantations on ACTH feedback mechanisms. *Endocrinology 76*, 811-18.

Critchlow, B. V. (1958). Ovulation induced by hypothalamic stimulation in the anesthetized rat. *Am. J. Physiol. 195*, 171-74.

Cutuly, E. (1941). Autoplastic grafting of anterior pituitary in male rats. *Anat. Rec. 80*, 83-97.

D'Angelo, S. A. (1963). Central nervous regulation of the secretion and release of thyroid stimulating hormone. In *Advances in Neuroendocrinology* (A. V. Nalbandov, ed.), pp. 158-205. Univ. of Illinois Press, Urbana.

D'Angelo, S. A., and A. S. Kravatz (1960). Gonadotrophic hormone function in persistent estrous rats with hypothalamic lesions. *Proc. Soc. Exp. Biol. Med. 104*, 130-33.

D'Angelo, S. A., J. Snyder, and J. M. Grodin (1964). Electrical stimulation of the hypothalamus: Simultaneous effects on the pituitary-adrenal and thyroid system of the rat. *Endocrinology 75*, 417-27.

Davidson, J. M. (1966). Control of gonadotropin secretion in the male. In *Neuroendocrinology* (L. Martini and W. F. Ganong, eds.), *1*, pp. 565-611. Academic Press, New York, London.

Davidson, J .M., and S. Feldman (1963). Cerebral involvement in the inhibition of ACTH secretion by hydrocortisone. *Endocrinology 72*, 936-46.

Davidson, J. M., and C. H. Sawyer (1961). Effects of localized intracerebral implantation of oestrogen on reproductive function in the female rabbit. *Acta Endocrinol. 37*, 385-93.

Davidson, J. M., A. N. Contopoulous, and W. F. Ganong (1960). Decreased gonadotrophic hormone content of anterior pituitary gland in dogs with hypothalamic lesions. *Endocrinology 66*, 735-40.

de Groot, J. (1962). In discussion, *Proc. Int. Union Physiol. Sciences. XXII. Int. Cong.* Int. Cong. Ser. 47, Part II, 623.

de Groot, J., and G. W. Harris (1950). Hypothalamic control of the anterior pituitary gland and blood lymphocytes. *J. Physiol (London) 111*, 335-46.

Dey, F. L. (1941). Changes in ovaries and uteri in guinea-pigs with hypothalamic lesions. *Am. J. Anat. 69*, 61-87.

Dierickx, K. (1966). Experimental identification of a hypothalamic gonadotrophic centre. *Z. Zellforsch. 74*, 53-79.

Egdahl, R. H. (1960). Adrenal cortical and medullary responses to trauma in dogs with isolated pituitaries. *Endocrinology 66*, 200-216.

Endröczi, E., and K. Lissák (1960). The role of the mesencephalon, diencephalon and archicortex in the activation and inhibition of the pituitary-adrenocortical system. *Acta Physiol. Acad. Sci. Hung. 17*, 39-55.

Endröczi, E., and K. Lissák (1963). Effect of hypothalamic and brain stem structure on pituitary-adrenocortical function. *Acta Physiol. Acad. Sci. Hung. 24*, 67-77.

Endröczi, E., and B. Mess (1955). Einfluss von Hypothalamusläsionen auf die Funktion des Hypophysen- Nebennierenrinden-Systems. *Endokrinologie 33*, 271-78.

Endröczi, E., S. Kovács, and K. Lissák (1956). Die Wirkung der Hypothalamus-reizung auf das endokrine und somatische Verhalten. *Endokrinologie 33*, 271-78.

Endröczi, E., K. Lissák, and M. Tekeres (1961). Hormonal feedback regulation of pituitary-adrenocortical activity. *Acta Physiol. Acad. Sci. Hung. 18*, 291-99.

Everett, J. W., and J. R. Harp (1960). Electrical induction of ovulation in the rat and the question of duration of the natural neurogenous stimulus. *1st Int. Cong. Endocrinol. Copenhagen, Advance Abstr. Short Communication* (F. Fuchs, ed.), p. 4. Periodica, Copenhagen.

Everett, J. W., H. M. Radford, and J. Holsinger (1964). Electrolytic irritative lesions in the hypothalamus and other forebrain areas: Effects of luteinizing hormone release and the ovarian cycle. *Proc. 1st Int. Cong. Hormonal Steroids I* (L. Martini and A. Pecile, eds.), pp. 235-46. Academic Press, New York.

Flament-Durand, J. (1965). Observations on pituitary transplants into the hypothalamus of the rat. *Endocrinology 77*, 446-54.

Flerkó, B. (1953). Einfluss experimenteller Hypothalamuslaesionen auf die Funktion des Sekretionsapparates im weiblichen Genitalrakt. *Acta Morph. Acad. Sci. Hung. 3*, 65-86.

Flerkó, B. (1957). Einfluss experimenteller Hypothalamusläsion auf die durch Follikelhormon indirekt hervorgerufene Hemmung der Luteinization. *Endokrinologie, 34*, 202-8.

Flerkó, B. (1966). Control of gonadotropin secretion in the female. In *Neuroendocrinology* (L. Martini and W. F. Ganong, eds.), *1*, pp. 613-668. Academic Press, New York, London.

Flerkó, B. (1968). Hypothalamic control of hypophyseal gonadotrophic function. In J. Szentágothai, B. Flerkó, B. Mess and B. Halász, *Hypothalamic control of the anterior pituitary*, pp. 249-342. Akadémiai Kiadó, Budapest.

Flerkó, B., and V. Bárdos (1960). Pituitary hypertrophy after anterior hypothalamic lesions. *Acta Endocrinol. 35*, 375-80.

Flerkó, B., and V. Bárdos (1961). Absence of compensatory ovarian hypertrophy in rats with anterior hypothalamic lesions. *Acta Endocrinol. 36*, 180-84.

Flerkó, B., and J. Szentágothai (1957). Oestrogen sensitive nervous structures in the hypothalamus. *Acta Endocrinol. 26*, 121-27.

Fortier, C. (1951). Dual control of adrenocorticotropin release. *Endocrinology 49*, 782-88.

Fortier, C., and J. de Groot (1964). Residual synthesis and release of ACTH following electrolytic destruction of the median eminence in the rat. In *Major Problems in Neuroendocrinology* (E. Bajusz and G. Jasmin, eds.), pp. 203-19. S. Karger, Basel, New York.

Fulford, B. D., and S. M. McCann (1955). Suppression of adrenal compensatory hypertrophy by hypothalamic lesions. *Proc. Soc. Exp. Biol. Med. 90*, 78-80.

Fuxe, K. (1964). Cellular localization of monoamines in the median eminence and the infundibular stem of some mammals. *Z. Zellforsch. 61*, 710-24.

Galicich, J. H., F. Halberg, L. A. French, and F. Ungar (1965). Effect of cerebral ablation on a circadian pituitary adrenocorticotrophic rhythm in C mice. *Endocrinology 76*, 895-901.

Ganong, W. F., and D. M. Hume (1954). Absence of stress induced and compensatory adrenal hypertrophy in dogs with hypothalamic lesions. *Endocrinology 55*, 475-83.

Ganong, W. F., D. S. Frederickson, and D. M. Hume (1954). Depression of the thyroidal iodine uptake by hypothalamic lesions. *J. Clin. Endocrinol. 14*, 773-74.

Gittes, R. F., and A. J. Kastin (1966). Effects of increasing numbers of pituitary transplants in hypophysectomized rats. *Endocrinology 78*, 1023-31.

Goldberg, R. C., and E. Knobil (1957). Structure and function of intraocular hypophysial grafts in the hypophysectomized male rat. *Endocrinology 61*, 742-52.

Goldfien, A., and W. F. Ganong (1962). Adrenal medullary and adrenal cortical response to stimulation of diencephalon. *Am. J. Physiol. 202*, 205-11.

Greer, M. A., and H. L. Ervin (1956). Evidence of separate hypothalamic centers controlling corticotropin and thyrotropin secretion by the pituitary. *Endocrinology 58*, 665-70.

Greer, M. A., and C. Rockie (1968). Inhibition of ether-induced ACTH secretion by Nembutal in the rat. *Excerpta Medica, Int. Cong. Ser. 157*, 79.

Greer, M. A., R. O. Scow, and C. Grobstein (1953). Thyroid function in hypophysectomized mice bearing intraocular pituitary implants. *Proc. Soc. Exp. Biol. Med. 82*, 28-30.

Guillemin, R., E. Sakiz, and D. N. Ward (1965). Further purification of TSH-releasing factor (TRF) from sheep hypothalamic tissues, with observations on the amino acid composition. *Proc. Soc. Exp. Biol. Med. 118*, 1132-37.

Halász, B. (1967). The role of the hypothalamic hypophysiotrophic area in the control of growth hormone secretion. Int. Symposium on Growth Hormone, Milan, *Excerpta Medica, Int. Cong. Ser. 142*, 13.

Halász, B., and R. A. Gorski (1967). Gonadotrophic hormone secretion in female rats after partial or total interruption of neural afferents to the medial basal hypothalamus. *Endocrinology 80*, 608-22.

Halász, B., and L. Pupp (1965). Hormone secretion of the anterior pituitary gland after physical interruption of all nervous pathways to the hypophysiotrophic area. *Endocrinology 77*, 553-62.

Halász, B., L. Pupp, and S. Uhlarik (1962). Hypophysiotrophic area in the hypothalamus. *J. Endocrinol. 25*, 147-54.

Halász, B., L. Pupp, S. Uhlarik, and L. Tima (1963). Growth of hypophysectomized rats bearing pituitary transplants in the hypothalamus. *Acta Physiol. Acad. Sci. Hung. 23*, 287-92.

Halász, B., L. Pupp, S. Uhlarik, and L. Tima (1965). Further studies on the hormone secretion of the anterior pituitary transplanted into the hypophysio-trophic area of the rat hypothalamus. *Endocrinology 77*, 343-55.

Halász, B., W. H. Florsheim, N. L. Corcorran, and R. A. Gorski (1967a). Thyro-trophic hormone secretion in rats after partial or total interruption of neural afferents to the medial basal hypothalamus. *Endocrinology 80*, 1075-82.

Halász, B., M. A. Slusher, and R. A. Gorski (1967b). Adrenocorticotrophic hor-mone secretion in rats after partial or total deafferentation of the medial basal hypothalamus. *Neuroendocrinology 2*, 43-55.

Halász, B., J. Vernikos-Danellis, and R. A. Gorski (1967c). Pituitary ACTH con-tent in rats after partial or total interruption of neural afferents to the medial basal hypothalamus. *Endocrinology 81*, 921-24.

Harris, G. W. (1948). Electrical stimulation of the hypothalamus and the mecha-nism of neural control of the adenohypophysis. *J. Physiol. (London) 107*, 418-29.

Harris, G. W., and D. Jacobsohn (1952). Functional grafts of the anterior pitui-tary gland. *Proc. Roy. Soc. B 139*, 263-76.

Hillarp, N. Å. (1949). Studies on the localization of hypothalamic centres con-trolling the gonadotrophic function of the hypophysis. *Acta Endocrinol. 2*, 11-23.

Hohlweg, W., and K. Junkmann (1932). Die hormonal-nervöse Regulierung der Funktion des Hypophysenvorderlappens. *Klin. Wochschr. 11*, 321-23.

Hume, D. M., and D. H. Nelson (1955). Effect of hypothalamic lesions on blood ACTH levels and 17-hydroxycorticosteroid secretion following trauma in the dog. *J. Clin. Endocrinol. 15*, 839-40.

Hume, D. M., and G. J. Wittenstein (1950). The relationship of the hypothalamus to pituitary-adrenocortical function. *Proc. 1st Clin. ACTH Conf.* 134-46.

Kanematsu, S., and C. H. Sawyer (1963). Effect of hypothalamic and hypophysial estrogen implants on pituitary gonadotrophic cells in ovariectomized rabbits. *Endocrinology 73*, 687-95.

Kanematsu, S., and C. H. Sawyer (1964). Effects of hypothalamic and hypophy-sial estrogen implants on pituitary and plasma LH in ovariectomized rabbits. *Endocrinology 75*, 579-85.

Kato, J., and C. A. Villee (1967). Preferential uptake of estradiol by the anterior hypothalamus of the rat. *Endocrinology 80*, 567-75.

Katsuki, S., and M. Mizuta (1958). Experimental studies on the hypothalamic control of the female gonadal function. I. Ovulation induced by electrical stimulation of the hypothalamus in rabbits. *Endocrinol. Japon. 5*, 185-91.

Katsuki, S., T. Ikemoto, H. Shimada, F. Hagiwara, and J. Kanai (1955). The functional relationship between the hypothalamus and the anterior pituitary-adrenal system. *Endocrinol. Japon. 2*, 303-12.

Kendall, J. W., A. K. Stott, C. Allen, and M. A. Greer (1966). Evidence for ACTH secretion and ACTH suppressibility in hypophysectomized rats with multiple heterotopic pituitaries. *Endocrinology 78*, 533-37.

Koibuchi, E. (1958). The effects of hypothalamic lesions on the pituitary-adreno-cortical system. *Endocrinol. Japon. 5*, 89-93.

Köves, K., and B. Halász (1969). Data on the location of the neural structures indispensable for the occurrence of ovarian compensatory hypertrophy. *Neuroendocrinology 4*, 1-11.

Laqueur, C. L., S. M. McCann, L. H. Schreiner, E. Rosenberg, D. McK. Rioch, and

E. Anderson (1955). Alterations of adrenal cortical and ovarian activity following hypothalamic lesions. *Endocrinology* 57, 44-54.

Laruelle, L. (1934). Le systeme végétatif mésodiencéphalique, partie anatomique. *Rev. Neurol. 61*, 808-42.

Leveque, T. F., and G. A. Hofkin (1961). Demonstration of an alcohol chloroform insoluble, periodic acid-Schiff reactive substance in the hypothalamus of the rat. *Z. Zellforsch. 53*, 185-91.

Lisk, R. D. (1960). Estrogen-sensitive centers in the hypothalamus of the rat. *J. Exp. Zool. 145*, 197-208.

Lisk, R. D. (1963). Maintenance of normal pituitary weight and cytology in the spayed rat following estradiol implants in the arcuate nucleus. *Anat. Rec. 146*, 281-91.

Löfgren, F. (1961). The glial-vascular apparatus in the floor of the infundibular cavity. *Lunds Universitets Arsskrift* N.F. Avd. 2. Lund Gleerup 57, 1-18.

Makara, G., and E. Stark (1968). Personal communication.

Mangili, G., M. Motta, and L. Martini (1966). Control of adrenocorticotropic hormone secretion. In *Neuroendocrinology* (L. Martini and W. F. Ganong, eds.), *1*, pp. 297-370. Academic Press, New York, London.

Marić, D. K., and M. B. Nikitovitch-Winer (1967). Post castration changes in hypophysis of female rats following the isolation of hypothalamus from CNS. *Prog. 49th Mtg. of the Endocrine Society*, p. 59.

Mason, J. W. (1958). Plasma 17-hydroxycorticosteroid response to hypothalamic stimulation in the conscious rhesus monkey. *Endocrinology 63,* 403-11.

Matsuda, K., M. A. Greer, and C. Duyck (1963a). Neural control of thyrotropin secretion: Effect of forebrain removal on thyroid function. *Endocrinology 73*, 462-66.

Matsuda, K., J. W. Kendall, Jr., C. Duyck, and M. A. Greer (1963b). Neural control of ACTH secretion: Effect of acute decerebration in the rat. *Endocrinology 72*, 845-52.

Matsuda, K., C. Duyck, J. W. Kendall, Jr., and M. A. Greer (1964). Pathways by which traumatic stress and ether induce increased ACTH release in the rat. *Endocrinology 74*, 981-85.

McCann, S. M. (1953). Effect of hypothalamic lesions on the adrenal cortical response to stress in the rat. *Am. J. Physiol. 175*, 13-20.

McCann, S. M. (1962). A hypothalamic luteinizing-hormone-releasing factor. *Am. J. Physiol. 202*, 395-400.

McCann, S. M., and J. R. Brobeck (1954). Evidence for a role of the supraoptico-hypophyseal system in regulation of adrenocorticotrophic secretion. *Proc. Soc. Exp. Biol. Med. 87*, 318-24.

McCann, S. M., and A. P. S. Dhariwal (1966). Hypothalamic releasing factors and the neurovascular link between the brain and the anterior pituitary. In *Neuroendocrinology* (L. Martini and W. F. Ganong, eds.), *1*, pp. 261-96. Academic Press, New York, London.

McCann, S. M., and K. L. Sydnor (1954). Blood and pituitary adrenocorticotrophin in adrenalectomized rats with hypothalamic lesions. *Proc. Soc. Exp. Biol. Med. 87*, 369-73.

McDermott, W. V., E. G. Fry, J. R. Brobeck, and C. N. H. Long (1950). Release of adrenocorticotrophic hormone by direct application of epinephrine to pituitary grafts. *Proc. Soc. Exp. Biol. Med. 73*, 609-10.

Mess, B. (1952). Influence of hypothalamic injury on spermatogenesis in albino rats. *Acta Morph. Acad. Sci. Hung. 2*, 275-85.

Mess, B., F. Fraschini, M. Motta, and L. Martini (1966). The topography of the neurons synthetizing the hypothalamic releasing factors. *Excerpta Medica, Int. Cong. Ser. 132*, 1004-13.

Michael, R. P. (1964). The selective accumulation of oestrogen in the neural and genital tissues of the cat. *Proc. 1st Int. Cong. Hormonal Steroids, Milan 1962, 2*, pp. 457-69. Academic Press, New York.

Newman, A. E., E. S., Redgate, and G. Farrell (1958). The effect of diencephalic-mesencephalic lesions on aldosterone and hydrocortisone secretion. *Endocrinology 63*, 723-26.

Nikitovitch-Winer, M., and J. W. Everett (1958). Functional restitution of pituitary grafts re-transplanted from kidney to median eminence. *Endocrinology 63*, 916-30.

Nikitovitch-Winer, M., and J. W. Everett (1959). Histologic changes in grafts of rat pituitary on the kidney and upon retransplantation under the diencephalon. *Endocrinology 65*, 357-68.

Nowakowski, H. (1951). Infundibulum und Tuber cinereum der Katze. *Dtsch. Z. Nervenheilk, 165*, 201-339.

Palka, Y. S., D. D. Coyer, and V. Critchlow (1968). Hypothalamic deafferentation and adrenal function. *Fed. Proc. 27*, 217.

Porter, J. C. (1968). Localization of CRF secreting elements. *Fed. Proc. 27*, 217.

Porter, R. W. (1953). Hypothalamic involvement in the pituitary adrenocortical response to stress stimuli. *Am. J. Physiol. 172*, 515-22.

Porter, R. W. (1954). The central nervous system and stress-induced eosinopenia. *Recent Prog. Hormone Res. 10*, 1-18.

Ramaley, J. A., and R. A. Gorski (1967). The effect of hypothalamic deafferentation upon puberty in the female rat. *Acta Endocrinol. 59*, 661-74.

Ramirez, V. D., R. M. Abrams, and S. M. McCann (1964). Effect of estradiol implants in the hypothalamo-hypophysial region of the rat on the secretion of luteinizing hormone. *Endocrinology 75*, 243-48.

Reichlin, S. (1966). Control of thyrotropic hormone secretion. In *Neuroendocrinology* (L. Martini and W. F. Ganong, eds.), *1*, pp. 445-536. Academic Press, New York, London.

Sawyer, C. H., C. K. Haun, J. Hilliard, and H. M. Radford (1960). Evidence for identical hypothalamic areas controlling ovulation and lactation in the rabbit. *1st. Int. Cong. Endocrinol. Copenhagen. Advance Abstr. Short Communications* (F. Fuchs, ed.), p. 574. Periodica, Copenhagen.

Schweizer, M., and M. E. Long (1950). The effect of intraocular grafts of anterior pituitary on the thyroid gland of hypophysectomized guinea pigs. *Endocrinology 47*, 454-57.

Shizume, K., K. Matsuda, M. Irie, S. Iino, J. Ishii, S. Nagataki, F. Matsuzaki, and S. Okinaka (1962). Effect of electrical stimulation of the hypothalamus on thyroid function. *Endocrinology 70*, 298-302.

Siperstein, E. R., and M. A. Greer (1956). Observation on the morphology and histochemistry of the mouse pituitary implanted in the anterior eye chamber. *J. Nat. Cancer Inst. 17*, 569-99.

Slusher, M. A. (1958). Dissociation of adrenal ascorbic acid and corticosterone responses to stress in rats with hypothalamic lesions. *Endocrinology 63*, 412-19.

Slusher, M. A. (1961). Effect of brain stem lesions on stress-induced cortico-steroid release in female rats. *Endocrinology 67*, 347-52.

Slusher, M. A. (1964). Effects of chronic hypothalamic lesions on diurnal and stress corticosteroid levels. *Am. J. Physiol. 206*, 1161-64.

Slusher, M. A., and V. Critchlow (1959). Effect of midbrain lesions on ovulation and adrenal response to stress of female rats. *Proc. Soc. Exp. Biol. Med. 101*, 497-99.

Slusher, M. A., and J. E. Hyde (1961). Inhibition of adrenal corticosteroid release by brain stimulation in cats. *Endocrinology 68*, 773-82.

Smelik, P. G., and C. H. Sawyer (1962). Effects of implantation of cortisol into the brain stem or pituitary gland on the adrenal response to stress in the rabbit. *Acta Endocrinol. 41*, 561-70.

Smelik, P. G., and C. H. Sawyer (1964). Hypothalamic structures involved in the adrenocortical feedback action on pituitary corticotrophin secretion. *Prog. Brain. Res. 5*, 132-34.

Spatz, H. (1951). Neues über die Verknüpfung von Hypophyse und Hypothalamus. *Acta Neuroveg. 3*, 1-49.

Story, J. L., J. C. Melby, R. H. Egdahl, and L. A. French (1959). Adrenal cortical function following step-wise removal of the brain in the dog. *Am. J. Physiol. 196*, 583-88.

Suzuki, T., E. B. Romanoff, W. P. Koella, and C. K. Levy (1960). Effect of diencephalic stimuli on 17-OHCS secretion in unanaesthetized dogs. *Am. J. Physiol. 198*, 1312-14.

Szentágothai, J. (1962). Anatomical considerations. In J. Szentágothai, B. Flerkó, B. Mess and B. Halász, *Hypothalamic control of the anterior pituitary*, pp. 19-105. Akadémiai Kiadó, Budapest.

Szentágothai, J. (1964). The parvicellular neurosecretory system. *Prog. Brain Res. 5*, 135-146.

Tejasen, T., and W. Everett (1967). Surgical analysis of the preoptic-tuberal pathway controlling ovulatory release of gonadotropins in the rat. *Endocrinology 81*, 1387-96.

Vernikos-Danellis, J. (1964). Estimation of corticotropin-releasing activity of rat hypothalamus and neurohypophysis before and after stress. *Endocrinology 75*, 514-20.

Vernikos-Danellis, J. (1965). Effect of stress, adrenalectomy, hypophysectomy and hydrocortisone on the corticotropin-releasing activity of rat median eminence. *Endocrinology 76*, 122-26.

Vigh, B., B. Aros, T. Wenger, E. Koritsánszky, and G. Ceglédi (1963). Ependymo-secretion (Ependymal neurosecretion). IV. The Gömöri-positive secretion of the hypothalamic ependyma of various vertebrates and its relation to the anterior lobe of the pituitary. *Acta Biol. Acad. Sci. Hung. 13*, 407-19.

Watanabe, S., and S. M. McCann (1968). Localization of FSH-Releasing Factor in the hypothalamus and neurohypophysis as determined by in vitro assay. *Endocrinology 82*, 664-73.

Wise, B. L., E. E. Van Brunt, and W. F. Ganong (1963). Effect of removal of various parts of the brain on ACTH secretion in dogs. *Proc. Soc. Exp. Biol. Med. 112*, 792-95.

Woods, J. W. (1962). In discussion, *Proc. Int. Union Physiol. Sciences, XXII. Int. Cong.* Int. Cong. Ser. 47, Part II, p. 612.

10
Feedback Control of Gonadotropin Secretion

JULIAN M. DAVIDSON

Introduction

General Considerations

The regulation of gonadotropin secretion, including feedback control, has been extensively reviewed in recent years (Everett, 1964; Bogdanove, 1964; Flerkó, 1966; Davidson, 1966a; McCann *et al.*, 1968). In this chapter, no attempt is made to review the field. Instead, data from recent work in this laboratory are presented and the discussions are centered on problems related to this work and other selected areas of current interest. References to much of the relevant literature dating from before 1965-66 can be found in Flerkó (1966) and Davidson (1966a).

Control Systems Concepts. For better or for worse the use of concepts, or at least terminology, borrowed from the engineering field of Control Systems Theory has become widespread among reproductive neuroendocrinologists. This is praiseworthy to the extent that it encourages thinking in objective, generalizable terms, and eventually it can lead to computer simulation of mathematical models. That such an approach has a place in physiology in general is unquestionable (Riggs, 1963), and that its application in certain areas of endocrinology can be useful in generating hypotheses for experimental testing has also been demonstrated (Yates, 1967). But is there as yet a place for this approach in pituitary-gonadal physiology?

Original work presented in this chapter was supported by National Institutes of Health grant HD 00778.

The vast majority of physiological studies in this field have been carried out without the benefit of chemical analysis of the steroids involved or any direct measure of gonadotropin levels other than crude, laborious, expensive, inaccurate, and often nonspecific biological assays. The system itself is more complex than the adrenal or thyroid systems appear to be, involving, in the female, two (or three) tropic hormones, two classes of steroids, marked cyclicity, and positive, negative, external, and probably internal short-loop feedback mechanisms. As a result, practically no sufficiently reliable quantitative data exist today which could be used to apply the systems analysis approach, although an interesting beginning at modeling the rat estrous cycle has been made (Schwartz and Hoffman, 1966).

Under these circumstances, how rigid need we be in application of control systems terminology? Although the present author does not lean far in this direction,[1] it would be imprudent to disregard the correct definitions of terms that originated in engineering systems theory. The day is not far distant when the application of gonadotropin radioimmunoassay and modern methods of analyzing circulating gonadal steroids will become widespread and routine among experimental endocrinologists. The combination of these two techniques will undoubtedly result in the collection of data amenable to this type of analysis. With such an eye for the hopefully not too distant future, we shall attempt, in this chapter, to avoid the blatant misuse of terms borrowed from Control Systems Theory. This will be accomplished in part by avoiding their use whenever feasible. In particular we shall generally avoid the terms "positive feedback" and "negative feedback." Although these terms mean approximately the same things to biologists and engineers, their proper use implies certain assumptions which the endocrinologist may not intend to make. Thus, if we speak of the negative feedback effect of progesterone on luteinizing hormone (LH) or follicle-stimulating hormone (FSH) secretion, this carries the implicit, but not necessarily correct, assumption that feedback inhibition of the gonadotropin will lead to a decline in the circulating progesterone level. Similarly, there are difficulties with the promiscuous use of the term "positive feedback," since, for example, to speak of a positive feedback effect of estrogen in stimulating ovulation implies a resultant increase in estrogen level which may not necessarily occur. Instead, when speaking of specific phenomena, the terms (1) "stimulatory" and (2) "inhibitory" feedback will be used to denote situations in which changes in circulating steroid levels are (1) positively

1. This should be obvious from the title of this chapter; in orthodox engineering parlance it is not the gonadotropins, but the steroids which are the "controlled variables."

or (2) negatively correlated with the resulting changes in gonadotropin secretion rate.

Control of Gonadotropin Secretion. The two classes of factors that influence gonadotropin secretion may be referred to as open loop and closed loop factors. Open loop behavior involves stimuli from both the external environment (e.g. light, sexual stimuli, etc.), and the internal environment (e.g. state of nutrition, maturational factors, etc.). Closed loop or feedback control involves regulation predominantly by circulating levels of hormones: we can distinguish positive (stimulatory) and negative (inhibitory) as well as internal and external forms of feedback. Internal, "short" feedback is not dealt with here, since it is fully discussed in Chapter 6. While we shall discuss only closed loop control, it should be clear that the relative importance of open and closed loop control of gonadotropin secretion is by no means understood. In the female, open loop behavior is clearly an important factor in the ovulatory release of gonadotropins, the best example of this being the effect of lighting conditions in rats. The reader may gauge, from the information presented here, what conclusions may be drawn about the physiological role of closed loop control, involving steroid hormones, in the events of the female reproductive cycle. It will also be seen that in the male little is known about whether day-to-day or minute-to-minute regulation of gonadotropin secretion is a function of feedback control.

Information about the effects on gonadotropin secretion of extreme increases (by injection) and decreases (by castration) in circulating steroid level has been collected over a period of many years in both males and females. Many of these studies on the feedback effects of extreme fluctuations in steroid level may have little bearing on the physiological situation. To the physiologist, the important questions have to do with the extent to which circulating gonadal steroid levels participate in the regulation of gonadotropin secretion under various circumstances in the life of the organism. Circumstances may arise in which steroid concentrations in blood approximate castration levels, as in the reproductive quiescence of seasonal breeders or in the post-menopausal state. However, the high levels reached in many experiments on steroid administration are probably beyond anything ever seen in nature. It is important, in experiments on feedback, to attempt to relate the phenomena under consideration to normal physiological situations.

Localization of Feedback Receptors

Where in the organism are located the sensors or receptors which respond to changes in circulating steroid levels by initiating a change in the secretion of gonadotropins? Theoretically, they could lie anywhere on the path of a neuroendocrine reflex leading from the nervous receptor which records stimuli from the internal or external environment to the effector-target organ—in this case the gonads. The three possible general sites for feedback action are, therefore, the brain, the anterior pituitary, and the testes or ovaries. Since feedback effects can be observed in their absence, the gonads may be eliminated from consideration. We are left with the question of whether the pituitary or the brain is the site of the various feedback actions of gonadal steroids, and, if the latter, which brain areas are involved.

The significance of this question stems not only from the fact that the precise points of feedback action need to be known in order to fully characterize neuroendocrine reflexes. It is also obviously essential for future studies on the cellular or molecular mechanisms of feedback action to determine the primary location of this action. For example, if a receptor is neural, its mechanism might be investigated by electrophysiological studies; different approaches would be required if the action is on the pituitary tissue. Conceivably, there might be multiple neural sites of the negative feedback action of one hormone, as has been suggested for corticosteroids (Dallman and Yates, 1967; Davidson et al., 1969; Corbin et al., 1965). More surprising is the evidence that some hormones (e.g. estrogens) may act both at the hypothalamic and pituitary levels (see below); such a dual feedback action on such different types of tissue suggests the possibility of multiple mechanisms of action of the same steroid at different locations.

It is important to note that not only is it necessary to establish whether the hormones can act on the pituitary or the hypothalamus, but where the action is under physiological circumstances. Thus it is possible that abnormally high concentrations of a steroid might have feedback action at an unusual site. This is a difficult problem to overcome, since most experimental manipulations that allow clear-cut separation of effects on the hypothalamus and pituitary involve gross changes in physiological condition (e.g. pituitary transplantation, in vitro incubation, etc.).

Methodology. The many experimental approaches which have been brought to bear on the localization problem differ greatly in their potential for providing information of value. Three approaches that have some relevance have been rather extensively studied in recent years: observation of the selective intracranial accumulation of systemically administered steroids (Jouan et al., 1967) and of the electrophysiological and cytological effects of such administration on the brain and pituitary (Sawyer, 1966; Kawakami and Sawyer, 1967; Lincoln and Cross, 1967; Szentágothai *et al.*, 1968; see Chapter 7). All three procedures are of general importance for the study of hormone-brain interaction. In relation to the specific localization problem, however, their main role is to provide suggestive evidence which can be followed up by more direct experimental approaches. In this role they have not yet been notably useful, and these results are not reviewed here. The reader should be cautioned against the danger of overinterpreting this kind of data, however. Estrogens, for example, undoubtedly have multiple diverse actions on the brain—stimulatory and inhibitory feedback effects, behavioral effects, etc. The fact that an estrogen is concentrated, for example, in the septum, does not tell us which of these functions it is fulfilling at that specific location. Furthermore, its accumulation, even by specific receptors, may have nothing to do with any of the functions of the hormone under consideration.

Another approach is to attempt the destruction by lesioning of possible sites of feedback action and then to study the results of the presentation of feedback signals (Davidson *et al.*, 1960; Barraclough *et al.*, 1964; Flerkó, 1966). The problem here is that destruction of the basal medial hypothalamus or adenohypophysis prevents secretion of gonadotropins even in the absence of feedback signals, and lesions may alter pituitary sensitivity to releasing factors.

Three methods are useful in providing evidence for or against possible pituitary involvement in feedback mechanisms. First, there is the in vitro investigation of secretion of gonadotropic hormones by incubated pituitaries under the influence of gonadal steroids. This method is useful to the extent that the incubated pituitary behaves in a manner similar to its behavior in in vivo conditions. Second, there is the measurement of changes in gonadotropin releasing factor (RF) activity in the hypothalamus in response to feedback signals. When such changes are found, it is clear that an effect of feedback-active hormones on the hypothalamus has been demonstrated, but this does not necessarily imply hypothalamic mediation of the feedback mechanism. Releasing factor content may not reflect the secretion or release of these agents; and the change in activity may be an indirect result of the feedback signal, secondary to primary changes in pituitary function. Third, one may study the effects of high concentrations of feedback-active steroids on sensitivity of the pituitary to releasing factors. If gonadotropin release in response to administered releasing factors is blocked by prior administration of gonadal steroids, this shows that the steroids can act at the pituitary level. However, for such experiments to be a reflection of the physiological situation it is necessary to administer "physiological" quantities of both releasing factor and steroid. It is doubtful that experiments which adequately meet these criteria have ever been performed.

The most direct approach is the production of changes in the local concentration of gonadal steroids at possible sites of feedback action. These changes can be brought about by injecting small quantities of the hormones in solution or suspension, by transplantation of endocrine glands, or by direct intracranial implantation of hormones (or hormone antagonists) in crystalline form. The third of these is the method of choice, since it allows us to produce a chronic and often highly localized change in hormonal concentration, following a single surgical intervention. However, a number of factors can result in mistaken conclusions based on implantation experiments, if inadequate controls are used. Thus the implanted material may diffuse to distant intracranial sites and act there; it may be absorbed into the systemic circulation with resultant possible sites of action anywhere in the organism; or the effects observed may be due not to feedback action, but to destruction of the tissue or its nonspecific irritation. These problems can be avoided by various control procedures, such as implantation of hormonally inert substances and quantities of hormones too small to be effective on systemic absorption, and by careful mapping of effective and ineffective sites to eliminate diffusion effects.

It might be argued that intracranial implantation of crystalline steroids results in a local concentration so high as to invalidate the results. However, because the steroids are relatively insoluble in body fluids, only the few cells in the immediate vicinity of the implant will be subjected to highly concentrated solutions of the implanted steroid; cells on the periphery of the feedback receptor may "see" little or no steroid. This can be studied by distributing implants of appropriate sizes in the vicinity of the "effective" region and observing the relationship of location to effect.

Inhibitory Feedback

Ovarian Steroids

Since the introduction of oral contraceptive agents, there has been much interest in the inhibitory feedback effects of estrogen and progesterone. Although these agents are probably all capable of preventing ovulation (Pincus, 1966), their antifertility effects in humans are not necessarily always the result of gonadotropic inhibition or even of anovulation since other effects sufficient in themselves to block fertility have also been observed (Østergaard and Starup, 1968; France and Pincus, 1964).

Inhibitory feedback regulation of LH secretion can be said to have physiological significance only if it is demonstrable that changes in levels of steroid within the range normally encountered in physiological conditions can affect the secretion or release of gonadotropins. Ramirez and McCann (1963) have compared the amount of estrogen required to maintain normal uterine weight (i.e. the "physiological" dose) with the amount whose administration resulted in a plasma LH value lower than that recorded in untreated spayed rats (the assay was not sufficiently sensitive to detect plasma LH in untreated normals). Animals were injected from the day of castration. More estrogen was required to prevent LH hypersecretion than to maintain the uteri, and this was interpreted as evidence that in the normal situation progesterone acts in combination with estrogen to restrain LH secretion. This evidence is not entirely convincing, however, since the doses used by Ramirez and McCann did not raise uterine weight above the level of diestrous control females. Recently Davidson et al. (1968) showed that the effective dose of estradiol benzoate for inhibition of pituitary castration cell formation in female rats three weeks after ovariectomy was roughly similar to that required to restore sexual behavior and uterine weight to normal levels. This experiment could provide no more than a crude approximation of the estrogen-gonadotropin relationship. However, the effective doses were considerably above those used by Ramirez and McCann (1963), suggesting that gonadectomy is followed by a decrease in sensitivity to gonadal steroids of various target organ responses including that of the feedback mechanism.

Progesterone inhibits the ovulatory surge of LH release, but apparently not basal secretion of the hormone (Rothchild, 1965). According to Giuliani et al. (1961) progesterone acutely depresses plasma LH in ovariectomized rats, but McCann (1962a) could show virtually no effect of progesterone unless estrogen was also administered. Although it is clear that combined estrogen-progesterone treatment is more effective than estrogen alone in inhibition of LH secretion (McCann, 1962a), the cyclic pattern of gonadotropin secretion in females makes it difficult to relate experimental findings to the normal physiological situation.

Even less is known of the ovarian steroid-FSH relationship, since FSH assay methods are less sensitive than LH methods and reliable measurements of plasma FSH cannot be made. This situation will undoubtedly improve soon with development of radioimmunoassays for blood FSH in animal species. For the present, little more can be said than that estrogen inhibits FSH secretion while progesterone does not appear to have much, if any, significant inhibitory effect (see Rothchild, 1965 for references).

To the extent that the compensatory ovarian growth which follows unilateral ovariectomy is due to increased FSH secretion, this phenomenon can be used as a means of studying the feedback effects of an acute submaximal decrease in circulating steroid level. Recently McLaren (1966) has attacked this concept and renewed the claim that compensatory ovarian hypertrophy (and superovulation) is due to increased utilization of FSH by the remaining ovary while blood concentration of FSH is unchanged. However, her conclusions are based in part on such inadequate criteria as measurements of pituitary gonadotropin content in unilaterally ovariectomized mice. Greenwald (1968) has since shown that there is no difference in the gravimetric or ovulatory response of one ovary in hypophysectomized rats, regardless of whether or not unilateral ovariectomy was performed.

Localization of Inhibitory Feedback by Estrogen. Estrogens have been investigated more than other steroids from the point of view of feedback receptor localization. Many of these studies were admirably reviewed by Flerkó (1966). A variety of indirect approaches have resulted in findings interpreted as indicating that the hypothalamus is the site of the estrogen inhibitory feedback receptor. These findings are as follows: prevention by anterior hypothalamic lesions of the gonadotropin-inhibitory effects of estrogen administration (Flerkó and Szentágothai, 1957); prevention of "compensatory" ovarian changes following hemicastration by atropine (Roos and Roos, 1966) or by anterior hypothalamic lesions (Assenmacher, 1957); failure of systemic administration of estrogen to block the effect of exogenous gonadotropin releasing factors (McCann, 1962b); changes in gonadotropin releasing factor activity of the hypothalamus following gonadectomy (Kobayashi et al., 1963); cytological changes in hypothalamic nuclei following changes in circulating estrogen levels (Flerkó, 1962); failure of estrogen to inhibit gonadotropin secretion by incubated pituitaries (Meites et al., 1966).

On the basis of a wealth of generally indirect evidence. Flerkó (1966) has argued for the inclusion of the anterior hypothalamus in a number of postulated estrogen-sensitive receptor areas. This conclusion has been considered in detail and rejected by Bogdanove (1964). To his findings may be added the results of recent investigations suggesting that the anterior hypothalamus is not essential to the estrogen feedback response. Thus Halász and Gorski (1967) found that complete deafferentation of

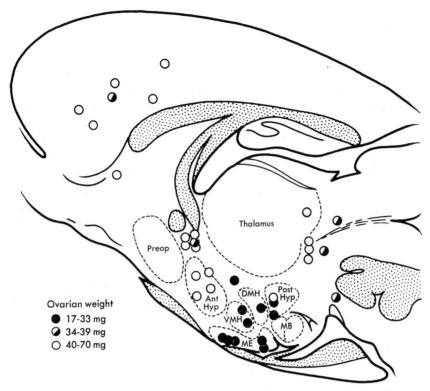

Figure 10-1 Sagittal diagram of rat brain showing location of chronic near-midline implants of estradiol benzoate (26 and 30 gauge tubing), with effects on ovarian weight. Effects of the two types of implant were similar, but note normal ovarian weights from implants in the anterior hypothalamus-preoptic area. (Data of Smith and Davidson.)

the medial basal hypothalamus did not prevent pituitary castration cell formation. Furthermore, Antunes-Rodrigues and McCann (1967) showed that castration still increased pituitary and plasma LH in rats with anterior hypothalamic lesions of the type which provoke constant vaginal estrus. The argument for hypothalamic involvement is weakened by the failure of several investigators to demonstrate "appropriate" changes in hypothalamic LRF content following castration or estrogen treatment (Moskowska and Kordon, 1965; Chowers and McCann, 1965). However, content need not reflect secretion, and in any case, more recent investigations have demonstrated decreases in LRF content (Piacsek and Meites, 1966) and FSHRF content (David et al., 1965) following estrogen treatment. More convincing evidence on this score would come from the demonstration of changes in secretion of releasing factors. In the absence of such information, the most direct available evidence comes from studies on intracranial implantation of estrogen, the first of which was reported by Lisk in 1960.

In the rabbit, estradiol benzoate implantation inhibits gonadotropin secretion when the implant is in the median eminence region, but not when it is in the pituitary (Davidson and Sawyer, 1961a; Kanematsu and Sawyer, 1964). The anterior hypothalamus has not been thoroughly investigated in the rabbit.

In the female rat, estrogen implants have been found effective in inhibiting gonadotropin secretion when placed either in the pituitary or the median eminence region, including the mammillary body (Chowers and McCann, 1967; Ramirez et al., 1964). However, basomedial hypothalamic implants have generally been more effective than pituitary ones (Ramirez et al., 1964). It is difficult to achieve precise localization with implants of undiluted estrogen because of diffusion from the site of implant (Smith and Davidson, 1968). Figure 10-1 shows the results of implantation of 26 and 30 gauge tubes containing estradiol benzoate at their tips in 30-day-old immature rats[2] for a period of 5 weeks. In this experiment ovarian and uterine atrophy resulted from placement of both 26 and 30 gauge implants at locations as far dorsal to the median eminence as the dorsomedial nucleus. However, anterior hypothalamic-preoptic implants were not effective in reducing ovarian or uterine weight. Lisk (1960, 1965) has also found that anterior hypothalamic implants were not effective. It seems as if the inhibitory effects that Flerkó and Szentágothai (1957) noted following ovarian transplantation in the anterior hypothalamus, as well as those noted by Fendler and Endröczi (1965/66), who used estrogen implants, might have resulted from diffusion of hormone to the median eminence. Surprisingly, Faure et al. (1966) have reported an inhibitory feedback effect of habenular implants of estrogen in female rabbits; recently, Motta et al. (1968) noted a similar effect in rats.

In summary, the evidence is generally in favor of the medial basal hypothalamus as the main site for negative feedback inhibition of gonadotropin secretion by estrogen in females, while the pituitary may be a secondary site of estrogen sensitivity. It is of interest, parenthetically, that while Chowers and McCann (1967) found estrogen implants

---

2. All studies reported from this laboratory were performed on rats of the Long Evans strain.

effective in both hypothalamus and pituitary in females, only hypothalamic implants were effective in males (Chowers and McCann, 1963).

Bogdanove has suggested that estrogen implants in the median eminence region may operate by release of the hormone into the hypophyseal portal vessel system with eventual perfusion of the anterior pituitary; intrapituitary implants may be ineffective due to the failure of single implants to perfuse the whole of the gland (Bogdanove, 1963, 1964). It must be admitted that this criticism (the "implantation paradox") has not been adequately countered as yet. In fact, Palka *et al.* (1966) have shown that H^3 labeled estradiol placed in the median eminence region does diffuse freely to the pituitary gland, although this does not mean it is physiologically active there. The best way to answer the question would be to determine whether intrahypothalamic estrogen implants decrease the secretion of gonadotropin releasing factor in animals with the pituitary transplanted outside the sella turcica. Although analogous experiments have been performed in males with testosterone (see below) and cortisol (Kendall and Allen, 1968), this approach has not as yet been applied to estrogen.

Localization of Inhibitory Feedback by Progesterone.   Despite progesterone's well-known inhibitory feedback action (Everett, 1964; Rothchild, 1965), studies on the localization of this effect using intracranial administration of progesterone have apparently not been published, and Kanematsu and Sawyer (1965) mention their failure to inhibit ovulation with intrahypothalamic progesterone in rabbits. One reason for this may

Table 10-1   Effects of median eminence implantation of progesterone and cholesterol on female reproduction. (Data from Smith, Weick, and Davidson.)

Steroid	N	Days of implantation	Ovarian weight (mg)	Uterine weight (mg)	Days of diestrus*	Days of estrus†
Cholesterol	7	28	74 ± 7	314 ± 20	2.7 ± 1.4	
Progesterone	6	28	61 ± 4	216 ± 29	11.1 ± 4.7	
Cholesterol	10	8	58 ± 3	229 ± 17		2.1 ± 0.4
Progesterone	10	8	49 ± 4	143 ± 10		0.5 ± 0.2

* Number of days of diestrus until first cycle.
† Number of days of estrous during experimental period. This parameter could not be used in the long-term experiment since normal cycling resumed after a mean of 11 days post implantation.

be that larger amounts of the crystalline hormone must be implanted than
the amounts that have been used for other steroids, if effects are to be
obtained. Furthermore, as we shall see, the effects of intracranially
implanted progesterone are considerably more transient than those of
estradiol or testosterone.

Recent unpublished experiments in this laboratory with E. R. Smith
and R. F. Weick have shown that inhibitory feedback effects may be
observed if 400μg pellet-type implants (Davidson and Feldman, 1963) of
crystalline progesterone are used. In initial experiments it was found that
hypothalamic progesterone implants in adult cycling females inhibited
vaginal cycling (Table 10-1), but only for an average of about 11 days,
following which regular cycles reappeared. Inspection of the implant
tubes on autopsy showed that the relatively large amount of implanted
progesterone had completely disappeared by about this time, suggesting
that the evanescence of the inhibitory effect was apparently due to rapid
absorption of the implanted steroid. As shown in Table 10-1, significant

Figure 10-2   Effects of 12 days' implantation of progesterone (shaded bars)
and cholesterol (open bars) in various intracranial locations, and of subcutaneous injection of 33μg/day progesterone (shaded bar) or oil vehicle (open
bar) on ovarian and uterine weight. Bars show means, vertical lines show
standard errors, and numbers at the bottoms of the bars show numbers of
animals, in this and subsequent figures. ANT HYP-POA, anterior hypothalamus, preoptic area.   (Data of Smith, Weick and Davidson.)

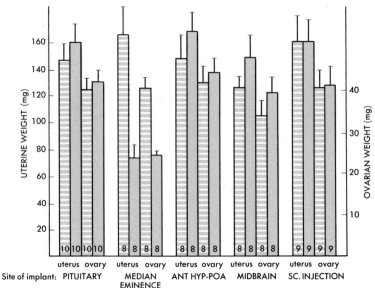

depression of uterine weight was observed in a long-term implantation experiment (28 days), as well as in a short-term one (8 days). Despite a trend toward decreased ovarian weight, no significant changes in this parameter were found. Furthermore, no effects of the progesterone implants on ovarian histology were observed. No conclusion on whether the secretion of FSH, LH, or both, had been inhibited could be drawn from these experiments.

Next, a series of experiments was performed in which similar progesterone implants were placed in the brain of 30-day-old females. The results of these experiments were equivocal; the extent of the ensuing changes in ovaries and estrous cycles depended on the date of vaginal opening, and the progesterone was often largely absorbed by that time. Finally, it was found that implantation on the day of vaginal opening gave the most clear-cut results: the changes in gonadotropin secretion were reflected in ovaries which had not previously ovulated.

Figure 10-2 shows the results of a definitive experiment in which progesterone was implanted on the day of vaginal opening into various locations in the hypothalamus, pituitary, and midbrain reticular formation area. Implantation in the median eminence effectively prevented or inhibited ovarian and uterine development. The weights of these organs were significantly lower than in the corresponding cholesterol-implanted controls, and estrous cycles were inhibited. No significant differences between control and experimental animals were observed in any of the parameters when implants were placed in the anterior pituitary, the anterior hypothalamus, or the midbrain reticular formation.

Histological examination of the ovaries from the animals with median eminence progesterone implants (but not the others) showed that there was an almost complete absence of corpora lutea (see Fig. 10-3). Well-developed follicles were present in all these ovaries, however, and the number and diameter of the follicles were not significantly different from controls. This suggests that the effect of intrahypothalamic progesterone implantation was to inhibit the secretion of LH, but that FSH secretion was unaffected, which is in line with the reported results of systemic progesterone administration (see Rothchild, 1965). In fact, the results of median eminence implantation could be duplicated by subcutaneous injection of 5 mg/day progesterone. When, on the other hand, the amount of progesterone implanted in the brain was divided into daily doses and administered throughout the experimental period, no changes in any parameter of reproductive function could be found (Fig. 10-2), suggesting that diffusion of hormone into the systemic circulation played no role in these experiments. Despite the large size of the implants, a

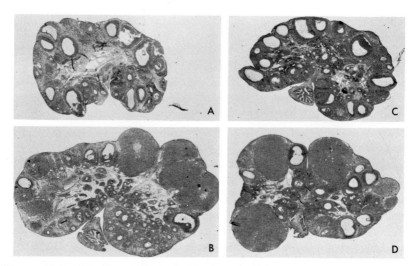

Figure 10-3   Histology of ovaries from rats with intrahypothalamic or sub-cutaneous progesterone administration.   A, progesterone implant in the median eminence; B, cholesterol implant in the median eminence; C, progesterone injection (5mg/day); D, oil vehicle injection.

surprisingly good localization of this effect was observed—the distance from the anterior hypothalamus to the median eminence is small.

The "implantation paradox" argument (Bogdanove, 1963) has not been eliminated as an explanation for these results. It should be noted, however, that the progesterone implants in this case occupied a much larger volume of the pituitary fossa than in previous experiments with other gonadal steroids; it is difficult to imagine that all parts of the pituitary were not reached by these large depots. Progesterone should now be added to the list of steroid hormones whose inhibitory feedback effect on pituitary tropic hormone secretion is apparently exerted at the level of the median eminence.

The gonadotropin inhibitory effects of the new synthetic progestational antifertility compounds are more potent than those of progesterone, and appear easier to demonstrate by intracranial implantation. Kanematsu and Sawyer (1965) have found that norethindrone implants in the median eminence of rabbits blocked mating-induced ovulation. Dörner and Döcke (1967) investigated the effects of chlormadinone implantation in rats. Gonadotropic inhibition in this case followed median eminence and pituitary implantation of the synthetic progestogen. Ectors and Pasteels (1967) found that anterior hypothalamic implants of medroxypro-gesterone in rats resulted in a pseudopregnancy-like condition; the results of median eminence implantation were not reported, so that diffusion to that area might have been envolved.

Inhibitory Feedback by Androgen

To what extent is pituitary LH secretion in males a function of the level of circulating testosterone? Virtually all studies relating to this question have been conducted with chronic administration of androgen and indirect measures of gonadotropin output, although, in one recent experiment, it was shown that a single high subcutaneous dose of testosterone propionate (1 mg) resulted in reduced plasma LH in castrate rats 72 hours later (Schally *et al.*, 1967). The first analysis of the testosterone-LH relationship in which a specific quantitative bioassay technique was used was done by Ramirez and McCann (1965). They investigated the effects of varying doses of testosterone propionate for 14 to 23 days, commencing on the day of castration, on plasma LH (ovarian

Figure 10-4   Plasma LH (per cent ovarian ascorbic acid depletion, OAAD) in normal male rats, castrates, and castrates treated with testosterone. "Assay control," OAAD, in assay rats injected with serum albumin.   Experiments of Davidson, Smith, Weick, and Rogers (unpublished) and Ramirez and McCann, 1965. See text for further details.

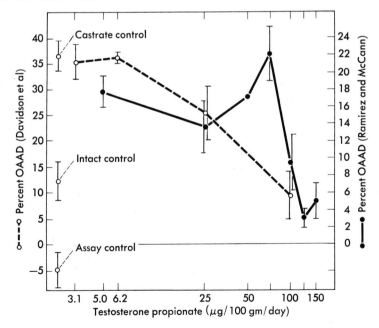

ascorbic acid depletion). Their data (see Fig. 10-4) show no significant reduction of the high castrate plasma LH level until a dose of 100μg/100gm body weight was reached. At 125μg the LH activity was further reduced, apparently to undetectable levels. The assay was insufficiently sensitive to detect LH in non-castrates.

We have recently reinvestigated the dose response curve, using the sensitive Bogdanove modification of the Parlow assay (Bogdanove and Gay, 1967a), and injecting 4ml plasma/100gm assay rat (unpublished data of Davidson, Smith, Rodgers, and Bloch). With this method, it was possible to detect significant ascorbic acid depleting activity in the plasma of intact (non-castrate) control animals. Adult orchidectomized rats were injected daily with testosterone propionate from the day of castration, and measurements were performed after two months of treatment.

The results (see Fig. 10-4) show that the negative correlation between administered testosterone and plasma LH activity extended over a considerable range of testosterone levels. The first decrease appeared between the doses of 12.5 and 25μg/100gm, and plasma LH activity in the 100 μg group was not significantly different from that in normal control animals. It has been suggested that the ovarian ascorbic acid test overestimates the amount of LH present in rat plasma (Pelletier, 1964) although McCann et al. (1968) disagree. At any rate, even if our measurements reflected a combination of LH activity (testosterone-suppressible) and a nonspecific, nonsuppressible component, this would not affect the conclusions to be drawn from the results.

These data suggest a more gradual inhibitory feedback slope of the

Table 10-2   Effects of testosterone propionate, injected daily from the day of castration for 2 months, on seminal vesicle and prostate weight (in mg) in rats weighing approx. 400 gm. (Data from Smith, Rodgers, Bloch, and Davidson.)

Testosterone dose (μg/100 gm/day)	No. of rats	Seminal vesicle weight	Ventral prostate weight
0 (castrate)	8	87 ± 6*	38 ± 3
3.1	8	107 ± 3	96 ± 9
6.2	8	176 ± 17	169 ± 11
12.5	7	317 ± 12	237 ± 21
25.0	7	428 ± 14	330 ± 25
100.0	6	630 ± 57	682 ± 89
0 (intact)	8	392 ± 26	424 ± 39

*mean ± standard error of the mean.

gonadotropin-testosterone relationship than was noted by Ramirez and McCann (1965). This seems more in keeping with a continuously operating negative feedback relationship over the range of plasma testosterone levels from castrate to normal. Ramirez and McCann (1965) concluded that since 100μg/100gm testosterone raised accessory sex gland weights to slightly supernormal levels, some testicular factor other than testosterone must operate to suppress LH secretion. A similar conclusion could be drawn from the data of Davidson et al. (Fig. 10-4) since accessory sex glands were restored in that experiment with approximately 25μg/100gm (see Table 10-2). In both cases, however, the conclusions must be tentative in view of the relative inaccuracy of the methods, and more studies of this problem should be carried out.

The suggestion that some testicular product other than testosterone is responsible for negative feedback inhibition of gonadotropin secretion in males is not new, however (see Davidson, 1966a). Recently, additional data have been added in the search for the elusive pituitary-inhibitory factor postulated to originate from the seminiferous tubules. Fachini (1966) has presented evidence of gonadotropin inhibitory activity in extracts of semen. Lacy (1967) has once again suggested, on the basis of histological evidence, that estrogen produced by the Sertoli cells might function normally to inhibit gonadotropin secretion. Other studies in which similar conclusions were reached relating to the antigonadotropic function of the seminiferous tubules are mentioned in the following discussion on FSH. The most interesting recent development in this area, however, is the demonstration by Voglmayr and Mattner (1968) that removal of the tubular products by cannulation of the vasa efferentia in sheep leads to a surprisingly large testicular hypertrophy in response to unilateral orchidectomy. The possibility arises that tubular secretions in sheep affect the pituitary after re-entering the bloodstream from the vasa efferentia. Active exchange of materials across the walls of these ducts have been clearly demonstrated by Waites et al. (1969).

Testosterone-FSH dose response relationships have not as yet been thoroughly investigated. Some of the inconsistencies in the literature relating to the effects of castration on pituitary FSH content appear to have been resolved, however, by Steinberger and Duckett (1966), who showed that there is a biphasic effect on FSH content, which decreases 1 week after castration and then rises above the normal level. Both Steinberger and Duckett (1966) and Katsh and Duncan (1968) believe that a tubular feedback-active substance exists; they base this belief on the finding of changes in pituitary FSH content following selective destruction of the seminiferous tubules. However, as pointed out most recently by Bogdanove and Gay (1967b), it is not at all clear what the relationship, if any, is between the content of FSH in the pituitary and its rate of secretion.

Localization of Androgen Receptor. Although considerably less work has been done on localization of the negative feedback receptor for androgen, the results are clearer than they are for estrogen. Implants of testosterone propionate in the median eminence region, but not in the pituitary, result in testicular and accessory sex gland atrophy in the dog (Davidson and Sawyer, 1961b) and the rat (Lisk, 1962; Smith and Davidson, 1967a, 1967b). In the rat, different areas of the hypothalamus have been carefully mapped, and the effect is well localized to the basal medial hypothalamic region (Lisk, 1960, 1962; Davidson, 1967). The problem of whether median eminence testosterone implants act merely via diffusion of the steroid to the pituitary has been investigated by Smith and Davidson (1967a). Testosterone implants were placed in the median eminence region of hypophysectomized rats with renal pituitary transplants that maintained testicular structure and spermatogenesis. Four weeks later, significant decreases in testicular weight and inhibition of spermatogenesis were noted. Since prostates were inhibited rather than stimulated by the implants, the results were not due to systemic release of testosterone.

Additional evidence for a hypothalamic site of testosterone negative feedback is provided by the experiments of Mittler and Meites (1966) and Martini *et al.* (1968), who found that castration increased and large doses of testosterone decreased the FSH releasing activity of the hypothalamus in male rats. Furthermore, Schally *et al.* (1967) demonstrated that testosterone treatment, even in high doses, did not block the activity of luteinizing hormone releasing factor (LRF). Finally, a recent abstract suggests that testosterone suppresses plasma follicle stimulating hormone releasing factor (FSHRF) activity in hypophysectomized male rats (Dickerman *et al.,* 1968).

If a median eminence receptor responds to elevations of circulating testosterone levels, does the same receptor also respond when the level is decreased below normal by initiating increases in gonadotropin secretion? This is not an artificial question; the possibility of separate receptors for the effects of high and low titers of feedback-active hormones has been proposed by Ganong (1963, p. 117) for corticoids, and by Sinha and Meites (1965/66) for thyroxine.

We have studied this question with the help of cyproterone (1, 2α-methylene-6-chloro-$\Delta6$-17α hydroxyprogesterone), a potent and specific antiandrogen. It was reasoned that upon intracranial implantation in crystalline form, this compound might bind to the testosterone receptors in the vicinity of the implant, thereby producing a local state of testosterone "deprivation." Initial experiments showed that implantation of 200 µg cyproterone in the median eminence region of adult male rats resulted in a slight stimulation of the seminal vesicles, but no effect on prostates or testes (Bloch and Davidson, 1967). Since the reproductive system of the adult male rat is relatively insensitive to gonadotropins or testosterone, further experiments were performed on 30-day-old rats. It was found that significant stimulation of seminal vesicles, prostates, and testes resulted from implantation of 100 µg cyproterone in the medial basal hypothalamus (Bloch and Davidson, 1967).

In further experiments, similar implants have been placed in the pituitary as well as in a number of other locations within the brain of 30-day-old rats (Bloch and Davidson, unpublished). Figures 10-5 and 10-6 show the results of three separate experiments; in the first two, cyproterone and cholesterol were implanted in the median eminence

Figure 10-5   Effects of intracranial cyproterone and cholesterol implants on ventral prostate weight of immature (30-day-old) male rats, implanted for 2 weeks. The first two pairs of bars represent two separate experiments, and all other bars represent results from a third experiment. A. Pit., anterior pituitary; A. Hy., anterior hypothalamus; P. Hy., posterior hypothalamus; CPU, caudate-putamen. (Data of Bloch and Davidson.)

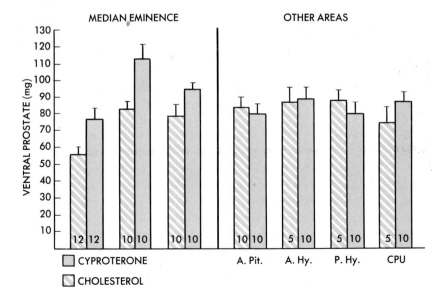

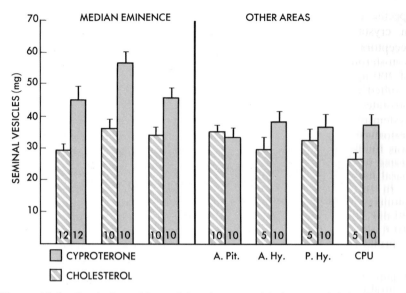

Figure 10-6   Seminal vesicle weights in rats with intracranial implants of cyproterone or cholesterol. See Fig. 10-5.

region, and in both cases there was significant stimulation of both seminal vesicles and prostates. In the third experiment, the results of implantation in the median eminence, anterior pituitary, anterior and posterior hypothalamus, and caudate-putamen were studied. No significant stimulation of accessory sex glands was found from implants in the pituitary gland or in extrahypothalamic regions, except for a significant difference

Table 10-3   Effects of median eminence implantation of cyproterone (Cyp) or cholesterol (Cho) on pituitary FSH content of 30-day-old male rats. (Bloch, Davidson, unpublished data.)

	Donors			Assay		
Steroid	Pituitary weight (mg)	Fraction of pituitary assayed	No. of Recipients	Ovarian weight (mg)	FSH‡ per pituitary gland (µg)	95% confidence limits
Cho	3.9 ± 0.2*	0.6	6	140.6 ± 8.1†	220.0	163–292
Cyp	4.4 ± 0.3	0.6	6	110.8 ± 11.3	144.0	96–219

* mean ± standard error of the mean.
† p < .05 vs. cyproterone group.
‡ NIH-FSH-S₃ equivalents.

that was found between cyproterone-implanted and cholesterol-implanted controls in the case of the seminal vesicles, in animals with caudate-putamen implants. This result was due to a control group with smaller prostates than any other in that experiment, not to higher weights in the cyproterone group. It appears, therefore, that the same basomedial hypothalamic region which responds to increases in testosterone concentration by decreasing gonadotropin secretion also responds to effective decreases in testosterone concentration by increasing the secretion of these hormones.

While the stimulation of accessory sex glands clearly indicates that LH secretion was enhanced by intrahypothalamic cyproterone implantation, it is not so clear what the effects on FSH secretion were. FSH assays were conducted on the pituitaries of groups of animals implanted with cyproterone or cholesterol in the median eminence region. As shown in Table 10-3, there was a decrease in pituitary FSH content in these animals. This result could be interpreted as signifying either a decrease in production of FSH or an increase in release with partial depletion of FSH stores. However, von Berswordt-Wallrabe and Neumann (1967) have demonstrated that a systemic injection of cyproterone resulted in decreased pituitary FSH content which was accompanied by increases in serum FSH. Arguing by analogy, it seems likely that the cyproterone implants had similar effects on FSH secretion, although we have not performed assays of FSH in the blood.

The above experiments were all conducted with the free alcohol form of cyproterone. Although cyproterone acetate is a considerably more potent antiandrogen on systemic administration, this does not appear to be the case with intracerebral implantation (Smith and Davidson, unpublished). As shown in Table 10-4, median eminence implantation of cyproterone acetate had no effect on the testes, seminal vesicles, or

Table 10-4   Effects of median eminence implantation of cyproterone acetate on male reproductive system; 100 µg was implanted two weeks before autopsy. (Smith and Davidson, unpublished data.)

Implanted steroid	Testes (gm)	Seminal vesicles (mg)	Ventral prostate (mg)
Cyproterone acetate (n = 8)	1.25 ± 0.03*	29.9 ± 2.8	83.2 ± 5.7
Cholesterol (n = 7)	1.32 ± 0.04	29.9 ± 2.8	90.0 ± 7.2

*mean ± standard error of the mean.

ventral prostates of 30-day-old rats, in direct contrast to the results with the free form of the steroid. Although the reason for this difference is not clear, it may possibly be connected with the fact that the acetate has marked progestational activity, unlike the free form. Conceivably the progestational action might have resulted in inhibition of gonadotropin secretion, thereby counteracting the antiandrogenic activity of the compound.

Recent work by Igarashi et al. (1967) suggests that decreased estrogen concentrations may also operate at the median eminence level. These authors reported that median eminence implantation of clomiphene resulted in stimulation of gonadotropin secretion in rats. Although all the actions of clomiphene on female reproduction are not yet understood, it does have antiestrogenic action. Thus the stimulatory effects of the implants might have resulted from a decreased "effective" estrogen concentration in the median eminence region.

Feedback Effects of Testosterone Compared with Behavioral and Androgenic Effects. We have seen that testosterone's feedback action is exerted directly on the hypothalamus. Another action of testosterone on the hypothalamus is that of activating structures responsible for the manifestation of male sexual behavior, as has been demonstrated in rats and capons (Davidson, 1966b; Lisk, 1967; Barfield, 1969). It is of interest to compare some characteristics of these two effects of testosterone on the brain with its effects on the reproductive system. Such comparisons, apart from their intrinsic interest, could be important for investigations of the biochemical mechanism of the actions of androgen.

Are the receptors for the two neural mechanisms—behavioral and feedback—coextensive in the brain? Apparently not. As shown above, the inhibitory feedback effect of testosterone in the rat is limited to the median eminence region of the hypothalamus. On the other hand, Lisk (1967) claims that the behavioral effect is limited to the anterior hypothalamic-preoptic region; we have also found that this is an effective site for testosterone implantation, although behavioral effects could be obtained throughout the hypothalamus (Davidson, 1966b).

How do the effects of testosterone compare with regard to the latency to loss of function following castration, and to its restoration following testosterone replacement therapy? Degenerative changes in the accessory sexual glands occur rapidly following removal of the rat's testes—the first histological changes being observable within hours (Burkhart, 1942; Price and Williams-Ashman, 1961). Behavioral responses, however, may persist for long periods of time after castration; complete behavioral responses are observed in some animals for several months (Davidson, 1966c). The behavioral and morphological responses to testosterone replacement in castrates also differ in their temporal pattern. Regrowth of the accessory sexual glands occurs rapidly (Burkhart, 1942; Price and Williams-Ashman, 1961), but the male's behavioral response to testosterone replacement is slow. In a recent experiment with adult male rats, normal behavior was only restored after two weeks of daily administration of a large dose of testosterone propionate (Smith, Rodgers, Bloch, and Davidson, umpublished). The temporal aspects of the feedback response to testosterone (as well as to estrogen and progesterone) are virtually unknown; this is an important dimension which should be added to our knowledge of the feedback mechanisms.

How do the dose-response relationships of the two hypothalamically mediated mechanisms compare? To study this question, behavioral and feedback responses to testosterone were compared in the same groups of castrate rats (for whom feedback responses are shown in Fig. 10-4). Behavioral tests were conducted twice weekly before and during the two-month post-castration period of testosterone administration; at its termination, accessory sex glands and plasma LH were studied. By the end of the experimental period all had achieved a steady state of behavioral performance, including both the group which received injections of vehicle only (no ejaculatory patterns) and that which received the highest dose of testosterone (100 per cent ejaculatory patterns on all tests).

A brief summary of results is shown in Table 10-5. Although further work is required to confirm the precise minimum effective doses for the various responses, some trends are clear from these results. If the amount of hormone required to maintain sex accessory glands (and pituitary weight) is the "physiological" dose, then it appears that the amount of hormone required to activate the behavioral receptor is below, and that

Table 10-5   Minimum doses of testosterone propionate (μg/100 gm body weight/day) required to maintain sexual behavior, pituitary weight, or plasma LH activity at approximately the level found in normal non-castrate adult males. with Fig. 10-1. (From Smith and Davidson, 1968.)
(Data from Smith, Rodgers, Bloch, and Davidson. See text for further details.)

Sex behavior	Seminal vesicles	Pituitary weight	Plasma LH level
12.5	25	25	>25 (100?)

required to maintain normal circulating LH levels above, the physiological range. The significance of the latter finding was discussed previously. The former finding suggests that the normal male rat has higher levels of blood testosterone than is "needed" for sex behavior, and this is in line with the failure of previous studies to show correlations between male sex behavior and variations in endogenous testosterone levels (Beach and Fowler, 1959; Whalen *et al.*, 1961). The point that is relevant to the present discussion, however, is the suggestion that there may be differences in responsiveness to testosterone of the two types of postulated cerebral receptor mechanisms.

Another way in which one can compare the functional characteristics of the different receptor mechanisms for testosterone is to examine their specificity, e.g. their ability to respond to estrogen. As is well known, the inhibitory feedback effect of estrogen in males is even more powerful than that of androgens; this effect has been directly demonstrated by intracerebral implantation of estradiol (Lisk, 1960; Chowers and McCann, 1963). In this respect the feedback response differs from that of the peripheral reproductive organs, since estrogen's effect on the accessory sex glands does not mimic that of testosterone (Greene and Thomson, 1941; Parkes and Deanesly, 1966, p. 682). The behavioral receptor has characteristics intermediate between those of the feedback and peripheral reproductive systems. There are indications in the literature that estrogen has a slight stimulatory effect on male sex behavior in castrate male rats (Ball, 1937; Beach, 1942). In order to establish the degree of such effects, a careful study of estrogenic action on the behavior of recently castrated male rats has recently been conducted (Davidson, 1968, unpublished). It was found that large doses of estradiol benzoate significantly slowed the castration-induced decline in male sex behavior and partially maintained most qualitative aspects of the behavioral patterns. It appeared from this study that estrogen did mimic the testosterone effect on behavior but that the sensitivity to estrogen was low. Far more estradiol benzoate was required than is needed to activate female sex behavior; and even very large doses (70 μg/day) did not maintain male behavioral patterns for long.

Finally, it is of interest to compare the various responses to cyproterone. This steroid has antiandrogenic effects on the male reproductive system (Neumann and Kramer, 1966; Junkman and Neumann, 1964) and also, as discussed above, on the hypothalamic inhibitory feedback mechanism (see Figs. 10-5 and 10-6). Recently, in this laboratory, G. J. Bloch has studied the effects of systemic and intracerebral administration of cyproterone on sex behavior in the male rat. On intrahypothalamic implantation, cyproterone had a definite stimulatory effect on male sex behavior; the decline in ejaculatory responses following castration was significantly slowed. A similar result was also found on systemic administration of cyproterone acetate to castrate male rats. Since cyproterone is not androgenic (myotrophic and accessory gland responses), it is unlikely that the differential effects on behavioral and feedback mechanisms are merely due to differential thresholds of androgenic effects. Rather these results suggest a molecular difference in the two types of hypothalamic receptors. Further information on these experiments and on others discussed in this section can be found in Davidson and Bloch (1969).

Stimulatory Feedback

The first observations relating to stimulatory effects of gonadal steroids on gonadotropic function date back to the early days of pituitary physiology. In 1934, Hohlweg demonstrated that estrogen administered to prepuberal rats led to premature luteinization of the ovaries, and later it was shown that this effect was dependent on the pituitary (Westman and Jacobsohn, 1938). Not long thereafter it was shown that progesterone could stimulate ovulation (see Everett, 1964). Recently, considerable new evidence has been collected on the stimulatory feedback effects of both estrogenic and progestational steroids, and the relevance of these observations to the physiological regulation of gonadotropin secretion is beginning to become a little clearer.

It is well established that estrogen or progesterone may advance the appearance of ovulation during normal estrous cycles in the adult rat, and evidence also exists for cows, rabbits, monkeys, and women (see Everett, 1964, for references). Second, ovulation may also be stimulated by estrogen and progesterone during the normally quiescent period of pregnancy, particularly on the fourth to the sixth days in rats (Everett, 1947; Brown-Grant, 1969a). A third group of observations relate to the stimulation of ovulation, luteinization, or even true precocious puberty in immature rats. It seems clear that the well-known induction of superovulation by pregant mare's serum (PMS) injections in immature female rats is mediated by stimulatory feedback effects of ovarian steroids (Rennels and O'Steen, 1967; Meyer and McCormack, 1967; Grayburn and Brown-Grant, 1968).

The evidence for stimulatory effects of testosterone in the male is slight and unconfirmed (Johnson, 1964; Taleisnik et al., 1968; see also

Davidson, 1967). Dörner and Döcke (1967) and Wagner (1968) have shown that the stimulatory feedback effect of estrogen in prepuberal rats can normally be demonstrated only in females. The ability to respond in this fashion apparently develops in the absence of testosterone during the neonatal "critical period." Thus, estrogen-induced luteinization did not occur in female rats treated neonatally with a single dose of testosterone, and neonatally castrated male rats with ovarian transplants did show this effect. An additional effect of estrogen (and possibly progesterone) on the pituitary is stimulation of prolactin secretion (see Rothchild, 1965). This may be regarded as a stimulatory feedback action to the extent that prolactin may be regarded as a luteotropic hormone.

The phenomenon of stimulatory feedback presents several difficulties. First, how can one steroid both stimulate and inhibit pituitary function? An early but recurring suggestion on how to explain this seeming paradox was that small amounts of estrogen might stimulate and large amounts of estrogen inhibit pituitary function (Zondek, 1935). However, estrogen can have stimulatory effects when administered in large doses (Hohlweg, 1934) and inhibitory effects can be revealed with chronic administration of low doses (Byrnes and Meyer, 1951). It has also been suggested that time is the important factor—stimulatory effects tend to result from acute exposure to steroids, and negative effects from chronic administration (see Flerkó, 1966). The situation is more complex than this, however. Chronic administration of small estrogen doses can also stimulate LH secretion (Callantine *et al.,* 1966); certain combinations of time and dose may provide the determining factor.

The ratio between circulating estrogen and progesterone concentrations in the present or immediate past may be the key to understanding why it is that a given steroid sometimes has stimulatory and sometimes inhibitory effects. There is evidence for estrogen-progesterone interactions in all three of the stimulatory feedback situations mentioned above: precocious stimulation of gonadotropic function in prepuberal animals, activation of ovulation in pregnancy, and advancement of ovulation in mature cycling females.

Progesterone has been shown to facilitate the induction of ovulation by estrogen in immature female rats (Döcke and Dörner, 1966). Progesterone also facilitates the superovulating effects of PMS or FSH in prepuberal rats (Meyer and McCormack, 1967) which appear to be mediated by estrogen (Rennels and O'Steen, 1967; Grayburn and Brown-Grant, 1968).

Success in inducing ovulation in pregnant rats depends on precise timing of the estrogen injection during the early days of pregnancy (Everett,

1947; Brown-Grant, 1969b). The possibility exists that success in this experimental situation depends upon a precise level of progesterone at the time of estrogen action; it is known that circulating progesterone levels are changing rapidly during this period (Fajer and Barraclough, 1967).

With regard to ovulation induction in adult animals, it was early suggested by Everett (1948, 1961) that the degree of success in stimulating ovulation by progesterone depends on pre-existing estrogen levels in the circulation. Support for this idea comes from the recent detailed investigations of Brown-Grant (1969a), who showed that exogenous progesterone inhibited (or delayed) ovulation at all stages in the rat estrous cycle except from the time of presumed onset of estrogen secretion until the time of the ovulatory release of LH, during which period the effect was stimulatory. The stimulatory effect of progesterone in immature rats also depended on previous exposure to endogenous or exogenous estrogen (Grayburn and Brown-Grant, 1968). The stimulatory phase of progesterone's effects on ovulation thresholds in the rabbit (Kawakami and Sawyer, 1967) is apparently also a function of high levels of estrogen.

Another difficulty has to do with the fact that stimulation of gonadotropin secretion by ovarian steroids could eventually lead to a runaway positive feedback situation which, if unchecked, would result in the organism rapidly becoming flooded with ovarian steroids. Two events may be responsible for shutting off stimulatory feedback. First, it may be assumed that with the passage of time the stimulatory effect is replaced with an inhibitory one. Thus, for example, we have shown that intracerebral estradiol implants in prepuberal female rats have an initial stimulatory effect (early vaginal opening) but, if they are left in place, there is eventual ovarian and uterine atrophy (Smith and Davidson, 1968). Second, ovulation presumably shuts off the source of estrogen secretion by destroying the follicle, and thereby terminates the positive feedback action.

To what extent can the experimental findings on stimulatory and inhibitory feedback be related to the naturally occurring events that control ovulation and reproductive function in the normal animal? This is the crucial question. The induction of ovulation in prepuberal animals and during pregnancy, although they provide useful information, are not analogous to usual physiological situations. The experimental findings on ovulation induction in adult animals, however, can be directly relevant. Recent advances in steroid analysis have resulted in a spate of studies on progesterone secretion in relation to the female reproductive cycle. It appears that a peak in progesterone levels in the rat is attained on the day of proestrus (e.g. Hashimoto and Melampy, 1967). Because of the difficulty in the chemical determination of blood estrogen, we do not have comparable information on estrogen secretion throughout the cycle. However, a number of ingenious experiments have recently been performed employing such biological criteria of estrogen levels as uterine weight and vaginal cornification following timed ovariectomy (Schwartz 1964; Barnea and Shelesnyak, 1968) and determination of the uterus to plasma concentration ratio of radioiodine following timed injections of progesterone (Brown-Grant, 1969a). It seems clear from these studies that estrogen reaches relatively high levels of secretion on the day before proestrus. Miyake (1968) has just reported estrogen bioassay data on ovarian venous blood showing the peak concentration 6 hours before the ovulatory surge of LH release. The conditions therefore exist, at least in rats, for an estrogen stimulatory feedback effect on the course of normal ovulation.

Feder et al. (1969) have now shown that progesterone does not reach peak plasma levels in the rat until shortly after the "critical period," indicating that this peak is not itself involved in stimulating ovulation. Similar findings for ovarian venous blood were reported by Miyake (1968). Of course it is conceivable that a stimulatory feedback effect of progesterone results from the initial rise in its secretion, rather than being a function of the peak attained only after LH is released. At the moment it seems likely, however, that estrogen exercises the primary stimulatory feedback effect in normal ovulation with progesterone playing, if anything, a subsidiary facilitatory role. It should be noted in this context that Neill et al. (1967), who studied plasma LH levels (by radioimmunoassay) and concurrently progesterone levels in women, could find no increase in progesterone until after the ovulatory surge of LH secretion had commenced.

The other species in which an appreciable amount of information on stimulatory feedback effects is available is the rabbit. In a recent, interesting study, Hilliard et al. (1967) found that ovarian vein levels of the characteristic progestin of the female rabbit—20α-hydroxypregn-4-en-3-one—were high between coitus and ovulation. Although mating induced LH release in ovariectomized rabbits treated with estrogen, this hormone disappeared from the circulation within 2 hours. LH levels could, however, be maintained for a longer period by injections of 20α-hydroxypregn-4-en-3-one immediately following mating. This evidence suggests that ovarian progestin in the rabbit has a stimulatory feedback effect which may be essential in maintaining sufficient LH secretion to produce ovulation following coitus.

Localization of Stimulatory Feedback Receptors

Estrogen. There is good evidence for an essential central nervous component in the ovulatory response to single injections of PMS in the immature rat (Strauss and Meyer, 1962), and this component, as mentioned above, probably involves a stimulatory feedback action of estrogen. Several investigators have shown that neural blocking agents similar to those effective in inhibiting ovulation in proestrous rats prevent PMS-induced ovulation, and the "critical period" phenomenon applies also to these immature animals (McCormack and Meyer, 1962). This is evidence that the postulated stimulatory feedback action in these animals is exerted on neural tissue. Quinn and Zarrow (1964) have shown that lesions in various parts of the medial preoptic-anterior hypothalamic region prevent PMS-induced superovulation, in contrast to animals with sham preoptic lesions, with lesions in lateral preoptic or other hypothalamic areas, or with medial preoptic lesions and HCG injections. These experiments supply suggestive evidence that, if the CNS component in PMS ovulation is due to the action of estrogen, that action may be exerted on the medial preoptic-anterior hypothalamic region. As mentioned earlier, however, other explanations are possible for these kinds of data.

What information can be obtained from the more direct method of intracranial implantation of estrogen? Davidson and Sawyer (1961a) interpreted their original experiments on estradiol benzoate implantation in rabbits to provide suggestive evidence that implants in the posterior median eminence had a biphasic effect on ovulation, since their ovulation-inhibiting effect was preceded by an apparent facilitation of copulation-induced ovulation. Subsequently, Kanematsu and Sawyer (1964) found an increase in the already high plasma LH activity following ovariectomy in rabbits with long-term (2 months) intrapituitary implants; median eminence implants reduced the level. Later Palka *et al.* (1966) showed increases in plasma LH 5 but not 18 days following median eminence implantation in female rats. Since these implants later produced severe gonadotropic inhibition, this was evidence for a biphasic effect of estrogen on the median eminence region—first stimulatory and then inhibitory feedback.

Döcke and Dörner (1965) have found that implants of estradiol benzoate dissolved in agar, when placed in the anterior hypothalamus or the anterior pituitary, are effective (to a greater extent than systemic injections) in inducing corpus luteum formation in immature rats. While agar implants presumably allow a more rapid spread of steroid than crystalline implants, it is noteworthy that the anterior pituitary was the most effective site of implantation. A puzzling but interesting finding is that lesions in the basal anterior hypothalamus prevented ovarian luteinization following intrapituitary estrogen implantation. This suggested to Döcke and Dörner (1965) that the lesion was reducing pituitary sensitivity to releasing factors, an interpretation also applicable to the above-mentioned experiments of Quinn and Zarrow (1964).

Smith and Davidson (1968) have studied the possible cerebral involvement in the precocious vaginal opening caused by estrogen in prepuberal rats. As was shown by Ramirez and Sawyer (1965), rats are very sensitive to this effect of estrogen. This was confirmed when we found (Smith and Davidson, 1968) that 30 gauge tubes containing estradiol benzoate at their tips were effective in advancing vaginal opening regardless of the location of the implants—including the cerebral cortex.

Figure 10-7   Sagittal diagram of rat brain, showing location of acute (48 hour) implants of estradiol benzoate, and effects on vaginal opening. Compare with Fig. 10-1.   (From Smith and Davidson, 1968.)

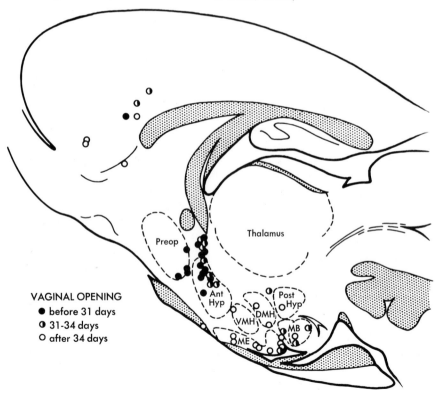

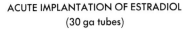

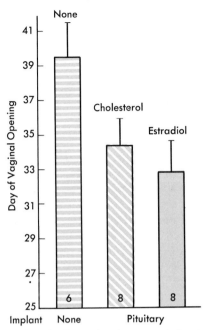

Figure 10-8   Dates of vaginal opening in untreated rats or rats with estradiol benzoate or cholesterol implants in the anterior pituitary. Implants made in 30 gauge tubes. (From Smith and Davidson, 1968.)

When these tubes were implanted at 26 days of age and removed 2 days later, however, it was possible to obtain a localization of this effect. Implants in the anterior hypothalamic or preoptic region (see Fig. 10-7) resulted in precocious vaginal opening, whereas implants in other areas of the brain, including the median eminence region, were ineffective. These procedures also resulted in true precocious puberty, unlike chronic basomedial hypothalamic implantation, which precipitated vaginal opening followed by inhibition of cycling and eventual ovarian atrophy. Although two other laboratories have found that precocious vaginal opening results from median eminence estrogen implants (Kannwischer *et al.*, 1967; Motta *et al.*, 1968), it is not clear if the effects noted by these investigators were due to diffusion of estrogen to the anterior region.

Intrapituitary implantation (for 48 hours as described above) also advanced the time of vaginal opening, but in this case it was found that the cholesterol-implanted controls also showed a similar effect (see

Fig. 10-8). We conclude that the stimulatory feedback effect of estrogen in prepuberal female rats is exerted specifically in the anterior hypothalamic-medial preoptic region. These experiments do not, however, rule out possible additional sensitive areas in the pituitary gland, although they suggest that mechanical trauma may stimulate gonadotropin release by the pituitary, and that considerable care must be exerted in interpreting effects of intrapituitary implants. The possibility that there are two sites of stimulatory feedback action, the anterior hypothalamus and the pituitary, is thus not inconsistent with the available evidence.

Progesterone Stimulatory Feedback Localization. Very little work has been done on the localization of progesterone stimulatory feedback. Barraclough *et al.* (1964) attempted to study this question by investigating the ovulation-inducing effect of progesterone in rats with various lesions in the preoptic area, all of which induced persistent estrous. Suprachiasmatic nucleus lesions did not prevent this effect of progesterone However, combined suprachiasmatic and medial preoptic area lesions resulted in anovulatory persistent estrous animals in which progesterone failed to induce ovulation. Barraclough (1966) does not consider these experiments as conclusive evidence that the site of stimulatory feedback action of progesterone is the preoptic area. In fact, his view is that progesterone "acts along the entire hypothalamic axis concerned with the regulation of adenohypophyseal gonadotropin secretion." Direct evidence from implant experiments in mammals is lacking. Ralph and Fraps (1960) did, however, demonstrate the induction of ovulation following intrahypothalamic, but not intrapituitary, injection of progesterone in hens.

Puberty

The mechanism of the onset of puberty is still one of the mysteries of biology. That the central nervous system is probably the prime initiator of puberty was most dramatically illustrated in the experiments of Harris and Jacobsohn (1952) which demonstrated the totipotentiality of the immature rat's hypophysis. One of the more attractive hypotheses in this area is that there is a change in the threshold of the negative feedback mechanism at this time such that the "gonadostat" is set at a higher level in the adult organism, thus supporting higher circulating concentrations of both gonadotropins and gonadal steroids (Ramirez and McCann, 1963; Donovan and van der Werff ten Bosch, 1965). There is much evidence for enhanced negative feedback sensitivity in prepuberal animals, dating back to the classic experiments of Moore and Price (1932).

Experiments on Puberty in the Male

Since it seems most likely that the inhibitory feedback action of testosterone is exerted at the basal hypothalamic level, the site of puberal change in inhibitory feedback setting should be demonstrable at this location. Experiments were therefore conducted to determine if a difference could be demonstrated in the effectiveness of 22-gauge implants in 30-day-old, 55-day-old (just after puberty), or adult (70 to 90-day-old) rats, as shown in Fig. 10-9. When testicular weight is compared at each of these ages in testosterone-implanted and cholesterol-implanted rats, it is clear that significant inhibition was present only in the prepuberal animals. Furthermore, there was an inverse relationship between age and degree of inhibition of the sexual accessory glands.

The very large differences in responsiveness of the prepuberal and adult median eminence region to testosterone implantation is clearly shown in Table 10-6. Measurements of the distance from the optic chiasm to

Figure 10-9 Testicular and accessory sex gland weights of rats implanted at various ages with cholesterol (Chol) or testosterone propionate (Tp). The bars indicate testis weight. Seminal vesicle and ventral prostate weights are expressed as percentage of the weights of cholesterol-implanted controls. (From Smith and Davidson, 1967a.)

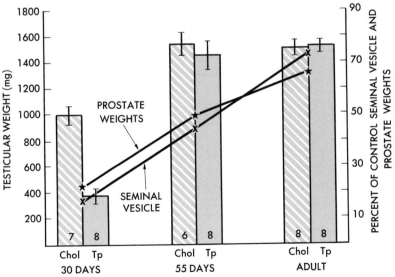

Table 10-6   Effects of hypothalamic implants of crystalline testosterone in prepuberal (30-day-old) and adult male rats. (From Smith and Davidson, 1967a.)

Type of implant	Surface area of implant	Age of rat at implantation	Testicular weight change (% of weight of cholesterol-implanted control)
20 ga ejected pellet	2.87 mm²	>70 days	80
22 ga fused pellet (not ejected)	0.086 mm²	30 days	38

the mammillary bodies showed that, after the age of 30 days, there was no appreciable increase in size of this region in which the negative feedback receptors are apparently located.

In this laboratory G. J. Bloch has also attempted to demonstrate a change in feedback sensitivity of the median eminence in relation to puberty by comparing the gonadotropin-stimulatory effects of the antiandrogen cyproterone in different periods before puberty. The intention was to produce the converse effect to that found in the above-mentioned experiment with testosterone implants. The greatest stimulation of seminal vesicles and ventral prostates resulted from implantation from 37 to 44 days of age (close to puberty); implants before this time were less effective (Bloch, 1968; Davidson and Bloch, 1969).

The differences in effectiveness of these implants were not as great as were noted previously for the inhibitory effect of testosterone implants; it was thought that perhaps the difference could be explained by a change in sensitivity of the accessory glands to gonadotropin-mediated testosterone secretion. Chorionic gonadotropin was therefore injected in approximately the dose required to duplicate the stimulatory effect of cyproterone implantation at different prepuberal ages. The period of maximal response to cyproterone implantation was not characterized by enhanced sensitivity to gonadotropin (Bloch, 1968; Davidson and Bloch, 1969). Thus it appears that, with advancing age toward puberty, decreases in effective testosterone concentration at the hypothalamic level have an increasingly greater stimulatory effect on gonadotropin secretion. Both the cyproterone and the testosterone implantation results are consistent with the hypothesis that the onset of puberty is related to a decreasing sensitivity of the hypothalamic inhibitory feedback receptor responsive to circulating testosterone levels.

Puberty in the Female

In the female rat there is also a decrease in the effectiveness of intrahypothalamic gonadal steroid implants after puberty. However, the difference is not as great as in the male (Smith and Davidson, 1968), suggesting a lesser change in inhibitory feedback threshold. It might be supposed, therefore, that some additional mechanism may be brought into play in the female. Furthermore, vaginal opening and the onset of mature reproductive function appear in the female rat in sudden, almost explosive fashion, unlike the more gradual development of the male. It seems as if a positive feedback mechanism would be appropriate for this trigger-like response. As mentioned above, very small amounts of systemic estradiol benzoate will precipitate true precocious puberty in the rat (Ramirez and Sawyer, 1965). This effect may be duplicated by acute intracerebral implantation of estradiol benzoate (Smith and Davidson, 1968). However, the effective area in this case (anterior hypothalamus) differs from that in which chronic implants caused inhibition of gonadotropin secretion (median eminence).

We have proposed the following tentative model for the events preceding puberty in the female rat (Fig. 10-10). We postulate that with advancing age there is a shift in the sensitivity of inhibitory feedback receptors in the median eminence region of the hypothalamus, involving an upward shift in the operating point of the system. This results in a rising level of circulating estrogen. At some as yet unspecified point in prepuberal life, this estrogen level reaches a threshold sufficient to activate a mechanism located in the medial preoptic-anterior hypothalamic region. As a result of activation in this area, impulses are passed to the median eminence, producing augmented levels of gonadotropin secretion. This causes the ovaries to secrete more estrogen and vaginal opening and ovulation then ensue. After this initial stimulus normal cycling is then commenced, for some unexplained reason, and continues throughout the animal's life. While we suspect that the postulated stimulatory feedback receptor in the anterior region might be the same as that which operates in response to rising estrogen levels to precipitate cyclic ovulation in the adult animal, there is as yet no direct evidence on this point. This hypothesis is, of course, no better than the still relatively sparse data which supports it. Hopefully it might serve as a framework around which to design future experiments, even if their outcome may be to invalidate that hypothesis.

It has been proposed (Bar-Sela and Critchlow, 1966) that the amygdala plays an important role in the onset of puberty in the female rat and that impulses pass from the amygdala, through the stria terminalis, to

Figure 10-10   Diagrammatic representation of hypothesis explaining the role of estrogen in the onset of puberty in the female rat. (From Smith and Davidson, 1968.)

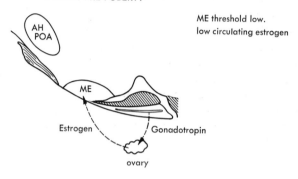

I: EARLY PRE-PUBERTY

ME threshold low.
low circulating estrogen

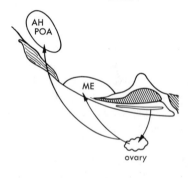

II: LATE PRE-PUBERTY

ME threshold rising.
↑ Estrogen level acts on anterior region.

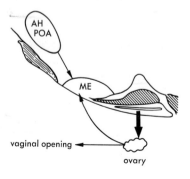

III: PUBERTY

Anterior region triggered to activate ME
↑ Gonadotropin release

the anterior hypothalamic region. This hypothesis is supported by the findings that lesions of the amygdala or stria terminalis precipitate precocious puberty in female rats, and stimulation in the same regions delay puberty. We have implanted estradiol benzoate in various regions of the amygdaloid area of 26-day-old rats, removing the implants 2 days later—the same design as was used in the experiments of Smith and Davidson (1968) mentioned above. These implants had no effect on the date of vaginal opening (mean date of vaginal opening in 20 rats with estrogen implants in the amygdala and surrounding regions: 39.7 $\pm$ 1.3 (SE); in 13 rats with cholesterol implants in this area: 40.6 $\pm$ 1.7). Although these findings do not invalidate the possible role of the amygdala in female puberty, they do suggest that the amygdala is not estrogen-sensitive in the same way as is the anterior hypothalamic region. Alternately, it may be that estrogen receptors in the amygdala may be more diffuse than those in the hypothalamus, so that it might be necessary to use bilateral implants of estrogen in order to demonstrate estrogen sensitivity in this location.

Concluding Remarks

The question posed at the beginning of this chapter about the precise physiological role of feedback mechanisms in the control of gonadotropin secretion has not been answered, yet it seems most likely that both stimulatory and inhibitory feedback of ovarian and testicular steroids are important components in that control. A much better answer to this question can come from careful quantitative studies, using the new methods of gonadotropin radioimmunoassay and steroid analysis, applied to measurements of plasma levels of these hormones in normal undisturbed animals.

The feedback mechanisms are established early in prepuberal life (see Donovan and van der Werff ten Bosch, 1965, for references), and, once established, are remarkably stable and persistent. Even in the "persistent estrous" state resulting from neonatal tetosterone treatment or hypothalamic deafferentation, the feedback response to ovariectomy persists (Gorski and Barraclough, 1962; Halász and Gorski, 1967). Flerkó has suggested, however, that the defect in these anovulatory rats results from a disturbance in feedback mechanisms (Flerkó et al., 1969); perhaps the defect is more subtle than can be revealed by ovariectomy.

The clearest evidence for localization of gonadal steroid feedback receptors relates to testosterone. A basomedial hypothalamic receptor for the testosterone inhibitory feedback mechanism seems well established; no evidence has yet appeared for an addititional site in the pituitary. Estrogen, on the other hand, may have a primary action on the basal medial hypothalamus with secondary effects on the anterior pituitary. The evidence for progesterone inhibitory feedback favors the same basomedial hypothalamic site. It is of interest that the principal site of inhibitory feedback action—the median eminence region—is also the area of highest concentration of the gonadotropin releasing factors (Mess *et al.*, 1967), an area which is the "final common path" for neuroendocrine stimuli. There is still only sparse information on the localization of stimulatory feedback receptors for estrogen and progesterone; it seems likely that these will be found in one or more of the following sites: median eminence, pituitary, and/or anterior hypothalamus.

Only very recently studies have begun to appear on the molecular mechanisms of steroid feedback action (Wakabayashi *et al.*, 1968; Crighton *et al.*, 1968). No doubt this field will be actively pursued in the near future. Steroid receptors are being sought and studied in peripheral tissues (Nolides and Gorski, 1966; Mercier *et al.*, 1968; Horton and Kato, 1968; Deakins and Rosmer, 1968). The extension of this type of work to brain tissue is an exciting prospect. In order for this work to be related to physiologic events much more information of a quantitative nature must be gathered on the functional characteristics of the feedback mechanisms. It should be borne in mind that the feedback-active hormones also have behavioral effects that are mediated by areas of the brain close to the feedback receptors; investigation of the comparative characteristics of the two types of central nervous system receptors might lead to advances in our understanding of both.

Acknowledgment

I am grateful to Dr. Keith Brown-Grant for reading the manuscript and for useful discussions.

References

Antunes-Rodrigues, J., and S. M. McCann (1967). Effect of suprachiasmatic lesions on the regulation of luteinizing hormone secretion in the female rat. *Endocrinology 81*, 666-70.

Assenmacher, I. (1957). Nouvelles donnees sur la role d'hypothalamus dans les regulations hypophysaires gonadotropes chez la canard domestique. *C. R. Soc. Biol. 245*, 2388-90.

Ball, J. (1937). Sex activity of castrated male rats increased by estrin administration. *J. Comp. Psychol. 24*, 135-44.

Barfield, R. J. (1969). Activation of copulatory behavior by androgen implanted into preoptic area of male fowl. *Hormones and Behavior*, in press.

Barnea, A., T. Gershonowitz, and M. C. Shelesnyak (1968). Assessment of ovarian secretion of oestrogen during the estrous cycle by use of biological criteria. *J. Endocrinol. 41*, 281-88.

Barraclough, C. A. (1966). Modifications in the CNS regulation of reproduction after exposure of prepuberal rats to steroid hormones. *Rec. Prog. Hormone Res. 22*, 503-39.

Barraclough, C. A., S. Yrarrazaval, and R. Hatton (1964). A possible hypothalamic site of action of progesterone in the facilitation of ovulation in the rat. *Endocrinology 75*, 838-45.

Bar-Sela, M. E., and V. Critchlow (1966). Delayed puberty following electrical stimulation of amygdala in female rats. *Amer. J. Physiol. 211*, 1103-7.

Beach, F. A. (1942). Copulatory behavior in prepuberally castrated rale rats and its modification by estrogen administration. *Endocrinology 31*, 679-83.

Beach, F. A., and H. Fowler (1959). Individual differences in the response of male rats to androgen. *J. Comp. Physiol. Psychol. 52*, 50-52.

Berswordt-Wallrabe, R. von, and F. Neumann (1967). Influence of a testosterone antagonist (cyproterone) on pituitary and serum FSH-content in juvenile male rats. *Neuroendocrinology 2*, 107-12.

Bloch, G. J. (1968). Effects of intracerebral implantation of an antiandrogen on gonadotropin function and mating behavior in rats. Ph.D. dissertation, Stanford University.

Bloch, G. J., and J. M. Davidson (1967). Antiandrogen implanted in brain stimulates male reproductive system. *Science 155*, 593-95.

Bogdanove, E. M. (1963). Direct gonad-pituitary feedback: an analysis of effects of intracranial estrogenic depots on gonadotrophin secretion. *Endocrinology 73*, 696-712.

Bogdanove, E. M. (1964). The role of the brain in the regulation of pituitary gonadotropin secretion. *Vitamins and Hormones 22*, 205-60.

Bogdanove, E. M., and V. Gay (1967a). Enhancement of the ovarian ascorbic acid depletion response during estrogen-prolonged pseudopregnancy. An improved bioassay for LH. *Endocrinology 81*, 1104-17.

Bogdanove, E. M., and V. L. Gay (1967b). Changes in pituitary and plasma levels of LH and FSH after cessation of chronic androgen treatment. *Endocrinology 81*, 930-33.

Brown-Grant, K. (1969a). The induction of ovulation by ovarian steroids in the adult rat. *J. Endocrinol.*, in press.

Brown-Grant, K. (1969b). The induction of ovulation during pregnancy in the rat. *J. Endocrinol.*, in press.

Burkhart, E. Z. (1942). A study of the early effects of androgenic substances in the rat by the aid of colchicine. *J. Exp. Zool. 89*, 135-65.

Byrnes, W. W., and R. K. Meyer (1951). Effect of physiological amounts of estrogen on the secretion of follicle stimulating and luteinizing hormones. *Endocrinology 49*, 449-60.

Callantine, M. R., R. R. Humphrey, and B. L. Nessett (1966). LH release by 17-β-estradiol in the rat. *Endocrinology 79*, 455-56.

Chowers, I., and S. M. McCann (1963). The effects on ACTH and gonadotropin secretion of implants of gonadal steroids in the hypothalamo-hypophysial region. *Israel Med. J. 22*, 420-32.

Chowers, I., and S. M. McCann (1965). Content of luteinizing hormone-releasing factor and luteinizing hormone during the estrous cycle and after changes in gonadal steroid titers. *Endocrinology 76*, 700-708.

Chowers, I., and S. M. McCann (1967). Comparison of the effect of hypothalamic and pituitary implants of estrogen and testosterone on reproductive system and adrenal of female rats. *Proc. Soc. Exp. Biol. Med. 124*, 260-66.

Corbin, A., G. Mangili, M. Motta, and L. Martini (1965). Effect of hypothalamic and mesencephalic steroid implantations on ACTH feedback mechanisms. *Endocrinology 76*, 811-18.

Crighton, D. B., S. Watanabe, A. P. S. Dhariwal, and S. M. McCann (1968). Failure of inhibitors of protein synthesis to affect the LH-releasing action of hypothalamic extracts *in vitro*. *Proc. Soc. Exp. Biol. Med. 128*, 537-40.

Dallman, M. F., and F. E. Yates (1967). Anatomical and functional mapping of central neural input and feedback pathways of adrenocortical systems. In *The Investigation of Hypothalamic-Pituitary-Adrenal Function* (E. H. T. James and J. Landon, eds.), pp. 39-72. Cambridge University Press, London.

David, M. A., F. Fraschini, and L. Martini (1965). Parallelisme entre le contenu-hypothalamique en FSH-RF (FSH releasing factor). *C. R. Acad. Sci. (Paris) 261*, 2249-51.

Davidson, J. M. (1966a). Control of gonadotropin secretion in the male. In *Neuroendocrinology* (L. Martini and W. F. Ganong, eds.), *1*, 565-611. Academic Press, New York.

Davidson, J. M. (1966b). Activation of the male rat's sexual behavior by intracerebral implantation of androgen. *Endocrinology 79*, 783-94.

Davidson, J. M. (1966c). Characteristics of sex behavior in male rats following castration. *Anim. Behav. 14*, 266-72.

Davidson, J. M. (1967). Neuroendocrine mechanisms in the control of spermatogenesis. *J. Reprod. Fert., Suppl. 2*, 103-16.

Davidson, J. M., and G. J. Bloch (1969). Neuroendocrine aspects of male reproduction. *Biol. of Reprod.*, in press.

Davidson, J. M., and S. Feldman (1963). Cerebral involvement in the inhibition of ACTH secretion by hydrocortisone. *Endocrinology 72*, 936-46.

Davidson, J. M., and C. H. Sawyer (1961a). Effects of localized intracerebral implantation of oestrogen on reproductive function in the female rabbit. *Acta Endocrinol. (Kbh) 37*, 385-93.

Davidson, J. M., and C. H. Sawyer (1961b). Evidence for a hypothalamic focus of inhibition of gonadotropin by androgen in the male. *Proc. Soc. Exp. Biol. Med. 107*, 4-7.

Davidson, J. M., A. N. Contopoulos, and W. F. Ganong (1960). Decreased gonadotrophic hormone content of the anterior pituitary gland in dogs with hypothalamic lesions. *Endocrinology 66*, 735-40.

Davidson, J. M., E. R. Smith, C. H. Rodgers, and G. J. Bloch (1968). Relative thresholds of behavioral and somatic responses to estrogen. *Physiol. Behav. 3*, 227-29.

Davidson, J. M., S. Feldman, E. R. Smith, and R. F. Weick (1969). Localization of steroid feedback receptors. *Proc. 3rd Int. Cong. Endocrinol., Excerpta Medica*, in press.

Deakins, S., and W. Rosner (1968). Electrophoretic studies of testosterone-binding proteins in human plasma. *3rd Int. Cong. Endocrinol., Excerpta Medica, Int. Cong. Ser. 157,* 158 (Abstract).

Dickerman, E., A. Negro-Villar, and J. Meites (1968). Plasma FSH-RF in hypophysectomized rats after treatment with testosterone propionate or reserpine. *24th Int. Cong. Physiol. Sci.,* Abstracts, p. 112.

Döcke, F., and G. Dörner (1965). The mechanism of the induction of ovulation by oestrogens. *J. Endocrinol. 33,* 491-99.

Döcke, F., and G. Dörner (1966). Facilitative action of progesterone on the induction of ovulation by oestrogen. *J. Endocrinol. 36,* 209-10.

Donovan, B. T., and J. J. van der Werff ten Bosch (1965). *Physiology of Puberty.* Williams and Wilkins, Baltimore.

Dörner, G., and F. Döcke (1967). The influence of intrahypothalamic and intrahypophyseal implantation of estrogen or progestogen on gonadotrophin release. *Endocrinologia Exp. 2,* 65-71.

Ectors, F., and J. L. Pasteels (1967). Action antiovulatoire medroxyprogesterone, implantee en quantites minimes dans l'hypothalamus anterieur de la ratte. *C. R. Acad. Sci. (Paris) 265,* 758-60.

Everett, J. W. (1947). Hormonal factors responsible for deposition of cholesterol in the corpus luteum of the rat. *Endocrinology 41,* 364-77.

Everett, J. W. (1948). Progesterone and estrogen in the experimental control of ovulation time and other features of the estrous cycle in the rat. *Endocrinology 43,* 389-405.

Everett, J. W. (1961). The mammalian female reproductive cycle and its controlling mechanisms. In *Sex and Internal Secretions* (W. C. Young, ed.), *I,* 497-555. Williams and Wilkins, Baltimore.

Everett, J. W. (1964). Central neural control of reproductive functions of the adenohypophysis. *Physiol. Rev. 44,* 373-431.

Fachini, G. (1966). "Inhibine" et structures gametogenes. *Ann. d'Endocrinol. 27,* 679-87.

Fajer, A. B., and C. A. Barraclough (1967). Ovarian secretion of progesterone and 20-α-hydroxypregn-4-en-3-one during pseudopregnancy and pregnancy in rats. *Endocrinology 81,* 617-22.

Faure, J., D. Vincent, and C. Bensch (1966). Couple habenulo-epiphysaire et regulation hypothalamique de la fonction gonadotrope chez le lapin femelle adulte. *C. R. Soc. Biol. 160,* 1557-60.

Feder, H. H., K. Brown-Grant, C. S. Corker, and D. Exley (1969). Systemic plasma progesterone levels during the pro-oestrous critical period in rats. *J. Endocrinol. 43,* xxix, (Abstract).

Fendler, K., and E. Endröczi (1965/66). Effects of hypothalamic steroid implants on compensatory ovarian hypertrophy of rats. *Neuroendocrinology 1,* 129-37.

Flerkó, B. (1962). Hypothalamic control of hypophyseal gonadotrophic function. In *Hypothalamic Control of the Anterior Pituitary* (J. Szentágothai et al., eds.), pp. 192-265. Publ. House Hung. Acad. Sci., Budapest.

Flerkó, B. (1966). Control of gonadotropin secretion in the female. In *Neuroendocrinology* (L. Martini, and W. F. Ganong, eds.), *I,* pp. 613-53. Academic Press, New York.

Flerkó, B., and J. Szentágothai (1957). Oestrogen sensitive nervous structures in the hypothalamus. *Acta Endocrinol. 26,* 121-27.

Flerkó B., B. Mess, and A. Illei-Donhoffer (1969). On the mechanism of androgen sterilization. *Neuroendocrinology*, in press.

France, E. S., and G. Pincus (1964). Biologically active substances affecting gonadotrophin-induced ovulation in immature rats. *Endocrinology 75*, 359-64.

Ganong, W. F. (1963). The central nervous system and the synthesis and release of adrenocorticotropic hormone. In *Advances in Neuroendocrinology* (A. V. Nalbandov, ed.), pp. 92-149. University of Illinois Press, Urbana.

Giuliani, G., L. Martini, A Pecile, and M. Fochi (1961). Studies on the luteinizing hormone release and inhibition. *Acta Endocrinol. (Kbh.) 38*, 1-12.

Gorski, R. A., and Barraclough, C. A. (1962). Studies on hypothalamic regulation of FSH secretion in the androgen-sterilized female rat. *Proc. Soc. Exp. Biol. Med. 110*, 298-300.

Grayburn, G. A., and K. Brown-Grant (1968). The role of oestrogen in the induction of ovulation in the gonadotrophin-treated immature rat. *J. Endocrinol. 42*, 409-16.

Greene, R. R., and D. M. Thomson (1941). Effects of estrogen on androgenic stimulation of prostate and seminal vesicle of the rat. *Endocrinology 30*, 85-88.

Greenwald, G. S. (1968). Influence of one or two ovaries on ovulation and ovarian weight in the hypophysectomized rat. *Endocrinology 82*, 591-96.

Halász, B., and R. A. Gorski (1967). Gonadotrophic hormone secretion in female rats after partial or total interruption of neural afferents to the medial basal hypothalamus. *Endocrinology 80*, 608-22.

Harris, G. W., and D. Jacobsohn (1952). Functional grafts of the anterior pituitary gland. *Proc. Roy. Soc. B 139*, 263-76.

Hashimoto, I., and R. M. Melampy (1967). Ovarian progestin secretion in various reproductive states and experimental conditions in the rat. *Fed. Proc. 26*, 485 (Abstract).

Hilliard, J., R. Penardi, and C. Sawyer (1967). A functional role for 20α-hydroxy-pregn-4-en-3-one in the rabbit. *Endocrinology 80*, 901-9.

Hohlweg, W. (1934). Veranderungen des Hypophysen-vonderlappens und des Ovariums nach behandlungen mit grossen Dosen von Follikelhormon. *Klin. Wochschr. 13*, 92-95.

Horton, R., and T. Kato (1968). Studies of testosterone-binding globulin. *3rd Int. Cong. Endocrinol., Excerpta Medica, Int. Cong. Ser. 157*, (Abstract) p. 160.

Igarashi, M., Y. Ibuki, H. Kubo, J. Kamioka, N. Yokota, Y. Ebara, and S. Matsumoto (1967). Mode and site of action of clomiphene. *Am. J. Obstet. Gynecol. 97*, 120-23.

Johnson, D. C. (1964). Effect of hypothalamic extracts on hypophyseal LH in immature male rats. *Proc. Soc. Exp. Biol. Med. 117*, 160-63.

Jouan, P., E. More, and S. Samperez (1967). Concentration de la testosterone-^{3}H par l'hypothalamus et l'hypophyseanterieure du rat castre. *Bull. Soc. Chimie Biol. 49*, 1614-15.

Junkman, N. K., and F. Neumann (1964). Zum Wirkungsmechanismus von Feten antimaskulen wirksamen Gestagenen. *Acta Endocrinol., Suppl. 90*, 139-54.

Kanematsu, S., and C. H. Sawyer (1964). Effects of hypothalamic and hypophysial estrogen implants on pituitary and plasma LH in ovariectomized rabbits. *Endocrinology 75*, 579-85.

Kanematsu, S., and C. H. Sawyer (1965). Blockade of ovulation in rabbits by hypothalamic implants of norethindrome. *Endocrinology 76*, 691-99.

Kannwischer, R., J. Wagner, and V. Critchlow (1967). Effects of intrahypothalamic estrogen implants on puberty in female rats. *Am. Assoc. Anatomists*, p. 268 (Abstract).

Katsh, S., and G. W. Duncan (1968). Pituitary gonadotropin content of aspermatogenic guinea pigs. *Proc. Soc. Exp. Biol. Med. 127*, 470-72.

Kawakami, M., and C. H. Sawyer (1967). Effects of sex hormones and antifertility steroids on brain thresholds in the rabbit. *Endocrinology 80*, 857-71.

Kendall, J. W., and C. Allen (1968). Studies on the glucocorticoid feedback control of ACTH secretion. *Endocrinology 82*, 397-405.

Kobayashi, T., T. Kigawa, M. Mizuno, and Y. Amemou (1963). Influence of rat hypothalamic extract on gonadotropic activity of cultivated anterior pituitary cells. *Endocrinol. Japon. 10*, 16-24.

Lacy, D. (1967). The seminiferous tubule in mammals. *Endeavour 26*, 101-8.

Lincoln, D. W., and B. A. Cross (1966). Effect of oestrogen on the responsiveness of neurones in the hypothalamus, septum and preoptic area of rats with light-induced persistent oestrus. *J. Endocrinol. 37*, 191-203.

Lisk, R. D. (1960). Estrogen-sensitive centers in the hypothalamus of the rat. *J. Exp. Zool. 145*, 197-208.

Lisk, R. D. (1962). Testosterone-sensitive centers in the hypothalamus of the rat. *Acta Endocrinol. (Kbh.) 41*, 195-204.

Lisk, R. D. (1965). Reproductive capacity and behavioral oestrus in the rat bearing hypothalamic implants of sex steroids. *Acta Endocrinol. (Kbh.) 48*, 209-19.

Lisk, R. D. (1967). Neural localization for androgen activation of copulatory behavior in the male rat. *Endocrinology 80*, 754-61.

Martini, L., F. Fraschini, and M. Motta (1968). Neural control of anterior pituitary functions. *Rec. Prog. Hormone Res. 24*, 439-96.

McCann, S. M. (1962a). Effect of progesterone on plasma luteinizing hormone activity. *Am. J. Physiol. 202*, 601-4.

McCann, S. M. (1962b). A hypothalamic luteinizing-hormone-releasing factor. *Am. J. Physiol. 202*, 395-400.

McCann, S. M., A. P. S. Dhariwal, and J .C. Porter (1968). Regulation of the adenohypohysis. *Ann. Rev. Physiol. 30*, 589-640.

McCormack, C. E., and R. K. Meyer (1962). Ovulating hormone release in gonadotrophin treated immature rats. *Proc. Soc. Exp. Biol. Med. 110*, 343-46.

McLaren, A. (1966). Regulation of ovulation rate after removal of one ovary in mice. *Proc. Roy. Soc. (Biol.) 166*, 316-40.

Meites, J., B. E. Piacsek, and J. C. Mittler (1966). Effects of castration and gonadal steroids on hypothalamic content of FSH-RF and LH-RF. *Proc. 2nd Int. Cong. Hormonal Steroids, Excerpta Medica, Int. Cong. Ser. 132*, 958-65.

Mercier, C., A. Alfsen, and E. Baulieu (1968). Plasma protein-binding testosterone. *3rd Int. Cong. Endocrinol., Excerpta Medica, Int. Cong. Ser. 157*, 159 (Abstract).

Mess, B., F. Fraschini, M. Motta, and L. Martini (1967). The topography of the neurons synthesizing the hypothalamic releasing factors. *Proc. 2nd Int. Cong. Hormonal Steroids, Excerpta Medica, Int. Cong. Ser. 132*, 1004-14.

Meyer, R. K., and C. E. McCormack (1967). Ovulation in immature rats treated with ovine follicle-stimulating hormone: facilitation by progesterone and inhibition by continuous light. *J. Endocrinol. 38*, 187-94.

Mittler, J., and J. Meites (1966). Effects of hypothalamic extract and androgen on pituitary FSH release *in vitro. Endocrinology 78,* 500-504.

Miyake, T. (1968). Interrelationship between the release of pituitary luteinizing hormone and the secretions of ovarian estrogen and progestin during estrous cycle of the rat. In *Integrative Mechanisms of Neuroendocrine System* (S. Itoh, ed.), pp. 139-49. Hokkaido University Medical Library Series No. 1, Hokkaido University School of Medicine.

Moore, C. R., and D. Price (1932). Gonad hormone functions, and the reciprocal influence between gonads and hypophysis with its bearing on the problem of sex hormone antagonism. *Am. J. Anat. 50,* 13-72.

Moskowska, A., and C. Kordon (1965). Controle hypothalamique de la fonction gonadotrope et variations du taux des GRF chez le rat. *Gen. Comp. Endocrinol. 5,* 596-613.

Motta, M., F. Fraschini, G. Giuliani, and L. Martini (1968). The central nervous system, estrogen and puberty. *Endocrinology 83,* 1101-7.

Neill, J. D., E. D. B. Johansson, J. K. Datta, and E. Knobil (1967). Relationship between plasma levels of luteinizing hormone and progesterone during the normal menstrual cycle. *J. Clin. Endocrinol. 27,* 1167-73.

Neumann, F., and M. Kramer (1966). Female brain differentiation of male rats as a result of early treatment with an androgen antagonist. *Proc. 2nd Int. Cong. Hormonal Steroids, Excerpta Medica, Int. Cong.* Ser. *132,* pp. 932-41.

Nolides, S., and J. Gorski (1966). Estrogen-induced synthesis of a specific uterine protein. *Proc. Nat. Acad. Sci. 56,* 230-35.

Østergaard, E., and J. Starup (1968). Occurrence and function of corpora lutea during different forms of oral contraception. *Acta Endocrinol. (Kbh.) 57,* 386-94.

Palka, Y. S., V. D. Ramirez, and C. H. Sawyer (1966). Distribution and biological effects of tritiated estradiol implanted in the hypothalamo-hypophysial region of female rats. *Endocrinology 78,* 487-99.

Parkes, A. S., and R. Deanesly (1966). The ovarian hormones. In *Marshall's Physiology of Reproduction* (A. S. Parkes, ed.), pp. 570-765. Little, Brown, Boston.

Pelletier, J. (1964). Dosage de l'hormone stimulant l'interstitielle (ICHS) dans le sang par la methode de l'acide ascorbique ovarien. *C. R. Soc. Biol. 258,* 5979-81.

Piacsek, B. E., and J. Meites (1966). Effects of castration and gonadal hormones on hypothalamic content of luteinizing hormone releasing factor (LRF). *Endocrinology 79,* 432-39.

Pincus, G. (1966). Control of conception by hormonal steroids. *Science 153,* 493-500.

Price, D., and H. G. Williams-Ashman (1961). The accessory reproductive glands of mammals. In *Sex and Internal Secretions,* (W. C. Young, ed.), *I,* 366-449. Williams and Wilkins, Baltimore.

Quinn, D. L., and M. X. Zarrow (1964). Inhibition of pregnant mare's serum-induced ovulation in the immature rat. *Endocrinology 74,* 309-13.

Ralph, C. L., and R. M. Fraps (1960). Induction of ovulation in the hen by injection of progesterone into the brain. *Endocrinology 66,* 269-72.

Ramirez, D. V., and S. M. McCann (1963). Comparison of the regulation of luteinizing hormone (LH) secretion in immature and adult rats. *Endocrinology 72,* 452-64.

Ramirez, V. D., and S. M. McCann (1965). Inhibitory effect of testosterone on luteinizing hormone secretion in immature and adult rats. *Endocrinology* 76, 412-17.

Ramirez, V. D., and C. H. Sawyer (1965). Advancement of puberty in the female rat by estrogen. *Endocrinology 76*, 1158-68.

Ramirez, V. D., R. M. Abrams, and S. M. McCann (1964). Effect of estradiol implants in the hypothalamo-hypophysial region of the rat on the secretion of luteinizing hormone. *Endocrinology 75*, 243-48.

Rennels, E. G., and W. K. O'Steen (1967). Alterations in LH and FSH content and weight of the anterior pituitary gland of immature female rats treated with PMS. *Endocrinology 80*, 82-88.

Riggs, D. S. (1963). *The Mathematical Approach to Physiological Problems.* Williams and Wilkins, Baltimore.

Roos, M., and J. Roos (1966). Mise en evidence d'un determinisme neuroendocrinien de la ponte provoquee par l'hemicastration chez la ratte. *C. R. Soc. Biol. 160*, 647-50.

Rothchild, I. (1965). Interrelations between progesterone and the ovary, pituitary, and CNS in control of ovulation and the regulation of progesterone secretion. *Vitamins and Hormones 23*, 209-327.

Sawyer, C. H. (1966). Effects of hormonal steroids on certain mechanisms in the adult brain. *Proc. 2nd Int. Cong. Hormonal Steroids, Excerpta Medica, Int. Cong. Ser. 132*, 958-65.

Schally, A. V., W. H. Carter, A. Arimura, and C. Y. Bowers (1967). Effect of purified luteinizing hormone-releasing factor on plasma and pituitary LH levels in castrated, testosterone pretreated male and female rats. *Endocrinology 81*, 1173-76.

Schwartz, N. B. (1964). Acute effects of ovariectomy on pituitary LH, uterine weight, and vaginal cornfication. *Am. J. Physiol. 207*, 1251-59.

Schwartz, N. B., and J. C. Hoffman (1966). A model for the control of the mammalian reproductive cycle. *Proc. 2nd Int. Cong. Hormonal Steroids, Excerpta Medica, Int. Cong. Ser. 132*, 837-43.

Sinha, D., and J. Meites (1965/66). Effects of thyroidectomy and thyroxine on hypothalamic content of thyrotrophin releasing factor and pituitary content of thyrotrophin in rats. *Neuroendocrinology 1*, 4-14.

Smith, E. R., and J. M. Davidson (1967a). Testicular maintenance and its inhibition in pituitary-transplanted rats. *Endocrinology 80*, 725-34.

Smith, E. R., and J. M. Davidson (1967b). Differential responses to hypothalamic testosterone in relation to male puberty. *Am. J. Physiol. 212*, 1385-90.

Smith, E. R., and J. M. Davidson (1968). Role of estrogen in the cerebral control of puberty in female rats. *Endocrinology 82*, 100-108.

Steinberger, E., and G. E. Duckett (1966). Pituitary "total" gonadotropins, FSH and LH in orchiectomized or cryptorchid rats. *Endocrinology 79*, 912-20.

Strauss, W. F., and R. K. Meyer (1962). Neural timing of ovulation in immature rats treated with gonadotrophin. *Science 137*, 860-61.

Szentágothai, J., B. Flerkó, B. Mess, and B. Halász (1968). *Hypothalamic Control of the Anterior Pituitary.* 2nd ed. Publ. House Hung. Acad. Sci., Budapest.

Taleisnik, S., J. J. Astrada, and L. Caligaris (1968). Sexual difference in the release of LH by progesterone. *Proc. 3rd Int. Cong. Endocrinol., Excerpta Medica, Int. Cong. Ser. 157*, 114 (Abstract).

Voglmayr, J. K., and P. E. Mattner (1968). Compensatory hypertrophy in the remaining testis following unilateral orchidectomy in the adult ram. *J. Reprod. Fert. 17*, 179-81.

Wagner, J. W. (1968). Luteinizing of ovarian transplants in PMS-primed immature male rats. *Am. Assoc. Anatomists*, p. 445.

Waites, G. M. H., T. W. Scott, and B. P. Setchell (1969). The testicular effluent and a comparison of testicular and ejaculated sperm. *Biol. of Reprod.*, Suppl., in press.

Wakabayashi, K., T. Ogiso, and T. Tamaoki (1968). Acute effects of androgen and estrogen on the promotion of amino acid incorporation into luteinizing hormone and protein in the anterior pituitary glands of male rats. *Endocrinology 82*, 721-30.

Westman, A., and D. Jacobsohn (1938). Endokrinologische Untersuchungen an ratten mit durchtrennten Hypophysenstiel. III Uber die luteinizierinde Wirkung des follikel Hormons. *Acta Obstet. Gynecol. Scand. 18*, 115-23.

Whalen, R. E., F. A. Beach, and R. E. Kuehn (1961). Effects of exogenous androgen on sexually responsive and unresponsive male rats. *Endocrinology 69*, 373-80.

Yates, F. E. (1967). Physiological control of adrenal cortical hormone secretion. In *The Adrenal Cortex* (A. B. Eisenstein, ed.), pp. 133-83. Little, Brown, Boston.

Zondek, B. (1935). *Die Hormone des Ovariums und des Hypophysenvorderlappens.* Springer-Verlag, Berlin.

11

Mechanism of Action
of Releasing Factors

IRVING I. GESCHWIND

Introduction

The study of the mechanism of action of hypothalamic releasing factors was the inevitable sequel to experiments whose major objectives were the purification of these same factors, and an outgrowth of a period in history when the elucidation of the intimate details of protein biosynthesis began to make possible the determination, at the molecular level, of the effects of hormones on the control of the rate of either specific or general protein synthesis. What these factors have contributed to this study has been mainly an excitement, for few, if any, of the releasing factors can be considered to be pure, and there appears to have been no need for the investigator to avail himself of the techniques for the study of subcellular protein biosynthesis. Indeed, experiments with crude and purified hypothalamic extracts ("purified" meaning having a single releasing factor activity) have, for the most part, given similar results, and an acute effect on protein synthesis has been difficult to demonstrate even with the macroscopic techniques employed.

Although the hypothalamic hypophysiotropic substances were called "releasing factors," most of the early evidence (see below) indicated a hormonogenic effect on the anterior pituitary as well, which probably should have suggested the adoption of a more appropriate nomenclature, perhaps "secretion factors." Just what is an appropriate nomenclature, however, is open to dispute. Most investigators would agree that the releasing factors do indeed promote a rapid release of hormones from the anterior pituitary, and that in chronic experiments the total amount of active hormone found is increased above control values. The immediate question is whether the latter effect is a direct consequence of releasing factor action. Attempts to answer this have been based on demonstrating a dependence of the release process on continued protein synthesis, an increased incorporation of radioactive amino acids into the hormones in acute experiments, and, by electron micrography, an effect on the protein synthetic machinery of the cell. Most of the investigative effort has been channeled to obtain the necessary experimental data to answer this question. By contrast, few investigations have been concerned with an unquestionable activity of the releasing factors, the process of release per se. It is the purpose of this review to point out what has been found in these areas, what conclusions can be drawn, and what generalizations about the process of secretion can be made.

The Secretory Process in Cells of the Anterior Pituitary

Our knowledge of the details of protein synthesis has come from biochemical studies of particulate and other subcellular fractions of many types of cells. To determine the fate of synthesized protein that is earmarked for export, studies by electron microscopy have been under- taken. From their studies on the exocrine cells of the mammalian pancreas, Palade and his colleagues (Palade *et al.*, 1962; Caro and Palade, 1964; Jamieson and Palade, 1966) formulated a scheme for the gradual packaging of the proteins as they moved through the cell, and for their release into the extracellular environment upon appropriate stimulation. Farquhar (1961) has studied these processes in cells of the anterior pituitary, and has modified Palade's scheme to account for what was observed in this gland. In a recent publication (Smith and Farquhar, 1966) she has summarized the findings for the prolactin-producing cells. The secretory proteins, as is true for all proteins, are synthesized on ribosomes, and are then transferred into the cavities of the rough-surfaced endoplasmic reticulum, from whence they are ferried, via intermediary vesicles, to the cisternae of the Golgi region. There they are condensed into small packets of secretory material which aggregate to form the mature secretory granules. These are finally discharged by a process of reverse pinocytosis (emiocytosis) which involves the coalescence of the limiting membrane of the granules with the apical cell membrane.

The kinetics of secretion granule synthesis in anterior pituitary cells has been determined by Racadot *et al.* (1965), using radioactive leucine as a label for autoradiography at the electron microscope level. Radioac- tivity first appears after 10 minutes in the endoplasmic reticulum, and by 30 minutes it is to be found in the Golgi complex. At 90 minutes the

Golgi complex no longer is labeled and radioactivity is restricted to some of the secretion granules dispersed in the cytoplasm.

A similar process, with slight modification, has been reported for the β-cells of the pancreatic islets (see, for example, the review by Lacy, 1967), so that the scheme appears to be a general one. Nevertheless, some details of the scheme, at least for some tissues, would appear to be uncertain. What has been followed, for example, is protein which is packaged in a zymogen or secretory granule, but we have no definite information on whether all exportable protein in such a cell must be so packaged. Another problem is whether discharge of granule contents can only occur after fusion of the granule membranes with the cell membrane. The possibility that fusion is a secondary event resulting from a change in membrane properties has been raised in a recent review (Schramm, 1967).

Evidence for an Effect of Releasing Factors on Protein Synthesis

Electron Microscope Studies

The detailed electron microscope observations reported by Farquhar and her colleagues have been used as a guide for a study of the action of releasing factors. Indeed, one may suppose that Smith and Farquhar's (1966) own study on the changes in the prolactin cells of lactating rats separated from suckling young, in which prolactin release is suppressed, is an example of the action of endogenous prolactin inhibiting factor (PIF). Under these circumstances there is a lag period of 10 to 12 hours during which prolactin synthesis continues and the prolactin content of the gland rises. Electron microscopy reveals that the protein synthetic and packaging apparatus (endoplasmic reticulum and Golgi complex) during this lag period is unmodified, and that there is an accumulation of mature granules. It is only after 12 hours, when synthesis of hormone is suppressed, that there is observed a rapid involution of organelles associated with protein synthesis. The excellent correlation between the assay information and the electron micrographs serves to corroborate the findings by the two techniques. It indicates that for PIF the immediate effect is on the release process, and that effects on synthesis are greatly delayed.

There is, however, a possibility that the above illustration is not an unambiguous example of PIF action, or that the conclusions drawn from it do not hold for other releasing factors. Fortunately, three separate reports have appeared, in abstract form, on the effect of growth hormone releasing factor (GRF) administration on the ultrastructure of cells of the rat anterior pituitary. In two of the experiments (Ashby et al., 1967; Clementi et al., 1967) crude sheep or rat extracts were employed as the source of the GRF, whereas in the third (Couch and Sawano, 1968) a highly purified porcine GRF was used, and in two of these studies the material was described as having been administered intracarotidly (Clementi et al., and Couch and Sawano). Couch and Sawano, who began sacrificing animals within ½ minute of completion of the injection, reported that by 2½ minutes there was a marked increase in extrusion of secretory granules from the somatotropes into the perivascular space. Neither of the other groups observed such an effect so early; Clementi et al. reported the first marked release by 15 minutes, while Ashby et al. noted the first evidence of granule depletion in the cells and repositioning of granules subjacent to the cell membrane at 30 minutes. Cytological evidence for increased protein synthesis was only observed by Clementi et al. at 30 minutes or later, when secretion of granules was no longer evident. On the other hand, Ashby et al. reported an increase in somatotrope granule content as early as 5 minutes, long before granule depletion was observed. If we ascribe the differences in the times when the releasing effects were observed to the purity of the preparations and to the presence of a growth hormone inhibiting factor (GIF) in the crude extracts, the increased granule content observed by Ashby et al. at early periods could have resulted from a rapid GIF effect, inhibiting release without immediately affecting synthesis (as with the prolactin experiments referred to above). We are then left with only the cytological observations of Clementi et al., of a slight dilatation of the endoplasmic reticulum and an enlargement of the Golgi complex at 30 minutes, as the sole evidence for increased synthesis of growth hormone. It is not possible, however, to state whether the effect on synthesis was a primary effect of the releasing factor, or whether it was secondary to the earlier release process.

Physiological and Biochemical Studies

Numerous experiments have been reported in which an effect of releasing factors on protein synthesis has apparently been demonstrated. These experiments have been of two general types: (1) those in which release and pituitary content of hormone have been measured after in vivo or in vitro administration of a releasing factor in order to determine whether the amount released, or the pituitary content alone, or the sum of the two, exceeds the amount originally present in the gland in situ, transplanted under the kidney capsule, or incubated in vitro, and (2) those in which the effect of a releasing factor on incorporation of a radioactive amino acid or monosaccharide into a pituitary hormone has been assessed.

There are also a few experiments designed to provide some generalizations about some of the actions of releasing factors without singling out specific factors or pituitary hormones. In one such study rat pituitaries were incubated for up to 2 hours in the presence of a mixture of radioactive amino acids or glutamic acid-^{14}C and either a hypothalamic or cerebral cortical extract (Grieshaber and Hymer, 1968). After the incubations in the presence of labeled glutamate, the gland protein specific activities were similar for the two types of extracts, but hypothalamic extract significantly increased the total (medium plus gland) activity per µg gland protein within 1 hour. With the amino acid mixture no significant differences were observed. It was concluded that hypothalamic extracts stimulated protein synthesis in pituitary explants and the release of the newly synthesized protein; that "the effect . . . is on a relatively small fraction of protein synthesis in the pituitary system, and when a labelled amino acid mixture is used the stimulatory effect is obscured"; and that "intracellular packaging of newly synthesized hormones into discrete populations of cytoplasmic granules may not be prerequisite to their release." It is extremely difficult to interpret these conclusions. On the one hand, we are anxious to know just what the "relatively small fraction of protein synthesis in the pituitary" that is stimulated by hypothalamic extract represents. On the other hand, if the fraction is indeed small, the data may be interpreted as meaning that the various releasing factors could not all be stimulating synthesis of their pituitary hormones. Indeed, the fraction may have nothing to do with hormones. Moreover, even if we were to admit an effect on synthesis, we would have to keep it in mind that, if the various releasing and inhibiting factors present in hypothalamic extracts have opposite effects, they might tend to cancel out each other's effects.

In still other experiments, polyribosomes were prepared and centrifuged in a gradient after a series of incubations for 90 minutes. No changes were produced by hypothalamic extract in the distribution of 260 mµ-absorbing fractions or in the specific activities in the finished protein fractions, but an increase in the relative specific activities of materials in the polysome fractions from hypothalamic extract incubates was observed. On the basis of this rather limited evidence the authors concluded that the protein-stimulating effect of hypothalamic extracts occurred at the polyribosme level (Grieshaber and Hymer, 1968).

RNA synthesis in the pituitary has also been examined, with divergent results with two different types of substrate. When rat pituitaries were incubated for 10 hours in the presence of tritiated uridine, a linear incorporation with time of radioactivity per μg DNA was found, and autoradiographs revealed that all types of cells at the periphery of the explant were labeled (Hymer and Stere, 1967). Neither incubation with hypothalamic extract nor prior injection of the extract into pituitary donors produced an uptake significantly different from that observed with extracts of the cerebral cortex. The conclusion was that hypothalamic extracts do not directly activate transcriptive processes within cells, and, therefore, the hormone specific mRNA molecules in the pituitary may be relatively long-lived. In contrast to the above, preliminary autoradiographic results obtained from addition of hypothalamic extracts to monolayer cultures of rat pituitary cells indicate a specific acceleration of RNA synthesis (Friend and Leavitt, 1967).

Corticotropin Releasing Factor (CRF): One direct experimental approach is to determine whether releasing factors can maintain or reactivate hormone synthesis in pituitary autografts beneath the kidney capsule. Critchlow *et al.* (1963) administered saline or posterior lobe CRF every 8 hours for 12 days to animals in whom autografts had just been placed, and found adrenal weights to be about 50 per cent heavier than those of controls, resting levels of plasma corticosterone to be normal (twice control) in treated animals, and the response to a challenging dose of CRF to be much greater in animals chronically treated with CRF (15.90 μg per cent corticosterone) than in those treated with saline (6.16 μg per cent). They concluded that CRF had maintained the synthesis of adrenocorticotropic hormone (ACTH) by the transplanted pituitary. Evans and Nikitovich-Winer (1965) modified the experiment so that rats which had received autografts 8 to 67 days earlier were continuously perfused into the renal artery with ovine median eminence or cerebral cortex extracts for 7 to 36 days. In 9 of 11 animals adrenal stimulation was observed 5 to 31 days after the onset of infusion of the median eminence extracts. Since autografts placed 8 to 67 days earlier contained very little hormone, the stimulation observed was considered to be evidence not only for a releasing action of the extract, but for a "tropic effect" on some other phase of pituitary function as well. It must be assumed that synthesis is one "tropic effect" that the authors had in mind.

The effects of stress, and more recently of median eminence extracts, on pituitary and circulating levels of ACTH in acute experiments, have been investigated by Vernikos-Danellis and her colleagues, and here we assume that the stress effects on the pituitary are primarily the result of increased CRF release. When normal rats are subjected to sham adrenalectomy under ether anesthesia, the pituitary ACTH concentration 4 hours later is 60 per cent of normal. If a second stress is applied at this time, circulating levels of ACTH increase to a maximum in 2½ minutes, at which time the pituitary shows a twofold increase in ACTH concentration. In rats 30 days after adrenalectomy, the resting pituitary ACTH concentration is 3 times normal, and the pituitary hormone level doubles 2½ minutes after ether stress. In rats 8 hours after adrenalectomy, the resting pituitary ACTH content is 40 per cent of normal, and it increases threefold in 2½ minutes after ether stress, while the plasma ACTH is increasing approximately 10 times (Vernikos-Danellis, 1963). The findings in all three experiments have been interpreted as indicating a rapid synthesis of ACTH during stress. The reviewer is impressed at the extreme rapidity of the considerable synthesis reported, but he also wonders whether other explanations are possible. In each of the experiments the increase in the amount of ACTH in the circulation was negligible compared to the marked increases in pituitary ACTH content. The assay of pituitary ACTH employed has sufficient selectivity that it can be considered specific for the hormone, and unaffected by the presence of other factors. However, it may be worthwhile to recall an earlier claim (Dasgupta and Young, 1958) indicating the presence in pituitary glands of a precursor molecule without biological activity, a precorticotropin, which may be activated. If such a molecule should exist, net increases in biological activity might occur rapidly in the absence of continuing protein synthesis. This possibility has been investigated (Marks and Vernikos-Danellis, 1963) by noting the effect of pretreatment with an inhibitor of protein synthesis, ethionine. This amino acid analogue produced an inhibition of ACTH release following stress within 1 hour after its injection in both intact and adrenalectomized rats, reinforcing the conclusion that synthesis of ACTH must occur.

In order to determine directly whether stress promotes increased synthesis of ACTH, studies on the uptake of serine-1-^{14}C into ACTH were undertaken (Jacobowitz et al., 1963). Ten minutes after the subcutaneous injection of the label, rats were stressed for 1 minute with ether and by sham laparotomy, and 2½ minutes later decapitated. Extracts of the anterior and posterior pituitary were subjected to paper chromatography and electrophoresis. Three spots were detected by autoradiography, with the greatest radioactivitiy in "spot 1" of the anterior pituitary. The activity of this spot doubled after stress, whereas those of the other two minor spots increased 3 to 4 times. Surprisingly, a similar "spot 1" was found in extracts of the posterior pituitary, and although its control radio-activity was 1/25th the value of the anterior pituitary "spot 1," its radioactivity increased 50 to 60 times after stress. Although the authors state that the R_f and electrophoretic mobility of "spot 1" are different from those of ovine or porcine ACTH, because of its autoradiographic prominence, because of an increased ninhydrin staining of the spot from extracts of stressed adrenalectomized animals, and because an eluate of the spot had adrenal ascorbic acid depleting activity, the authors consider it rat ACTH. They conclude, in agreement with the results of Vernikos-Danellis, that acute stress causes an increased synthesis of ACTH.

Results similar to the above were obtained by Vernikos-Danellis (1965) with rat median eminence extracts. The intracarotid injection of the equivalent of a single median eminence into a normal rat produced a fivefold increase in pituitary ACTH concentration in 1¼ minutes, while injection of 0.4 of a median eminence in adrenalectomized rats blocked with cortisol resulted in a fourfold increase in pituitary hormone concentration within 2½ minutes. In both these experiments the period of pituitary increase coincided with the period of a maximum ACTH release. The conclusion drawn from these experiments was similar to that already presented: CRF influences the synthesis of ACTH. Direct support for this conclusion has come from in vitro incorporation experiments, the details of which have been available only in an abstract (Uemura, 1968). When pituitary glands were incubated with rat hypothalamic extract, incorporation of phenylalanine into "ACTH" was increased. The "ACTH" fraction was apparently rather specific since the incorporation of phenylalanine-^{14}C into the "ACTH" was increased after adrenalectomy, whereas the incorporation of isoleucine, an amino acid not present in any known ACTH, was not changed.

Gonadotropin Releasing Factors in General. In their study of pituitary autografts Evans and Nikitovitch-Winer (1965) observed definite gonadotropic effects in animals perfused with median eminence extracts: in 4 of 11 animals vaginal estrus was observed and large follicles were found in the ovary. In another 5 animals the latter effect was also seen. If it is assumed that these effects are brought about by release of both luteinizing hormone (LH) and follicle stimulating hormones (FSH), then the appropriate releasing factors in the extracts were obviously stimulating the dormant grafts to synthesize these proteins.

A different approach has been taken by Kobayashi and his colleagues (1964, 1965) who have cultured colonies from single anterior pituitary cells or the anterior pituitary itself. Appropriate cultures released gonadotropins for a period of less than 2 weeks. When hypothalamic extract was added during the third week, elevated gonadotropin levels were found in both the cells and the medium after 1 week of treatment. Unfortunately, the assay employed, the mouse uterine weight method, is a general assay for gonadotropins and cannot be used as a specific assay for LH or FSH.

In the above experiments it could also be shown that, whereas cells treated with a hypothalamic extract showed a positive periodic acid-Schiff (PAS) reaction, control cells, when incubated with a cerebral cortical extract, were PAS-negative. Actual *de novo* synthesis of protein was followed in these cultures by measuring autoradiographically the uptake of tritiated leucine added to the cultures on the second and fourth days following the addition of the extract. In the absence of the extract, acidophiles and chromophobes showed a greater uptake than did the PAS-positive cells, but when hypothalamic extract was present the uptake of only the PAS-positive cells was accelerated. These results are somewhat surprising, for if we are dealing with a full complement of pituitary cells —basophiles, acidophiles, and chromophobes—and a crude hypothalamic extract which apparently contains all the releasing factors and PIF, it is difficult to understand why only the PAS-positive cells were affected by the extract. One should also note that only *uptake* was measured. This should not be equated with protein synthesis, and especially not the synthesis of any particular protein.

In contrast to the above, a few experiments have been carried out in which LH and FSH were separately determined; these experiments can be considered specific for luteinizing hormone releasing factor (LRF) and follicle stimulating hormone releasing factor (FSHRF).

LRF. One line of evidence in favor of an effect of LRF on LH synthesis derives from studies carried out on pituitary and plasma LH levels in the cyclic rat (Schwartz and Bartosik, 1962; Ramirez and McCann, 1964; Schwartz and Caldarelli, 1965), in which it was found that pituitary LH levels on the afternoon of proestrus are little changed from those on the morning of proestrus, although plasma LH levels are higher in the afternoon than they are in the morning of proestrus. The apparent maintenance of pituitary levels in the face of elevated plasma levels led Schwartz and Caldarelli (1965) to conclude that "when rapid LH release starts at 2 P.M. of proestrus, synthesis is speeded up to the same extent; only after 4 P.M. does release continue in the absence of matching synthesis." However, it can be simply calculated from the total increment in plasma LH level (approximately 100 mμg/ml; Ramirez and McCann,

1964), and the half-life (30 minutes) and distribution volume (3 per cent of body weight) of rat LH (Gay and Bogdanove, 1968), that an increase in secretion rate of less than 900 mμg/hour for the 2-hour period from 2 to 4 in the afternoon would allow the plasma LH levels to attain the observed maximum in a 200-g rat, while decreasing pituitary LH content by less than 1.8 μg. This amount is probably insufficient to have been detected as a significant depletion. Therefore there would be no need to postulate any increase in synthesis during these two hours. Continued secretion at this rate would not further increase the plasma concentration of LH materially, but a decrease in pituitary LH content would become evident.

A more direct approach was to study the effect of purified LRF on LH synthesis by monolayer cultures of rat anterior pituitary gland (Cohen et al., 1966) by first depleting nearly all of the LH present by incubating the cultures for 1 hour with LRF, and, after the cells were washed, to reincubate them with and without additional LRF. Bioassays indicated that cells reincubated with LRF accumulated about twice as much LH as did controls in 2 to 4 hours, which suggested that LRF can stimulate LH synthesis in vitro. Unfortunately, the statistical significance of the differences reported is open to question.

A similar conclusion to that drawn by Cohen et al. was arrived at by Jutisz and his colleagues (Jutisz et al., 1967) as a result of experiments designed to demonstrate a dose-response relationship between a purified LRF and the LH released during a 2-hour incubation. The pituitary donors were rats which had been ovariectomized at 30 days of age and given a single injection of 25 μg estradiol benzoate and 12.5 mg progesterone 4 to 8 weeks later. Three days after the injection the pituitaries were removed and incubated with varying doses of LRF, and the LH release during the incubation determined by bioassay. The maximum release rate found, approximately 5 μg/mg pituitary, was just about double the bioassayable LH concentration of 2.7 μg/mg in nonincubated pituitaries.

These results would seem to indicate that synthesis of LH must have occurred, if a process akin to the activation process referred to above had not taken place. If synthesis is stimulated, it should be possible to demonstrate it directly by measuring the incorporation of a radioactive amino acid or appropriate monosaccharide into the glycoprotein LH under these incubation conditions. What is required is a simple method for the isolation of the small quantities of LH present. This has been accomplished by employing a specific and selective antiserum to precipitate the LH as part of an antigen-antibody complex (Wakabayashi and Tamaoki, 1965; Samli and Geschwind, 1967). When rat pituitaries from ovariectomized rats, some of which had been treated 3 days previously with a single injection of 50 μg estradiol benzoate plus 25 mg progesterone, were incubated for 4 hours in the presence of hypothalamic extract and L-leucine-^{14}C or D-glucosamine-^{14}C, incorporation of the label per mg pituitary was not different from that found in control incubations (Samli and Geschwind, 1967). Simultaneous determination of LH release revealed a definite enhancement by the extract even at much lower concentrations than used for the incorporation experiments. In contrast to the results of Jutisz et al. (1967), referred to above, in none of the experiments in which animals had been pretreated with estradiol and progesterone did the amount of LH released in 4 hours exceed 30 per cent of that present initially in the pituitary. However, animals of a different age were employed, and the dose of extract may not have been optimal. In experiments in which normal pituitaries were incubated for 24 hours with extract and label, only a suggestive effect on synthesis was found.

These results were interpreted as indicating the absence of a direct effect of LRF on LH biosynthesis either at the level of peptide bond formation or of saccharide attachment to the completed polypeptide chain. The validity of the interpretation depends upon a number of factors: the adequacy of the antiserum, the normalcy of the incubated half-pituitaries, the provision of an environment capable of supporting maximum protein synthesis, and intracellular pools of free amino acids whose sizes are not altered by the extract. Given these, it should be possible to obtain a direct measure of synthesis that avoids the problem of activation. The technique for this should also allow resolution of possible effects on peptide synthesis and possible effects on addition of carbohydrate to the glycoprotein. Moreover, when coupled with specific immunoassays or bioassays, and with inhibitors of peptide bond formation (see below), the problem of activation itself can be attacked.

FSHRF. In a study of the kinetics of FSH release and synthesis following treatment of rats with rat stalk-median eminence extracts (Corbin and Story, 1966), it was found that maximum depletion of about 50 per cent of the pituitary FSH content occurred 45 minutes after the injection, as measured by the Steelman-Pohley assay. Restoration of the original FSH level occurred over a 4-hour period, and a rate of resynthesis of 15 μg of FSH (S-1 equivalent) per hour per mg pituitary was calculated. In experiments such as the above, however, at least three additional questions should be answered before we can consider them relevant to the problems at hand. First, is pituitary depletion always to be equated with release? This interpretation has been rather universally accepted, but in light of the findings that lysosomes in anterior pituitary cells incorporate and degrade secretory granules—a regulatory disposal mechanism for overproduced secretory products (Smith and Farquhar, 1966)—evidence of an increased amount of the hormone in the extracellular environment should be presented. Second, a question asked above, is an increase in content or restoration of a hormone level in the pituitary to be equated with synthesis? Third, does restoration occur, and if so, is it at the same rate, when depletion is promoted by some other means, e.g. by high $[K^+]$ in in vitro experiments? The answer to the last question may allow us to decide between the alternatives of primary and secondary effects of a releasing factor on protein synthesis.

More definite evidence of FSH synthesis was obtained from 4-hour incubations of pituitary glands obtained from ovariectomized rats which had been pretreated with estradiol and progesterone (Jutisz and de la Llosa, 1967). At the end of the incubation period the sum of the bioassayable FSH in the medium and pituitary from experiments in which FSHRF was added was greater by about 40 per cent than that found for control incubations; the sum in the latter was equal to the pituitary FSH content of the nonincubated pituitary.

Thyrotropin Releasing Factor (TRF). In the experiments with renal pituitary autografts mentioned above (Evans and Nikitovitch-Winer, 1965), stimulation of the thyroid was observed in 9 of the 11 rats perfused with extracts of the median eminence, and so the conclusions drawn with respect to CRF and gonadotropin releasing factors apply to TRF as well. Another type of in vivo experiment is that reported by Bowers *et al.* (1967), who labeled the thyroid glands of mice with [131]I 24 hours prior to administering a purified porcine TRF, and then followed ^{131}I release from the thyroid—as a reflection of thyrotropin (TSH) released—and pituitary TSH content. Injection of large doses of TRF led to an increase in blood ^{131}I levels without any change in pituitary TSH levels, leading to the suggestion that TRF produces an increased rate of synthesis of TSH as well as release. However, it is doubtful that the small changes in pituitary TSH content resulting from increased release in these experiments can be accurately measured.

Organ culture experiments have also demonstrated an apparent TRF effect on synthesis (Sinha and Meites, 1966; Mittler and Redding, 1968). In these experiments, rat pituitaries were incubated for 4 to 9 days and hypothalamic extract or purified TRF was added for the last 3 to 6 days.

When the media and pituitary explants were assayed for TSH, the total amount found exceeded both the total of control incubations and the original TSH contents of the pituitaries. In the experiments of Sinha and Meites, at the end of 6 days with hypothalamic extract 50 to 97 per cent more TSH was recovered from the media and explants than was initially contained in the fresh pituitary.

Finally, data bearing more directly on the question have come from two groups of investigators who have measured incorporation of radioactive amino acids into "TSH" in the presence of either hypothalamic extract or purified TRF, and have arrived at diametrically opposite conclusions. In the first experiment (Solomon and McKenzie, 1964) the extract was added during the third hour of incubation of the pituitary, and it not only produced an increased content of TSH in the medium, but also promoted the incorporation of label into a large molecular weight component of the medium which was excluded from Sephadex G-25, and which on Sephadex G-100 had a "distribution coefficient identical with TSH." The latter was apparently the only way the material was identified, and it seems highly improbable that even if TSH were present in the fraction from Sephadex G-100 that it was a homogeneous component. Certainly the three glycoprotein hormones of the anterior pituitary will behave similarly on Sephadex G-100, as will dimers of growth hormone and of prolactin, and undoubtedly other nonhormonal proteins of the pituitary. A later experiment made use of an antibody to TSH for the isolation of the hormone as part of an antibody-antigen complex (Wilber and Utiger, 1968b). Although release was stimulated by addition of TRF to the culture, no change in the incorporation of either L-leucine-^{14}C or D-glucosamine-^{14}C into TSH was observed after either 4 or 24 hours of incubation. These results are similar to those found for LRF by Samli and Geschwind (1967).

GRF. To this reviewer's knowledge no studies of the effect of median eminence extracts or of GRF on the maintenance or stimulation of growth hormone (GH) release from transplanted pituitaries have been reported. Other types of approaches, similar to those already outlined for other releasing factors, have been utilized, in addition to the aforementioned electron microscope studies.

Analysis of the restoration of rat pituitary GH levels after depletion induced by rat hypothalamic extract (Müller and Pecile, 1966) demonstrated complete repletion in less than 5 hours. The questions raised in reference to the similar studies of Corbin and Story (1966) on FSHRF are equally pertinent here. The first question, that of equating depletion with release, is an even more serious one in this context, since factors other than GH affect the tibia test used for the bioassay of GH (Geschwind and Li, 1955), and since it has not been possible to demonstrate unequivocally a GRF action in rats using radioimmunoassay techniques (see, for example, Garcia and Geschwind, 1968).

Evidence for an effect of GRF on GH synthesis was first reported in experiments in which rat pituitaries were cultured with hypothalamic extract for 6 days (Deuben and Meites, 1964); 4 to 6 times more GH was found in the medium than was found in control experiments (no additions or addition of cerebral cortex extracts). Since in separate control experiments it was demonstrated that about 80 per cent of the hormone originally present in the gland was released in the first 6 days of culture, it would seem that at least 3 to 5 times more GH than was originally present in the gland must have been released under the influence of the hypothalamic extract. One report of pituitary incubations carried out for only 4½ to 5 hours (Symchowicz et al., 1966), and purporting to demonstrate stimulation of GH synthesis, is not so convincing. One series of incubations for 4½ hours with a crude porcine hypothalamic extract failed to yield evidence for an effect on hormone release at any dose level, yet at all dose levels there was a similar increase in pituitary GH content. In a second series of incubations for 5 hours, an irregular increase in the GH content of the incubation medium was found. Apparently no control experiments using extracts of other parts of the brain were undertaken. A more satisfactory series of experiments has involved incubations of rat pituitaries for 6 or 24 hours in the presence of a purified porcine GRF (Schally et al., 1968). Incubation of the pituitaries of normal, unmanipulated animals with GRF failed to reveal an effect on GH synthesis. However, if the pituitary donor had first been exposed to a temperature of 4°C for 60 to 75 minutes, to deplete the pituitary GH, GRF was capable of increasing pituitary GH content by 250 to 400 per cent at the same time that it promoted release of the hormone into the medium. This led the investigators to suggest that the same substance increased synthesis and release. A report that would appear to be somewhat in conflict with the above has been published by Krulich et al. (1967). When normal rat pituitaries were incubated for 5 hours in control experiments, it was found that the decrease in pituitary GH could be completely accounted for by the increase in GH in the medium. When GRF was added, release of GH was stimulated and the decrease in pituitary GH content was prevented, so that the total amount of GH in the system exceeded control (or initial) values. These same experimenters have also provided data showing that experiments on GH release or synthesis in which crude hypothalamic or median eminence extracts are employed must be interpreted with caution, for a fraction which inhibited GH release (GIF) could be obtained upon fractionation of crude extracts. Although this fraction by itself did not affect pituitary GH content, it diminished or abolished the effect of GRF on both release and pituitary content when administered together with GRF. The investigators concluded that while GRF stimulates both release and synthesis of GH, GIF opposes both actions. What is disturbing in the three reports just referred to is the lack of consistency—no effect on release in one, and no effect on synthesis in the unmanipulated animal in a second.

One study has also been reported in which the investigators made use of labeled amino acids (MacLeod and Abad, 1968). Rather than using an immunoprecipitation technique to purify the GH, these authors first purified the pituitary homogenates and media on Sephadex G-10 and then electrophoresed the fractions on a gel. After staining the gel, the absorbance of the bands was determined and the individual bands were counted. In incubations of 3 to 21 hours in the presence of one of three different radioactive amino acids, stalk-median eminence extracts were found not to alter the incorporation of the label into the GH band, or the retention of the radioactive GH by the incubated pituitary.

PIF. It has been reported (Nicoll and Meites, 1962) that the rat pituitary in organ culture in the absence of hypothalamic extract releases an amount of prolactin which in a single day far exceeds that initially present in the pituitary. This suggests that PIF inhibits prolactin synthesis as well as release. However, the conclusion is debatable since in the case of this hormone a prohormone has been postulated (Carlisle, 1957). The reviewer is aware of only a single study in which useful data are presented with respect to an effect of PIF on prolactin synthesis: the abstract of MacLeod and Abad (1968). Incorporation of amino acids into prolactin occurred at the same rate as into GH, but prolactin differed from GH in that the labeled hormone was predominantly released into the medium, rather than being stored in the gland. When extracts were added, neither the incorporation rate nor the distribution of prolactin was changed. Thus, no effect on synthesis was seen.

Studies with Antibiotics

For a number of years several antibiotics have been used as specific inhibitors of either DNA-dependent RNA synthesis (e.g. actinomycin D) or of peptide bond synthesis (e.g. puromycin and cycloheximide). Although their specificities have frequently been questioned, they have been extensively employed in studies of the mechanism of hormone action. Of late, the reports of their use frequently carry caveats indicating that the investigator is, and the reader should be, aware that the effects found may not be the result of an inhibition of RNA or peptide bond synthesis but may result from some other unknown function of the antibiotic. In releasing factor studies the antibiotics have been mainly employed to determine whether the release process per se is dependent upon *de novo* protein synthesis, and whether release of a given hormone is dependent upon continued hormone synthesis.

Answers to the first question have been offered by a number of investigators for other systems in which secretion occurs. For example, nondependence of secretion of chymotrypsinogen, parotid amylase, epinephrine, thyroid hormones, and HCl on protein synthesis has been demonstrated after inhibition of protein synthesis by puromycin and cycloheximide (Bauduin *et al.,* 1967). Answers to the second question for a number of secreted proteins or polypeptides other than those of the anterior pituitary are also available. The secretion of specific antibody by isolated lymph node cells following treatment with puromycin was found to be not completely independent of protein synthesis (Helmreich *et al.,* 1962). Insulin release in vitro in response to glucose was not inhibited by 3.4×10^{-4} M puromycin (Coore and Randle, 1964). According to one group of investigators, although not confirmed by others, 5×10^{-4} M dinitrophenol failed to inhibit insulin release (Grodsky and Bennett, 1963). This dose inhibited incorporation of radioactive valine into proteins. A priori, continued protein hormone synthesis may be required for secretion when the available intracellular pool of hormone is quite small.

CRF. In their studies on the effects of stress on the synthesis of ACTH, Marks and Vernikos-Danellis (1963) found that the increase in blood ACTH 2½ minutes after stress was prevented by administration 1 hour earlier of 50 mg of ethionine (an analogue of methionine and an inhibitor of RNA and protein synthesis). In a subsequent report (Vernikos-Danellis, 1964) a similar inhibition was produced by 25 μg actinomycin D administered ½ hour before imposition of the stress. The author's conclusion was that synthesis of new hormone is essential for the reponse of the pituitary to stress (and presumably to CRF). Another conclusion, incidentally, is that some type of new or continuing RNA synthesis is ultimately required for the release of ACTH to occur. A somewhat similar experiment with different time relationships has been carried out by Estep *et al.* (1967). Rats were treated with 30 mg puromycin intravenously 2 minutes prior to, and 40 to 50 minutes after, laparotomy, and pituitary ACTH content and the incorporation of valine-^{14}C into pituitary protein were determined. In the control groups ^{14}C incorporation increased linearly with time, whereas in the puromycin group incorporation was less than 10 per cent of control values at all times. Two hours after the laparotomy the differing rates of incorporation were reflected in the pituitary ACTH contents, which were about 50 per cent of the control value in the puromycin group. Despite this, the plasma ACTH level and half-life in the latter group were the same as in the former. In these experiments, in which the response to stress was investigated after 2 hours, rather than after 2½ minutes, and in which a different inhibitor from those used by Vernikos-Danellis was employed, it appeared that ACTH could be released for an extended period of time even when continuing synthesis of hormone was largely prevented.

LRF.   When pituitaries from castrated rats which had been injected with 25 µg estradiol benzoate and 12.5 mg progesterone 3 days earlier were incubated for 2 hours in the presence of 2×10^{-4} M puromycin, the incorporation of ^{14}C-amino acids was reduced to about 5 per cent of the control value. Incubation with 10 µg of actinomycin D per ml caused 84 per cent inhibition of tritiated guanosine incorporation into RNA (Jutisz *et al.*, 1966). In the presence of a purified LRF and puromycin the amount of LH released into the medium was only 46 per cent of that found with LRF alone. This reduction was statistically significant. The amount of LH released in the presence of LRF and puromycin was significantly greater than that released in the absence of both. Actinomycin D, however, did not significantly affect the LRF-induced release of LH. Since the puromycin inhibition of LH release was incomplete, while the inhibition of protein synthesis was virtually complete, the authors concluded that LRF must act on the step where carbohydrate is added to the polypeptide—either on the synthesis of the carbohydrate moiety or on its attachment to the polypeptide chain. Puromycin would not be expected to affect either of these processes, so that preformed polypeptide chains might still have carbohydrate attached to them to render them biologically active. However, no replacements could be synthesized as these would be used up, and a partial inhibition of release would be detected. Furthermore, since LRF continued to show an effect, albeit diminished, even in the presence of puromycin, the effect of LRF could not have been on the synthesis of peptide bonds. The failure of actinomycin D to affect release was interpreted as reflecting the adequacy of the levels and the long life of mRNA, sufficient to allow LH synthesis for the 2-hour incubation period.

As noted earlier, no effect of LRF on the incorporation of either leucine or glucosamine could be demonstrated when we used, in some of the experiments, the same type of pituitary donor as Jutisz *et al.* employed for their inhibitor studies (Samli and Geschwind, 1967). Moreover, under incubation conditions with 4×10^{-4} M puromycin in which 94 per cent of the incorporation of leucine-^{14}C into pituitary LH was prevented, no significant effect of the inhibitor on either basal or LRF-induced release was noted (Samli and Geschwind, 1967). In addition, neither basal nor LRF-induced release was affected by 1 or 2×10^{-4} M dinitrophenol, which inhibited incorporation of leucine-^{14}C into LH by 61 and 74 per cent, respectively (Samli and Geschwind, 1968). The failure of puromycin or actinomycin D, in doses which produce 92 per cent inhibition of protein synthesis and 73 per cent inhibition of RNA synthesis, to affect either basal or LRF-induced release of LH has also been reported for normal pituitaries incubated for 6 hours (Crighton *et al.,* 1968).

FSHRF.   In experiments in which the treatment of the pituitary donors, the incubation conditions, and the concentrations of inhibitors were identical to those referred to above for the study of LRF action (Jutisz *et al.,* 1966), the mechanism of FSHRF action has also been investigated (Jutisz and de la Llosa, 1967). Puromycin decreased FSH release in response to ovine FSHRF by 39 per cent, while actinomycin D decreased it by 21 per cent. In addition, both produced a significant decrease in pituitary FSH content of about 30 per cent when FSHRF was present in the incubation medium. According to the authors, the partial inhibitions of release observed here, similar to effects reported by the same investigators for LRF, cannot be simply explained. Presumably the postulated effect on carbohydrate attachment had lost some attractiveness to them, for the same arguments applied in that case could apply here as well. The decrease in pituitary FSH content in the presence of the inhibitors and FSHRF was taken to be an indication that, in the absence of the inhibitor, FSH was being synthesized during the incubation period.

Although they found "no block" of FSH release in response to porcine FSHRF when pituitaries from similar donors were incubated in the presence of only 2 µg/ml actinomycin D, Schally *et al.* (1967) state that their results and those of Jutisz and de la Llosa are "not necessarily at variance" because of the dose differences and because "we did not attempt to quantitate partial inhibition." In separate experiments the same authors treated castrate rats, which had been pretreated with testosterone, with 100 μg of actinomycin D per 100 g body weight 24 hours before sacrifice. Depletion of pituitary FSH measured 20 minutes after the intracarotid administration of FSHRF was found not to have been affected by treatment with the antibiotic. It should be pointed out that no data were given to indicate the effectiveness of the low dose of actinomycin used in the in vitro experiments in inhibiting pituitary RNA synthesis nor of the effectiveness 24 hours after administration of the dose used in the in vivo experiments.

In the experiments of Watanabe *et al.* (1968) a *tenfold* greater concentration of actinomycin, 20 μg/ml, inhibited RNA synthesis approximately 73 per cent, and a dose of 5 μg/ml had no effect on hypothalamic extract-induced FSH release. These pituitary incubations lasted 6 hours. Under conditions where at least 93 per cent of protein synthesis or 73 per cent of RNA synthesis was inhibited, and where the basal release of FSH was unaffected, the quantity of FSH released in response to a hypothalamic extract was reduced to that found in control incubations with cerebral cortical extract in the absence of any antibiotic. Both antibiotics seemed to behave in an "all-or-none" fashion, for 5 μg/ml of either was ineffective, and no dose-response relationship could be detected for effective doses of 10 to 100 μg/ml of puromycin or 10 to 40 μg/ml of actinomycin. Jutisz and de la Llosa (1967) found that similar quantities of these two antibiotics produced significant decreases in pituitary FSH content when FSHRF was present, but Watanabe *et al.* failed to observe any effect of either antibiotic on FSH content in the presence or absence of hypothalamic extract.

TRF. The effect of puromycin and actinomycin D on TRF action has been examined both in in vivo experiments in mice and in in vitro experiments with rat pituitaries, and all authors are in agreement: neither antibiotic has any effect on TSH release. In the experiments of Schally and Redding (1967) neither pretreatment of pituitary donor rats with large doses of actinomycin D (200 μg per 100 g body weight) 3 hours prior to pituitary removal, nor addition of 1 to 10 μg/ml of the antibiotic to the incubation medium, nor combined in vivo and in vitro treatments, affected the TRF-induced TSH release. Actinomycin D in concentrations up to 50 μg/ml failed to affect TRF-stimulated TSH release from incubated rat pituitaries in the experiments of Vale *et al.* (1968). An inhibitor of peptide bond synthesis, cycloheximide, was also without effect at concentrations of 100 μg/ml. This dose produced 96 per cent inhibition of radioactive leucine incorporation in their experiments. Cycloheximide was also without effect in the experiments of Wilber and Utiger (1968a), in which TSH release was determined by a radioimmunoassay. In mice, neither 1.5 mg puromycin (Bowers *et al.,* 1968a) nor as much as 20 µg actinomycin D (Bowers *et al.,* 1968b) produced any significant change in the in vivo release of TSH in response to exogenous porcine TRF. In the latter experiment 20 µg inhibited tritiated uridine incorporation into pituitary RNA by 50 per cent without affecting leucine-^{14}C incorporation into pituitary protein.

GRF.   There is only one report on the effects of any antibiotic on GRF action (Schally *et al.,* 1968). Administration of 100 µg actinomycin D per 100 g body weight to pituitary donor rats 3 hours before pituitary removal did not appear to prevent increased release of GH, but incubation of pituitaries with 1 µg/ml actinomycin D successfully prevented the increased release of GH into the medium in the presence of a purified porcine GRF.

Section Summary

The evidence that increased "synthesis," as measured by an increase in total bioassayable hormone, occurs after in vivo or in vitro administration of releasing factors appears overwhelming. On the other hand, when direct measurement of radioactive amino acid incorporation into the protein hormone has been carried out in in vitro experiments, no effect of hypothalamic extracts or purified releasing factor has been observed in three reports for LRF, TRF, and GRF. In one in vivo experiment, the claim has been made that stress enhances incorporation of label into "ACTH" within 2½ minutes of its application, and in one in vitro experiment the incorporation of a radioactive amino acid into "ACTH" was reported to be enhanced by rat hypothalamic extract. Since some of the conditions under which in vitro experiments were carried out were the same for "total hormone content" and the negative "incorporation" studies, no simple answer to the lack of agreement is forthcoming. The results of the "total hormone content" experiments of various investigators are not in agreement, particularly with GRF. However, experiments on this particular releasing factor may present special problems due to the possible presence of GIF in crude extracts. They also suffer from the fact that evidence for true synthesis has generally not been reported, and it is possible that other alternatives could explain some of the effects observed. In the case of the "incorporation" experiments, there are only single reports for any given releasing factor. Emphasis has been placed on the discrepancy between results obtained in in vitro experiments for the two types of studies, for here a direct comparison can be made, and one cannot fall back on the argument that in vitro systems are inadequate for duplicating in vivo conditions, effects, and results. This argument, of course, can be raised in comparing the in vivo "total hormone content" data and the in vitro "incorporation" data.

Almost all active investigators of this problem fall into one of two classes: those who believe that releasing factors directly affect both release and synthesis, and those who favor the view that synthesis is a secondary consequence of some other process, usually secretion itself, which is stimulated by the releasing factors. This latter view was first advanced by Samli and Geschwind (1967) for LRF action, and by Jutisz and de la Llosa (1967, 1968) for FSHRF action. It does not require that release occur in order for synthesis to take place, but rather that release stimulate an ongoing process to greater production. In practice it is possible at times to produce selective effects on either synthesis or release (Samli and Geschwind, 1968; Grodsky and Bennett, 1966). No one has suggested that there are discrete releasing and synthesis-stimulating factors, nor that releasing factors for different hormones behave differently. Those who believe in a duality of action simply point to the preponderance of evidence reviewed above as sufficient support for their views. For the others, support comes mainly from the negative incorporation experiments, and from the experiments of Nicoll and Meites (1962), which, although of the "total hormone content" type, indicate that cells releasing prolactin maximally in the absence of hypothalamic intervention also synthesize rapidly. These facts are clearly consistent with a secondary response of synthesis to the release process, although they are consistent with other hypotheses as well. No direct evidence favoring a secondary response has been demonstrated, and the question may be asked why increased incorporation has not been found following stimulation of release by either releasing factors or high concentration of potassium ($[K^+]$; see below) in incubations lasting at least 24 hours. Mechanisms in which the secretion process acts to stimulate protein synthesis are not new, having previously been advanced for the exocrine pancreas on the basis of studies on stimulation of enzyme release with parasympathomimetic drugs (Junqueira et al., 1958; Junqueira, 1965).

The experiments recounted indicate that continued or *de novo* protein or RNA synthesis is not required for LRF- and TRF-stimulated release, and other examples of normal release in the presence of blocked protein synthesis suggest that this may be generally true. However, for the promotion of FSH release by FSHRF, a partial or complete inhibition of release is indicated when protein or RNA synthesis is inhibited. One single report claims this to be true also for GH release, while the reports for CRF action (resulting from stress) are not consistent. If we restrict our discussion to FSHRF, we may ask just what sort of protein must be synthesized. An obvious candidate is FSH itself, and no incorporation studies have been done which might eliminate this possibility. Hormone synthesis may be required for release if the pool of hormone is not large, but, from the data of Watanabe *et al.* (1968) for FSH, this does not appear to be the case; over the 6 hour incubation period in their studies probably less than one-third the FSH originally present was released. It is possible that all of the FSH present is not part of a readily releasable pool, a situation postulated for vasopressin in the posterior lobe (Sachs *et al.,* 1967). Another possibility is that protein synthesis may be required for the release process per se, although it is difficult to imagine what is unique about FSH release which makes it different from that of LH or TSH, for example. The suggestion has been made that the protein whose synthesis is required may affect lysis of the FSH storage granules in the cytoplasm or that it may "promote transport of FSH across the cell membrane" (Watanabe *et al.,* 1968).

Finally, the problem of activation deserves comment. Older evidence, referred to above (Carlisle, 1957; Dasgupta and Young, 1958), suggested the possibility that hormones exist in the anterior pituitary in an inactive form that is capable of being activated, and it has been pointed out that a proper combination of assays, measurement of incorporation of radioactive amino acids, and judicious use of antibiotics can be used to cast light on this problem. Recently, the whole concept of prohormones has been brought to the fore again by the finding that vasopressin appears to be synthesized as part of a biologically inactive precursor molecule (Sachs *et al.,* 1967), and by the isolation of a proinsulin (Steiner *et al.,* 1967; Chance *et al.,* 1968). The possibility that releasing factors may act directly or indirectly in activating a pituitary prohormone was suggested by Samli and Geschwind (1967), and was implicit in the earlier suggestion of Jutisz and his colleagues (1966). In this latter instance the polypeptide chain of a glycoprotein to which the carbohydrate has as yet not been added can be considered an inactive precursor; one need not always imagine the classical type of activation which is found in the transformation of chymotrypsinogen to chymotrypsin or presumably, proinsulin to insulin, in which peptide bond cleavage occurs. However, at a time when it was still hoped that all releasing factors might act in a similar fashion, a specific effect on the attachment of carbohydrate to the polypeptide chain had to be restricted to the glycoproteins, and could not apply to GH or ACTH, for example.

Energy Requirements for the Release Process

The energy requirements for protein release have been extensively investigated. One of the first systems examined was the secretion of amylase by the pigeon pancreas in vitro (Hokin, 1951). In this system, release was completely inhibited by the presence of 1×10^{-4} M dinitrophenol (DNP), 1×10^{-4} M CN^- and by anaerobiosis, and 60 per cent inhibited at 1×10^{-5} M concentrations of the inhibitors. Analogous findings were reported (Bdolah et al., 1964) for epinephrine-induced and high [K^+]-induced amylase and deoxyribonuclease secretion by slices of rat parotid gland, but both 1×10^{-3} M N-ethylmaleimide and iodoacetate were without effect. In a recent review on secretion (Schramm, 1967), this dependence of protein release on energy has been considered virtually absolute, and it is stated that one of the "characteristics of the process of protein secretion" is that "energy is essential and most systems are dependent on its supply by oxidative phosphorylation." Certainly, most findings with hormones are consistent with this view. The release of insulin in response to a glucose load was found to be inhibited by 2.5×10^{-4} M DNP (Coore and Randle, 1964) and by 3×10^{-4} M DNP, and 1×10^{-3} M CN^- (Malaisse et al., 1967a), although, as indicated earlier, Grodsky and Bennett (1963) did not observe this inhibition with 5×10^{-4} M DNP.

Vasopressin release has also been examined for its energy dependence (Douglas et al., 1965). The release induced by high [K^+] was found to be inhibited by 5×10^{-4} M DNP, 1×10^{-2} M CN^-, 3×10^{-3} M iodocetate, 2×10^{-3} M amytal, and 7.2×10^{-3} M antimycin A, but cold-induced release was not blocked by DNP. p-Chloromercuribenzoate at 2.5 and 5×10^{-4} M, and N-ethylmaleimide at 1 and 2×10^{-2} M stimulated release by themselves, even in the absence of Ca^{++}. Both of these compounds are sulfhydryl-blocking reagents, as is iodoacetate under appropriate conditions, and they may simply have made the cells "leaky." Neither high [K^+] nor electrical stimulation induce vasopressin discharge in the absence of Ca^{++} (see below).

Since this survey appears to suggest that there is an energy requirement for protein release, we may inquire at what step in the release process the energy is required. If continued or *de novo* protein synthesis were a requirement for release, then the energy would be needed for that synthesis. In the case of insulin, at least, experiments with puromycin (Coore and Randall, 1964) rule out a dependence on synthesis. Another possibility is that ATP is required for $3',5'$-cyclic AMP formation. Cyclic AMP has been implicated in amylase release from parotid slices (Bdolah and Schramm, 1965) since enzyme release is promoted by 1 to 2 mM O',N-dibutyryl cyclic AMP and by 1 to 10 mM theophylline, an inhibitor of the phosphodiesterase which hydrolyzes the nucleotide. Epinephrine, which stimulates amylase secretion, produces a fourfold increase in the concentration of cyclic AMP in the slices (Rasmussen and Tenenhouse, 1968). Cyclic AMP and theophylline have also been found to stimulate insulin release. Theophylline injected intravenously into a fasted adrenalectomized rat at a dose of 15 mg produced an increased release of insulin which could be detected within 1 minute, and which at its peak was some 10 times greater than the baseline value (Turtle et al., 1967). In studies in vitro, insulin release from rat pancreas was increased by either 1.4 mM theophylline or 7.6 mM cyclic AMP (Malaisse et al., 1967b). A generalized theory of cyclic AMP action on membranes has recently been offered by Rasmussen and Tenenhouse (1968), and the possibility exists that cyclic AMP may be the mediator for releasing factor action. However, the hypothesis that the energy requirement for release simply involves the utilization of ATP as a substrate for cyclic AMP formation has been ruled out by the finding that DNP blocks the theophylline and O',N-dibutyryl cyclic AMP effects on amylase release (Bdolah and Schramm, 1965). It is possible that either the transport of the secretory granule to the cell membrane or the fusion of the two membranes requires some energy dependent steps.

Do the actions of releasing factors on the pituitary show a dependence on energy, and does cyclic AMP play a part in the release process? In their study of the mechanism of action of LRF, Samli and Geschwind (1968) studied the effects of certain inhibitors of energy transfer on LH release. Media containing 1×10^{-3} M CN$^-$, and 1 to 2×10^{-4} M DNP did not affect release of LH in the presence of hypothalamic extract. At higher concentrations (1×10^{-2} M CN$^-$ and 5×10^{-4} M DNP, as well as 1×10^{-3} M arsenate) large amounts of LH were released into the medium even in control experiments, probably as a result of cell death or of markedly altered membrane permeability. The antibiotic oligomycin, at a concentration of 2×10^{-7} M, partially inhibited the LH response to hypothalamic extract. At 1, 2 and 4×10^{-6} M, the release, with or without extract, was greater than control release, and at concentrations greater than 4×10^{-6} M, LH release occurred in large amounts irrespective of whether the extract was present or not. This inhibitor routinely produced pituitaries which appeared swollen at the end of the incubation. In these studies protein synthesis was also measured as an index of the inhibition of energy transfer, and inhibition of synthesis in excess of 75 per cent was observed only under conditions which promoted high control release. In the other experiments, the continuing synthesis at a rate that was 25 per cent or more of normal was felt to indicate that adequate energy sources were still available, so that no firm conclusions could be drawn. Subsequently, 10^{-4} M DNP and 2 μg/ml oligomycin were reported to have produced inhibitions of 78 per cent and 55 per cent, respectively, of TRF-induced TSH release from incubated rat pituitaries (Wilber and Utiger, 1968a). In a similar system, it has been claimed that 10^{-4} M DNP and 10^{-2} M CN^- had no effect (Guillemin, 1969). However, in the latter study, 1 μg/ml oligomycin and 10^{-3} M iodoacetate were inhibitory. Furthermore, in a report available only in abstract form (Bowers et al., 1968c) it is stated that, in in vivo studies on TRF action in mice, oligomycin, but not DNP, decreased the amount of the TSH released. From the above data, it is difficult to draw any firm conclusions on the dependence of pituitary hormone release on energy; certainly the results are not as clear-cut as they have been reported to be in other tissues.

The first report of an attempt to determine the effect of cyclic AMP on pituitary hormone release was that of a study of the release of GH from incubated slices of heifer pituitaries (Schofield, 1967). In this study, 6.7 mM theophylline was found to promote a mean stimulation of release of 31 per cent over a 2-hour period. Although the effect was statistically highly significant for each 30-minute interval examined, it was quite small in magnitude. Recently, it has been reported that, in men, infusions of cyclic AMP or its dibutyryl derivative cause a highly significant increase in the circulating GH level from 1 mμg/ml to 14 mμg/ml. Unfortunately, this report has only appeared in abstract form (Levine, 1968).

In other studies, neither cyclic AMP nor its dibutyryl derivative were found to promote TSH release from incubated rat pituitaries, but the effect of TRF was enhanced by the addition of theophylline (Guillemin, 1968). In unpublished experiments with Drs. J. Garcia and M. Samli, we were not able to demonstrate an effect of cyclic AMP on either GH or LH release from rat pituitaries. Addition of 6 mM cyclic AMP to incubated rat pituitaries has been reported to consistently induce ACTH release (Fleischer and Vale, 1968).

These experiments, as was true for those in which the dependence of release upon energy sources was examined, do not allow any firm conclusions to be drawn. However, the rather consistent effects of theophylline point to the involvement of cyclic AMP in the release process, *if* this xanthine derivative has no other effect than that of inhibiting phosphodiesterase.

Cation Requirements for the Release Process

The effects of selected cations on the release process have been elucidated by W. W. Douglas and his colleagues in the course of an extensive series of investigations. The initial studies were concerned with catecholamine discharge from the adrenal medulla, and used acetylcholine or 56 mM K^+ to provoke the discharge. The ability of high concentrations of K^+ to increase catecholamine output had been observed earlier in experiments involving arterial injection of KCl into the denervated cat adrenal (Vogt, 1952). It was quickly established that the presence of Ca^{++} was required for release in response to acetylcholine or K^+ (Douglas and Rubin, 1961); that acetylcholine promoted an eightfold increase in the uptake of ^{45}Ca by the medullae of perfused cat adrenal glands in vitro (Douglas and Poisner, 1962a); that Mg^{++} inhibited the acetylcholine-induced or high $[K^+]$-induced release, and that this inhibition was overcome by increasing the concentration of Ca^{++} (Douglas and Rubin, 1963); that Na^+, K^+, and Cl^- were dispensable for the release process, with omission of Na^+ or K^+ actually potentiating the response (Douglas and Rubin, 1963); that in the presence of normal concentrations of Ca^{++} (2 mM), 5 mM Ba^{++} stimulated release; that this effect could be blocked by raising the $[Ca^{++}]$ to 6 mM (Douglas and Rubin, 1964a,b); and that Sr^{++} and Ba^{++} could substitute for Ca^{++} (Douglas and Rubin, 1964b).

Investigations were also carried out on the release of vasopressin from the posterior pituitary, and similar observations were made. It was found that K^+ at concentrations greater than 30 mM promoted vasopressin release from the isolated rat posterior lobe, with maximum release being observed at concentrations of 60 and 90 mM, the release thereafter falling off (Douglas and Poisner, 1964a); that the effect of high $[K^+]$ or of electrical stimulation of the severed stalk was enhanced in Na^+-free media, whereas Mg^{++} inhibited the response to either stimulus (Douglas and Poisner, 1964a; Mikiten and Douglas, 1965); that the presence of Ca^{++} was required for release in response to the high $[K^+]$ stimulus (Douglas and Poisner, 1964a) or to electrical stimulation (Mikiten and Douglas, 1965); and that ^{45}Ca uptake was increased about fivefold by high $[K^+]$, whereas Mg^{++} reduced the uptake by about 30 per cent

(Douglas and Poisner, 1964b). At about the same time, Dicker (1966) reported that high $[K^+]$ had no effect on release of vasopressin from pituitaries of young rats up to 15 days of age. He also reported that 5×10^{-4} M ouabain, an inhibitor of the Na^+-K^+-activated ATPase and the "sodium pump," promoted, by itself, a fivefold increase in release from the pituitaries of adult rats, an effect which was only slightly inhibited by the absence of Ca^{++} from the medium.

These results led Douglas and Rubin (1963) to advance the concept of "stimulus-secretion coupling," analogous to "excitation-contraction coupling" for the events in muscle, in which calcium entry into a cell when the cell is stimulated is a *sine qua non* for initiating secretion. For the acetylcholine-activated catecholamine extrusion mechanism, it was proposed that the inducer brought about an increase in the permeability of adrenal medullary cells to calcium, and that ionic calcium entering the cell in some way activated the extrusion mechanism in the cell (Douglas, 1966). In order to study the secretion phenomenon more completely, Douglas and his colleagues undertook an analysis of the effects of acetylcholine on the membrane potential of isolated adrenal medullary cells. They found that this substance, as well as other secretagogues, depolarized the cells (Douglas *et al.*, 1967a). These investigators then suggested that depolarization of the membrane might cause the secretory granules to be attracted to it, or might bring about some configurational changes in the apposed membranes which would be conducive to rupture, thus leading to release of the granule contents. Depolarization itself, however, did not appear to be tightly coupled to secretion, since it could be demonstrated that excess K^+ or acetylcholine still depolarized the cells under conditions where release failed to occur, i.e. when the medium was devoid of Ca^{++} or contained an excess of Mg^{++} (Douglas *et al.*, 1967b). Moreover, in a Na^+-free medium the cells were hyperpolarized, and despite some depolarization by acetylcholine they remained hyperpolarized, yet release was actually augmented. This has now led to the suggestion that acetylcholine in some way modifies the membrane to make it more permeable to commonly occurring cations such as Na^+ and Ca^{++}, and that, although this increase in permeability causes depolarization, the depolarization itself is not an important factor in stimulus-secretion coupling. Rather, it is the entry of calcium into the cell which is the important event. As attractive as this hypothesis is, it is incomplete since it in no way provides an explanation for the heightened response in the absence of Na^+, or for the enhancement of release by ouabain, an inhibitor of the "sodium pump." Inhibition of the "sodium pump" may be a common denominator. High $[K^+]$, which also stimulates release, activates the "sodium pump," but the high $[K^+]$ effect may represent another form of activation (see below).

The cations found to be required for release of catecholamines and vasopressin seem to be almost universally required for release processes. The absence of calcium from fluid perfusing the acetylcholine-stimulated cat submaxillary gland *in situ* led to a striking decrease in salivary secretion of water, electrolytes, and protein (Douglas and Poisner, 1962b). The stimulation of amylase secretion from pigeon pancreas slices by acetylcholine was also found to be dependent upon the presence of calcium (Hokin, 1966). Rather surprisingly, Bdolah *et al.* (1964) reported that calcium could be omitted from the medium in which slices of rat parotid gland were being incubated without affecting epinephrine-evoked release of amylase. This finding was not confirmed by Rasmussen and Tenenhouse (1968). Our own experience with calcium deprivation in systems in vitro (Samli and Geschwind, 1968) would suggest that a complexing agent, such as ethylenediaminetetraacetic acid (EDTA), may have to be used in order to remove last traces of calcium, and there is no evidence in the report of Bdolah *et al.* that this was used. In some of these same experiments, in which the presence of K^+ was found to be necessary for the epinephrine-induced enzyme release, 60 mM K^+ has been found to stimulate amylase release (Bdolah *et al.*, 1964), and also to increase cyclic AMP formation threefold, both in the presence and in the absence of Ca^{++} (Rasmussen and Tenenhouse, 1968). Moreover, the increase in cyclic AMP induced by epinephrine was found to occur in the absence of Ca^{++} or in the presence of high $[Mg^{++}]$ (10 mM), conditions under which amylase secretion was inhibited. Thus, Ca^{++} is not required for cyclic AMP formation, and cyclic AMP formation cannot by itself induce protein release. In a completely different type of system, the polymorphonuclear leucocyte stimulated by staphylococcal leucocidin, the discharge of intracellular granule-enclosed enzymes also requires the presence of calcium (Woodin and Wieneke, 1963, 1964).

Within the past year, similar studies have been extended to the problem of insulin release. Calcium is required for glucose-stimulated release of the hormone from the perfused rat pancreas (Grodsky and Bennett, 1966; Curry *et al.*, 1968) and for the release induced by a number of secretagogues from pieces of rabbit pancreas (Milner and Hales, 1967a). In the latter system, elevated $[Mg^{++}]$ inhibited secretion (Milner and Hales, 1967a), while elevated $[Ba^{++}]$ stimulated it (Milner and Hales, 1968). Grodsky and Bennett (1966) also found that $[K^+]$ elevation provoked increased insulin release in the absence of glucose, but, unlike other systems investigated (see Douglas and Poisner, 1964a) only a doubling of the normal $[K^+]$ was required. Moreover, this system appears to differ from other systems studied, in that it possesses a requirement for Na^+ (Milner and Hales, 1967b); in the absence of this cation, release of insulin in response to glucose and other secretagogues, including Ba^{++} (Milner and Hales, 1968), is inhibited. That the "sodium pump" may be involved is indicated by the fact that 1×10^{-6} M to 1×10^{-5} M ouabain and a K^+ -free medium stimulate secretion; in both conditions the pump is inhibited. For the ouabain effect to be observed both Na^+ and Ca^{++} must be present (Milner and Hales, 1968).

One last point is worthy of mention before we turn to the ionic requirements for hypothalamic releasing factor action, for it is pertinent not only to those studies, but also to the theory of the mechanism of action of any inducer of the release process. If optimum quantities of inducers are employed, and if inducers generally act to enhance permeability and entry of Ca^{++}, what will the magnitude of the release effect be when two widely different kinds of inducers, such as high $[K^+]$ and a releasing factor specific for a system (e.g. acetylcholine, glucose, epinephrine), are jointly employed? In one experiment, when high concentrations of K_2SO_4 (79 or 126 mM) were employed to depolarize the adrenal medulla, the addition of acetylcholine produced an increase in catecholamine release, even though the high $[K^+]$ had markedly stimulated release (Douglas and Rubin, 1963). In a second experiment, the combination of 60 mM K^+ and epinephrine produced no greater increase in amylase secretion from the incubated parotid gland than either did alone (Bdolah et al., 1964). Thus, in the two systems, dissimilar effects were reported.

The stimulating effect of a five- to tenfold increase in $[K^+]$ on release of hormones from incubated pituitaries has been demonstrated for LH (Samli and Geschwind, 1968; Vale and Guillemin, 1967; Wakabayashi et al., 1968), for TSH (Vale and Guillemin, 1967), and for ACTH (Vale and Guillemin, 1967); for LH, only a minimal effect was found with a fivefold increase of $[K^+]$ (Wakabayashi et al., 1968). The presence of Ca^{++} was found to be required for the potassium effect on release of LH (Samli and Geschwind, 1968; Wakabayashi et al., 1968) and of TSH (Vale and Guillemin, 1967), and for the releasing factor-induced releases of LH (Samli and Geschwind, 1968) and TSH (Vale et al., 1967b). Although Wakabayashi et al. (1968) claimed only a partial inhibition of LH release, when EDTA was used to complex available Ca^{++}, confirmation of the report of complete inhibition was obtained (McCann, personal communication). So-called "control release" of LH and TSH was not affected by calcium deprivation, and it has been suggested that this release represents loss of hormone from cut surfaces or through cellular breakdown (Samli and Geschwind, 1967, 1968; see Schramm, 1967). In the particular case of LH release, it has been found that pituitaries incubated with 59 mM K^+ and hypothalamic extract responded with an additive or even greater effect (Samli and Geschwind, 1968; Wakabayashi et al., 1968).

A requirement for Ca^{++} has also been described for spontaneous release of prolactin from incubated pituitaries, as measured by acrylamide gel electrophoresis and densitometry (Parsons, 1968). In these experiments, pituitaries incubated in Ca^{++}-free media not only released less prolactin, but, in addition, were more greatly depleted of prolactin at the end of the experiment, suggesting that calcium was also required for synthesis. The release of only one adenohypophyseal hormone by its releasing factor has been said not to be dependent on the presence of Ca^{++}; this hormone is FSH (Jutisz and de la Llosa, 1968). For the release of FSH by FSHRF, K^+ was reported to be necessary.

Finally, 1×10^{-4} M ouabain did not affect releasing factor-induced release of either LH (Samli and Geschwind, 1968) or TSH (Wilber and Utiger, 1968a).

Section Summary

The experiments of Douglas and his colleagues have led to a hypothesis for the mechanism of action of at least one set of inducing agents, acetylcholine and other adrenal medullary secretagogues. Presumably, something similar happens normally as a result of the arrival of nerve impulses in the posterior pituitary after discharge down the hypothalamo-hypophyseal tract. Basically, a membrane is modified to allow Ca^{++} to enter, and it is Ca^{++} that triggers release, possibly with the help of cyclic AMP (Rasmussen and Tenenhouse, 1968). The question then arises, how does Ca^{++} effect release? Many suggestions have been offered. In the specific instance of vasopressin release, Thorn (1965) has suggested that Ca^{++} may inhibit the binding of vasopressin to its complexing proteins, the neurophysins. Other possibilities are that Ca^{++} may modify the membrane to allow emiocytosis to occur either by producing a conformational change in the proteins of the membrane (see Douglas et al., 1967a; Matschinsky and Ellerman, 1968), or by activating a lytic system, such as phospholipase, which affects membrane lipids (see Matschinsky and Ellerman, 1968). Another possibility is that, in conjunction with ATP, Ca^{++} may promote adherence between the secretory granules and the plasma membrane (Woodin and Wieneke, 1964). However, Milner and Hales (1967a) state that the granule certainly cannot be the sole site of Ca^{++} action in the pancreatic islets, for in the rabbit fetal pancreas the β-cells do not contain granules, yet in the absence of Ca^{++}, glucose-provoked insulin release is inhibited. Suggestions by the Hokins, that phospholipid turnover was important in the secretory process, and the finding that CRF promoted the incorporation of ^{32}P into phospholipids of incubated rat pituitaries (Hokin et al., 1958), led to studies of whether calcium deprivation affected phospholipid synthesis (Hokin, 1966). In the experiments with pigeon pancreas slices in which Ca^{++} was found necessary for the acetylcholine-stimulated release of amylase, phospholipid synthesis was little affected by the absence of Ca^{++}.

Curry et al. (1968), impressed with their finding that the total amount of insulin released was dependent upon $[Ca^{++}]$ up to 4 to 5 mEq./1., hypothesized that Ca^{++} was bound stoichiometrically and had some role to play other than just maintaining the integrity of the cell membrane. Woodin and Wieneke (1964), on the other hand, felt that the actual secretory process required that both Ca^{++} and ATP be removed from the membrane, the latter by hydrolysis, so that the membrane would become more permeable and less strong mechanically. Rasmussen and Tenenhouse (1968) argued that a Ca^{++}-ATP complex dissociated, with the Ca^{++} acting in the cytosol and the ATP, utilized as a substrate for adenyl cyclase, being coverted into cyclic AMP. They postulated that the cyclic AMP might act either by altering the permeability of cellular membranes to Ca^{++} or by affecting the binding of Ca^{++} to membranes.

Whatever the specific locus of Ca^{++} action is, it is not on the protein synthetic process. Protein synthesis appeared normal in the absence of Ca^{++}, as well as when $[K^+]$ was increased (Samli and Geschwind, 1968; Grodsky and Bennett, 1966). This is important, for it offers the scientist another dissecting tool: puromycin inhibits synthesis without affecting release, while Ca^{++}-deprivation inhibits and high $[K^+]$ activates release without affecting protein synthesis.

Inhibitors of Releasing Factor Action

One possible additional way of studying mechanism of action of releasing factors is to study how substances such as target organ hormones affect their action. The first report of such an effect was on the inhibition of TRF-stimulated release of TSH from pituitaries which were derived from rats pre-treated with 200 µg thyroxine 24 hours prior to removal of the gland, or were pre-incubated for 15 minutes in a medium containing 1 µg of thyroxine (Guillemin et al., 1963). The report has been amply confirmed, and this system is the only one which has been extensively investigated.

The inhibition of TRF action by thyroxine or triiodothyronine administration has been demonstrated for rat pituitaries both in vivo (Vale et al., 1967a; Averill, 1968) and in vitro (Schally and Redding, 1967; Vale et al., 1968; Wilber and Utiger, 1968a), and for mouse pituitaries in vivo (Redding et al., 1966; Bowers et al., 1967, 1968a, b). In his studies in rats, Averill (1968) found that thyroxine administered 2 hours, but not 17 hours, prior to an intrapituitary infusion of TRF prevented TSH release. TSH release was measured by the blood TCA-precipitable radioactivity in animals whose thyroids were prelabeled with ^{131}I 3 to 5 days earlier. In mice it was found that maximum inhibition of the TRF effect occurred when triiodothyronine was administered 45 minutes or more before the injection of the TRF (Bowers et al., 1968a). A number of investigators have shown that the magnitude of the thyroid hormone effect is dose-dependent (Bowers et al., 1967; Wilber and Utiger, 1968a), and that by increasing the dose of TRF it is possible to overcome the inhibition produced by the thyroid hormones (Vale et al., 1967a; Bowers et al., 1967). In addition to effects on TSH release, effects of the prior injection of thyroid hormone in mice on pituitary TSH content in TRF-treated animals have been described. With a dose of 10 µg of thyroxine, significant elevation of pituitary TSH was described in TRF-treated mice (Redding et al., 1966), while with a dose of 2.7 µg only a prevention of the TRF-induced depletion was found (Bowers et al., 1967). Since, in the latter experiments, release was inhibited without a concomitant increase in the pituitary TSH level, the authors suggested that thyroxine blocks both the synthesis and release of TSH which follow TRF administration. It is not readily apparent, however, why a fourfold larger dose of thyroxine should permit the synthesis.

Very recently, two important further developments have been described. One is that thyroxine also inhibits the high $[K^+]$-invoked release of TSH, for pituitaries pre-incubated in 1.25 µg/ml thyroxine do not respond to the presence of 25mM K^+ (Vale and Guillemin, 1967). The other is that antibiotic inhibitors of RNA or protein synthesis prevent, and may sometimes reverse, the thyroid hormone effect. Puromycin (2 mg) or cycloheximide (400 µg) given at the same time as triiodothyronine prevents the inhibition of TRF action in the mouse by the thyroid hormone, without affecting the uptake of the triiodothyronine by the anterior pituitary (Bowers et al., 1968a). Interestingly, when the dose of thyroid hormone is increased, the amount of antibiotic must be increased to override the inhibition by the former; why there is a quantitative relationship between dose of triiodothyronine and dose of puromycin is unknown (Bowers et al., 1968a). Inhibition by cycloheximide has also been found with rat pituitaries which had been pre-incubated with thyroxine for 15 minutes (Vale et al., 1968). This antibiotic was found not only to prevent the thyroxine effect, but to reverse it as well; significantly more TSH was released by pituitaries incubated with thyroxine, cycloheximide, and TRF, than with TRF alone, suggesting that the antibiotic reversed the effect caused by endogenous thyroxine in vivo which also persists in vitro. Actinomycin D has also been shown to prevent the thyroxine effect in vitro (Schally and Redding, 1967; Vale et al., 1968) and in vivo (Bowers et al., 1968b). In the latter studies it was found that, unlike its action in experiments with puromycin, triiodothyronine did not override the effect of the antibiotic when the amount was increased, and in the in vitro studies this inhibitor was shown only to prevent, and not to reverse, the action of the thyroid hormone (Vale et al., 1968).

When the above findings are considered in relation to the previously reviewed reports indicating that these same antibiotics have no effect on TRF-induced TSH release, it is obvious that the thyroid hormones and TRF are not competing for the same site of action. Obviously, both RNA and protein synthesis are required for the thyroid hormone effect, and since actinomycin does not reverse the action of thyroxine, but only prevents it, once the RNA is formed it would appear to be stable. The reversibility of the thyroxine effect by cycloheximide, however, indicates that the protein has a rather short half-life, disappearing quickly, and not being replaced because of the cycloheximide inhibition (Vale et al., 1968). What is the function of this labile protein? Vale and his colleagues (1968) suggest as possibilities that it may act to prevent TRF effects by removal of Ca^{++} from some specific sites, or by stabilizing membranes involved in the release of TSH or the membrane of TSH secretion granules.

A few other inhibitors of releasing factor action are known. Growth hormone, for example, was found to prevent the pituitary depletion of GH by intracarotidly administered median eminence extract when given intraperitoneally at a dose of 1 mg/100 g body weight 15 minutes before injection of the extract (Müller et al., 1967). When given alone 30 minutes before sacrifice of the recipient, the same dose of GH had no effect on pituitary GH concentration. Dexamethasone, a synthetic corticoid, has been found in experiments in vivo in rats to prevent the increase in plasma corticosterone that follows the intravenous injection of CRF, and in studies obviously modeled on those with the thyroid hormones recounted above, prevention of the dexamethasone effect could be obtained if actinomycin D or cycloheximide, 100μg/100 g body weight, was administered 30 minutes before the steroid was given (Arimura et al., 1968). The result with cycloheximide is somewhat surprising, since it has been reported by many investigators that both puromycin and cycloheximide prevent the in vivo action of ACTH on the adrenal (see Garren et al., 1965; Estep et al., 1967). Therefore, it ought not to be possible to detect the action of CRF when using steroid secretion as an indicator of its action in animals treated with these antibiotics. Dexamethasone has also been found to be an inhibitor of the ACTH-releasing action of lysine and arginine vasopressin (10 to 100 mU/ml) in studies in vitro with rat pituitaries (Fleischer and Vale, 1968). The effect is an interesting one even if, despite the similarity to the report of Arimura et al. (1968), the ACTH-releasing action of vasopressin may not be a proper model for the mode of action of CRF.

Conclusions

One of the reviewer's preconceptions before writing this review was that in different organs the process of secretion, and more especially polypeptide and protein secretion, and perhaps even more especially polypeptide and protein hormone secretion, would be governed by the same factors. On the basis of the pioneer work in the field one might imagine that some specific stimulus acts upon a cell to cause it to release its product, and for that release Ca^{++} must be present, and energy is required. To this could be added the finding that high $[K^+]$ may be a nonspecific stimulus for release, exerting its effect mainly, if not entirely, by depolarization of cell membranes. This in turn suggested that the specific stimuli may also act as depolarizers. Finally, more recent experiments suggest that 3',5'-cyclic AMP may be the "second messenger" between the stimulus and the release event, indicating that the primary effect of a specific stimulus may be to activate adenyl cyclase. If all of this were true, then of course there would be no need to establish for releasing factor action what has already been established for the release of molecules other than the anterior pituitary hormones. However, at least one hypothalamic factor, PIF, inhibits release, and this would seem to be without precedent in other fields.

The reviewer was not prepared to find, therefore, that, whereas 1 to 5

$\times$ 10^{-4} M DNP and 1×10^{-4} to 1×10^{-2} M CN$^-$ depress the release of amylase, insulin, and vasopressin, 1 and 2×10^{-4} M DNP and 1×10^{-3} and 1×10^{-2} M CN$^-$ have no effect on LH and TSH release, or that, while 1×10^{-6} to 5×10^{-4} M ouabain stimulates vasopressin and insulin release, 1×10^{-4} M has no effect on either LH or TSH release. In addition, release of amylase and release of insulin, but not of LH, GH, or TSH, are promoted by cyclic AMP or its O',N-dibutyryl derivative.

What have held fast are the requirement for Ca^{++} and the stimulating action of high [K$^+$]. That the former is not involved in the activation of adenyl cyclase has now been shown for amylase secretion from rat parotid gland slices (Rasmussen and Tenenhouse, 1968). This might suggest that the effect of Ca^{++} is somewhere within the cell, rather than, or in addition to, its membrane. That high [K$^+$] is not acting solely by depolarizing the cell is supported by the arguments offered by Douglas and his colleagues (1967b), and by the findings that high [K$^+$] stimulates cyclic AMP formation three- to tenfold, not only in parotid gland slices (Rasmussen and Tenenhouse, 1968), but also in slices of guinea pig cerebral cortex (Sattin and Rall, 1967) and in rat diaphragm as well (Lundholm et al., 1967).

In evaluating the reported failure of cyclic AMP to stimulate hormone release from the pituitary, the major problem of adequate cellular penetration by this nucleotide should be kept in mind. As reviewed above, limited results with theophylline suggest that cyclic AMP may be involved in releasing factor action. It is tempting to speculate that the intervention of this nucleotide offers a common mode of action for all releasing factors, and that an inhibitory factor such as PIF may act by depressing the activity of a free-running adenyl cyclase or by activating the phosphodiesterases of the prolactin-secreting cells. With either purified releasing or inhibiting factors, or with monolayer cell cultures, estimation of cyclic AMP levels would be rewarding. This picture may be much too simple, however, for how does acetylcholine further stimulate catecholamine release (Douglas and Rubin, 1963) or hypothalamic extract further stimulate LH release (Samli and Geschwind, 1968; Wakabayashi et al., 1968) in the presence of a high K$^+$ concentration?

Recent reports suggest that the question of enhanced protein synthesis following releasing factor administration may also involve cyclic AMP. In one study 1×10^{-3} M cyclic AMP, or better yet 1×10^{-3} M cyclic AMP plus 1×10^{-3} M dimethylaminopurine or theophylline, could replace the requirement for 1×10^{-3} M ATP plus 2.5×10^{-4} M guanosine triphosphate (GTP) in an in vitro enzymatic "releasing system" which promoted the release of radioactive proteins from isolated liver polysomes pre-labeled with valine-^{14}C (Khairallah and Pitot, 1967). The effect of cyclic AMP would, of course, have to be on the translation event in protein synthesis. A similar conclusion was drawn from experiments with *E. coli* cells treated with Tris-EDTA to make them more permeable to the nucleotide. In this experiment, it was shown that 1×10^{-4} to 1×10^{-3} M cyclic AMP could cause a 150 to 300 per cent increase in the induced production of β-galactosidase and tryptophanase (Perlman and Pastan, 1968). A more striking effect of 1×10^{-3} M cyclic AMP was observed in cells in which synthesis of β-galactosidase and tryptophanase was repressed by the presence of 1×10^{-2} to 1×10^{-1} M glucose and 1×10^{-2} M pyruvate, respectively, in the medium, for a threefold increase in the rate of synthesis of β-galactosidase and a twenty-seven-fold increase in the rate of production of tryptophanase occurred.

Thus, with evidence of the importance of cyclic AMP for both the release and synthetic processes, the activation of adenyl cyclase looms more dominantly as the means by which releasing factors may affect these processes. However, it would appear that for neither process is an increase in cyclic AMP levels in itself sufficient to explain all the effects observed.

References

Arimura, A., C. Y. Bowers, and A. V. Schally (1968). Suppression by dexamethasone of the action of hypothalamic CRF: Its elimination by actinomycin D or cycloheximide. *Fed. Proc. 27*, 5.

Ashby, E., P. Coates, L. Krulich, A. Dhariwal, and S. M. McCann (1967). Early ultrastructural changes in somatotrophs under the influence of hypothalamic releasing factors. *Am. Zool. 7*, 714.

Averill, R. L. W. (1968). Interactions of thyroxine and TRF on TSH release. *Excerpta Medica, Int. Cong. Ser. 157*, 93.

Bauduin, H., J. Reuse, and J. E. Dumont (1967). Non-dependence of secretion on protein synthesis. *Life Sci. 6*, 1723-31.

Bdolah, A., and M. Schramm (1965). The function of 3',5'-cyclic AMP in enzyme secretion. *Biochem. Biophys. Res. Comm. 18*, 452-54.

Bdolah, A., R. Ben-Zvi, and M. Schramm (1964). The mechanism of enzyme secretion by the cell. II. Secretion of amylase and other proteins by slices of rat parotid gland. *Arch. Biochem. Biophys. 104*, 58-66.

Bowers, C. Y., A. V. Schally, G. A. Reynolds, and W. D. Hawley (1967). Interactions of L-thyroxine or L-triiodothyronine and TRF on the release and synthesis of thyrotropin from the anterior pituitary gland of mice. *Endocrinology 81*, 741-47.

Bowers, C. Y., K.-L. Lee, and A. V. Schally (1968a). A study on the interaction of the thyrotropin-releasing factor and L-T$_3$: Effects of puromycin and cycloheximide. *Endocrinology 82*, 75-82.

Bowers, C. Y., K.-L. Lee, and A. V. Schally (1968b). Effect of actinomycin D on hormones that control the release of thyrotropin from the anterior pituitary glands of mice. *Endocrinology 82*, 303-10.

Bowers, C. Y., K.-L. Lee, and A. V. Schally (1968c). *In vitro* studies on the mechanism of TSH release. *Clin. Res. 16*, 33.

Carlisle, D. B. (1957). The direct action of anterior pituitary extracts on the initiation of lactation in the rabbit. *Physiol. Comp. Oecol. 4*, 295-312.

Caro, L. G., and G. E. Palade (1964). Protein synthesis, storage, and discharge in the pancreatic exocrine cell. *J. Cell Biol. 20*, 473-95.

Chance, R. E., R. M. Ellis, and W. W. Bromer (1968). Porcine proinsulin: characterization and amino acid sequence. *Science 161*, 165-67.

Clementi, F., G. De Virgiliis, and J. Meldolesi (1967). Ultrastructure of the growth hormone-producing cells of the rat pituitary after injection of a hypothalamic extract. *Excerpta Medica, Int. Cong.* Ser. *142*, 33-34.

Cohen, A. I., E. C. Nicol, and W. F. White (1966). Stimulation of LH synthesis by LHRF in monolayer cultures of rat anterior pituitary. *Prog. 48th Mtg. Endocrine Soc.*, 33.

Coore, H. G., and P. J. Randle (1964). Regulation of insulin secretion studied with pieces of rabbit pancreas incubated *in vitro*. *Biochem. J. 93*, 66-78.

Corbin, A., and J. C. Story (1966). Depletion and resynthesis of pituitary FSH: Time course of events following treatment with hypothalamic FSH-RF. *Experientia 22*, 694-95.

Couch, E. F., and S. Sawano (1968). Electron microscope studies of somatotrophs of rat pituitary after injection of purified GRF. *Excerpta Medica, Int. Cong.* Ser. *157*, 195-96.

Crighton, D. B., S. Watanabe, A. P. S. Dhariwal, and S. M. McCann (1968). Failure of inhibitors of protein synthesis to affect LH-releasing action of hypothalamic extracts *in vitro*. *Proc. Soc. Exp. Biol. Med. 128*, 537-40.

Critchlow, V., H. S. Lipscomb, and R. Guillemin (1963). Effect of CRF on maintenance of the adrenocorticotrophic function of anterior pituitary grafts. *J. Endocrinol. 25*, 465-72.

Curry, D. L., L. L. Bennett, and G. M. Grodsky (1968). Requirement for calcium ion in insulin secretion by the perfused rat pancreas. *Am. J. Physiol. 214*, 174-78.

Dasgupta, P. R., and F. G. Young (1958). Activation of hormonal secretions: Precorticotropin. *Nature 182*, 32-34.

Deuben, R. R., and J. Meites (1964). Stimulation of pituitary growth hormone release by a hypothalamic extract *in vitro*. *Endocrinology 74*, 408-14.

Dicker, S. E. (1966). Release of vasopressin and oxytocin from isolated pituitary glands of adult and new-born rats. *J. Physiol. (London) 185*, 429-44.

Douglas, W. W. (1966). Calcium-dependent links in stimulus-secretion coupling in the adrenal medulla and neurohypophysis. In *Mechanism of Release of Biogenic Amines* (U. S. von Euler, S. Rosell, and B. Uvnäs, eds.), pp. 267-88. Pergamon, Oxford.

Douglas, W. W., and A. M. Poisner (1962a). On the mode of action of acetylcholine in evoking adrenal medullary secretion. Increased uptake of calcium during the secretory response. *J. Physiol. (London) 162*, 385-92.

Douglas, W. W., and A. M. Poisner (1962b). Importance of calcium for acetylcholine-evoked salivary secretion. *Nature 196*, 379-80.

Douglas, W. W., and A. M. Poisner (1964a). Stimulus-secretion coupling in a neurosecretory organ: The role of calcium in the release of vasopressin from the neurohypophysis. *J. Physiol. (London) 172*, 1-18.

Douglas, W. W., and A. M. Poisner (1964b). Calcium movement in the neurohypophysis of the rat and its relation to the release of vasopressin. *J. Physiol. (London) 172*, 19-30.

Douglas, W. W., and R. P. Rubin (1961). The role of calcium in the secretory response of the adrenal medulla to acetylcholine. *J. Physiol. (London) 159*, 40-57.

Douglas, W. W., and R. P. Rubin (1963). Mechanism of catecholamine release from the adrenal medulla and the role of Ca in stimulus-secretion coupling. *J. Physiol. (London) 167*, 288-310.

Douglas, W. W., and R. P. Rubin (1964a). Stimulant action of Ba on the adrenal medulla. *Nature 203*, 305-7.

Douglas, W. W., and R. P. Rubin (1964b). The effects of alkaline earths and other divalent cations on adrenal medullary secretion. *J. Physiol. (London) 175*, 231-41.

Douglas, W. W., A. Ishida, and A. M. Poisner (1965). Effect of metabolic inhibitors on the release of vasopressin from the isolated neurohypophysis. *J. Physiol. (London) 181*, 753-59.

Douglas, W. W., T. Kanno, and S. R. Sampson (1967a). Effects of acetylcholine and other medullary secretagogues and antagonists on the membrane potential of adrenal chromaffin cells: An analysis employing techniques of tissue culture. *J. Physiol. (London) 188*, 107-20.

Douglas, W. W., T. Kanno, and S. R. Sampson (1967b). Influence of the ionic environment on the membrane potential of adrenal chromaffin cells and on the depolarizing effect of acetylcholine. *J. Physiol. (London) 191*, 107-21.

Estep, H., P. F. Mullinax, R. Brown, K. Blaylock, and E. Butts (1967). Increased ACTH release without increased synthesis. *Endocrinology 80*, 719-24.

Evans, J. S., and M. B. Nikitovitch-Winer (1965). Reactivation of hypophysial grafts by continuous perfusion with median eminence extracts. *Fed. Proc. 24*, 190.

Farquhar, M. G. (1961). Origin and fate of secretory granules in cells of the anterior pituitary gland. *Trans. N. Y. Acad. Sci. 23*, 346-51.

Fleischer, N., and W. Vale (1968). Vasopressin induced ACTH release *in vitro*— Inhibition by glucocorticoids and possible mediation by cyclic AMP. *Clin. Res. 16*, 266.

Friend, J. P., and W. W. Leavitt (1967). Preparation of rat pituitary monolayers as a means of studying the effects of hypothalamic extracts on pituitary cells. *Am. Zool. 7*, 201-2.

Garcia, J. F., and I. I. Geschwind (1968). Investigation of growth hormone secretion in selected mammalian species. In *Growth Hormone* (A. Pecile and E. E. Müller, eds.), pp. 267-91. Excerpta Medica Found., Amsterdam.

Garren, L. D., R. L. Ney, and W. W. Davis (1965). Studies on the role of protein synthesis in the regulation of corticosterone production by adrencorticotropic hormone *in vivo*. *Proc. Nat. Acad. Sci. (U.S.) 53*, 1443-50.

Gay, V. L., and E. M. Bogdanove (1968). Disappearance of endogenous and exogenous luteinizing hormone activity from the plasma of previously castrated, acutely hypophysectomized rats: An indirect assessment of synthesis and release rates. *Endocrinology 82*, 359-68.

Geschwind, I. I., and C. H. Li (1955). The tibia test for growth hormone. In *Hypophyseal Growth Hormone, Nature and Actions* (R. W. Smith, Jr., O. H. Gaebler, and C. N. H. Long, eds.), pp. 28-53. McGraw-Hill, New York.

Grieshaber, C. K., and W. C. Hymer (1968). Effect of hypothalamic extracts on protein synthesis in rat anterior pituitary tissue. *Proc. Soc. Exp. Biol. Med. 128*, 459-63.

Grodsky, G. M., and L. L. Bennett (1963). Insulin secretion from the isolated pancreas in absence of insulinogenesis: Effect of glucose. *Proc. Soc. Exp. Biol. Med. 114*, 769-71.

Grodsky, G. M., and L. L. Bennett (1966). Cation requirements for insulin secretion in the isolated perfused pancreas. *Diabetes 15*, 910-13.

Guillemin, R. (1969). TSH-RF: RF model study. *Proc. 3rd Int. Cong. Endocrinol.*, Excerpta Medica, Amsterdam, in press.

Guillemin, R., E. Yamazaki, D. A. Gard, M. Jutisz, and E. Sakiz (1963). *In vitro* secretion of thyrotropin: Stimulation by a hypothalamic peptide (TRF). *Endocrinology 73*, 564-72.

Helmreich, E., M. Kern, and H. N. Eisen (1962). Observations on the mechanism of secretion of γ-globulins by isolated lymph node cells. *J. Biol. Chem. 237*, 1925-31.

Hokin, L. E. (1951). Synthesis and secretion of amylase by pigeon pancreas *in vitro*. *Biochem. J. 48*, 320-26.

Hokin, L. E. (1966). Effects of calcium omission on acetylcholine-stimulated amylase secretion and phospholipid synthesis in pigeon pancreas slices. *Biochim. Biophys. Acta 115*, 219-21.

Hokin, M. R., L. E. Hokin, M. Saffran, A. V. Schally and B. U. Zimmermann (1958). Phospholipids and the secretion of adrenocorticotropin and of corticosteroids. *J. Biol. Chem. 233*, 811-13.

Hymer, W. C., and A. Stere (1967). Effect of hypothalamic extracts on RNA synthesis in rat anterior pituitary tissue. *Proc. Soc. Exp. Biol. Med. 125*, 1143-49.

Jacobowitz, D., B. H. Marks, and J. Vernikos-Danellis (1963). The effect of acute stress on the pituitary gland: Uptake of serine-1-^{14}C into ACTH. *Endocrinology 72*, 592-97.

Jamieson, J. D., and G. E. Palade (1966). Role of the Golgi complex in the intracellular transport of secretory proteins. *Proc. Nat. Acad. Sci. (U.S.) 55*, 424-31.

Junqueira, L. C. U. (1965). Aspects of the biology of the animal cell secretion. In *Funktionelle und Morphologische Organisation der Zelle: Sekretion und Exkretion*, pp. 27-35. Springer-Verlag, Berlin.

Junqueira, L. C. U., H. A. Rothschild, and I. Vugnam (1958). The action of atropine on pancreatic secretion. *Brit. J. Pharmacol. 13*, 71-73.

Jutisz, M., and M. P. de la Llosa (1967). Studies on the release of FSH *in vitro* from rat pituitary glands stimulated by hypothalamic FSH-RF. *Endocrinology 81*, 1193-1202.

Jutisz, M., and M. P. de la Llosa (1968). Studies on the mechanism of action of FSH releasing factor. *Excerpta Medica, Int. Cong. Ser. 157*, 137-38.

Jutisz, M., A. Bérault, M.-A. Novella, and F. Chapeville (1966). Sur le mécanisme d'action du facteur hypothalamique LRF *in vitro*. *C. R. Acad. Sci. (Paris) 263*, 664-67.

Jutisz, M., A. Bérault, M.-A. Novella, and G. Ribot (1967). Étude de l'action du facteur hypothalamique LRF chez le rat *in vivo* et *in vitro*. *Acta Endocrinol. 55*, 481-96.

Khairallah, E. A., and H. C. Pitot (1967). 3',5'-Cyclic AMP and the release of polysome-bound proteins *in vitro*. *Biochem. Biophys. Res. Comm. 29*, 269-74.

Kobayashi, T. (1965). Studies on gonadotropin-releasing factor of rat hypothalamus. *Excerpta Medica, Int. Cong. Ser. 87*, 306-8.

Kobayashi, T., T. Kigawa, M. Mizuno, and H. Sato (1964). Studies of the gonadotropin secretion of the anterior pituitary cells cultivated *in vitro*. *Gunma Symp. Endocrinol. 1*, 249-63.

Krulich, L., A. P. S. Dhariwal, and S. M. McCann (1967). Effect of growth hormone-releasing and inhibiting factors on synthesis and release of GH "*in vitro*" in the rat. *Excerpta Medica, Int. Cong. Ser. 142*, 32.

Lacy, P. E. (1967). The pancreatic beta cell: Structure and function. *New Eng. J. Med. 276*, 187-94.

Levine, R. A. (1968). Stimulation of plasma insulin and growth hormone in man by cyclic 3',5'-AMP. *J. Clin. Invest. 47*, 62a.

Lundholm, L., T. Rall, and N. Vamos (1967). Influence of K-ions and adrenaline on the adenosine-3',5'-monophosphate content in rat diaphragm. *Acta Physiol. Scand. 70*, 127-28.

MacLeod, R. M., and A. Abad (1968). Influence of hypothalamic extract on growth hormone and prolactin synthesis *in vitro*. *Fed. Proc. 27*, 319.

Malaisse, W., F. Malaisse-Lagae, and P. H. Wright (1967a). A new method for the measurement *in vitro* of pancreatic insulin secretion. *Endocrinology 80*, 99-108.

Malaisse, W. J., F. Malaisse-Lagae, and D. Mayhew (1967b). A possible role for the adenyl cyclase system in insulin secretion. *J. Clin. Invest. 46*, 1724-34.

Marks, B. H., and J. Vernikos-Danellis (1963). Effect of acute stress on the pituitary gland: Action of ethionine on stress-induced ACTH release. *Endocrinology 72*, 582-87.

Matschinsky, F. M., and J. E. Ellerman (1968). Metabolism of glucose in the Islets of Langerhans. *J. Biol. Chem.* 2730-36.

Mikiten, T. M., and W. W. Douglas (1965). Effect of calcium and other ions on vasopressin release from rat neurohypophyses stimulated electrically *in vitro*. *Nature 207*, 302.

Milner, R. D. G., and C. N. Hales (1967a). The role of calcium and magnesium in insulin secretion from rabbit pancreas studied *in vitro*. *Diabetologia 3*, 47-49.

Milner, R. D. G., and C. N. Hales (1967b). The sodium pump and insulin secretion. *Biochim. Biophys. Acta 135*, 375-77.

Milner, R. D. G., and C. N. Hales (1968). Cations and the secretion of insulin. *Biochim. Biophys. Acta 150*, 165-67.

Mittler, J. C., and T. W. Redding (1968). Stimulation of TSH secretion by TRF in organ cultures of anterior pituitary. *Excerpta Medica, Int. Cong. Ser. 157*, 93.

Müller, E., and A. Pecile (1966). Growth hormone resynthesis in the pituitary after depletion induced by a hypothalamic extract. *Experientia 22*, 108.

Müller, E. E., S. Sawano, A. Arimura, and A. V. Schally (1967). Mechanism of action of growth hormone in altering its own secretion rate: Comparison with dexamethasone. *Acta Endocrinol. 56*, 499-509.

Nicoll, C. S., and J. Meites (1962). Estrogen stimulation of prolactin production by rat adenohypophysis *in vitro*. *Endocrinology 70*, 272-77.

Palade, G. E., P. Siekevitz, and L. G. Caro (1962). Structure, chemistry and function of the pancreatic exocrine cell. In *Ciba Foundation Symposium on the Exocrine Pancreas* (A. V. S. de Reuck and M. P. Cameron, eds.), pp. 23-55. J. and A. Churchill Ltd., London.

Parsons, J. A. (1968). Calcium ions and release of prolactin from female rat adenohypophyses *in vitro*. *Excerpta Medica, Int. Cong. Ser. 157*, 75.

Perlman, R., and I. Pastan (1968). Cyclic 3',5'-AMP: Stimulation of β-galactosidase and tryptophanase induction in E. coli. *Biochem. Biophys. Res. Comm. 30*, 656-64.

Racadot, J., L. Olivier, E. Porcile, and B. Droz (1965). Appareil de Golgi et origine des grains de sécrétion dans les cellules adénohypophysaires chez le Rat. Étude radioautographique en microscopie électronique après injection de leucine tritiée. *C. R. Acad. Sci. (Paris) 261*, 2972-74.

Ramirez, V. D., and S. M. McCann (1964). Fluctuations in plasma luteinizing hormone concentrations during the estrous cycle of the rat. *Endocrinology 74*, 814-16.

Rasmussen, H. and A. Tenenhouse (1968). Cyclic adenosine monophosphate, Ca^{++}, and membranes. *Proc. Nat. Acad. Sci. (U.S.) 59*, 1364-70.

Redding, T. W., C. Y. Bowers, and W. Locke (1966). *In vivo* depletion of pituitary TSH content by thyrotropin releasing factor. *Prog. 48th Mtg. Endocrine Soc.*, 122.

Sachs, H., R. Portanova, E. W. Haller, and L. Share (1967). Cellular processes concerned with vasopressin biosynthesis, storage and release. In *Neurosecretion* (F. Stutinsky, ed.), pp. 146-54. Springer-Verlag, Berlin.

Samli, M., and I. I. Geschwind (1967). Some effects of the hypothalamic luteinizing hormone releasing factor on the biosynthesis and release of luteinizing hormone. *Endocrinology 81*, 835-48.

Samli, M. H., and I. I. Geschwind (1968). Some effects of energy-transfer inhibitors and of Ca^{++}-free or K^+-enhanced media on the release of luteinizing hormone from the rat pituitary gland *in vitro*. *Endocrinology 82*, 225-31.

Sattin, A., and T. W. Rall (1967). The effect of brain extracts on the accumulation of cyclic 3',5'-AMP in slices of guinea pig cerebral cortex. *Fed. Proc. 26*, 707.

Schally, A. V., and T. W. Redding (1967). *In vitro* studies with thyrotropin releasing factor. *Proc. Soc. Exp. Biol. Med. 126*, 320-25.

Schally, A. V., E. E. Müller, and S. Sawano (1968). Effect of porcine growth hormone-releasing factor on the release and synthesis of growth hormone *in vitro*. *Endocrinology 82*, 271-76.

Schally, A. V., T. Saito, A. Arimura, S. Sawano, C. Y. Bowers, W. F. White and A. I. Cohen (1967). Purification and *in vitro* and *in vivo* studies with porcine hypothalamic FSH-RF. *Endocrinology 81*, 882-92.

Schofield, J. G. (1967). Role of cyclic 3',5'-AMP in the release of GH *in vitro*. *Nature 215*, 1382-83.

Schramm, M. (1967). Secretion of enzymes and other macromolecules. *Ann. Rev. Biochem. 36*, 307-20.

Schwartz, N. B., and D. Bartosik (1962). Changes in pituitary LH content during the rat estrous cycle. *Endocrinology 71*, 756-62.

Schwartz, N. B., and D. Caldarelli (1965). Plasma LH levels in cyclic female rats. *Proc. Soc. Exp. Biol. Med. 119*, 16-20.

Sinha, D. K., and J. Meites (1966). Stimulation of pituitary thyrotropin synthesis and release by hypothalamic extract. *Endocrinology 78*, 1002-6.

Smith, R. E., and M. G. Farquhar (1966). Lysosome function in the regulation of the secretory process in cells of the anterior pituitary gland. *J. Cell Biol. 31*, 319-47.

Solomon, S. H., and J. M. McKenzie (1964). Studies on the hypothalamic thyrotropin releasing factor. *Canadian Med. Assn. J. 90*, 487.

Steiner, D. F., D. Cunningham, L. Spigelman, and B. Aten (1967). Insulin biosynthesis: Evidence for a precursor. *Science 157*, 697-700.

Symchowicz, S., W. D. Peckham, R. Oneri, C. A. Korduba, and P. L. Perlman (1966). The effect *in vitro* of purified hypothalamic extract on the growth hormone content of the rat pituitary. *J. Endocrinol. 35*, 379-83.

Thorn, N. A. (1965). Role of calcium in the release of vasopressin and oxytocin from posterior pituitary proteins. *Acta Endocrinol. 50*, 357-64.

Turtle, J. R., G. K. Littleton, and D. M. Kipnis (1967). Stimulation of insulin secretion by theophylline. *Nature 213*, 727-28.

Uemura, T. (1968). Studies on the biosynthesis and release of ACTH. *Endocrinol. Japon. 15*, 130-31.

Vale, W., and R. Guillemin (1967). K$^+$-induced stimulation of thyrotropin release *in vitro*. Requirement for presence of calcium and inhibition by thyroxine. *Experientia 23*, 855-57.

Vale, W., R. Burgus, and R. Guillemin (1967a). Competition between thyroxine and TRF at the pituitary level in the release of TSH. *Proc. Soc. Exp. Biol. Med. 125*, 210-13.

Vale, W., R. Burgus, and R. Guillemin (1967b). Presence of calcium ions as a requisite for the *in vitro* stimulation of TSH-release by hypothalamic TRF. *Experientia 23*, 853-55.

Vale, W., R. Burgus, and R. Guillemin (1968). On the mechanism of action of TRF: Effects of cycloheximide and actinomycin on the release of TSH stimulated *in vitro* by TRF and its inhibition by thyroxine. *Neuroendocrinol. 3*, 34-46.

Vernikos-Danellis, J. (1963). The effect of acute stress on the pituitary gland: Changes in blood and pituitary ACTH concentrations. *Endocrinology 72*, 574-81.

Vernikos-Danellis, J. (1964). Neuroendocrine factors affecting the synthesis and release of ACTH. *Excerpta Medica, Int. Cong. Ser. 83*, 549-55.

Vernikos-Danellis, J. (1965). Effect of rat median eminence extracts on pituitary ACTH content in normal and adrenalectomized rats. *Endocrinology 76*, 240-45.

Vogt, M. (1952). Secretion of the denervated adrenal medulla of the cat. *Brit. J. Pharmacol. 7*, 325-30.

Wakabayashi, K., and B.-I. Tamaoki (1965). *In vitro* biosynthesis of luteinizing hormone in the anterior pituitary gland. *Endocrinology 77*, 264-72.

Wakabayashi, K., H. P. G. Schneider, S. Watanabe, D. B. Crighton, and S. M. McCann (1968). Studies on the mechanism of action of the gonadotropin releasing factors on the pituitary. *Fed. Proc. 27*, 269.

Watanabe, S., A. P. S. Dhariwal, and S. M. McCann (1968).   Effect of inhibitors of protein synthesis on the FSH-releasing action of hypothalamic extracts *in vitro*.   *Endocrinology 82*, 674-84.

Wilber, J. F., and R. D. Utiger (1968a).   *In vitro* studies on mechanism of action of TRF.   *Proc. Soc. Exp. Biol. Med. 127*, 488-90.

Wilber, J. F., and R. D. Utiger (1968b).   Personal communication.

Woodin, A. M., and A. A. Wieneke (1963).   The accumulation of calcium by the polymorphonuclear leucocyte treated with staphylococcal leucocidin and its significance in the extrusion of proteins.   *Biochem. J. 87*, 487-95.

Woodin, A. M., and A. A. Wieneke (1964).   The participation of calcium, adenosine triphosphate and adenosinetriphosphatase in the extrusion of the granule proteins from the polymorphonuclear leucocyte.   *Biochem. J. 90*, 498-509.

Index